FAMILY MATTERS

HOME TO HEATHER CREEK

FAMILY MATTERS

Diann Hunt

Guideposts
NEW YORK, NEW YORK

Guideposts.org
(800) 932-2145
Guideposts Books & Inspirational Media

Cover by Lookout Design, Inc.
Interior design by Cindy LaBreacht
Typeset by Nancy Tardi

Printed in the United States of America
10 9 8 7 6 5 4 3 2

To my Monday Mentors who truly have taught me
that we can make a difference in the daily things of life.
I am blessed to call you friends!

Acknowledgments

Special thanks to Beth Adams and Fiona Serpa for their ability to blow away the debris and find the gold. You both are amazing and I am blessed to be on your team!

Special thanks to Karen Zimmerman for her gracious help on the medical issues of this book and thanks also to my critique partner, Colleen Coble, for her expertise and constant encouragement.

To my husband who stands by me every step of the way, my world is a better place because of you.

And finally, a huge, heartfelt thanks to you, the readers, who graciously give of your time to take this journey with me. Hope you enjoy it!

—Diann Hunt

Home to Heather Creek

Before the Dawn

Sweet September

Circle of Grace

Homespun Harvest

A Patchwork Christmas

An Abundance of Blessings

Every Sunrise

Promise of Spring

April's Hope

Seeds of Faith

On the Right Path

Sunflower Serenade

Second Chances

Prayers and Promises

Giving Thanks

Holiday Homecoming

Family Matters

FAMILY MATTERS

Chapter One

Emily Slater had never seen her friend this upset. Ever. Red, swollen eyes. Skin as pale as the bathroom walls. The knot in Emily's stomach tightened as she stood beside the sink in the girls' restroom at Bedford High School and waited for Ashley Givens to pull herself together.

Grabbing her long, auburn curls into her fist, Ashley turned on the faucet and splashed water on her face with her free hand. Emily yanked a couple of rough paper towels from the dispenser and stuffed them into Ashley's groping fingers.

"Thanks." Ashley wiped the moisture from her face.

Emily hoped no one else would walk in so they would have time to talk privately before the next-period bell rang.

"I'm sorry, Em. I'm still trying to get my mind wrapped around it all."

"What all?"

Color seeped slowly back into Ashley's face, and she took a deep breath. Through thick, wet lashes, she looked at Emily. The pain Emily saw in her friend's eyes frightened her. She placed her hand on Ashley's shoulder. "What is it? It can't be that bad."

Ashley swallowed hard. "It *is* that bad."

One look at her friend's face made Emily's pulse kick up a notch and caused her legs to tremble. She knew this was worse—far worse—than any boyfriend trouble or grade problem.

"Mom has a doctor's appointment this afternoon."

Emily's mouth went dry.

More tears drizzled down Ashley's face. "She found a lump . . ." she cleared her throat, "in her breast." She rolled the paper towel around in her hand. Staring straight into Emily's eyes, she whispered, "I'm scared."

Emily pulled Ashley into a hug. "It may be nothing. Like Grandma always says, 'Don't borrow trouble.'"

"I sure hope you're right." Emily noticed Ashley twisting the paper more before she finally tossed it and pulled out her makeup bag. She dabbed a little blush on her cheeks.

Emily faced the mirror and ran a comb through her blonde hair and touched up her sheer lip gloss.

The door swished open and another student breezed in with a handbag and backpack.

Ashley swiped her hand across her face and stuffed her makeup back into her bag. "We'd better go. The bell is about to ring." She sniffed. "Do I look all right?"

"You look great." Emily figured a little white lie wouldn't hurt, just this once. "I'll see you at lunch, okay?"

Ashley nodded. They shoved through the door and stepped into the hallway.

"Em?"

Emily turned back around. "Yeah?"

"Thanks."

"You're welcome." Emily smiled and headed down the hall toward her class, all the while telling herself everything would be fine.

Just the way she had the day of her mother's accident.

LATER THAT MONDAY, the sweet aroma of chocolate chip cookies wafted from the oven and filled the kitchen while the winter winds swooshed against the old farmhouse. Charlotte Stevenson wiped the flour from the countertop and rinsed out her washcloth. She shoved back a strand of brown hair from her face and figured she must look a sight.

"This winter seems worse than last year, don't you think?" Emily asked, putting away the flour.

"Maybe. We've certainly had our share of snow already this year."

"Well, I'm ready for spring."

Charlotte chuckled. "I'm afraid you'll have to wait a little bit for that."

Emily lined the next cookie sheet with dollops of dough. "Thanks for doing this, Grandma. It makes me feel better."

"Me too," Charlotte said, lifting a smile. She glanced at the clock for the hundredth time in the last half hour and wondered why Ashley hadn't called yet to tell Emily about her mom's doctor visit. There was probably no reason to worry, she told herself, or they would have heard something by now. Most likely the lump was nothing. Besides, God was in control, as always, and there had been huge strides in breast cancer research in recent years. Melody Givens would be fine.

Emily walked over to the cabinet and pulled out a large dinner plate.

"Are you planning to eat a lot of cookies?" Charlotte asked with a chuckle.

Emily took a surprised look at the plate in her hand and blushed. "I meant to pull out another cookie sheet."

Charlotte merely nodded but said nothing.

The shriek of the phone made them both jump. Their gazes collided.

"You want to get it or shall I?" Charlotte asked.

"How about you?"

"Hello?" It took only a second for Charlotte's spirit to dip. "Sure, Brad, just a moment." She turned a disappointed face toward Emily and then took the phone into the family room. "Bob, it's Brad Weber. That part you wanted had to be back-ordered."

Her husband sat in his easy chair, watching a game show. He hauled his paunchy, six-foot-one self out of the chair and met Charlotte halfway.

She handed him the phone and then turned back toward the kitchen. Taking a deep breath, she wiped her hands on her apron. It was silly to get this stirred up. Melody would be absolutely fine. Why did Charlotte's mind always jump to the worst-case scenario? She needed to trust that the Lord knew exactly what he was doing because, of course, he did.

When Charlotte stepped back into the kitchen, Emily was sitting at the table, staring at her fingers. Charlotte's heart constricted at the sight. Her granddaughter had been through so much with her own mother's death and having to move from California to Nebraska. Seeing Ashley's mother in a health crisis undoubtedly brought back some of the familiar pain. Charlotte hoped she could get Emily to talk about it.

The buzzer on the stove went off.

"I'll get it." Emily hopped up from her chair and grabbed a potholder. The sweet scent of fresh-baked cookies burst from the oven when she pulled out the tray.

"Mmm, those smell pretty good. I think we should sample them to make sure, don't you think?" Charlotte tossed Emily a wink.

"Yeah." Emily pulled two small plates from the cupboard and set them on the table with a couple of napkins.

A knock at the back door gave Charlotte a start. She laughed. "Guess I'm a little nervous." She walked over and opened the door to see her dear friend and neighbor Hannah Carter. "Now how did you know we just pulled a batch of chocolate chip cookies from the oven?" Charlotte stepped aside so Hannah could enter.

Beyond Hannah, frosted tree limbs stood silhouetted against mingling hues of scarlet and tangerine as the sun splayed across the horizon, bidding adieu to the sleepy town of Bedford. Charlotte lingered a slight moment, taking in the scene, before closing the door.

"Women's intuition," Hannah said as she stepped inside, already pulling off her coat and scarf. "I hope you don't mind me dropping by. Frank had a meeting, and I wanted some company."

Charlotte gave her a knowing smile. "Well, you've come to the right place." Charlotte gave a nod toward Emily, who quickly gathered a plate and a glass of chilled milk for their guest while Charlotte scooped more cookies onto a serving dish.

Soon they all settled at the table.

"So how's that new grandson of yours?" Hannah asked with a twinkle in her eyes.

"He's an angel. Perfect in every way. Babies smell so sweet and—"

"Sweet?" Emily made a face. "I don't think they smell so sweet."

The older women laughed.

"Well, I don't think she meant all the time," Hannah said before biting into her cookie.

Charlotte thought about her grandson for a moment before her thoughts drifted over to Denise's children and the days she had missed with them when they were tiny. San Diego had been much too far away from Bedford, Nebraska, to keep close contact. The result was years of regret, but there was nothing she could do about it now. The important thing, she told herself, was to make a difference from this point forward.

And that's what she and Bob had been trying to do since Denise's death: provide a loving home to her children—their grandchildren—Sam, Emily, and Christopher.

Emily and Hannah slipped into a conversation about school while Charlotte silently whispered a prayer in her heart for each of her grandchildren. Time passed so swiftly. It seemed only yesterday she had held her own three children in her arms.

Toby, their Australian shepherd-blue heeler mix, barked at Charlotte, no doubt wanting a cookie.

"How many times do I have to tell you, Toby? Dogs can't eat chocolate." Charlotte sighed. Then she got up from the table and pulled a doggie treat from under the cabinet. "Here. I'm sure this is just as good."

"Don't bet on it, Toby," Hannah muttered with a chuckle.

Emily finished her cookies and excused herself to go upstairs. Charlotte and Hannah talked of baby Will's habits and his feeding schedule. His big sisters, it seemed, were adjusting well to him and helped Anna by fetching diapers and such in her times of need.

"You could never tell Anna just had a baby. She looks just wonderful," Charlotte said.

"I'm not surprised. That girl is always put together well." Hannah took another ambitious bite from her cookie.

Charlotte smiled. Her daughter-in-law rarely had a hair out of place or a soiled spot on her clothes. Charlotte couldn't imagine how she did it.

Contentment settled upon her as she visited and laughed with her best friend, absolving every thought of worry from her mind.

Until the phone rang.

Chapter Two

Emily ran to the phone. "Hello?"

"It's me," Ashley said. "Mom has to go in for a biopsy in the morning."

"Oh." Pause. "Is your dad going?"

"I think so."

"They're probably just checking to be safe, you know?" Emily said, her stomach beginning a slow coil.

"Yeah." Such a tiny word, spoken with volumes of doubt.

"You okay?"

"I guess. Mom is trying to act like it's no big deal, making jokes and all, but I know it is. She's cleaning house like crazy. She got rid of so many things out of her closet, I don't think she has anything left."

"Anybody would be a little, you know, nervous about it. But it's gonna be fine, Ash. You'll see." Even as the words spilled from her tongue, Emily wondered why she was saying them. Life didn't always turn out fine. She didn't want to build Ashley's hopes, but neither did she want to worry her. How did her grandma always know what to say?

"Well, I just wanted to let you know. Sorry I didn't call sooner. Dad took us out for dinner. I think he was trying to keep Mom's mind off things—either that or keep her out of the closet."

They shared a chuckle.

"Hey, I've gotta go. I'll see you at school tomorrow."

"Okay. Thanks for calling, Ashley," Emily said, trying to sound upbeat. She clicked off the phone, her thoughts swirling with fear for her friend. Without warning, memories of her mom's accident came to mind—their neighbor showing up with the police officers while Emily was watching TV with her brothers, the chills that ran up her arms when they announced the news, the tears—and fears—that followed. She shook herself.

She threw away her cookie. Her stomach rumbled, but this time not from hunger.

She was a little awkward with praying, but in the quiet of that moment, Emily lifted a prayer for her friend and her family. Mothers weren't supposed to die when their kids were young.

So why did they?

BOB STEVENSON BRUSHED HIS TEETH in the bathroom. The smell of freshly laundered sheets wafted in to him as Charlotte folded back the covers on the bed and plumped the pillows. Easing out of her slippers, she slid between the cool sheets with a sigh. It had been a long day.

"I wasn't sure you heard me in the hubbub of conversation when I told you about Ashley's call to Emily?"

Bob climbed into his side of the bed. "Yeah, I heard what you said about Melody. That's too bad. Hopefully, it'll turn out to be nothing."

"Yes, let's hope so."

He reached over and gave Charlotte a kiss good night, a

practice they'd started on day one of their marriage. He smelled of peppermint, and just a hint of aftershave lingered still. After a meaningful hug, Charlotte picked up the novel from her nightstand and cracked it open.

The phone rang. The clock beside her bed said ten o'clock.

"Wonder who that could be?" Charlotte reached for the phone. "Hello?"

"I'm sorry to bother you this late, Charlotte, but I have a favor to ask of you." Melody's voice sounded tired.

"Absolutely. What do you need?"

"I'm sure Emily told you what's going on with me."

"Yes, she did. How are you holding up?"

"I'm doing all right. Listen, Russ was planning to go with me tomorrow to the surgeon's office, but to be honest he makes me nervous. He's pacing the floors, and asking me every ten seconds if I need anything. He did the same thing when I was pregnant with the kids."

Charlotte laughed. "At least he's concerned, right?"

"I guess. The worst of it is that this is the slow time of year for a carpenter, so that gives him too much time to worry. Fortunately, he got a call tonight from someone who wants to discuss new kitchen cabinets. We can use the money, so I encouraged him to go over there tomorrow. But the only way he will agree to that is if someone goes with me. And I don't want Ashley to go. She's too upset as it is." She paused. "Would you consider going with me? The appointment is at nine tomorrow morning."

"I'd be happy to go with you."

"I don't know why Russ is making such a fuss. I'll be fine, come what may. In fact, I've already spotted a gorgeous red wig that I plan to buy if chemo is in my future."

She laughed. "People just may see Russ sportin' a new woman around town."

That was Melody—always easing the tension with humor.

"Let's not borrow trouble," Charlotte said.

"Spoken like a true friend."

"Who will be manning the diner?" Charlotte asked.

"I called Esther Showalter. She's always ready and willing to help out in the kitchen. Says it gives her purpose. Bless her."

"She is a great support," Charlotte agreed.

All sweetness and cuddles—that's what Denise used to say about Esther. Denise had loved her like another grandmother. It had broken Esther's heart when Denise died.

"Listen, I'd better let you go."

"How about I pick you up at eight?" Charlotte suggested.

"That will work."

"Okay. I'll be at your house then."

"Sounds good."

"And Melody?"

"Yeah?"

"I'll be praying for you."

"Thanks."

Bob was already fast asleep when Charlotte hung up the phone. Deciding she wasn't in the mood to read after all, Charlotte placed her novel on the stand. She eased into her place under the soft folds of their comforter. The chimes on the front porch whistled and whined as the winter winds swirled them to a tangle. The windows rattled, and Charlotte sunk farther into the covers.

The night was cold and dark. Just like life at times. She knew the only way to get through the harsh, cold realities of life was prayer. So she pushed through the fears, the pain, the uncertainties that faced Melody—that faced all of them, really—and focused her attention on the one who had everything under control.

Lord, it's me again . . .

MELODY KICKED THE BOTTOMS of her boots against the car's door frame to shake off the snow. Then she eased into the car and closed the door. She smelled of vanilla shampoo. "Good morning."

Charlotte smiled and returned the greeting.

Sporting rosy cheeks and a woolen hat, scarf, and gloves, she appeared more like a woman about to go out with a friend than one who faced a needle biopsy.

"How do you stay so positive and trusting at a time like this?" Charlotte asked.

Melody shrugged. "Doesn't do much good to be otherwise. Gotta take the good with the bad."

Charlotte patted her hand. "Remember, you're not alone."

"I remember."

A light snow forced Charlotte to turn on her windshield wipers. "I'll be so glad when it's spring."

"Yeah, me too. There's something so rejuvenating about it all."

Spring meant life. New opportunities. New beginnings. That's what Charlotte prayed for her friend. And she absolutely would not allow her thoughts to go anywhere else.

"Thanks for taking me this morning, Charlotte. It's no small trip, and I really appreciate it." Melody tugged the red woolen cap closer to her ears.

Charlotte adjusted the heater. "That's what friends are for, you know."

They passed the twenty miles to Harding Memorial Hospital, where Dr. Douglas Grady had his offices, with chitchat about the family and avoided talk of the unknown future.

Once they had pulled into a parking place, they vacated the car and headed toward the hospital door, leaving a trail of footprints in the fresh snow.

"I feel a little silly that you have to come with me. I'm a grown woman, after all."

"Hey, in times like these we all need a friend." Charlotte smiled. "So fill me in on what exactly is going on."

"Not much to tell, really. It all started when I took a shower the other morning and found a slight bump. I called the doctor, and they worked me in. They performed a mammogram, which led to an ultrasound, which ultimately brought me here. The surgeon will look over my case and tell me what happens next."

They walked through the front doors of the brick building. "It shouldn't take long to discuss the process. Just in case, I hope you brought something to read." Melody looked down at Charlotte's bag.

"I brought my embroidery."

"What are you working on?" They stopped just inside the door so Melody could look at the signs. "This way." They walked down a scrubbed hallway, boots sounding against the tile, and turned right.

"I'm working on some hand towels for Miss Middleton."

"That's nice. How is she doing?"

"She's great. Emily still goes over to visit now and then. I would never have imagined Emily would have a friend in her eighties." Charlotte chuckled.

"Yeah, that's pretty cool."

They walked to the end of the hall, took a left, and landed in the suite of Dr. Grady. The waiting room smelled of antiseptic and lemon-scented furniture polish. A woman with bright eyes and a sincere smile greeted them. Melody stated her business as Charlotte scanned the room for a suitable place to hang out for the next hour or so. Spotting a coffeemaker, she walked over to a tan vinyl chair near it.

While Melody filled out some paperwork at the counter, Charlotte breathed in the scent of coffee. Funny, she had always wondered why doctors' offices offered caffeine to a lobby full of people who were no doubt already anxious. But sitting here now, she realized there was something more to it. The fragrance brought comfort. Memories of lingering over kitchen tables with loved ones. Conversations that strengthened and deepened over every cup. She chuckled quietly as she poured herself a cup. She should do a coffee commercial.

"Writing an autobiography would have been faster than answering all their questions piece by piece," Melody said with a heavy breath when she slipped into the seat beside Charlotte.

"Guess they have to check every nook and cranny."

"I guess." She inhaled deeply. "Mmm, that smells good."

"Want some?"

"I can't have any caffeine until after the test." She pulled open a magazine and flipped through. "I sure hope the diner is all right this morning."

"You've got good help. It'll be fine."

"You're right."

Melody crossed her legs and began to swing her top leg

back and forth, back and forth. Charlotte's heart went out to her. Though she knew Melody tended to be a ball of energy, Charlotte suspected her friend's body language had a little more to do with anxiety over her future than pent-up energy.

The wooden door swung open, and a nurse wearing a long, blue top printed with pictures of black stethoscopes and white nurse's caps stood at the entrance. She looked at her chart and then called out, "Melody Givens."

"Guess that's me." Melody grabbed her bag and tossed a pleading glance toward Charlotte.

Charlotte squeezed Melody's hand. "I'll be praying."

"Thanks."

Lifting a prayer, Charlotte watched her friend slip through the door.

"Is that your daughter?"

Charlotte turned to a woman seated nearby.

"No, just a friend." She almost added that Melody had been her daughter's friend but stopped herself. She didn't want to get into that discussion.

The woman nodded and said nothing more. But her question had sent Charlotte's thoughts in Denise's direction. She hadn't been there in her daughter's last minutes, and that was that. The thought troubled her, although she knew she couldn't blame herself. Denise had chosen to move to San Diego, and that was a far cry from Bedford, Nebraska.

She had to put those thoughts aside. For now, she had a friend who needed her.

Chapter Three

Hey, Ashley, how're you doing?" Emily rushed to join her friend in the school hallway. A kid scarfing down a sausage and egg biscuit walked past them, sending the spicy aroma their way.

Ashley shrugged. "I'm okay. I'll be better after Mom's biopsy is over and I talk to her."

"Will she know anything today?" Emily waved at a couple of friends as they passed her.

"I don't think so. I think she said it would take a few days to find out."

"That stinks."

"I know." Ashley sighed.

Feet scuffled and conversations murmured along the hallway, punctuated by occasional giggles and short squeals. Emily searched for the words to encourage her friend. "Hey, you want to come over and study tonight?" What a lame thing to say. Of course, she wouldn't want to come over tonight.

"Thanks, but I think I'd better stay home and help Mom."

Well, duh. "Oh yeah, sure. What was I thinking?" Emily chided herself.

Ashley turned to her. "I know you're trying to help. I suppose you know better than anyone how I feel."

Emily's gaze fixed on her notebook, and she nodded.

Just then the bell rang. The girls looked at one another, said good-bye, and then dashed off to their next classes.

Emily slid into her seat in English class, but her teacher's words seemed to evaporate into the air. She wiped her sweaty palms on her jeans. Her heart ached with a sense of loss that could never be fixed. She'd lost her mom. But she would do anything and everything she could to help Ashley and her mom, come what may. She didn't ever want her friend to go through what she had gone through.

Not ever.

MELODY REJOINED CHARLOTTE in the waiting room. Charlotte gathered her things, and they headed back toward the car, leaving behind the scents of coffee and antiseptic.

"You okay?" Charlotte asked.

"Yeah, I'm fine."

Charlotte didn't want to make her talk till they got to the car so Melody wouldn't feel uncomfortable.

Once they got in the car, Melody turned to her. "So it's like this. Dr. Gray examined me, and he recommends that I have an excisional biopsy, rather than the needle biopsy they first mentioned, which means he'll remove the entire mass and biopsy it afterward. He'll do the surgery there in the hospital, but I'll be an outpatient. He said he assumes the mass is most likely a fibroadenoma, which means a benign tumor that's nothing to worry about. But in this day and age, they don't like to take chances, so they'll biopsy it this way to be one hundred percent sure."

"Sounds like a good idea." Charlotte took a moment to digest the information. "So when is the biopsy scheduled?"

"Tomorrow afternoon."

Charlotte's heart twisted. They weren't waiting around. That was good. But why did life have to be so hard? If only she could find the words to comfort her friend. These were anxious times, to be sure.

"They had a cancellation."

Melody must have sensed Charlotte's concern—or possibly had the same concern herself.

"I've heard they do these things more as a precaution than anything. Many times it's nothing," Charlotte said.

"Yeah, the doctor said that. Still, I have a feeling about this."

Charlotte didn't like the sound of that at all. "What do you mean?"

"I don't know, really. The doctor's demeanor, the way he guarded his words . . . I get the feeling there is more going on here."

"Well, let's not worry about that until we get there. Face this thing one day at a time, knowing the Lord is with you and so are your many friends."

Melody turned a grin to Charlotte. "You're right. In the meantime, let's get some lunch. My treat."

"The diner?"

"No. I'm not ready to work just yet." She chuckled.

Such a sweet chuckle, as though Melody hadn't a care in the world. But Charlotte knew there was so much more going on behind that smile. So much more.

LATER THAT AFTERNOON, Christopher twirled the pencil between his fingers, causing lead to stain his fingertips, while Miss Luka droned on about a special project. The tip was sharp, so he had to be careful. He sniffed. He liked the smell of sharpened pencils—except that it reminded him of school, and who wanted to be at school when he could be snowmobiling on the farm? He wondered if Sam might drive the snowmobile and attach the tire tube on the back so he could ride behind him like they had done with Uncle Pete a few weeks ago. Most likely they'd have to wait for Uncle Pete.

Christopher's thoughts tuned back into Miss Luka just as she said, "Your project assignment is to create a family tree." To further drive salt into the wound, she wrote the words in big, sharp letters across the blackboard.

Miss Luka's chalk screeched across the board, matching his sentiments exactly. Christopher didn't like this idea one little bit. Didn't she know he had plans to go riding in the snow?

"Go as far back as possible on both sides of your family. Research is key. Internet, library, family, extended family—go where you need to go, talk to those who may be of help, and document everything. Then, once you trace back a few generations—the further back, the better—I'd like you to tell me what you know about each person. A small paragraph for every individual."

Christopher's sixth-grade class let out a collective groan.

"It won't be as bad as all that," Miss Luka encouraged. "In fact, you may find that it's actually fun to trace your roots."

It sounded like a whole lot of work to Christopher. He wondered if she sat up at night thinking of these projects. His grandma had said sometimes people drink some kind of tea before bed to help them sleep better. Maybe he'd suggest that to Miss Luka. He had no doubt she could use more sleep.

The bell rang. Chatter exploded in the room. Papers shuffled, notebooks snapped closed, and book bags shifted as students spilled into the hallways. Christopher passed Miss Luka's desk and continued out the door, glad the school day was over.

The bad part about Miss Luka announcing the assignment just before the bell rang was that it put him in a bad mood. Who wanted to write about family stuff?

He stumbled onto the bus and plopped down in his seat, the cold vinyl making cracking noises as he eased into place. He dropped his book bag on the seat beside him to discourage anyone from sitting down.

His thoughts meandered to his dad's visit last month. Christopher had liked spending time with him. His dad made him feel special. That's why it didn't make sense to Christopher that his dad hadn't stayed for Christmas. Sure, he sent gifts, but anybody could do that. Why didn't his dad want to stick around and hang out with them? Didn't he like being with them? Wasn't that what families were supposed to do—spend time together?

Frost iced the windowpane. He fogged the window with his breath and tried to wipe a clean circle so he could see out. Clad in coats and boots and lugging their book bags, students hustled to their buses; some chatted in clusters. Keeping his gaze fixed outside, he tried to figure out how he was going to tackle this latest assignment and wished he could just forget it.

What was the big deal about learning family ancestry anyway? He'd rather play on the farm and hang out with their dog Toby or his friend Dylan.

Dylan hadn't been at school today. Christopher wondered what he'd say about the assignment. He thought for a moment. It might be kind of cool for Dylan to find out more about his Native American heritage. But Christopher's heritage? B-O-R-I-N-G.

The ride home seemed to take forever, but finally he reached the farm and headed straight for a snack when he stumbled in through the back door of the kitchen.

"Where's Grandma?" he asked Emily while plunging his hand into the cookie jar.

"She's still out with Mrs. Givens."

He grabbed a handful of the cookies his sister and grandma had made last night and started stuffing them into his mouth. In between bites he asked, "Do you know when she'll be home or what's for dinner?"

Emily's jaw went slack. "Mrs. Givens is going through a crisis, and all you care about is dinner?" She stomped out of the kitchen. "Unbelievable."

Christopher stared after her. What crisis was she talking about? Emily was such a drama queen. He reached once more into the cookie jar and grabbed another cookie. With Grandma out, there was no telling when they would eat dinner.

This day just kept getting worse.

EMILY WAS GATHERING UP her homework from the kitchen table when Charlotte stepped through the back door and into the kitchen.

"How did it go?" Emily asked.

Charlotte kicked the snow from her boots and pulled them off at the door. She shook the chill from her bones.

"It went all right. A little different than expected. After examination, the surgeon decided she needed an excisional biopsy, which they'll do tomorrow afternoon. She won't know anything definitive for a while." Once her boots were off, Charlotte shook the snow from her coat and hung it on the coat tree just inside.

"How is Mrs. Givens? Is she upset? Afraid?"

Emily had so many questions. Charlotte wasn't necessarily up for them, but she knew Emily was concerned too. She turned around and came face-to-face with her granddaughter.

Emily stepped back. "Oh, sorry."

Charlotte smiled. "It's all right. I know you're worried too. Let's start supper." Charlotte washed her hands at the porcelain sink and dried them on a hand towel.

"Would you get me some kidney beans out of the cupboard? I think I'll make a kettle of chili tonight."

Emily complied.

"Now. About Mrs. Givens. She's doing fine, really. Her spirits are up. You know her. She doesn't let much get her down."

Emily smiled and nodded.

Charlotte fried some ground turkey breast with onion and green pepper. Emily took one look and scrunched her nose.

"Don't worry," Charlotte said. "I'll set aside some meatless chili for you. In fact, let's throw a few more vegetables into your pot. Charlotte grabbed a couple of cans of garbanzo and black beans and spilled them into a second pot. "Cut up some celery, and we'll throw that in too."

Emily did her part and then set the table.

"Grandma, do you think it's harder to lose someone suddenly or to know ahead of time that they're . . . well, you know."

Charlotte saddened as she thought of the pain all this must be stirring in Emily's mind.

"I don't think it's ever easy either way, but somehow we get through it, one day at a time." Such a trite answer, but Charlotte wasn't at all sure what else to say.

After adding the soup beans, tomatoes, and sauce to the meat mixture, Charlotte sprinkled on the chili, trying to hold back a sneeze as the seasoning tickled her nose.

"Yeah." Emily placed the last soup bowl on the table. "It just seems so unfair."

Charlotte stirred Emily's chili, rinsed her hands under the faucet, and wiped her hands on a dishtowel again. She walked over to her sweet granddaughter and pulled her into a sideways hug. "Listen, honey, it may not be anything."

Emily kept her gaze fixed on the floor. Charlotte suspected she was hiding tears she didn't want her grandmother to see. "Yeah, you're right."

"Hey, Grandma." Christopher stepped into the kitchen.

"Hi, kiddo." She released Emily and walked toward the stove. "Getting hungry?"

"I sure am."

Charlotte chuckled. "Well, I hope you're hungry for chili."

He stepped up to the pot on the stove. "Sure. That smells really good."

"Chili? Did someone say chili?" Charlotte's younger son, Pete, walked into the room, his usual smile in place. He walked over to his mom and gave her a hug. "Mmmmm, the chili *does* smell good." He rubbed his hands together. "Long day on the farm. I'm starved."

"I thought you and Dana went shopping for dishes and such for your wedding."

He let out a long, dramatic sigh. "That too."

Charlotte chuckled. Shopping was not a forte of the Stevenson men.

"You'd better go shopping for groceries. I hope Dana realizes just how much you like to eat," she said with a shake of her head.

"I think she has an idea." Pete dipped his hand into the cookie jar and grabbed one.

Charlotte put her hands on her hips. "Make sure you save room for dinner, Peter Stevenson. Now, you boys shoo out of this kitchen and let Emily and me get our work done here."

Pete looked at Christopher. "Guess we're getting thrown out."

"But I have to tell you something, Grandma," Christopher said.

Charlotte finished stirring the chili, and tapped the wooden spoon against the lip of the kettle. She turned to Christopher. "Yes?"

"Miss Luka is making us research our family tree."

The expression on Christopher's face almost made her laugh, but she knew this was quite serious for him. In fact, she wasn't at all sure this was coming at a good time, just on the heels of his father's visit. She hoped it wouldn't stir up some worrisome emotions.

"Oh?"

"I have no idea how to find out that stuff."

"There's all kinds of help on the Internet, you goof," Charlotte's oldest grandson, Sam, said as he stepped into the kitchen.

"That's what Miss Luka said," Christopher admitted glumly.

Sam walked over and tousled Christopher's hair.

"Hey, stop it."

"I'll help you out, little brother, if you need it."

Christopher brightened. "You will?"

"Sure." Sam stuck his hand into the cookie jar and pulled out the last cookie.

"What are you kids doing? Stop eating cookies before dinner."

Sam shrugged.

Charlotte turned the heat off under the chili. "Now, someone go get Grandpa. It's time to eat."

Charlotte watched them all dash to the family room. If she didn't know better she'd say they'd been fasting for weeks, judging by the way they hovered in the kitchen. She shook her head and collected two potholders from the cabinet drawer—one with the picture of a pig, the other a picture of a cow. A Mother's Day present from Bill twenty-plus years ago. They had their share of stains and were frayed on the edges, but she kept them anyway. Some things, no matter how ragged, earned an eternal place in her kitchen drawer—and her heart.

Carrying the pot over to the table, Charlotte gave it one last enthusiastic stir while the gang stumbled into the room.

The kids had finally settled into the normal routine of eating dinner together, come what may. Obviously, her daughter hadn't been able to manage that tradition with her work schedule at the time. Looking around the table now, Charlotte was glad she took measures to make mealtime an important event in their family. And right now, she couldn't help wondering how mealtime was going in another home across town.

Chapter Four

Sam and his friend Jake Perkins crawled into Sam's car after school. The scent of cold pizza lingered.

"Dude, smells like something died in here."

"Aw, it's not that bad. By the way, there's some old pizza in the backseat if you want it. It's stayed plenty cold in the car."

Jake cringed. "I think I'll pass."

"Suit yourself."

Sam started the engine and then jumped out to brush the snow from the windows. His fingers burned from the cold. Grandma always scolded him for not wearing his gloves, and right now, he wished he had listened.

He hustled to get back inside and cranked up the heater. With great drama, the heater clicked, thumped, whined, and then belched out a blast of cold air. Sam looked at Jake and shrugged. "It gets worse before it gets better." He guided the car out of the school parking lot.

Jake laughed.

"I don't know how you guys stand this stuff," Sam said with a shiver.

"Listen to you, Mr. San Diego Man. You're one of us now, bro. Get used to it."

"No offense, but I'll never get used to it."

Jake looked at him.

"What?"

"Do you hate it that much?"

"No, I don't hate it," Sam said, trying to soften his distaste for the weather. "I'm just not a fan of snow."

Jake shrugged and looked out the window. "I don't mind it so much. Guess because I've grown up with it." He turned the volume knob on the radio. "So how's it going with you and Arielle?"

"Okay, I guess."

"Uh-oh, that doesn't sound so good."

"Oh, you know girls. They're hard to figure."

"What's the problem?"

Sam pulled the car to a standstill at a stoplight. "All she wants to talk about is college, and she gets mad that I'm not all excited about it. Sometimes it drives me crazy. Just because I'm not all that thrilled with the idea of college doesn't mean I have no ambition. I'm only trying to figure out where to go from here, you know?"

"No kidding. You'd better watch yourself. From what I hear, if you let a woman boss you once, it's all over, bro."

"She's not gonna boss me; I can tell you that. I like Arielle and all that, but I don't want her telling me what to do."

"That's right. I'm just saying, put your foot down right now," Jake said as though they were having a serious meeting.

Sam decided he'd better change the subject. "What did you think about that Career Day thing they're planning at school next week?"

Jake shrugged. "Okay, I guess."

"Think you'll end up at the University of Nebraska?"

"Yeah, probably. Don't know what I'll do yet, though."

"Maybe we'll figure it out by the time we get to school."

"I've been on the college track all along since my dad keeps telling me how important it is to get a good education. I know it's true, but sometimes I think it would be nice to just check out for a while and travel or something."

Sam grinned. "Yeah, I know. That would be way cool."

"So do you think you'll get accepted at one of the colleges where you applied?" Jake asked.

"Don't know why not. My grades aren't all that bad. I need a soccer scholarship, though."

They simultaneously released sighs.

"They should give kids a grace period, like two years or something, where we can just think about it and then decide. But my dad said it's college or work. 'No laying around,' as he put it." Jake shook his head and made a face.

"I'm pretty sure my grandparents feel the same way. Maybe we'll figure something out next week."

"Maybe." Jake didn't sound all that hopeful. "I thought you wanted to do something with flying."

"Yeah, flying is cool, but I'm not sure yet." Sometimes Sam just wanted to be a little kid again.

After he dropped Jake off at his house, he drove on to the farm, thankful Emily had gotten another ride home tonight—at least until he could get his car cleaned. He opened the glove compartment and grabbed the can of spray deodorant he kept there for emergencies and then gave the backseat a good dousing.

Not quite the smell he was going for, but it worked.

"WELL, THIS IS A LIVELY GROUP if ever I've seen one," Pete said as he and Dana walked into the family room.

Emily was on the sofa working crochet stitches. She looked over to where Grandma sat in her rocking chair, embroidering, and Grandpa sat in his easy chair watching reruns of *The Price Is Right.*

"Where are Christopher and Sam?" Pete asked.

"Sam's upstairs doing homework, and Christopher is in the kitchen helping himself to the peanut butter cookies I just made," Grandma said.

"Ah, so that's what I smell."

That was one thing Emily loved about living with Grandma and Grandpa; their home always smelled of baked bread or cookies. It held happy smells—smells that made Emily feel safe and content all at the same time.

Pete looked over at her. "Haven't you finished that yet?" He pointed to the half-finished baby blanket in Emily's hands. "Bill's kid will be driving before you get it to him."

Emily winced. "I know. But I want it to be perfect for him." Her fingers kept working the soft blue yarn while she talked. "Besides, I've been busy with school." She loved the feel of the soft yarn between her fingers.

Pete made a face. "How can that be? You just had two weeks of Christmas vacation."

"Believe it or not, I have an English project due in a couple of weeks, so that's been on my mind."

Pete shook his head. "Teachers can be ruthless. Especially those English teachers." He winked at Miss Simons, who happened to be a high school English teacher.

She nudged him in the side. "You'd better watch yourself."

Pete put his arm around her. "There are always exceptions to the rule."

Emily smiled but wasn't about to say anything. She and everyone else at Bedford High School knew that

Miss Simons had a reputation for being a tough but fair teacher. In fact, once Miss Simons and Pete got engaged, Emily's friends teased her and Sam that they would soon become the teacher's pet. Emily resented the insinuation, but Sam hoped they were right.

"Crocheting and knitting take time, especially when you make it as nice as Emily does." Miss Simons smiled at her.

"Thanks." Emily stuck her tongue out at Pete, and he did the same thing back to her.

Grandma shook her head. "You two are hopeless." She turned to Miss Simons. "So how are the wedding plans coming along?"

Pete made a face. "Oh man, don't get her started."

That caught everyone's attention—well, all except for Grandpa. He was trying desperately to guess the price of a cruise vacation to the Bahamas for *The Price Is Right.*

Grandma put aside her embroidery. A frown tugged at her lips and eyes. "What's wrong?"

"I'm going to leave you women to your girl talk and join Christopher in the kitchen before he eats up all the cookies." Pete was already halfway out of the room before anyone could respond.

Miss Simons sighed. "I've never considered myself to be a super picky person, but I'm beginning to wonder." She looked up at them, her dark eyes revealing frustration. "I can't seem to find a wedding dress anywhere—at least not in my price range."

"I'm sure that's not an easy choice."

Miss Simons rattled off the different wedding shops she'd visited without luck. "It's very frustrating." She shook her head, causing her straight, dark hair to brush the tops of her shoulders.

"You should look online," Emily suggested.

"I'm afraid to do it that way. You know how you just can't tell if it's what you want until you try it on."

Emily nodded and thought a moment. "Hey, I have an idea!"

Miss Simons and Grandma both looked at her.

"How about I make it for you? Didn't you say Aunt Rosemary made your wedding dress, Grandma?" She didn't give Charlotte any time to answer. "We could create the dress together—I'll sketch it out for you, and then we could shop for the material together, and then I could make a pattern, and then I could sew it for you and fit it on you along the way, and you can come check on my progress and—"

"Whoa, just a minute there," Grandma said.

"What?"

"That's a big order."

"And I'm just not sure about that," Miss Simons said.

"Why not? You said you loved the dress I made for the prom."

"Well, yes, I did, but—"

"I can do it, Miss Simons." Emily laid aside her yarn work and scooted toward the edge of the sofa, feeling as though she could fly at any moment. "I know I can totally do this."

"Emily, that's a huge—"

"If you don't like it, you can always do something else. What have you got to lose? You haven't found anything yet. All you would be out is the material if you don't like it. This could be the start of my fashion career."

Miss Simons's gaze scanned the floor as though searching for an answer. Emily could almost hear the *Jeopardy* clock ticking—the way she heard it every night when her grandpa watched the program on the television. Emily wanted to say more but decided she'd better not push too hard or Miss Simons would get scared off.

Emily looked at her grandma, who shrugged in response.

Miss Simons finally looked up. "Let me think about it a day or two. Okay, Emily? I can't wait any longer than that. I have to do something soon, so I promise to let you know. I think it's a great suggestion. I just need to think it through. All right?"

"Sure, that's fine." Excitement swelled through Emily's stomach and shot through her body merely thinking there was a possibility she might get this job. She knew she should not get her hopes up, but it was too late. Until Miss Simons told her no, there was hope that she, Emily Slater, could actually create a wedding dress. Who knew? One day she just might become the next Vera Wang.

Grandma always told them to dream big. That's exactly what she was doing.

"CAN I GET YOU some more coffee?" Charlotte asked Hannah Carter as they sat at Charlotte's kitchen table the next morning.

Hannah and Charlotte had been friends and neighbors for over thirty years and their regular visits were as much a part of their routine as sweeping the kitchen floor.

"No, thanks. I need to get back once I finish this cup. I've got a ton of laundry to do. I have no idea how Frank and I manage to go through so many clothes in so little time." Hannah's long, thin fingers worked the ends of her graying blonde hair.

"It doesn't take long. Add three more people to that, and you're doing laundry most every day." Charlotte took a sip from her coffee, allowing the warmth of it to soothe her.

"I don't know how you do it. I really don't. I'm sure it doesn't get any easier as we get older. I know how tired I get and, no offense, you're older than me."

Charlotte stared her down. "I'm wiser too, remember."

"Yes, there's that."

They shared a friendly laugh.

"I'm so glad that Melody got through her biopsy all right yesterday," Hannah said.

"Yes, she came through it fine. They won't know anything for a while, of course."

"This has to be a scary time. Good news or bad, it's hard to wait."

"I can only imagine."

"I'm glad there are so many people helping with the diner."

"Me too," Charlotte said. "Thanks for your part in that, friend."

"Hey, it's the least I can do. I'm glad to help." Hannah drained the last bit of coffee from her cup. "Well, I guess I'd better get back to that laundry, though I hate to face the cold again." She glanced out the kitchen window. "It's coming down pretty good out there."

"Yeah, I see that. They're predicting another six inches on Saturday."

Hannah sighed as she stuffed her arms through her coat sleeves. "I'm so ready for spring."

"That makes two of us."

"Funny how the snow can look so beautiful, like the

world is perfect, and be so deadly at the same time, you know? Well, thank you for the coffee, my friend. I'll talk to you soon." Hannah tromped off the front porch, her boots leaving fresh tracks behind in the newly fallen snow.

Charlotte thought of what Hannah had said about the snow. Just like life, so perfect one minute, and yet . . . No, she couldn't—she *wouldn't*—think that way.

She went back to the kitchen to put their cups in the dishwasher and clean off the table. The morning's Scripture verse that Bob had read at breakfast came to mind. Proverbs, she thought it was. "A friend loves at all times."

That was certainly how it had been with Hannah over the years. She had stood by Charlotte while her children were growing up. Though Hannah and Frank had no children of their own, they had served as Aunt Hannah and Uncle Frank as devotedly as any blood relatives could have.

Precious few enjoyed the blessings of a friend like Hannah. Charlotte prayed she could offer that kind of friendship to others. After all, she was on this earth to do what she could to help others, and that's what she intended to do. She had never been one to sit on her hands when someone was in need, and she was thankful for that. Plenty of people had reached out to the Stevensons, and the Stevensons tried to do the same.

She shook her head. Why her mind was shooting off in that direction this morning, she had no idea. Most likely her concern for Melody had taken her there. Friends might be helping out more at the diner in the days ahead. Time would tell. She could only hope her fears were unfounded.

Chapter Five

"Are you coherent enough to talk or are you still feeling loopy from the drugs yesterday?" Charlotte asked Melody over the phone.

"Well, Russ tells me I'm loopy and it has nothing to do with the drugs."

Charlotte laughed, carrying the phone in one hand and her mug of coffee with the other as she headed toward the kitchen table.

"How did it go?"

"Went all right. Russ was actually a big support. He was still with me when I woke up and they showed me the mass. Ashley was grossed out when I told her that."

Charlotte laughed, but worry constricted it.

"It was bigger than I had anticipated. They sent me home to take care of the incision and said I could go back to work in a couple of days."

"When will you know the biopsy results?"

"I go back to the surgeon next week."

A quickening rolled in Charlotte's belly just knowing the anxiety her friend must be going through.

"So weird. There is no cancer on either side of my family. They all die from heart attacks and strokes instead." She chuckled. "As if that's any consolation."

"Is Ashley holding up all right?"

"For some reason, this has been really hard on Ash, and I'm not sure exactly why."

"Maybe Emily has shared some of her struggles," Charlotte said.

"Maybe."

"Well, we'll be here for her."

"I knew I could count on you, Charlotte. I guess I'd better go. I'm feeling a little tired, and Dr. Grady said I needed to rest."

"Of course. Before you go, could I pray with you?"

"There's nothing I would appreciate more."

In the quiet of that winter day, as a soft wind whistled and swirled around the old homestead and a gentle snow drifted against the windowpane, Charlotte and Melody prayed together, knowing without a doubt that God had heard their prayer and the answer was on its way.

Hopefully, it would be the answer they longed to hear.

LATER THAT AFTERNOON, the kids came bursting through the back door, smelling of book bags, school lockers, and fresh snow.

"Take off your wet boots," Charlotte called out as she walked down the hall toward the kitchen.

The kids pulled off their boots and stacked them neatly by the door.

"Sorry, Grandma," Christopher said.

Yanking off their wet woolens and coats, they put them in their places.

"What's for dinner? I'm starved," Sam said.

"Whatever it is, it sure smells good," Christopher said, taking a deep whiff.

Charlotte smiled. "Stuffed chicken, mashed potatoes and gravy, sweet potatoes, and salad."

"Anybody we know?" Sam asked with a wink.

"What?" Charlotte didn't know what he was getting at.

"The chicken. Anyone we know?"

Charlotte swatted him with the dishtowel. "Oh, you."

"Grandma, I can't wait to show you the two sketches I came up with for Miss Simons," Emily enthused.

Even though she had been in school all day, Emily still smelled as fresh and sweet as a scrubbed apple. The scent reminded Charlotte of Denise.

"Did she say you could do it?"

"Yeah. She caught me in the hall at school and told me to go ahead with it."

"That's wonderful, honey. I'd like to see your sketches." Charlotte walked with them toward the stairway. "But remember, I'm not the one you have to please."

"I know. But still I want your opinion."

"All right. I'll look at them after dinner. You kids get your homework done. By that time, dinner should be about ready."

They nodded and ran up the stairs.

Charlotte's heart squeezed when she looked at Emily. She knew Emily loved Ashley's family, and if they had a long road ahead of them, no doubt Emily would be walking that road with them.

They all would.

AFTER GRANDPA SAID GRACE for the meal, Sam and Christopher started passing the bowls, taking more than their fair share of food.

"Hey, save some for the rest of us," Emily growled when Sam took a double helping of potatoes.

He scooped a bite onto his fork. "Sorry."

She grunted. He obviously wasn't sorry in the least.

"There's plenty for everyone," Grandma said.

"Just make sure there's plenty for me," Grandpa said with a grin as the bowls made their way to him.

Amid the sounds of silver scraping stoneware, Emily and her brothers spilled stories of their day around the dinner table. It had taken them awhile to get used to eating dinner together. To Emily it had seemed as though they had taken a step back in time when they first moved to Nebraska. But now she almost looked forward to dinner together—except when Sam was in a bad mood. Then he usually picked at her and caused her mood to go south. She didn't like those dinners. But tonight was good.

While Christopher talked about the family tree he had to get started on, Emily's mind drifted to the wedding dresses she had sketched. They were so cool. One of the girls at school called them "eclectic." Emily liked that. Made it sound like she was on the cutting edge of fashion.

Grandma talked about God giving people gifts, and Emily wondered if this just might be hers. Maybe she would go to college and pursue a degree in some kind of fashion. They had lived in California before. It didn't seem so far-fetched to her that she could one day work for the stars. She could own her own boutique where all the big-name stars would come to buy one of her original designs. She smiled at the thought.

"Why do you have that goofy grin on your face?" Sam asked, nudging her and shaking his head.

"Shut up." She glanced up at her grandparents. "Sorry." Better that she beat them to the punch. They didn't like their grandchildren to say "shut up" to one another, but it had just sort of slipped out. Sam had a way of making her feel stupid.

"Did you tell Emily about Mrs. Givens?" Grandpa asked Grandma.

Emily's attention shot toward Grandma. "You know something?" A burning sensation balled in her stomach when she saw the look Grandma gave to Grandpa.

"Oh, sorry," he said.

"Not much, really. Just that she had her biopsy and everything went well. She'll go back next week for the results."

"You don't think it's bad, do you?" Emily asked.

Forks stopped sliding across plates, hands came to a standstill, and all eyes turned to Grandma.

She swallowed. "I have no way of knowing, honey, but we can always pray for the best."

The burning in Emily's stomach grew more intense. She scooted her food around her plate with her fork and finally looked up. "I just wondered—did you pray for our mom?" One look at the sadness on her Grandma's face, and Emily wished she could take back the words. Heat climbed her cheeks. Still, although she already knew the answer in her heart, she couldn't deny the question had smoldered inside her for months.

Now she could feel everyone looking at her.

"Yes, we prayed for your mom," Grandma whispered. "We prayed for her—and for all of you kids—every day. But remember, she . . . she was gone before we knew about the accident."

"May I please be excused?" Emily asked.

"Yes, honey," Grandma said, though the words sounded distant to Emily.

Her wobbly legs barely carried her to the top of the stairs. She ran into the familiar comfort of her room, closed the door behind her, and threw herself on the bed. Maybe everything would turn out all right for Ashley's mom, but maybe not. There were no guarantees.

She breathed deeply of the sweet smell that lingered on her yellow-and-blue patchwork quilt and the pillows on her bed. She tried to find comfort in the scent, but right now, she hurt too much.

"Mom, why did you have to leave us?" Emily hugged her pillow tight against her chest and released her fear through tears that fell upon the pillow.

Were the tears for herself? Her mom? Ashley? Ashley's mom? Emily wasn't sure. She knew only that an ache grew in her chest that took her breath away. Why didn't God fix it? Make everything better?

A few minutes later a soft knock on her door told her Grandma was on the other side.

"Emily, do you want to talk now or should I come back later?"

"You can come in," Emily said.

Grandma stepped inside, her face full of compassion. "Are you all right?" She walked over to the bed and sat down beside Emily.

"I just don't know what I will say to Ashley if—if—" Emily twisted the edge of the sheet between her fingers. "I feel so helpless."

"I know. That's the hardest part in situations like this.

Now you know how mothers feel when their children are sick." Grandma smiled.

Suddenly, Emily realized this whole thing was likely stirring up hard memories of her mom for Grandma too.

"I'm sorry, Grandma." Emily reached over and hugged her. It had taken awhile for Emily to get comfortable sharing hugs with her grandparents, but they'd been there long enough now, and Grandma didn't give up, always hugging whether they accepted and received her hugs graciously or not.

"It may be nothing. But if it's something, we'll get her through it. With God's help, we'll get the whole family through it," Grandma said.

Emily nodded. Fresh tears slipped down her cheeks and moistened her dry lips.

"The women at church have already rallied around Melody and her family, helping at the diner. Esther Showalter has been working hard, but she can't handle it all alone, and not knowing what the future holds, we set up a schedule of workers till Melody gets through this. With everyone pitching in, it will make things much easier. Melody is greatly relieved to know she doesn't have to hurry back."

"That's great." Emily yanked a tissue from a nearby box and then wiped her face.

"In the meantime, maybe you and Ashley could come up with some way you might help out at the diner."

"That's true," Emily said, her mind already leaving her own pain behind to think of ways to help.

"The most important thing is that Ashley knows you're there for her. Sometimes it's enough to know there are people who care and are standing by to help in any way they're needed."

"Yeah." The more she talked to Grandma, the more the burning in Emily's stomach lessened.

"You think she'll be all right, Grandma?"

She smiled and tucked a strand of hair behind Emily's ear. "It's hard to say what the future holds, so we'll just have to wait and see. In the meantime, if they need us, we'll be there for them."

Peace flowed through Emily like warm chocolate, followed by the strong determination to help her friend in her hour of need.

"I don't know how you do it."

"Do what?"

"Carry everybody's struggles and not let it get to you."

"That's because I carry my burdens to the Lord and leave them there." She paused. "Well, most of the time I leave them there." Another pause. "Okay, I *try* to leave them there."

They laughed together.

"Oh, I wanted to show you these." Emily reached for her sketchpad and opened it.

"Those are nice, Emily."

"You think so?"

"Yes, you are very talented."

"I just hope Miss Simons likes them."

"Me too. But even if she doesn't, just remember, it's only her opinion. It doesn't mean they're bad designs."

"Thanks."

"Well, I'd better get back downstairs before the boys eat up all the chocolate cake."

"Chocolate cake?"

Grandma smiled. "Want some?"

Emily nodded vigorously. She got up and walked with her grandma toward the bedroom door.

"Grandma? Thanks."

Charlotte gave Emily a sideways squeeze. "The Lord will help all of us. You'll see."

Emily nodded and followed her grandmother down the stairs, all the while hoping Grandma was right.

Chapter Six

Charlotte looked with gratitude at the names of the six women on the church hospitality committee who had offered to help out at Mel's Place. Shoving her notebook aside, she folded her hands and briefly closed her eyes. *Thank you, Lord, for providing the workers to help Melody keep the diner going so she has one less thing to worry about while her life is so uncertain.*

Just as she finished her prayer, Bob shoved through the back door. He yanked off his boots and hung his coat on the rack. "Boy, it's cold out there."

"How are the animals?"

"They seem to be all right. Can't leave 'em out long though. That wind has a bite in it, that's for sure."

Charlotte promptly got up and started the coffee for Bob. "Let me get you some coffee to warm you up."

"Sounds good." He settled into a seat in the breakfast nook. "The chickens sure are plumped up today." Bob gave a laugh.

Charlotte chuckled. "From the sounds of it, if we had feathers today, we'd be plumped up too." She placed a mug of hot coffee in front of him and slipped into a seat across from him.

Bob curled a big, calloused hand around the mug. "Thanks." He took a sip. "What are you up to today?"

"Cleaning the house, doing chores, working a little on the bookkeeping, working on the schedule for the diner. As you know, some of the ladies from the church are helping out there."

Bob scratched his head. "That's faithful people doing the Lord's work."

"It sure is."

"Glad to see it."

"Me too. The Givenses are good folks, and they're known in this community. They deserve a good response."

"They sure do," Bob agreed. "If it comes down to it, and you need help from the men, let me know. I'll get a group together."

"That would be great."

"You seen that boy of ours around?"

"Pete? I think he's staying out in the field, hiding from Dana." Charlotte grinned.

"I wouldn't doubt it. Can't say I blame him."

"Oh, you." Charlotte playfully tapped him on the arm. "You men are all alike."

"What? Just because we don't like shopping for dishes?" He shook his head. "Get some paper plates and be done with it." Bob grunted.

"Think Bill and Anna will make it over tomorrow?"

"The boys at the supply store say we're supposed to get more snow tomorrow, so I wouldn't count on it. Don't want them to get stranded somewhere."

"Oh my, no," Charlotte said, mortified at the thought.

"You're just itching to get your hands on that baby again, aren't you, Grandma?"

She smiled. "And you're not?"

"Sure I am—want him to know his grandpa, after all."

"I've been thinking about one of our other grandsons today."

"Which one?" Bob asked.

"Christopher. This family tree project has me wondering if Christopher will need to talk to Kevin and what that might mean."

Kevin's recent visit had not only caused an upheaval in the family, it had brought fresh fears as well. Fears of him taking the children, fears of what kind of father he would be.

Bob sighed. "He *is* their dad, Charlotte. We just have to trust the Lord with it. Might not be a bad idea for Kevin to get to know Christopher a little more anyway."

"And vice versa."

"Right."

Private fears kept Charlotte from responding further. One day at a time—that was all they could do.

"WELL, I DON'T KNOW what you expected, little brother. It costs money to get information." Sam walked into the kitchen behind Christopher and drank from a glass of water. "I'm going to bed."

Charlotte said good night and watched him disappear into the hallway. She turned to see Christopher slumped down in a seat at the breakfast nook with Toby coiled in a heap at his feet. She walked over and sat across from him.

"Want to talk about it?"

"No."

She waited.

"I just don't understand how we're supposed to make a family tree when we can't get anything we want off the Internet without paying for a download of this or that." His pudgy fingers raked the hair from his forehead.

"Now, don't you worry. There has to be a way." Charlotte thought a moment. "What about the library? Didn't you say Miss Luka said to check there? They could certainly give you some direction."

"Yeah, she did say to check there. Dylan needs to work on his family tree too. Do you think you could take us there tomorrow?"

Charlotte inwardly winced at all she had to do the next day, but one look at the hope in her precious grandson's eyes and she knew she would help him out.

"Absolutely. How about we plan for around two o'clock?"

"That would be great! Thanks, Grandma." Christopher reached over and gave her a hug. It was short, sweet, and to the point, but she'd take it.

He smelled of chewing gum and fabric softener. She smiled. Every day he seemed to get a little taller. Before she knew it, he would be as tall as his Uncle Pete.

Time goes much too fast.

Her throat constricted with thoughts of Denise. She'd never get to see her children grown to adulthood. No matter how many times Charlotte rolled the matter around in her head, she never seemed to quite settle things in her mind. Yes, God's peace enveloped her and continued even now, but she wondered if parents who had lost children ever truly stopped grieving for them. She didn't think so. At least she didn't see that happening for her. In the meantime, she prayed that Melody would have more time. Lots more time.

"HOW'S TRUDY DOING?" Bob asked when Charlotte stepped through the back door early Saturday morning.

"I thought I would never get milk out of that cow this morning."

"Must be too cold."

"I think it was me. My fingers were too stiff to get the job done." Charlotte hung her coat on the rack. "Finally managed it though."

She lifted the bucket as proof of victory and walked it over to the sink to pour its contents into a container. "It's so cold out there today." She shivered.

"I wish you would have let me do it."

"You were sleeping so peacefully. I just couldn't wake you."

"I'm a lucky man." Bob grinned at her and then folded his newspaper and laid it on the table. He walked over to the kitchen window and peered out. "Looks like we're getting a start on those six inches they're predicting."

Charlotte sighed. "I fear you're right." She put the milk in the refrigerator.

"Where are the kids?" Bob asked.

"Let's see: Emily is out in the barn grooming Stormy. Sam went out for breakfast with Jake, and then he was going to work for a while at the airport. Hopefully, he'll get back before we get too much snow."

Charlotte pulled out a bottle of cleaning liquid from under the sink. With a little elbow grease, she gave the kitchen sink a thorough scrubbing, the pine scent gaining momentum with every stroke.

"I sure wouldn't want to be out in that open field today with the wind whipping around me," Bob said.

"That makes two of us."

"Where's Christopher?"

"He's up in his room playing with the DS that Kevin got him at Christmas."

Once the sink was polished, Charlotte put the cleanser away, washed and dried her hands, and then joined Bob at the table.

"Is his room cleaned up?" Bob wanted to know. He was not one for letting the kids slack off their chores.

"Yes, it is. I'm taking him and Dylan to the library later today. This family tree thing has him in a tizzy. Emily wants to go along too and look at fashion magazines. Get some ideas for Dana's wedding dress, I suppose."

Bob nodded but didn't say anything.

"I still don't like the family tree idea," Charlotte said, shaking her head. "I've got to let it go though."

Bob rubbed a hand along the back of his neck. A shaft of sunlight peered through the window and landed on the sink and countertop, as though spotlighting Charlotte's scrubbing efforts.

"It will work itself out," Bob said matter-of-factly.

"I'm sure you're right. Christopher doesn't seem any more excited about it than we are."

He chuckled. "You're right about that." He shoved away from the table. "I'd better get back to work."

"What's on your agenda today?"

"By the looks of things, I need to help Pete make sure the livestock are warm enough, have plenty of feed, all that."

"Emily's fed the chickens and the barn cats, so you don't need to worry about that."

At the mention of food, Lightning, Christopher's brown tabby, came prancing into the kitchen for her breakfast. She purred and tangled herself about Charlotte's feet.

"All right, all right. Hold still so you don't trip me,"

Charlotte said with a chuckle. After pouring fresh water and cat food for Lightning, Charlotte placed the bowls by the coat rack at the back door. "Here you go."

"Where's Toby?" Bob asked.

"He's up in Christopher's room. Where else?"

"Yeah, I should have known. If you ask me, that dog is becoming sissified."

Charlotte laughed. "You can't blame her. She doesn't want to be out in the cold and snow any more than we do."

Bob reached over and gave Charlotte a peck on the cheek. Then he sunk deep into his jacket, opened the back door, and braved the icy wind. A blast of chilled air whipped through the kitchen, lifting a paper napkin from the table to float upon the momentary breeze and land on the floor.

Charlotte picked it up and tossed it in the trash.

"Grandma, are you still going to take Dylan and me to the library?" Christopher stood before her in rumpled Spider-Man pajamas, hair askew, his skin all aglow. Toby happily trotted up beside him, tongue dangling from the side of her mouth—proof positive the two of them had been romping about upstairs.

"Yes. Remember, I told you we would leave around two o'clock. Should I plan to pick up Dylan or will he meet us there?"

"We need to pick him up. Could he come over to our house after that? Maybe stay for supper?"

Charlotte mentally scurried through her to-do list. "I suppose that would be all right."

"Great. Thanks, Grandma."

Christopher took off, most likely to get away before she could change her mind. Charlotte heard him tromping up the stairs, Toby's paws padding along behind him.

Chapter Seven

I'm going to run an errand while you all are at the library, but I won't be gone long," Charlotte said, glancing at the gathering snowfall. "We don't want to get caught in the snowstorm if it gets worse."

Dylan and Christopher exchanged wide grins and both said at the same time, "Cool."

Charlotte rolled her eyes. "I'll be back in an hour. Let Emily know if you get into any trouble."

Emily rolled her eyes. "Thanks a lot."

The boys grinned and trotted happily toward the library door. When they got there, Christopher bent over, molded a snowball between gloved hands, and then lifted an ornery grin toward Dylan. Just as he was about to throw it, a thin, gray-haired woman with wire-rimmed glasses that made her eyes look twice their size pecked on the door window and shook her head. Christopher dropped the snowball. Dylan pointed at him and started laughing.

"You'd better watch yourself," Emily said, pulling open the library door, "or you'll be waiting for Grandma out in the cold."

Once they stepped into the library the old woman's taut lips and stern brows reinforced Emily's message that they'd better behave or else. It seemed that the regular librarian, Edna, was on vacation and had been temporarily replaced.

"I'm going to look through the magazines. Let me know if you need me—and stay out of trouble," Emily warned.

Christopher made a face.

Once Emily had walked away, Dylan turned to Christopher and whispered, "Are you sure it will work for me to ask your grandma to let me stop by my house on our way home? Won't she be suspicious when I carry out the ant farm covered with a blanket?"

"She won't pay any attention," Christopher said, hoping he was right. "Just tell her it's a game we're gonna play."

Dylan sighed, his eyes twitching.

"Don't worry."

"You'll have to tell her about the ant farm sooner or later," Dylan said.

"I know. I will, when the time is right."

"Sure wish I could keep it," Dylan said with regret.

"You'll still get to watch them at my house."

"Yeah, as long as your grandparents don't make you get rid of them too."

"Yeah," Christopher said, feeling glum at the thought.

Dylan tapped Christopher's arm. "I think she's the one we have to ask for help." Dylan pointed at the old woman who had frowned at them moments before.

Christopher's jaw dropped. His gaze frantically searched his surroundings. There had to be another way. "Are you sure?"

Dylan shrugged. "See for yourself."

"Follow me."

Christopher led the way, aimlessly walking up and down the aisles as he searched for another way to get help.

"Come on. Your grandma will be back in an hour. We've got to get help."

"Oh, all right." Christopher trudged toward the information desk. "You ask her."

"Excu—" Dylan's voice cracked and he cleared his throat. "Excuse me, ma'am. We were wondering if you could help us."

She looked at Christopher as though intently searching for possible flaws on the page of a book. Finally, she let out a grunt and asked for specifics.

Christopher had a feeling it was going to be a long hour before Grandma came to get them.

CHARLOTTE WALKED into Mel's Place to see how things were going. The smells of frying hamburgers and onion rings swirled about her. Esther Showalter spotted Charlotte and sent a hearty wave her way. Charlotte smiled and waved back.

The church women covered the serving and cash register, and Esther appeared to be holding down the kitchen duties today.

Charlotte said hello to the ladies and then walked into the kitchen, where Esther lifted the onion rings from a searing hot vat of grease and put them aside to drain.

With her hands on her hips, Charlotte stared at her. "What are you doing here? You've put in far too much time here lately. You need to let others help."

Esther held up her hand. "Now, before you get in an uproar, just hold on right there. I had the whole day off yesterday while Alice Mayfield filled in for me. It was time to come in. I'll get lazy and soft if I don't keep busy."

Downy-soft hair the color of fresh-fallen snow, cheery pink cheeks, eyes filled with merriment, and a puffy midsection made Esther look like Mrs. Claus. Her appearance made her easy to love.

Charlotte shook her head. "I give up. There's no keeping you down."

Esther gave a heartfelt chuckle that shook her belly. "You're right there." She put together a couple of hamburgers with all the fixings and scooped the onion rings onto the plates alongside the sandwiches. Then she put the plates in the window for the servers to pick up and deliver. She turned to Charlotte. "How's our girl doing?"

"So far, so good. 'Course we won't know anything for a while. She's resting, and that's good."

Esther nodded. "I'm so thankful for all the helpers. God is good."

"He is indeed," Charlotte said. Right then she noticed Lydia Middleton at one of the tables with another lady Charlotte didn't know. "I'll be right back."

She walked over to Lydia's table. "Hello, Lydia, how are you?"

Lydia's gray eyes brightened at the sight of Charlotte. "Hello, dear. Good to see you. This is my friend, Emma Green. Emma, this is Charlotte Stevenson."

"Hello," the elderly woman said with a shaky voice.

"Melody told me she received a lovely card from you, Lydia," Charlotte commented.

"I made up my mind a long time ago that as long as I have breath in me and the ability to write, I will let others know how much they mean to me. My mama taught me that. She said people don't take the time to tell each other how much they love them. 'Never miss an opportunity, Lydia,' she would say." Lydia smiled. "What an old woman I am. I've gone on and on, boring you with my talk."

Charlotte smiled and patted Lydia's shoulder. "Not at all. It's always a pleasure to talk with you." A glance at the clock told her it was time to pick up the kids. "I'm afraid I'll have to go now though. The kids are at the library, and I need to pick them up. It looks like the snow is already starting to come down more heavily."

"I'll have to get going myself," Lydia agreed. "Tell Emily I'll look forward to our next visit."

"I sure will. Nice to meet you Mrs. Green."

The old woman nodded and smiled.

Charlotte quickly said her good-byes to Esther and the other ladies and then headed out the door, all the while praying she could be just like Lydia Middleton one day.

AFTER BROWSING THROUGH a few Web sites, poring through genealogy books, and checking out a couple of how-to books, the boys went outside just in time to see Grandma pulling the car up to the library.

"Where's Emily?" Grandma asked.

"She's coming. She's getting some magazines," Christopher said.

"How did it go?" she asked when they climbed into the car.

"Oh, all right, I guess," Christopher said.

Dylan's eye twitched, but he didn't say anything.

"The online stuff wasn't much help, as I already knew. The librarian did give us some books, but I don't know that they're gonna help that much. She said the best way was to keep searching through genealogy books and e-mail family members who might be able to help us."

"Yeah," Dylan said. "Like we didn't know that." More twitching.

"Well, I suppose it's a start," Grandma said.

"I s'pose," Christopher said, using Grandma's word. "I guess I'll start with my dad. He told me to e-mail him when I had time, so I might as well."

Christopher noticed that Grandma didn't say anything. She probably felt sorry for him that he had to do all that work. Maybe she'd make some more cookies.

With her arms full of magazines, Emily stepped into the car, and they were soon on their way.

The snow was so thick now, that Grandma had to turn on her wipers to see to drive.

"Hey, Grandma, Dylan forgot his sleeping bag. Could we swing by his house and get it?"

Charlotte gave a nervous look. "Can't he borrow one of ours? The weather isn't all that great, and I'd like to get home."

"It will only take a second," Dylan piped up.

"Oh, all right. But do hurry."

Emily had her nose buried in a magazine, and Christopher prayed she'd keep it that way when Dylan came out with the ant farm. Then he wondered how God felt about such prayers. He had a feeling that, since they were sneaking around, God wouldn't answer it, but he figured it didn't hurt to ask.

"Here we are," Grandma said when they pulled up to Dylan's place.

"I'll be right back." Dylan dashed from the car.

Christopher wanted to go too but was afraid it would

raise suspicion. Dylan returned in a hurry, a sleeping bag over the ant farm.

"What in the world is that?" Grandma asked.

"Oh, I think Dylan grabbed a game for us to play too. I guess he doesn't want the snow to get on it," Christopher said, feeling a nudge of guilt for fibbing.

"Thanks, Mrs. Stevenson," Dylan said, settling into the car.

As they got back on the road toward home, Christopher asked her what was for dinner.

"How about spaghetti, garlic bread, and salad?"

"Mmmm, sounds great. Cookies too?"

"Yes, cookies too. If you keep eating all these cookies, I'm going to have to teach you how to make them."

Christopher didn't like the sound of that at all.

Dylan snickered.

Before long Grandma pulled the car into the driveway and the boys hopped out before she could say another word about cooking. The only thing Christopher wanted to do in the kitchen was eat.

But first they'd go to his room and put away the ant farm.

"DID BILL AND ANNA CALL to cancel for dinner?" Charlotte asked when she spotted Bob in the kitchen as she and the kids pushed through the back door.

"Not that I know of, but I didn't check the machine for messages," Bob said.

"Oh my. I hope they didn't head out in this weather," Charlotte said in a worried voice.

Then she turned to the boys. "You boys go get washed up for supper."

"Okay, Grandma."

Christopher and Dylan happily obeyed. Emily had already gone up to her room to pore over her magazines.

"Where's Sam?" she asked Bob, pulling a box of spaghetti from the pantry.

"Sam isn't home from the airport yet."

She turned around. "Oh dear."

"Now, Charlotte, don't expect the worst."

"I just don't like him out in this stuff, Bob. It's getting really bad."

"You want to call and check on him?"

"Yeah, maybe I'll do that. And I'll check to see if there's a message from Bill while I'm at it." She put the spaghetti down just as the phone rang.

Bob was closest to the phone, so he answered it.

"Hello? Okay, where are you?"

Charlotte knew from the sound of Bob's voice that Sam was stuck somewhere. They should have reminded him to get home before the snow got too heavy. In fact, it seemed ridiculous that airports were open on days such as this anyway. The more she thought about it, the more worked up she got. She filled the kettle with cold tap water and placed it on the stove, lighting the fire beneath it.

Bob hung up the phone.

"Well, I hope you have enough spaghetti."

She turned to face him. "What's wrong?"

"That was Bill. They're stuck in a snowdrift. I'll get Pete to go with me and see if we can dig them out. Better get the extra blankets and beds ready. Looks like we'll be having overnight company."

Chapter Eight

"You'd better take Arielle home, Sam. The roads are getting bad, and I don't want you two getting stuck here," said Ed Haffner, owner-operator of the county airport.

"Guess Dad shouldn't have dropped me off here today. Sorry, Uncle Ed." Arielle looked at him through dark blue eyes and flicked her long, raven ponytail behind her shoulder.

"No problem, honey. I just want you kids to be safe."

Sam and Arielle pulled on their warm winter wraps and gathered their things to go.

"I'll be back to work next week," Sam said.

"With the uncertainty of this weather, it's probably a good idea to call the airport before you come in, Sam. No need to make the trip if we're shut down," Ed said.

"Okay."

"I'm going to close up for today." Ed turned off the coffee-maker and stuffed some paperwork in his right top drawer.

The moment Sam and Arielle stepped through the office door, a sharp wind hit them.

"It's freezing out here," Arielle said, pulling her coat farther up her neck and burrowing her chin deeper into her woolen scarf.

"Yeah, let's hurry."

Sam ran to the car with Arielle right on his heels. He unlocked her door and then ran around to his door, climbed inside, and started the engine. The heater went through its usual drama and finally sputtered a thin veil of heat into the car. Sam got out and scraped the thickening ice off the windows.

Snowflakes clung to his eyelashes. The icy air bit into his cheeks, stinging them. He could hardly move his fingers and vowed never to go out of the house in the winter again without gloves.

Once the windows were cleared, he jumped back in the car and sat for a moment, shivering. Right now, he would sell his brother to get a good heater for his car.

"Are you all right?"

"Yeah, just freezing, that's all," he said through chattering teeth.

He sat there a moment, briskly rubbing his hands together, waiting for the car to warm up. When his fingers finally tingled back to life, he backed up the car and nosed it toward the road.

"The snow sure is coming down," Arielle said. "A big mug of hot chocolate with marshmallows sounds great to me right about now. How about you?"

"Yeah, that does sound good."

Heavy winds picked up the fallen snow, sending glistening sparkles swirling through the air. Sam struggled to keep the car on the road and out of the huge snowdrifts heaped along the roadsides.

"Hey, maybe school will get canceled on Monday," Sam said.

Arielle looked at him with utter horror. "No, we don't want that! It could throw off Career Day. I'm really looking forward to that."

"Don't you already know you want to be a social worker?"

"Yes, but there's still a lot to learn about all the facets of the job. And I'd love some guidance about which classes will be most helpful."

Her eyes twinkled at the thought of college and careers. Sam just didn't get that.

"What about you? Now that applications are in, have you thought about what you want to major in?"

Sam cleared his throat. Did he really want to get into this discussion with her right now while their lives hung in the balance in this snowstorm? He didn't think so.

"I'm still thinking." He knew his comment lacked the enthusiasm she wanted, but he didn't care. They weren't married. He didn't owe her an explanation.

"You don't sound very excited about it." Her expression held a challenge.

Here we go again.

"Look, Arielle, I'm just not sure what I want to do with my life yet. We can't all be like you."

"Just what do you mean by that?" She folded her arms in front of her and glared at him.

"Only that I'm busy and haven't had time to think about it."

"You've had as much time as anyone else, Sam. You think you're the only one who's busy around here? I'm trying to keep up my grades so I can make it to a decent college and see my dreams fulfilled. Not to mention, I'm working after school at the pharmacy."

"I do my share of work at the airport, not to mention on the farm."

"Yes, but there's always time to plan for the future."

"What's it to you, anyway, Arielle? What do you care if I have my life all mapped out or not?" His voice reverberated off the car ceiling.

That question seemed to hit her like a punch, taking the fight right out of her. The look in her eyes immediately brought him pain.

He'd pay for that. He didn't know how or when, but he'd pay.

"WHAT'S THAT PERFUME?" Charlotte looked up from her embroidery when Emily entered the family room.

Emily smiled. "You noticed."

"What is it?"

"Cachet. Mom used to wear it. It's still available but hard to find in the stores—especially around here. Anyway, Ashley found it online and bought me a bottle. I forgot to tell you."

Charlotte's heart lodged in her throat. She had bought that scent for Denise a long time ago. It had a light, flowery scent. If she wasn't wearing apple-scented lotion, she smelled of Cachet.

"It's lovely," Charlotte said, trying to quell the memories it conjured up.

Emily looked completely satisfied. Obviously, the familiar scent brought her comfort. Who was Charlotte to argue with that?

Charlotte glanced at the clock on the wall for the hundredth time in the last ten minutes. Bob wasn't home yet with Bill and his family. Sam still wasn't home either, and she wasn't able to reach him on his cell phone. The wind had picked up momentum, whipping around the heavy snow as fast as it fell.

"I sure wish they'd hurry up and get here." Emily said, as though reading Charlotte's thoughts. She plunked into a chair near Charlotte.

"Yeah. Me too."

"Funny how something can look harmless and yet cause so much trouble."

Charlotte looked up in surprise. Emily's comment held such depth—Charlotte wondered if she even realized it.

Emily looked at her and shrugged. "You know, kind of like life. One minute you're happy and everything is going great. The next minute, your world sort of falls apart."

She did realize it. Obviously, the perfume or maybe this thing with Melody was bringing back memories of Denise to both of them.

"Emily—"

Christopher and Dylan walked into the room. "Hey, Grandma, when are we gonna eat?"

"Yeah, I'm hungry too," Emily said.

Deep moment over.

"I suppose we'll have to go ahead without everyone else. I had hoped we could all eat together, but it's getting late."

Charlotte lifted back the curtain and looked outside. Though the sky had disappeared into thick darkness, everything else was covered by a blanket of white as far as the eye could see. So pretty, yet so dangerous. Life could change faster than a weather report.

"Let's head for the kitchen, kids."

She didn't have to tell Christopher twice. He led the way. They had no sooner sat down to their meal when the back door burst open, allowing a gust of winter's chill to enter. One by one Bill and his family piled in amid greetings of relief and welcome.

Soon they were all seated at the dinner table, which was laden with spaghetti and thick sauce, parmesan cheese, large chunks of warm garlic bread fresh from the oven, and a crisp salad, just tossed. Ice water and hot coffee completed the menu.

"What happened out there?" Charlotte asked Bill.

"We got caught in a snow bank, Grandma. It was awesome," Bill's younger daughter, Jennifer, said.

The adults laughed.

"Well, I don't know how 'awesome' it was, but it definitely was an adventure," Bill said.

"It wasn't awesome at all," Anna said with a frown. "I told Bill it was dangerous to take a baby out in this weather."

She was put out to say the least, and Charlotte wasn't so sure she could blame her. Still, she was glad to have everyone safe at the farm. Hopefully, Sam would join them soon.

"We'd better figure out sleeping arrangements," Charlotte said to keep her mind off of Sam. "Let's see, Pete—you could bunk in with Sam so that Bill, Anna, and the baby can have your room. Dylan will be with Christopher, and the girls can sleep in Emily's room." Charlotte thumped back in her chair. "Yes, that will work. Is that all right with all of you?"

Everyone nodded.

"I'm getting worried that Sam still isn't home," Bob said.

Charlotte agreed. "I called the airport while you were out getting Bill, and there was no answer."

"Did you try his cell phone?"

"Yes, but no answer. I'll try again." Charlotte excused herself from the table.

Charlotte called Sam's cell phone, but it went directly to voice mail.

"Nothing. Do you think I should call Arielle?"

"Might not be a bad idea," Bob said.

Charlotte looked up Arielle's parents' phone number and called them. She quickly explained her business, and Arielle let her know that Sam had dropped her off more than a half hour ago. He should have been home by now. Thanking her, Charlotte hung up the phone and turned to tell Bob.

"We're right on it," Pete said, tossing the last bite of garlic bread into his mouth. He backed his chair away from the table, causing its wooden legs to groan with the effort.

"Where will you go?" Emily asked. "I know the road he takes to Arielle's house. Want me to go with you?"

"Can me and Dylan go too?" Christopher asked, hopeful.

"You may not," Charlotte said with a stern voice.

Christopher's and Dylan's faces showed their disappointment, but she wasn't about to let them go out in this weather.

"Good idea, Emily. Make sure you dress plenty warm enough and join us out in the truck," Bob said.

"Why don't you stay here, Dad? Pete and I will take Emily and go," Bill said.

"You sure?"

"We're sure. No sense in all of us going."

Bob settled back into his chair, for which Charlotte was grateful. There were some perks to having adult children, after all.

"You kids be careful," Charlotte called out. She knew that was just plain silly. Of course they would be careful. Still, the mother and grandmother in her could not keep silent.

Once they left, the minutes seemed to crawl by at a snail's pace. Charlotte tried to occupy her thoughts by playing with Bill's girls, talking with Anna, and cuddling the baby, but her thoughts kept going back to Sam, wondering if he was all right.

"There's Uncle Pete," Jennifer called out from the family room nearly an hour later.

Charlotte practically raced to the front door. She watched as Emily and Sam climbed out of the truck. Sam had his hand up to his head. Charlotte's pulse quickened. She opened the front door for the kids to step inside.

"Are you hurt, Sam?"

Sam pulled down the rag he had been holding against his forehead and revealed a three-inch gash. Though the cut was fairly superficial, the bleeding made it appear much worse.

Madison took one look at it and started crying, which caused baby Will to cry too.

"We'd better get you stitched up," Charlotte said, tugging on Sam's arm, leading him to the bathroom.

"What? You're going to do it?"

The look on his face, along with her relief that everyone was safe at home, made Charlotte chuckle. "No, I meant that I have butterfly bandages that can do the trick for us. What happened anyway?"

"Someone crossed into my lane. I swerved to miss them, and my car spun out of control on the snow. Ended up in a ditch. We just left my car there. Uncle Pete says we'll go get it tomorrow."

Charlotte thought of all that could have happened and breathed a prayer of thanks.

"I tried to call you, but your cell phone wasn't on or something. I couldn't get through," she said.

"It was on, but there was no signal. Just a dead spot, I guess."

"Well, I'm glad you're all right and that you're getting your car tomorrow. We don't need anyone going back out in that mess tonight."

"Yeah, I guess."

Charlotte cleaned his wound and then pulled the bandages from the medicine cabinet, ripped the paper away, and stuck a couple on Sam's forehead. He winced only for a second.

"There. Good as new."

"Thanks."

There was something different about Sam tonight; she couldn't put her finger on it, but he seemed preoccupied. "You all right?" she asked. "I mean, I know you've just been through a lot, but is there anything else wrong?"

Sam blinked. "Uh, no. No, I'm fine." He lifted a forced smile and walked away.

She would keep an eye on him. Something was up. She'd get it out of him, one way or another.

Chapter Nine

Twinkling stars still hung suspended in the early morning sky when Charlotte heard the giggles and patter of little feet in the hallway, followed by Bill's firm whispers for the girls to be quiet.

"But, Daddy, did you see outside? We could make a snow fort today." Jennifer's voice was high and breathless.

Charlotte glanced at the clock. They didn't have to get up for chores for another fifteen minutes yet. What were the girls doing up so early? Rising from the bed, she pulled on her robe and shuffled over to the window. One glance outside, and she stopped in her tracks. There would be no church today. Large, wavy drifts of soft white lay upon the ground like thick mounds of icing on a cake. No wonder the girls were itching to get out there.

She quietly stepped across the room so as not to wake Bob and moved into the hallway.

"Grandma! Did you see outside?" Jennifer asked, face all aglow.

"Yeah, we want to make a snowman." Madison's eyes were as wide as full moons.

Charlotte scrunched down and hugged them both. "It does look mighty tempting out there, doesn't it?"

Little heads bobbed enthusiastically.

"Tell you what. Let's get some breakfast, and then maybe after everyone has eaten, it will warm up a little so Mommy and Daddy might let you go outside. But we'll have to wait and see, okay?"

Their pudgy faces wavered somewhere between hope and despair.

"Go get washed up so you can help Grandma in the kitchen."

Their feet kicked up full throttle as they ran to the bathroom to wash their hands.

Soon, amid yawns, disheveled hair, and pajamas, the family gathered around the table. Normally, they dressed before eating, but this morning there was something very relaxing and happy about it all, Charlotte decided.

"Here, Mommy, have this one. I made it myself," Jennifer announced proudly, pointing to an oblong-shaped pancake.

Anna smiled. "It looks delicious." She lifted the pancake with her fork and put it on her plate.

"I can't remember the last time we got snowed in," Bill said. "Makes me feel like a kid again." He passed the plate of pancakes to Christopher.

"Hey, Uncle Pete, could you hook that big tire tube on the back of the snowmobile and pull us around?" Christopher asked before scooping three pancakes onto his plate.

"Yeah, that would be cool." Dylan's eyes twitched only slightly this morning.

Pete rubbed his jaw. "Well, now, I don't know. I need to check on our neighbors. Maybe Sam could take you out today."

Hope stretched their eyes wide open as the boys eagerly sought Sam's response.

Charlotte wanted to mention that since they were all together it might be a good time to work on their family tree, but she hated to ruin the boys' excitement with thoughts of schoolwork, so for now, she kept silent. Though she hadn't grown completely at ease with the snowmobile idea, she knew she couldn't shelter the kids forever.

"I guess I can take you out," Sam said.

"Can we go on the snowmobile too, Sam?" Madison wanted to know.

"Um—" Sam looked at Bill and Anna.

"Oh no, girls, not with Sam driving," Anna spoke up.

Charlotte noted Christopher sighed with relief.

Amid the clanging of silverware and thumping of glasses against the wooden table, happy chatter abounded. Charlotte and Bob shared a glance and a smile. There was just something special about unexpected family gatherings such as these.

Once breakfast was over and the chatter had ceased, Bob cracked open the family Bible to the bookmark and began reading from Isaiah 26. Charlotte's gaze swept across her family sitting reverently at the table while Bob read the Scripture. Her heart swelled with gratitude for family.

When Bob read the words of Isaiah 26:3: "You will keep in perfect peace him whose mind is steadfast, because he trusts in you," Charlotte's heart turned toward someone else. And immediately she asked God to grant perfect peace to the Givens household—both today and in the days ahead.

AFTER THE MORNING CHORES had been tended to, the kids settled into the winter wonderland with all its pleasures.

"Hi, Grandma," Christopher waved wildly at his grandmother, who sat on the front porch swing, mummified in layers of warm clothes, her gloved hands wrapped tightly around a cup of hot coffee.

By the looks of her, Christopher figured older people couldn't handle the cold. So he thought it was pretty awesome that she would come out just to watch them on the tire tube. Just then Grandpa came out and joined her. Christopher was also glad he didn't have to worry about her going into his room and finding the ant farm. His teeth chattered slightly, from excitement or the cold, he couldn't be sure.

Pete looked the snowmobile over, took a wrench to it, and then announced it ride-worthy.

Madison and Jennifer were already busy making a snowman. A wimpy, girly snowman, Christopher thought.

Dylan laughed and pointed. "Look at that."

"We'll have to show them how to make a *cool* snowman when we're done riding, okay?" Christopher said to Dylan, who nodded enthusiastically.

Heavy snow weighed on the branches of the poplar trees in the yard. A ground squirrel, plumped by the cold and with a plume of a tail, scampered from tree to tree in search of who knew what.

Sam walked over to the boys and watched as Pete harnessed the tire tube to the snowmobile. Sam climbed onto the machine, causing the cold metal to groan in protest. Pete said something to Sam, and he nodded, checking the front dashboard and settling into a comfortable position on the seat.

Toby barked and circled a couple of times, no doubt wanting to get going. But Grandpa called Toby over. He said Toby had to stay home.

Christopher looked at Toby's sad eyes as she sat beside Grandpa on the porch and decided he'd play with her and give her a treat when they got back.

Uncle Pete looked at the machine and then over at Christopher and Dylan. "I think she's ready to go."

Christopher wondered how Uncle Pete could tell the snowmobile was a *she*.

The boys piled onto the big tire tube and hollered, "We're ready!"

Sam cranked the engine to life and eased the snowmobile forward. Christopher sure hoped he would go faster out in the meadow. But for now he knew Sam had to be careful in front of Grandma.

"Be careful out there," Grandma called out.

Christopher and Dylan waved at Grandma and Grandpa, who waved back from the porch.

Once they were out in the open space, Christopher called out, "Go faster!"

Sam grinned and then turned around and revved the

engine a noticeable amount, causing the tube to slide across the frozen road. Christopher laughed so hard that it nearly took his breath away.

The laughter seemed to encourage Sam; he kicked things up a notch. The steel runners of the snowmobile cut through the snow, turning to send the tube sliding about willy-nilly on the deserted field.

The boys laughed and squealed—though Christopher would never outright admit that they actually *squealed*. Christopher and Dylan hunkered into the ride. Their thick, gloved fingers dug into the tire as they hung on for dear life.

The wind whipped through Christopher's hat and stung his ears. It pricked his face like tiny needles, though it didn't really hurt. He laughed out loud, but the cold hurt his teeth so he closed his mouth. It was hard to laugh with his mouth closed.

Snow-covered trees flashed past them in a blur. He couldn't tell if Dylan's eyes were twitching. He couldn't even see his eyes. For that matter, he couldn't see his face. Dylan's head had dropped down and forward like a quarterback rushing with the football. Screams blasted through the morning air, startling Christopher. He looked for the source. Suddenly Dylan's head lifted, and his mouth was opened wide enough to swallow a whole package of marshmallows. That was the source.

Then Christopher heard another scream. A blood-curdling scream. A familiar scream.

His own.

Despite the danger inherent in their speed, the thrill of

it made him gasp with sheer energy. Grandma would have a fit, but right now he didn't want to think about that. A ride at the fair couldn't beat this.

On the far side of the field, the tube seemed to roam freely as Sam sped up, going as fast as he dared. Christopher's lips felt glued to the northernmost top of his gums. Dylan's lips were stretched too, and Christopher thought he looked like Emily's horse, Stormy. That made him laugh all the more, which, of course, made his teeth hurt.

Just when Christopher thought he couldn't take it anymore, a strong jolt caused them to look at the towrope, which had suddenly frayed to no more than a single strand.

"Hang on!" he cried out to Dylan.

Christopher dug his fingers deeper into the tube and braced himself for a fall. The tube broke free of the machine, and the boys tumbled and spun across the slick ground until they finally landed in a nearby ditch.

With nothing broken, the boys laughed with relief as Sam came back to check on them. "Hey, you guys ok?" he asked.

"Yeah, we're okay," Christopher responded. "But how are we gonna get the tire reattached to the snowmobile?"

"You just watch the master," Sam replied.

Christopher wasn't so sure he considered Sam a master of anything, but he hoped his brother knew what he was doing. He did not want to be stranded out here in the cold or have to walk home through all this snow. Sometimes having fun could be a lot of work.

Chapter Ten

By the time the kids got back to the farm, Charlotte was standing outside on the porch, hands on her hips, watching them.

"Where have you been? I was getting worried about you." They looked guilty. All three of them.

"Just out having fun, Grandma," Sam said, a little too chipper.

"Yeah, it was awesome," Christopher said, eyes bright, cheeks aglow with winter fun.

Maybe she was just imagining a problem, she told herself. Christopher looked plenty happy. But something about Sam said they were hiding something.

"Well, get the machine put away, and you kids come in for some hot chocolate. I was just about to make some for the girls."

"Great," Christopher and Dylan said in unison.

In no time they had gathered in the kitchen for a winter warm-up and were talking and laughing and sharing stories.

"Did you see our snowman, Christopher?" Madison asked while sipping her hot chocolate.

"I sure did. It's . . . nice."

"I helped too," Jennifer said.

"We're gonna make one too," Christopher said, "if it's okay with Grandma." He turned to her. "We can go back outside, right?"

"If you're not too cold and you dress warm enough."

"What are you going to do this afternoon, Emily?" Grandma asked.

"I thought I would look at some wedding dresses online and then sketch another idea for Miss Simons."

Pete walked into the kitchen. "Too bad she didn't get snowed in with us. You girls could have talked wedding dresses all day." He laughed, pouring himself a cup of hot chocolate.

"Were you able to help the neighbors get out of their driveways?" Charlotte asked Pete. Then she set the cookie jar in the middle of the table. "I should have pulled this out earlier. No more than two each. I need to make some more."

Pete talked to Grandma about the snow in town, the people he had helped, and how he wanted to get back out there and help some more. Sam took the opportunity to reach into the cookie jar and help himself to two thick peanut butter cookies.

"Hey, Sam, want to come back out with me and see if we can rescue any stranded motorists?" Pete asked.

"Nah. I need to make a couple phone calls. Maybe later?"

"I thought you liked being a hero." Pete teased him. "It's a good way to impress the ladies, right?"

"I'll leave that up to you today. I've had enough of being out there in the cold. Besides, my lady doesn't seem too impressed with anything I do lately, and I'm sure this would be no different."

"Suit yourself," Pete said.

Sam looked around the table and excused himself so he could go call Arielle and see if things were still strained between them.

"ARE YOU SNOWED IN?" Sam asked when Arielle answered the phone.

"Yeah. How about you?"

"Yep."

"What have you been doing this morning?"

"I took my little brother and his friend for a ride on a tire tube behind Uncle Pete's snowmobile."

"Sounds like fun," she said.

"Yeah, it was a blast."

"What are you doing the rest of the day?" she asked.

"I have to go get my car." He explained what happened after he dropped her off last night.

"I'm glad you're all right."

"That makes two of us."

Silence.

"So what are you up to?" he asked.

"Finishing up some homework and looking through college brochures."

Okay, he so didn't want to go there.

"Maybe you could look through the brochures of the colleges where I applied. It might spur some ideas for the direction you want to go. There's no time like the present," she urged.

The more he talked to her, the more he wondered if she would be a nagging wife. Not that he wanted to get married, but it just seemed she had the makings of one.

"Yeah, maybe," he said, not feeling the least bit obligated to commit his day to what she wanted him to do.

She changed the subject, and their conversation took a better turn. She almost sounded like the old Arielle, the less-controlling Arielle. He liked her. He wished the other one would go away.

"Sam, you want to build a snow fort?" Emily asked.

"Yeah, be there in a minute." He wanted to get off the phone with Arielle before she could launch into another speech about how he should spend his life. "Guess I'd better go. My little brother wants to build a snow fort."

"That's sweet," she said. "Talk to you soon."

"Okay, bye." Sam grabbed his winter wraps and put them on. His eyes landed upon a college brochure lying on a nearby stand. He walked past it, barely giving it a glance. There'd be time to study it later. For now, he had a snow fort to build.

AFTER CREATING A SECOND plump, sturdy snowman complete with corncob pipe, button nose, two eyes made out of walnuts, and a woolly scarf and hat, Madison and Jennifer went inside to watch a kids' movie while Christopher, Dylan, Emily, and Sam stayed outside for a round of snowball fights.

Toby tried to join them, attempting to jump in the knee-deep snow and struggling with every pounce. At one point, she finally gave up and rolled around, ultimately landing on her back with her paws kicking upward in sheer delight, her back nuzzling the ground as she enjoyed a healthy wallow in the fresh snow. Sam couldn't help laughing at her.

The younger boys made a fort on one side of the poplar trees, and then Emily and Sam made a fort on the other side. The fort would hold each side's snowballs and help protect them from the onslaught of snowy missiles coming their way. Once they were ready, the war began.

As snowballs flew overhead, Toby barked furiously, at first seeming out of sorts about it all. Then, with all the squealing and laughter, Toby's bark changed from concern to playfulness.

Sam couldn't remember when he'd had such fun. Sometimes he thought the teenage thing was way overrated. Why did he have to act like a grown-up when he'd rather be a kid?

A snowball whacked him upside the right arm. "Uh-oh, buddy, you're getting it now," he yelled to Christopher.

Forming a hard ball of snow between the palms of his hands, he blasted it through the air, straight toward Christopher, and thumped him on his left leg. The snow was too soft to hurt all that much, but hard enough to pack, which made the snowball fight all the more fun.

For the next half hour, they relentlessly walloped one another until, breathless and tired, they finally trudged into the house to get warm.

BY THE TIME THE FAMILY gathered around the evening meal of homemade vegetable soup, french bread, and salad, a fresh snowfall had begun.

"Doesn't look as though we'll have school or work tomorrow," Bill said. "I can't even get back home in this weather."

Sam liked the idea of no school.

"That will give your mom here all the more time to fuss over baby Will," Grandpa said with a grin.

Grandma laughed. "That's true. You won't hear me complaining."

"Maybe we'll get some extra time to work on the family tree thing," Christopher said to Dylan.

"Yeah."

"I can work on Miss Simons's wedding dress sketches," Emily chimed in.

"I wish you would. She's driving me crazy with worries about her dress," Pete said. "She's a nervous bride; that's for sure."

"It's natural," Grandma said.

"Aw, I don't know why women get all stirred up about these things. I'd marry her wearing sackcloth." Pete laughed.

Grandpa laughed too. But Anna shook her head and tsk–tsked.

Pete stared at her. "I can think of worse."

She ignored him and went back to her soup. "While you all were playing in the snow today, I've been busy," Grandma said, no doubt trying to steer the conversation away from Aunt Anna and Uncle Pete.

She walked over to the counter and uncovered two warm apple-caramel pies. Sam's stomach gurgled in response. He could hardly wait to dig in.

"That looks delicious, Grandma," Sam said, already grabbing dessert dishes and placing them on the table for everyone.

Somehow Grandma could always save the day with her award-winning pies.

Chapter Eleven

"Hey, Ash. Are you snowed in?" With the cordless phone in her hand, Emily snuggled deep into the folds of the blankets on her bed.

"Yeah. How about you?"

"Yeah. I think everyone is. Our house is so crowded with Bill and Anna and their kids and Christopher's friend Dylan. But I wish you could have been here too when the snow hit."

Ashley grunted. "At least you didn't have to play chess all day with your brother."

Emily laughed. "Brett sure does like to play that, doesn't he?"

"Yeah."

"How's your mom?"

"She's fine. You know Mom. You'd never know she had a problem by watching her. She's just as upbeat as ever. Sometimes I wish she'd talk to me about it, but she says she'll be fine. I sure hope she's right."

Silence hung between them.

"Wish I could do something," Emily said, hating the feeling of helplessness.

"You are, just by being there. I don't know what I'd do without you, Em."

"Thanks." Another pause. "Have you told Ryan yet?" Emily asked, referring to Ashley's boyfriend.

"Yeah, but he'd already heard about it. You know how small towns are."

"Yeah."

"He's kind of driving me crazy right now."

"Why?"

"I don't know. Just kind of acting immature and stuff. He says I'm acting too serious these days. He can't understand what my family is going through, so I just let it drop."

Emily didn't know what to say to that.

"I'll just be glad when it's all over," Ashley said. "If Mom is right and everything turns out fine, we'll just get through this and forget it ever happened."

Emily knew some things weren't so easy to move beyond, but she didn't want to discourage Ashley. Her friend needed all the hope she could get right now.

"We'll get through it, Ashley. And I promise, I'll be there for you."

Emily knew the pain of things not turning out as planned. That would explain the niggling doubt that tugged at her. But then she shook her head, as if to clear away the doubts. Things would turn out fine for Ashley's mom.

They just had to.

CHARLOTTE TOSSED AND TURNED in bed. In her dreams, the family gathered at the table, eating, laughing, talking together. A smell wafted through the air. Not the smell of sloppy joes and chips, but rather the sweet, fresh scent of apples mingling with Cachet perfume. Charlotte would know that scent anywhere. In her dream, her heart lurched in her chest the moment she looked across the table and saw not Emily, but Denise.

Charlotte bolted upright. Perspiration dotted her forehead and neck. Thankfully, Bob barely stirred and then immediately settled back into a rhythmic pattern of breathing. Easing into her robe and slippers, Charlotte got up and went into the bathroom to wipe her face and the back of her neck with a washcloth. She then walked into the family room and sat down in her rocking chair.

A bigger chasm of time swelled between these dreams now; they came less frequently than they had right after Denise died, but still they unsettled her. The only peace and strength Charlotte could find came from the Lord, so she pulled open her Bible to read.

Denise had been a big part of their lives, and they would never forget her. Charlotte would hold her daughter's memory close for as long as she had breath in her. She could only hope and pray that one day she would see her daughter again.

Until then, from time to time she would allow herself a few tears. Tears of grief but also of release, each one bringing her that much closer to letting go of the daughter she tried so desperately to hold on to. Cleansing tears.

And after that, she'd wash her face and help those around her who needed her. Like Melody Givens.

In the wee morning hours, before the sun had peeked into the night sky, Charlotte Stevenson once again left her grief behind and lifted the concerns of her friend Melody to the Lord, knowing he had full control of the situation and would give them strength to face it all, come what may.

Relaxed by God's presence, Charlotte was able to slip back into bed and rest as she hadn't in a very long time.

"HEY, I GOT AN E-MAIL from Dad," Christopher announced as everyone but Emily sat in the family room watching the movie *The Shaggy Dog*.

Charlotte and Bob exchanged a glance.

"What does he say?" she asked.

Christopher's brows knit together in a puzzled expression. "He said Sam told him about the family tree project, and he listed some of our relatives."

"Hope that's okay, Christopher," Sam said. "I thought it might help."

"Yeah, it's okay. I was afraid to write to him, so it's cool that you did."

"Why were you afraid, nerd? He's our dad," Sam said.

Charlotte cringed at the way Sam talked to his brother, but Christopher didn't seem to mind.

"I know. I just didn't want to write to him."

"That's weird," Sam said.

Though Charlotte liked Dylan, she was glad he finally had been able to go home today. He and Christopher seemed to struggle in settling down to work when they were together. The house was much quieter with Bill, Anna, and the kids gone as well.

"Hey, Sam, do you know Great-Uncle Richard?"

"Never heard of him."

Christopher shrugged. "I guess he's already been working on the family tree on Dad's side, so Dad told me to e-mail him." Christopher's bright eyes looked at Sam. "He might save me a lot of time."

Kids today. Always looking for an easy way out, Bob thought.

Christopher's fingers tapped across the keyboard. Charlotte didn't want to think where this little project might lead them. She only hoped it would not stir up trouble.

"You need to get busy on our side of the family too, you know," Bob said.

"That's right," Charlotte said.

Christopher got up from the computer desk. "I'll be right back," he said, dashing up the stairs.

"Uh-oh, You're in trouble now," Sam said. "He told me his teacher said they needed to be like news reporters and interview people."

"Why didn't he do it before now?" Charlotte asked.

"He didn't know how to get started, I think. So I contacted Dad for him."

Although she didn't know how all this research might affect the family, Charlotte was impressed that Sam thought to help out his little brother.

Christopher bounded into the room, pad of paper and pen in hand. He looked at his grandparents. "Are you watching that?" Christopher pointed to the television.

Bob blinked.

Charlotte chuckled. "We've seen it several times already."

"Yeah, I'm not really watching it either," Sam said. "Want me to turn it off, Grandpa?"

"I suppose," Bob said with reluctance.

"I'll leave you two to the reporter," Sam said with an ornery grin. "I've got some homework to finish."

Charlotte wanted to point out that this was Monday and what if they hadn't had a snow day from school? But she didn't want to start a battle right now.

"Okay, so Grandma, let's start with you," Christopher said in his most professional voice. "Are you from Bedford?"

"Born and raised." Her grandson had a lot to learn about the family. Maybe this would be a good thing after all. "My parents were William and Opal Coleman."

Christopher scrunched his nose. "Opal? I thought that was a stone or something."

"It is. But it was also a popular name back then."

He shrugged. "What else?"

"My dad ran the town's movie theater, but it burned down."

"Wow, that's cool." Christopher scribbled furiously on his pad of paper.

"Well, I don't know how cool it was that it burned down, but I guess it was cool that he owned the theater. I got to go to the movies for free." She smiled.

"Why do you think I married her?" Bob asked with a wink.

"My mom was a kindergarten teacher. Let's see . . . and my grandparents had a farm east of this farm. Don't know if you remember that I had a brother, Chet, who died about ten years ago."

"No, I didn't know about him."

A shadow crossed her heart. Her grandchildren hardly knew their own family.

Christopher scribbled on his paper. "What about you, Grandpa?"

Bob scratched his jaw. "Well, let me think here a minute. My parents were Les and Mildred Stevenson. They owned this farm, so I grew up on it with your Great-Aunt Rosemary.

Christopher nodded.

"I had an Uncle Matthew Stevenson, my dad's brother, who moved to Cincinnati to work for a newspaper. Met a woman and they settled there. He was a reporter like yourself," Bob said with a wink.

Charlotte noted that Christopher sat up a little taller in his seat.

"He eventually ran the paper. Pretty impressive, I thought, but I never wanted to be anything but a farmer, just like my dad."

Charlotte smiled as she listened to her husband open up about his family.

"Uncle Matthew finally tired of all that and settled in a small town and ran a little paper there. Hattie Creek, I think, was the name of the town." He stretched his legs a bit, but the look in his eyes told them he was still thinking.

"My mom loved to cook. She could take anything and turn it into a feast." He looked at Charlotte. "Just like your grandma here."

Christopher smiled. "I always thought it would be cool to be a writer. Is your uncle still living?"

"No. But his son took over the paper. Come to think of it, Uncle Matthew worked on the family tree once. I remember Dad saying maybe he could get copies one day, but I don't think he ever did. Why don't you try looking up that paper so you can get a hold of his son?"

"Wouldn't that be your cousin?" Charlotte interjected.

"Sure would."

"How come you don't talk to him?"

"That's a good question. I guess it's because we never really got to know one another, with them living in Ohio and us living here, and everyone so busy. We didn't have all the ways to communicate back then like we do today. Trips were harder to take too."

Christopher nodded. "Do you know your cousin's name?"

"Let me think." Bob paused. "Luke. That's what it was. Luke Stevenson. I remember that because they were both Bible names. You might find something about him on the computer. I'm sure you could find the name of the paper. I just can't remember it right now. Had the name *Sun* in it, or something like that. If you can't find it, let me know and I'll do some checking around. See what I can find."

"Thanks, Grandpa." Christopher looked at both of them. "This really helps. You know, this isn't so bad." He grinned, said good night, and then turned to go. Before they could blink, he swiveled back around and looked at them. "If something happens to Mrs. Givens, do you think people will remember her?"

A gasp caught in Charlotte's throat.

"Well, of course they will remember her," Bob said. "Why do you ask?"

"Just wondering why some people are remembered and some aren't." He stared at the floor a minute while thinking. "I don't want people to forget me."

Charlotte's breath stopped short. Obviously the thing with Melody, or maybe it was the family tree—or both—was affecting them all.

"People don't remember so much what you said or what you did, but they remember how you made them feel," Bob said. "Now, that's something worth remembering."

Charlotte wasn't sure she wanted to think about that one.

Seemingly satisfied, Christopher nodded, thanked his grandpa, and then headed up to his room.

Just then the phone rang. Charlotte went over to answer it.

"Charlotte, this is Melody."

Fear shot through Charlotte. "What is it?" Instinctive

concern for her friend caused her to say it more abruptly than she'd intended to.

"I'm sorry to call at bedtime. I've had a whirlwind day, and I'm just now getting around to calling."

"Oh? Are you all right?"

"Yes, yes, I'm fine. But the surgeon's office called, and they got the biopsy results and it's a cancerous tumor. He was reluctant to tell us on the phone, but with the weather so bad he didn't want to drag us up to Harding."

Charlotte's mind raced with what she could do—what she should do.

"I have to have another surgery to make sure all the cancer has been removed."

"I see," Charlotte said, her stomach sinking.

"Dr. Grady will confer with the oncologist, Dr. Carrington, and on Friday, I'll meet with a team of doctors to go over the best course of treatment. It sounds exhausting, doesn't it?"

"It sure does." Charlotte's thoughts were spinning.

"Well, those are the plans at present. The reason I called, I was wondering if the ladies who are working at the diner—"

"Before you go any further," Charlotte said, "everyone told me they were in it for the long haul, if need be. So the diner is covered. Also, we want to see to it that your family is fed so you can concentrate on getting well. We'll start tomorrow. I'll make the necessary calls tonight."

"You don't need to feed us," Melody protested.

"Consider it done, friend. We are here for you."

"Charlotte?"

"Yes."

"I'm scared."

"I know, Mel. Me too."

Chapter Twelve

Sam had crawled out of bed before sunrise to milk Trudy so Charlotte could get to the restaurant early. Yesterday was a blur, and here it was Wednesday already. Charlotte had a feeling the next few weeks would melt together and slip into oblivion.

She pulled her blue Focus out of the drive and waved at Sam, who headed across the yard beneath the pale moonlight, looking barely alive.

She yawned. Though normally a morning person, Charlotte was feeling a bit weathered today. The stress of Melody's news had taken its toll on her. Winter winds whipped across the open fields as she edged her car down the snow-drifted country roads. The windshield wipers ticked off an even tempo while her mind muddled through her morning steps.

The kids' lunches waited on the kitchen countertop. Pete and Bob could come to the restaurant for breakfast. The kids would have to resort to cereal. A pang of guilt shot through her, but she ignored it. For now, she had no choice in the matter.

Mentally, she clicked off her to-do list. Once she finished at the restaurant, she'd dash home to throw in a load of laundry and start supper. After kitchen cleanup, she'd make sure the kids completed their homework and follow up with Christopher on his family tree project.

Her Focus groaned and sputtered as she slid into a parking slot at the restaurant. She couldn't blame it, really. She had groaned and sputtered a bit herself this morning.

The zipper on her coat had slipped downward, so she pulled it closer to her neck and then braced against the cold. Her car door screeched with resistance as cold metal scrunched together. The sharp, icy winds blasted against her coat and nipped at her ankles as she ran toward the restaurant entrance. Once inside, the smells of spicy sausage, hot coffee, and warm biscuits greeted her. The heat seeped through her skin, thawing her cheeks and tingling fingers.

With Charlotte's frequent visits to the restaurant and her friendship with Melody, people here knew her well. Most folks in Bedford knew one another. That's what she loved about living in a small community.

"Good morning," Esther said.

"Morning. How are you?"

"I'm much better now that you're here." Esther pulled Charlotte into an enormous hug. Something about the older woman made Charlotte remember fondly the hours she'd spent as a child in front of a warm, crackling fire on the family hearth, cuddled on her grandmother's lap while she told Bible stories.

"Is there a problem?"

Esther led the way back to the kitchen. "No, no, no. I'm just glad you're here. That's all. Good of you to help with the cooking, Charlotte. So like you."

"I've had the best of teachers, you know." She winked at the older woman.

"Hi, Charlotte," Ginny said, chewing and smacking her gum with gusto. Though Ginny was a tad scatterbrained, Mel employed her full-time as a waitress for the restaurant. Melody could always see beyond folks' limitations and did what she could to help them.

"How are you, Ginny?" Charlotte marveled that the woman's long, reddish hair could fit in the hairnet.

"Doing good."

They had little time for idleness before the patrons started streaming in for breakfast. Charlotte and Esther worked side by side, talking of family news, recipes, and their concerns over Melody. If Charlotte had to work away from home for the time being, she couldn't think of anyone with whom she'd rather work than Esther Showalter.

When Pete and Bob walked in for breakfast, she greeted them and then went back to work. It made things much easier when the men took it all good-naturedly like this.

Hopefully, Bob would understand if she had to work the morning shift for more days than they had planned.

LATER THAT EVENING, Emily picked up the phone and called her youth pastor's wife.

"Hello?" Andrea Vink answered.

"Hi, Andrea. This is Emily Slater."

"Yes, how are you, Emily?"

"I'm good. Do you have a minute?"

"Sure do. What's up?"

"Well, you know about Melody Givens."

"Yes."

"I wanted to run an idea by you—a way that maybe the teens could get involved in helping the Givens family."

"Okay, great. Let's hear it."

"Ashley told me that business has picked up lately so the restaurant is a little shorthanded. I know some of the girls in the youth group have worked in restaurants before. I wondered if we could offer our services as a group."

"Wow, that's a great idea! It's easy to see the apple doesn't fall far from the tree in your family."

Emily smiled.

"I'll make some calls tomorrow. We'll have a group assembled before you know it."

"Great, thanks."

"Thank *you*. It's a wonderful idea. I'll keep you posted on how it comes together."

"Sounds good. I'll talk to you later."

Emily walked into the kitchen just as Uncle Pete and Miss Simons stepped through the back door.

"Hi," she said.

"Hi, yourself. What's everybody eating for supper around here tonight?" Uncle Pete asked.

"Well, Grandma had to go back to the restaurant, so it's every man for himself tonight. There's leftover meatloaf, if you want it." She reached into the refrigerator and pulled out the plate of cold meatloaf.

Pete frowned. "Not exactly what I had in mind." He turned to his fiancée. "You want to go to the restaurant?"

"Sure."

"Wait," Emily said.

They looked at her.

"I need to talk to Miss Simons, show her a couple of my sketches."

Pete sighed. "You want to stay long enough for that?"

Dana smiled. "That's fine." She eased off her coat, and Pete hung it up for her.

"Only a few minutes though. I'm hungry," he said.

Emily nodded. "Be back in a jiff." She ran up the stairs, grabbed her sketchpad, and came back to the kitchen.

She and Miss Simons sat at the table. Uncle Pete went in to the family room to watch a little news while the ladies talked shop.

Emily's heart skipped double time as she pulled open her sketchpad. She had to admit she loved working on this dress. Not only was it an honor to do this for Miss Simons, but Emily also loved the whole process of creating a design.

Flipping open her pad, she stopped at the three sketches she had created so far, presenting the first one to Miss Simons.

"As you can see, this one has a draped bodice. I was thinking silk material. See how all this beautiful material would hang in the front here? Nice, huh?" She looked up at Miss Simons, smiling.

"*Hmm*, could I see the others too?"

"Sure." Emily turned the page. "Now, this one has an artsy flair. With the contrasting flower, sort of cool and unexpected, don't you think?"

Miss Simons looked at her. "I certainly do. How about the next one?"

"This one isn't as artsy. Actually, you might think it's boring, but you said to show you different styles, so that's what I'm doing."

Miss Simons nodded.

"Pretty much self-explanatory. Straight gown with a flare from the midcalf down. Not much to it, really."

"I like that one best."

Emily tried not to show her surprise. She didn't like this one at all, but to each her own.

"You ready yet?" Uncle Pete stood in the doorway, patting his belly.

"Yes, I'm ready." She smiled and then looked back at Emily. "We're not quite there yet. Just remember: for me, simple is better."

Emily nodded and watched as the two of them put on their coats and headed into the wintry evening.

She sighed. There was no accounting for taste.

SAM'S CAR CLANKED and chugged up the driveway. The way it carried on, Sam wondered if it would make it through the snow tonight. He'd be glad when he could afford something nicer to drive.

As soon as that thought hit his mind, Arielle's words followed. "You need a good college education to make a decent life for yourself these days. Otherwise, you end up flipping burgers at some old mom-and-pop joint."

He had reminded her of Mrs. Givens's nice restaurant and how they did just fine for themselves. But she argued that's because they were the owners, not just the cooks. He could have argued on about the nice people who had worked there, but remembering they were either part-timers working their way through school or retired folks adding to their established income, he decided against it.

He shoved the car door open with his foot, the metal protesting every inch, and then gave it a hard slam.

Okay, he knew Arielle was right. He had to get a college education, and he would. But that didn't mean he had to be happy about it.

The professions represented at Career Day all needed college educations. He suspected the educators had planned it that way. Maybe he should just chuck it all and head back to San Diego. He kicked the heavy snow from his path, sending a spray of white through the air.

Sometimes he just wanted to be little again—like he had been when his mom was still with them, and they'd spent afternoons on the sunny beaches of California. He looked at the snow surrounding him. Life had changed dramatically since then. Since his mom died, the cold realities of life had set in. Sure, his grandparents made life bearable, but there was no denying that his life would never be the same.

Though he would never admit it to anyone else, Sam sometimes wondered if he was ready to enter the "grown-up world." In some ways, he couldn't wait. In other ways, the idea scared him.

"Hope you grabbed something to eat on the way home," Grandpa said when he walked through the door.

"Why? Are we out of food?" He wondered if his grandparents had gone to college.

"Well, cooked food, yes." Grandpa opened the refrigerator door. "I guess there's a slice or two of meatloaf still left, if you want it."

Something in Grandpa's eyes said he wanted it. "No, you go ahead. I'm not hungry." Sam moved through the kitchen toward the hallway.

"Now, hold on a minute. You have to eat something or your grandma will have my hide. Why don't you join me here at the table a minute?"

The last thing Sam wanted to do was have a heart-to-heart talk with Grandpa right now. He slumped into the chair.

Grandpa heated the meatloaf in the microwave, grabbed two plates, and gave them each a slice. He pulled the applesauce from the fridge and the homemade bread from the breadbox.

"Thanks," Sam said.

After a quick prayer over their food, they started to eat. Sam hadn't realized he was so hungry.

Silence hovered over the table. Grandpa cleared his throat.

"How was your day?"

Sam looked up in surprise. Grandpa didn't usually ask about things like that. "Okay, I guess."

"Any more thought about your college major?"

"No."

"That's all right, boy. It takes time to figure these things out."

Hope sliced through him. "Really?"

"Really. It's best to wait till you've got a good idea of what you want to do before you pour your life into a career you don't want."

"Did you ever think you wanted to do something other than farming?"

"Never did. It was all I had ever known and all I wanted to do. Something about working with dirt, I guess." Grandpa grinned up at Sam.

"Pete was the same?"

"Yep. But, see, Bill didn't want that. It took him awhile to tell us. But the way I see it, life's too short to do work you don't enjoy."

"But that's just it. How do people know what they want to do? I just don't have any idea what to do."

Grandpa nodded. "Well, you like airplanes, don't you?"

"Sure. But I'm not sure what I'd do with it."

"Isn't that why they have advisers at school, to help you with that?"

"I guess."

"I think the most important thing you should know is that it matters most that you enjoy what you're doing. Ecclesiastes tells us, 'Then I realized that it is good and proper for a man to eat and drink, and to find satisfaction in his toilsome labor under the sun during the few days of life God has given him—for this is his lot.'" Grandpa looked at him and gave a short grunt. "Sounds like wise counsel to me. Give it some thought."

Grandpa got up, walked over to the sink, rinsed out his plate, and then placed it in the dishwasher before walking out of the room.

Sam sat in his chair, pondering Grandpa's words and thinking how thankful he was that Grandpa understood. If only he could get Arielle to understand.

Chapter Thirteen

Grandpa sipped his coffee, and Christopher gulped down some orange juice while Grandma got her coat on to go to the restaurant the next morning.

"You sure you boys will be all right?" Her face scrunched with worry.

"We'll be fine, Grandma." With meals in an upheaval these days, Christopher thought maybe he could talk her into buying some of those breakfast treats that she normally refused to buy. He made a mental note to ask her when she was in a really good mood.

"They'll be fine. Stop worrying," Grandpa said.

"Make sure Emily gets her room cleaned up and Sam gets his English paper turned in." She looked at Christopher. "You keep working on your family tree project. I'll be checking on your progress this weekend."

"Okay."

Grandma turned to go and then swiveled back around to Grandpa. "I almost forgot to tell you. Bring Emily to the restaurant after school. I need her to help me take dinner over to the Givenses tonight."

"Will do," Grandpa said with a grin. "Now don't worry. We've got things covered."

After a sigh, she said, "Thank you. Love you all." She opened the door and disappeared into the wind.

"She sure is busy," Christopher said, his cheek slumped in his hand. "Just like when she first started working at Bedford Gardens."

"I know. But it won't last forever." Grandpa glanced at the clock. "What are you doing up so early anyway?"

"Couldn't sleep."

Toby sat on her haunches beside Christopher, her furry coat askew, her eyes drooping.

"That's odd."

"Yeah, I guess."

"Something on your mind?"

"Yeah. Food."

Toby whined a tad and licked her chops on cue as though she understood completely. Sometimes that dog just amazed Christopher.

"That's why you couldn't sleep?"

Christopher nodded. "My stomach gurgled all night. Rumbled. Complained."

"Mine too," Grandpa said.

"What are we gonna do about it, Grandpa?"

"I'm not sure. What do you think we should do?"

"Can we hire a cook?"

"I don't think Grandma would go for that—not when we have all these adults around. Seems like one of us should take over her job, don't you think?" Grandpa asked.

"But—"

"Go upstairs and get ready for school. We'll talk later."

Christopher had no clue what that was all about. The

way he saw it, his stomach still rumbled, and Grandpa hadn't so much as offered a crumb.

He and Toby slogged up the stairway to his room, and Christopher closed the door behind them. The last thing he needed was for Emily or Sam to discover his secret.

Walking over to his closet, he pulled open the door, reached for the box in the back, and pulled it out. The ants were busily at work, as always. Christopher sure was glad he wasn't an ant. Then again, if he were, he might not be hungry.

Toby whined some more, looking quizzically at the ant farm. "Don't you go getting any ideas. I mean to keep these insects safe, do you hear me?"

Toby cocked her head sideways.

"You're still my favorite though."

Toby perked up and scooted closer to Christopher, who gave the canine a friendly scratch on the head.

Christopher had meant to tell Grandma and Grandpa about the ant farm before now, but everything went crazy once Mrs. Givens got sick. Could he help it that Dylan's parents made him get rid of the ants? Dylan had no one else to turn to, so Christopher had to help him. He helped a friend in need. Grandma would like that. Yeah, that was the excuse he'd go with.

He thought about the ants and his family tree project. Funny how similar ants and humans could be. Working together and working hard. Just like everyone was doing for Mrs. Givens. Which made him think of something else.

His mom used to sing in the kitchen when she cooked. It was a happy tune. Whenever he had heard her singing it, it made him feel better no matter what was going on. But now he couldn't remember the tune.

One thing he did remember was that she smelled like apples. He had told her so once and she told him she used apple lotion. He remembered that because he wondered how people made lotion out of apples. He also remembered too that every time he smelled it, it made him happy.

WITH THE RELIABILITY of Sam's car in question this morning and the kids having to wait on the bus, Grandpa offered to pick everyone up after school. Afterward, he dropped Emily off at the restaurant to help out, like Grandma had asked him to, and then he brought Sam and Christopher home.

"We eating at the restaurant tonight, Grandpa?" Christopher asked hopefully after glancing at the bare countertop.

"Not tonight."

"What are we eating?" Sam asked.

His stomach must have been growling too, Christopher thought.

Grandpa smiled, walked over to the stove, lifted the big pot from the burner, and placed it on a hot pad on the table. It resembled soup, but it smelled funny.

"What is it?" Christopher wanted to know, watching it closely for signs of life.

"It's stew," Grandpa said proudly.

Christopher had never seen stew look like that before. The meat looked really weird. Was it chicken? Was it beef?

There were vegetables he didn't recognize too. He stole a glance at Sam and could tell Sam hadn't ever seen anything like it either.

Christopher's gaze swept the area. "Where's Toby?"

Grandpa blinked. "Toby? I'm not sure. I haven't seen her around for a while."

"You boys get cleaned up for dinner and then come on down."

"What about Uncle Pete? Don't we have to wait on him?" Christopher asked.

"He'll be here. Now, go get washed up."

Sam and Christopher headed toward the stairs.

"Here, Toby. Here, girl," Christopher called.

Just then Toby came out of Christopher's room, tail wagging, happy to see them.

"There you are." Christopher scrunched down and hugged the dog's neck. He leaned in and whispered into the hound's ear, "Stay away from the stew."

"You'd better get scrubbed up. You heard Grandpa," Sam said.

"Yeah." Christopher stood up, his gaze fixed on Toby's with one long look of warning. Then Christopher trudged toward the bathroom as though walking a plank to his final reward.

Funny thing: His stomach wasn't gurgling anymore.

"DID SOMEONE FROM CHURCH drop this off for us?" Uncle Pete asked.

"Nope," Grandpa said. "I made it myself."

Uncle Pete's jaw dropped. "You did?"

Christopher's spoon slipped from his fingers and landed with a thud right in his stew. A thud? Should silverware make a thud when dropped in stew? He didn't think so. The stew was thick like paste. If the bottom of his spoon disappeared, Christopher feared he would have to take a rebellious turn.

"Get the washcloth and dab that stew off your shirt," Grandpa said.

Christopher wanted to slip out of the house and beg Grandma to come back.

"I didn't know you knew how to cook," Sam said.

"Well, I learned how today."

The way Uncle Pete and Sam glanced at each other, Christopher could tell they didn't believe it either. One thing was for certain: whoever had taught Grandpa to cook should be fired.

"Do we have any flour, Grandpa?"

"Flour? Well, no, actually we don't. I used it all this afternoon."

Christopher had no trouble believing that.

"We're out of flour?" The saliva left Christopher's mouth.

"Yes, why?"

"Can I say the blessing, Grandpa?" Christopher asked.

Grandpa, Uncle Pete, and Sam all looked at him in shocked surprise.

"Well, yes, of course, Christopher," Grandpa said.

"Dear Lord, please, please, please bless this food to our bodies. Remember that story my Sunday school teacher told us? About death in the pot and how Elisha had to throw flour in the stew to make it edible? Could we use something else if we need to? Just let us know. Thanks. Amen."

Christopher opened his eyes and picked up his spoon. He had the distinct impression Grandpa was watching him. He looked up, and sure enough he was.

"What's wrong?"

Sam snickered beside him.

"What makes you think there's death in this pot?"

"When Grandma cleaned the refrigerator one day I was in the room with her. She pulled something out and said it looked like death warmed over. It looked an awful lot like this stew."

Sam and Uncle Pete laughed right out loud, but Christopher didn't know what was so funny. Especially when he saw the look on Grandpa's face.

He sure wished Grandma would get home soon.

CHARLOTTE COULD BARELY STAND by the time she stumbled through the door later that evening. Emily looked just as tired. The two of them took off their coats at the door and hung them up.

"I sure am tired," Emily said. "I'm going up to my room to do my schoolwork and then I'm going on to bed. 'Night, Grandma."

Charlotte reached over and hugged her. "Good night, dear. Thank you for all you did to help today. I know that meant a lot to Ashley and her mother."

Emily smiled. "I was glad to help." She turned and left the room.

In the mood for some tea, Charlotte poured tap water into the teakettle and placed it on the burner.

"Hi, Grandma," Christopher said, walking into the kitchen. He walked over and hugged her. The clean scent of soap lifted from him, telling her he'd already had his bath. She wanted to kiss his scrubbed cheeks but knew he felt much too grown-up for that.

"Well, that was an unexpected surprise. How are you?" She could tell he missed her, which delighted her to no end.

"Hungry."

"Oh? Didn't you have dinner?"

"Yeah."

"I didn't see you at the restaurant. Did someone bring over something?" Charlotte walked to the cabinet to get a mug.

"No. Grandpa made us stew."

His comment made her stumble slightly. She turned to him. "Are you sure Grandpa made it?"

Christopher made a face. "I'm sure."

"Now, Christopher, I doubt it was that bad."

He made a small circle on the floor with his bare toes. "Well, no one died, so that's good."

Charlotte struggled to keep from laughing.

"When are you coming back to cook for us, Grandma?"

Her heart melted that Bob would try to pitch in and help in this way. He hadn't responded so well when she filled in part-time for the activities director at Bedford Gardens a few months ago. Maybe he had learned something from that experience.

"Did you have any stew left over?" she asked.

Christopher nodded. "Lots of it. Grandpa tried to feed it to Toby, but she didn't want it either."

Charlotte gasped. "Toby eats everything."

"Exactly. 'Course, I warned her, so that's probably why."

"Oh dear."

"He won't make us eat it tomorrow, will he, Grandma?"

Charlotte smiled. "No, honey, he won't make you eat it tomorrow." Charlotte thought a moment. "Hannah is just as busy as I am. Trying to make everyone's schedules work has been quite challenging." She pulled her teacup from the cupboard and poured steaming water into it. "Still, maybe I can arrange for someone to help you guys out." She dunked the peppermint teabag into the hot water.

Hope lit up Christopher's face. "Really?"

"I don't know if I can find anyone, but I'll see. We don't want to make Grandpa feel bad, Christopher. That was a kind thing he did to help with the meals."

Christopher nodded and stared at the floor.

"He may have to continue to cook for you awhile. In the meantime, you help him as best you can, and encourage him, all right?" The peppermint scent immediately calmed her frayed nerves and soothed her aching muscles.

"Yes ma'am."

"All right, now you'd better scoot off to bed."

"Grandma?"

"Yes?"

"How soon you gonna ask someone?"

Chapter Fourteen

"What're you doing there, son?" Grandpa asked when he walked into the room and found Christopher sitting at the computer.

"Working on my family tree project. Miss Luka gave us some Web sites to visit to see if we could pull up some more information. My dad gave me the name of someone to contact too. A distant relative who has already done some of the work. So I'm waiting to hear back from that guy."

Toby slept on a rug nearby, her lip snarling while a slight growl rumbled in her throat. Christopher figured she was chasing a chicken in her dreams.

"Did you find anything on that Ohio newspaper I told you about?"

"Yeah. I found the newspaper. It's called *Hattie Creek Herald*."

"Is that right? I didn't remember that."

"It had a place where I could contact them, so I just sent a note. We'll see if anyone gets back to me."

Grandpa stood over Christopher, seemingly mesmerized by the computer screen.

"You ever use the computer, Grandpa?"

"Not much. I don't understand all that stuff. I've been watching PBS on TV, and it mentioned some cooking sites on the Web. I was kind of curious about them."

"Do you have their addresses?"

"Addresses?"

Christopher felt kind of important with Grandpa seeking his advice on the computer. "Pull up a chair. Let me show you a thing or two."

Grandpa shrugged, got a chair from the kitchen, and carried it into the family room.

Over the next hour, Christopher showed him how to get online and how to plug a Web site into the address line and navigate a little from there.

"I think that's about all my head can handle for now," Grandpa said. He patted Christopher's shoulder. "You're a fine teacher."

"Grandpa, do you think it's lying if you keep a secret?"

Grandpa rubbed his jaw. "Well, now, that all depends. What kind of secret?"

"Well, let's just suppose someone has something they're not sure they're allowed—"

"Anybody home?" Charlotte's voice called through the kitchen.

"There's Grandma. Looks like I won't get to cook dinner tonight." Grandpa got up from the chair and carried it back to the kitchen.

Christopher tried not to appear too excited about Grandma's early arrival, but his taste buds jumped to life.

"I'd almost forgotten what you look like," Grandpa said, pulling Grandma into his arms.

Christopher stopped in his tracks and scooted out of sight. He peeked around the corner at his grandparents.

"Did I ever tell you that you have the prettiest blue eyes I ever saw?"

"Bob Stevenson, what's gotten into you?" Grandma let out a giggle that sounded like the girls at school.

"Just miss you, that's all. Can't a man miss his wife?"

Christopher liked seeing them hug and smile at each other like that.

He started to walk away when he heard Grandma say, "How about chicken pot pie for dinner?"

Christopher licked his lips and figured he'd pretty much died and gone to heaven.

"What's up with you?" Sam asked.

Christopher could have asked him the same thing considering the stupid goofy grin on Sam's face.

"Grandma's cooking chicken pot pie for dinner."

Sam's eyes grew wide. "Yum."

Christopher nodded in awe.

"What's going on?" Emily asked.

"Grandma's gonna cook tonight," Sam said. "She's making chicken pot pie."

Uncle Pete came up behind them, eyes bright and shiny. "Mom's cooking tonight?"

The three kids nodded in unison.

Uncle Pete looked down at his gut and patted it. "Did you hear that? You get to eat real food tonight."

As the kids looked on, no one noticed Grandpa stepping into the hallway.

"Hey, are you kids spying on us?"

They all jumped.

"We're just excited to see Mom, that's all," Uncle Pete said.

"Well, aren't you sweet." Grandma reached over and gave Uncle Pete a kiss on the forehead.

AFTER DINNER CHARLOTTE, Bob, Pete, and Dana sat around the table, drinking from mugs of steaming coffee and chatting leisurely while the kids watched a movie in the family room.

"So how are the wedding plans coming along?" Charlotte asked.

"You know, I've been so caught up in the wedding dress deal that we haven't discussed the bridal party yet." Dana looked at Pete, her face framed with worry.

Pete took a drink from his coffee and said, "That's something we should be doing soon?"

Dana sighed. "Yes, it's something we should be doing soon."

He lowered his mug to the table, the ceramic making a thud against the wood. "Okay, I'll start thinking about it. How many guys do I need?"

Dana thought a moment. "Let's see. I'm thinking three bridesmaids, so you'll need three guys for the wedding party, and then a couple of ushers." She took a drink, her gaze staring at a distant wall as though her thoughts had taken her elsewhere.

Pete scratched his head. "I don't know if I have that many friends."

"I can go to town and scrounge up a couple for you, if need be," Charlotte offered.

Pete grinned. "I may call on you."

"Oh, you." Dana waved him off.

"Are you and Emily any closer to a wedding dress style?" Charlotte asked.

Dana shook her head. "Not yet. I think we're on different pages. She's on the young page, and I'm on the old."

Charlotte chuckled. "I'm sure it's not that bad. You'll figure out something."

Obviously tired of wedding talk, Pete moved the conversation to the weather. Charlotte pondered Emily and Dana's dilemma with the dress and prayed they could work something out. Though a wedding is a wonderful family event, on more than one occasion she'd seen it stir up trouble within families. She hoped that wouldn't be the case for them.

Besides, it was out of her control, and she wasn't about to worry about it.

Not yet, anyway.

"CHARLOTTE, THIS IS MELODY."

"Hey, how did it go today?"

"All right, I guess. Let me just say there is no room for modesty in the hospital."

Charlotte laughed.

"I saw the team of doctors I told you about. Our heads were spinning by the time we got out of there. We got many of our questions answered, and they're giving us till

Monday to decide which surgery I should have, a lumpectomy or full mastectomy, that sort of thing."

Charlotte couldn't imagine having only a couple of days to make such a monumental decision.

"They'll schedule the surgery accordingly for next week."

They weren't wasting any time.

"Well, it sounds as though you have everything under control. Hannah alerted our prayer chain, so you're covered in prayer. I've got the restaurant covered, so no worries there."

"What would I ever do without my dear friends?" Melody asked.

"That's what Christian love is all about."

"Very true. Thank you so much, Charlotte. I'll keep you posted on any developments. In the meantime, thank you for handling the restaurant for me. It's such a load off my mind."

"You need to concentrate on getting better."

"That's what the doctor says too. Well, I'll talk to you later this weekend. Just wanted you to know what's going on."

"Thank you, Melody. We're praying for you."

"Thanks."

Charlotte hung up the phone and stared at it in its cradle, remembering another phone call a few years back that forever changed her world. Funny how one phone call could do that.

Chapter Fifteen

Christopher heard someone plunking around in the kitchen, and hope surged through him. Saturday morning meant pancakes, biscuits and gravy, and eggs. His stomach urged his legs to walk—no, run—to the kitchen. When he got to the kitchen doorway, he came to a screeching halt.

Grandpa stood there in overalls, sprinkled with flour, whipping something up in a bowl. Grandma must have gotten him some more flour.

"What are you doing in here?" Christopher asked.

"I'm fixing breakfast." A smile creased Grandpa's face. Christopher rarely saw that happen. Not that Grandpa had a sour attitude; he just seemed more a man of little emotion—as far as Christopher could see.

"Grandma's not here?"

"Nope."

Christopher tried not to show his disappointment, but he wondered if life would ever be the same again. He took a couple of steps closer—as close as he dared—and peered over the bowl. "What are you fixin'?"

"Blueberry pancakes," he said proudly.

"Is that what those lumps are?" Christopher asked, pointing.

Grandpa glared at him. "I haven't added the blueberries yet."

"Oh." Christopher glanced at the oven and peered inside. "What are those?"

"Close that door or you'll ruin 'em," Grandpa snapped. "They're biscuits."

Christopher had never seen such little biscuits. He knew he'd better not say anything about it though.

"You making gravy too?"

Another glare from Grandpa.

"Just asking."

"Well, don't. Get washed up." Grandpa wasn't smiling anymore.

Christopher worried about the growing vein in Grandpa's forehead, so he ran upstairs to the bathroom to wash his hands.

Sam stopped at the bathroom door. "Is it safe to go downstairs?"

Christopher finished washing his hands. "Grandpa's cooking."

Sam made a face. "What is it?"

"Pancakes with blueberries. And biscuits—I think."

"What do you mean, you think?"

"They don't look like biscuits. They're tiny."

"Well, if they taste good, that's all that matters."

"I guess. Not much else we can eat anyway."

Uncle Pete joined them as they made their way to the kitchen.

"I'm surprised you didn't go to the restaurant, Uncle Pete," Sam said.

"Me too," Christopher said.

"I was thinking of going, but it looks like Dad already has breakfast underway," Uncle Pete told the boys.

"That's right, gentlemen. As you can see, I have plenty here." Grandpa spread his hand across the kitchen. The timer went off, and Grandpa pulled the junior biscuits out of the oven. They were dark. Very dark. In a moment of silence, everyone just stared at them.

Grandpa noticed. "Throw on a glob of gravy, and they'll be good as new," he said with a smile.

For the first time ever in Christopher's young life, he worried about his digestive tract.

They sat down at the table, and before Christopher could open his mouth to say a word, Grandpa glared at him. "I'll do the praying this morning."

He asked a quick blessing, and Christopher lingered a little longer on his own private prayer—until Grandpa cleared his throat. Then he opened his eyes. If Grandpa kept cooking, Christopher was sure to grow up a praying man.

Uncle Pete loaded the little biscuits on his plate like polka dots, and then he globbed on the gravy. The gravy didn't pour as it usually did. Instead, Uncle Pete had to dish it out with a spoon—which it stuck to like a thick ball of goo. Uncle Pete didn't seem to mind.

Christopher and Sam exchanged a glance. Something was seriously wrong with Uncle Pete.

"I'll heat the syrup," Christopher said, tucking the container in the microwave for a few seconds. At least Grandma had made the syrup, so Christopher knew that was good.

He made his way to the table, piled a couple of lumpy pancakes onto his plate, and then poured on the syrup.

Uncle Pete talked about the farm with Grandpa while Christopher tried to figure out what was sour in his pancakes. One bite of a lone blueberry and he knew. They were as sour as could be. Obviously not yet ripe. He poured on more syrup.

Sam hardly touched his food, but Uncle Pete practically licked his plate clean. Christopher couldn't figure it out. Either he liked Grandpa's cooking, or he was downright starving to death.

Christopher pushed pieces of pancake around on his plate. He wasn't all that hungry.

"Are you gonna play with your food or eat it?" Grandpa asked.

"I'm not real hungry."

"I'll eat 'em," Uncle Pete said while everyone looked at him in complete and utter disbelief.

Christopher shoved his plate over to him before he could change his mind.

"You've got a bottomless pit for a stomach, son," Grandpa said.

"What got you started cooking anyway?" Uncle Pete asked between bites.

Grandpa shrugged. "Your mom is busy, and I've been watching a cooking show on PBS. I figured if I could run a farm, I could whip up a few meals. How hard can it be?"

Pretty doggone hard, as far as Christopher could tell.

Grandpa pinned Christopher with his gaze. "I know I'm not great at it yet, but I'll figure it out."

Christopher wasn't about to argue. It took everything in him not to squirm under Grandpa's gaze. Happily, just then someone knocked at the back door.

"I'll get it," Christopher said, already on his way to answer it. He pulled open the door, and Mrs. Carter greeted him with a big smile.

"Good morning. Hope you haven't had your breakfast yet. I've got hot cinnamon rolls fresh out of the oven." She stepped through the door and looked at everyone sitting at the table. "Oh, good. I'll just place these on the counter, and you can have one when you're finished there."

Christopher's mouth salivated before the pan hit the counter. He grabbed a plate from the cupboard.

"Thanks, Hannah. That's mighty nice of you," Grandpa said, though Christopher thought he looked a little put out.

"Glad to do it. I made some for Frank and me this morning and thought your family might like some since I knew Charlotte would be at the restaurant. I'm headed over there myself in a couple of hours." She waved good-bye.

"I thought you weren't hungry," Grandpa groused at Christopher.

"Well, I don't want to be rude when Mrs. Carter went to all that trouble."

Everyone laughed. Everyone except for Grandpa.

"OH, BOB, THANKS for meeting me for lunch," Charlotte said, pulling up a chair across from him at the restaurant.

"Pretty sad that I have to come to a restaurant to see my wife," he said, but there was no hint of remorse in his voice.

"I'm sorry, honey."

"Oh, don't worry about it. I'm just teasing you."

Once their orders were placed and drinks were on the table, Charlotte began. "Okay, the reason I needed to talk to you is that we haven't had time at home, and I needed to get started on this. I talked with Melody, and they're having insurance issues. It seems they'll be responsible for a big chunk of the medical expenses, and, of course, they don't have that kind of money. But you know how Melody feels about charity, so I wasn't quite sure what to do. Being the wise man that you are, I was wondering what your thoughts might be on the matter." She smiled up at him.

Bob thought for a few minutes. Charlotte drank her coffee in silence, giving him time to mull over the problem in his mind.

"Would they mind if word got out that they need some wisdom for financial needs?"

"No, they won't mind. I told her she couldn't stop the Lord from doing what he needs to do. I think it's more a matter of them not wanting to put people out."

"Yeah, that's what I figured. Well, we could let folks know that this would be a good time to support the restaurant."

"Yeah, that's good. Business has already picked up some lately. Another thing is we're low on meat. They don't have the money for more right now. How can we feed people if we're out of food?"

"I can pull a few strings with the farmers in town. I think some of 'em would be willing to donate a cow or pig or a chicken or two to help fill their freezers."

"That's a great idea, Bob." Excitement shot through her. Now they were getting somewhere.

"There's a young woman on staff whose brother runs a T-shirt shop in Harding. She said he offered to make T-shirts with the logo 'Stirring up a cure' for folks to buy. Donations could go to Melody's family."

"Sounds to me as though the Lord is already working in the situation."

Charlotte smiled. "You're right." She placed her hand on Bob's. "I knew you would help me figure this out. You truly are a wise man."

"Spread the word," he said.

The server brought their lunches of chicken salad sandwiches, apple slices, and cottage cheese.

"Is your sugar staying in check?" she asked after Bob prayed over their meal.

"Yep. You think I get off track when you're not around?" he teased.

"Just checking."

"It's really a good thing you're doing here, Char," he said. "You're a great friend to people. I'm lucky to call you my wife."

"Boy, we both are getting sentimental in our old age, huh?"

"I guess."

"So how are things on the home front?"

Bob sighed. "Coming along. I've been watching a cooking show and trying my hand at it. I'm really enjoying it. But Emily is never home to eat. Sam is rarely hungry. Christopher avoids it like the plague, and I think I could serve Pete dog food and he'd never get enough."

Charlotte laughed out loud at this. "Oh my," she finally said when she calmed down. "That was funny."

"I'm serious. I don't know how you do it."

"Well, it's a chore to keep everyone happy; that's for sure. You just do what you can. Trust me, when Christopher is hungry enough, he'll eat. Don't worry about Emily. She eats here with me. Pete has a hollow belly, so you'll never fill him up. And Sam, I'm not sure. What's he been up to?"

Bob shrugged. "I can't keep up with these kids."

Charlotte nodded.

"So when do you think Melody will be up and back at work?"

"Hard to say. Depends on what kind of surgery she has, I guess. But if I know her, she'll be back as soon as possible."

"How do you like your supervisor job?"

"It's fine," she said. "But I miss my regular job at the farm. And I miss my volunteer work at Bedford Gardens."

"Yep, we'll be glad when things are back to normal," Bob nodded. "That was good chicken salad."

"Thanks. I made it."

"I'll have to get your recipe."

Charlotte laughed.

"Well, I guess I'd better go. I'll go over to the tractor supply and see if I can round up a few farmers and get the word out about donating meat. I'll let you know how that goes."

"Sounds good. Thanks, honey."

"You're welcome. Be home for dinner?"

"Yeah. Emily and Ashley went over to the library for a while to work on the wedding dress designs. I'll pick her up on my way home, and we'll both be home for dinner."

"Sounds good. See you then."

Charlotte watched Bob leave the restaurant, thinking how thankful she was to call such a man her husband. The clap of a dish shattering on the floor sounded from the kitchen. Charlotte drank the last of her coffee and headed back to work. Duty called.

Chapter Sixteen

The library smelled of old books and stale air, like a room that had been boarded up for some time. The only sound came from the wooden floor that creaked as patrons walked across the boards.

"What do you think of this dress?" Emily asked Ashley, pointing to a wedding dress in a catalog.

Ashley scrunched her nose. "Too frilly for my tastes."

"Yeah, it's a little unruly." Dust escaped the pages while Emily fanned through the catalog and made her sneeze.

"What do you have sketched out so far?" Ashley asked.

Emily shoved her sketchpad toward Ashley. "Take a look."

Ashley browsed through the sketches. "You're so talented, Emily. These are great. I really like this one." She pointed to the one with the layers of fluffy material.

"Thanks. That's one of my favorite ones, too. I'm not sure Miss Simons liked it though."

"Why do you say that?"

"She didn't say much." Emily shrugged. "Just a hunch, I guess."

"She's probably still trying to figure out what she wants. Didn't you say she's looked everywhere and can't find anything?"

"Yeah."

"I'll bet that's it. It's one of those she'll-know-it-when-she-sees-it kind of things."

"I guess you're right. Hope I can come up with something for her."

"It sure is an honor that she asked you to design it for her. I can't imagine. I'd be so nervous." Ashley grew quiet, as though lost in thought.

"You okay?"

"Yeah. I'll be better when Mom is through all this stuff. You know, the hospital stay, her treatment, all that."

"Yeah, I understand." Emily didn't know what else to say.

"I'm sorry," Ashley said.

"About what?"

"That your mom didn't make it."

"Not much we can do about it." Emily didn't want to talk about it. "So, what's going on with you and Ryan?" Ashley shrugged.

"You still like him?"

"Yeah, I guess. We're not serious or anything."

"Oh?"

"You know what I mean."

"No, I don't."

"I just can't deal with it right now. He's mad at me about that. Says he doesn't understand why I don't want to talk to him. But I just don't feel like discussing things that don't matter. Because what's going on in my world is huge right now, and talking about stupid school things just seems trivial to me."

"Yeah, I see what you mean."

A wave of relief seemed to wash over Ashley. "Really? You get it?"

"Sure, I do."

"Well, Ryan doesn't. We're not talking much. He says every time he's tried to talk to me to help me through this, I've shut him down. I guess I have, but why can't he understand what I'm going through?"

"Because he's a guy and, well, he's not going through it."

Ashley let out another sigh. "I just don't need the pressure right now."

"Does that mean you're not dating him anymore?"

She blinked. "I don't think it means that. We've just sort of cooled off for now. He's finally giving me space to deal with this stuff with Mom. We'll be okay—I think."

Emily nodded and closed the catalog. "Okay, I've gotten a few more ideas. We can go. It's almost time for Grandma to get here."

The girls walked to the library door and watched for Emily's grandmother. They didn't talk much, each seemingly lost in her own thoughts. Emily could hardly wait to show Miss Simons her latest ideas. She had no doubt Uncle Pete's fiancée would like one of them.

"HEY, HE WROTE BACK, Grandpa!" Christopher yelled from the computer desk, causing Toby to bark.

"What are you talking about?" Grandpa asked.

"Your cousin, Luke Stevenson. He wrote me back."

"He did?" Grandpa got up from his chair and walked over to the computer. "What did he have to say?"

"He said it was good to hear from me and he'd be glad to help me any way he can, but that he doesn't have a whole lot of information on the family. But at least he sent me an attachment with some pictures."

"Wow, that's great." Grandpa seemed as excited as Christopher. "Let's see what it is."

When Christopher clicked on the attachment, it revealed a picture of Luke with his wife and two boys with a note that said it was taken before the boys left home.

"Well, will you look at that," Grandpa said. "He's the spittin' image of my uncle." Grandpa looked at Christopher. "His dad."

Christopher nodded.

"Never thought I'd get the chance to talk to him again."

Christopher felt slightly proud that he had brought Grandpa and his family into contact with one another.

"That's my aunt and uncle," Grandpa said, referring to the second picture of Luke with his parents when he was a kid. "How about that." Grandpa studied the picture a moment longer.

"Here's another one," Christopher said, clicking the attachment button. Up came a picture of Luke with a couple of other people.

"What's the note on the bottom of the picture say?"

"It says, 'This is my son Aaron and his wife, Megan.'"

Christopher clicked on another attachment. "This one says, 'This is our other son Kyle with his wife, Amber.'"

Grandpa shook his head. "My, my. The computer is something else, isn't it?"

Christopher could tell Grandpa's opinion of the computer had changed in that moment. His voice held a new respect. Maybe between looking up cooking sites and seeing e-mails with attachments like this, he'd become a computer geek like the rest of them.

"You be sure and thank him for sending that to you. I'll sit down and write him tomorrow when you have time to show me how."

"Okay," Christopher said, excited for the opportunity.

Grandpa walked away, and Christopher made notes on his paper, filling in the family information he had so far, and saving it to his explanatory key. He'd take it to the library and print off the pictures for his notebook soon.

Once he finished making his notes, he ran up to his room to check on the ant farm. Making sure his bedroom door was closed, he pulled it out of his closet and checked on the insects. He had been checking online and found out this gel ant farm was the best kind to own. He didn't have to worry about feeding them or giving them water because all the nutrients and water were self-contained in the tunnels. Good thing, or Grandma and Grandpa might have discovered them by now.

Not that they would mind. At least he didn't think they would. He just had to find the right time to tell them.

He watched the black insects as they worked their way through the tunnels, removing debris, keeping the place clean. It really amazed him to watch them.

Once again it reminded him of how people were helping out at the restaurant while Mrs. Givens was recovering. And how Grandma and Grandpa had come to their rescue when their mom died. Everyone working together. Funny how even insects knew to do that.

He put the ant farm away and looked at his room.

Clothes strewn about, toys here and there, scattered school papers.

He quickly set about cleaning.

ARIELLE SHOWED UP at the airport just as Sam was leaving. They decided to go to the Harding Pizza Parlor for dinner. On the way there they talked about the airport and the cold weather, but nothing of significance. Sam wondered if something was wrong, but he didn't really want to talk heavy tonight, so he let it go.

"Boy, I sure am hungry," he said when they got out of the car.

"Me too."

The cold wind whipped through his hair, making him shiver. He plunged one hand into his coat pocket and with the other, opened the door to the pizza parlor. Arielle stepped inside, and then he followed her.

The room pulsed with upbeat music and energetic chatter. The place smelled of pizza sauce and sausage. After eating Grandpa's attempts at cooking, Sam could hardly wait to sink his teeth into a slice of pizza.

"Let's sit over there," Arielle said, pointing to a booth in the back of the room.

After placing their order, Sam leaned back in his seat and relaxed.

"Long day?" Arielle asked.

"Yeah. I've been picking up the slack on some of the chores while Grandma and Emily help out at the restaurant."

"That's nice. How is Mrs. Givens doing, do you know?"

"Okay, I guess. They don't tell me a lot. I guess she has some more surgery coming up."

Arielle nodded.

For reasons Sam couldn't put his finger on, things between them seemed awkward. Arielle fidgeted with her fingers. She must have sensed it too.

"So what did you do today?"

"Oh, just ran through some college catalogs, dreaming about where I might end up next year."

His spirit sank. Not that again.

Just then the server arrived with their drinks. He hoped that was enough distraction to carry the conversation elsewhere.

"Have you had a chance to look through your brochures, come up with any ideas for a degree yet?"

"Not yet." His lips tightened.

"Listen, Sam, I'm not trying to tell you what to do—"

Yes, you are.

"—but I just want to encourage you. The possibilities are endless. We might even end up at the same school. Wouldn't that be cool?"

He took a deep breath. "Sure. But the truth is, if I don't get a soccer scholarship, I'm not even sure I want to go to college. It's a lot of money."

"Of course, it's a lot of money. You get what you pay for, Sam."

"I don't want to talk about it, Arielle. Why can't you let it drop?"

"Fine." She fluffed the napkin in her lap with a snap, indicating all was *not* fine.

Fine. Two could play this game.

The server brought their pizza, and they started eating, Sam thinking this night hadn't turned out at all like he had planned. He wished he hadn't wasted his money on Arielle, considering the way she was acting. Who knew what Arielle was thinking? By the way she was biting into her pizza, Sam thought, he didn't want to know her thoughts.

Several slices of pizza later, Arielle was the first one to speak. She pushed aside her plate and let out a sigh.

"Sam, we need to talk."

Why did girls do that? Not say anything all evening and then get all serious and say, "We need to talk"? He didn't get it.

"Okay."

"I know you're tired of me asking you about the future."

Well, duh.

"But it's important to me."

Hello? This is not all about you.

"I'm big on dreams, goals—ambitions. You know?"

Yeah, I've noticed.

"There's nothing wrong with waiting, Arielle. Not everyone has to make a decision right out of high school. Even Grandpa said so."

"It's your choice, I guess. I just don't understand it. Aren't you anxious to get started on your future?"

"I don't want to talk about it right now, Arielle." These discussions got them nowhere.

"You never want to talk about it. You have no ambition. You talk about going to your dad's. What would you do there? What kind of job would you get?"

"I said I don't want to talk about it."

The server brought their bill, and Arielle immediately stood up. "I want to go home."

"What?" Just like that? He had bought her dinner, and this was the thanks he got?

"You heard me. I want to go home. I have a headache, and I just want to go home."

"Fine."

"Fine."

Sam paid for their meal, and then they headed for home. The icy chill outside was nothing compared to the polar conditions inside the car. They rode in silence, and when Sam pulled up to her house, Arielle got out of the car and slammed the door.

Something told him their relationship was on thin ice. And right now, he just didn't care.

"IT WAS SO NICE to have you kids at church with us this morning," Charlotte said to Bill and Anna as they settled into a lunch of chicken, asparagus, mashed potatoes, and salad.

"We knew you could hold out only so long without sharing your grandson with your friends," Bill teased.

Charlotte grinned. "They were certainly impressed with our little guy."

"Can we talk about our grandson *after* prayer? I'm hungry," Bob said.

"I suppose," Charlotte said.

Bob offered grace, and they passed the serving bowls.

"Sure was a good message today on trusting, wasn't it?"

Bob plopped a hefty helping of mashed potatoes onto his plate.

"Yes. I wished Melody could have heard it, but I didn't see her there," Charlotte said.

"Yeah, I didn't see Ashley either," Emily joined in.

Bill closed his eyes when he took a bite of the potatoes. "Mom, your potatoes can't be beat."

Anna shot him a frown.

He cleared his throat. "By anything except Anna's, of course."

"Of course," Charlotte said with a smile.

"You barely covered your tail on that one, brother," Pete said with a hearty laugh. Dana nudged him in the side.

Anna turned to Dana. "What's new with the wedding planning?"

Dana exchanged a quick glance with Emily and then said, "It's coming along."

"You haven't chosen the bridal party yet, have you?" Anna asked, her nose hiked a bit.

"Well, no, we haven't. We were discussing recently that we had to get on that. How did you know?" Dana asked sincerely.

"You haven't mentioned it to Bill."

Pete stopped eating and stared at her.

"What?" Anna asked, hand against her chest. "I assume you're planning to make your brother the best man. That's what most people do."

Pete looked clueless.

"Well, I'm sure Dana and Pete will make their decision on the bridal party in due time," Charlotte jumped in.

Just then the phone rang, and Charlotte was thankful to be saved by the bell.

"Hello?"

"Hi, Charlotte. This is Melody. Just wanted to check in with you. "

"Oh?" Charlotte's heart thumped a drum roll.

"I've decided to go ahead and have a lumpectomy. Once I speak with the doctor tomorrow I'll find out the surgery schedule. I was wondering if it would be possible to meet at the restaurant tomorrow afternoon—say, around two o'clock? I'd like to go over some things with you and just touch base."

"Oh, Melody. You've had so much on your plate. I'd be happy to meet with you anytime and help in any way I can."

"Great. Then I'll see you tomorrow. Oh, and Charlotte?"

"Yes?"

"Please, keep praying."

A prayer was on Charlotte's lips before the phone hit the cradle.

Chapter Seventeen

Sam stomped the snow from his boots in the chicken coop as he made the rounds. Plump chickens stared him down, daring him to move them from their warm nests.

"Sorry, gals, it's gotta be done." He dreaded this part. Some of the more crabby ones pecked at him, so he kept his gloves on—which probably didn't help since his gloves were rough and cold.

He'd named one of the feisty ones Arielle as a joke, and now it seemed especially fitting.

He hated to be out this early in the morning, but Grandma and Emily had been working so hard lately, it didn't seem right to leave them with it all.

Surprising a chicken when he reached under her, she cackled and fluttered but held her ground. He was able to pull out a soiled brown egg, so it had been worth her cantankerous clucking. It helped too that he didn't know what she said.

As he made his rounds to each nest, his mind drifted to Arielle—again. He hadn't called her yesterday, and fortunately, he'd managed to avoid her at church. He didn't want to talk to her just yet. What would he say? They had come to a crossroads where they couldn't agree, so where would they go from here?

After he had a basket of eggs, he headed toward the house. A gray sky, still tinted by night shadows, loomed overhead. Gusty winds whistled through the farmland, shaking tree limbs and clawing at Sam's face and neck. He forced his thoughts on San Diego. And to think he once thought the winters were cold there. If he'd only known how cold life could get.

Sam brushed the snow from the shoulders of his coat and pushed through the back door. The smell of sizzling bacon and eggs and simmering oatmeal greeted him. Hanging up his coat, he marveled that Grandpa seemed to be getting a handle on cooking. But when he walked into the kitchen, he saw Grandma standing there with her apron on, turning the bacon in the skillet.

"Grandma, I thought you'd be at the restaurant this morning."

She turned to Sam and smiled. "Nope. Got someone else to fill in today so I can get some work done around here."

Sam took a deep breath. "That smells awesome."

"Good. Wash up for breakfast and join the others. It's almost ready."

He turned to go.

"And Sam, thanks for all the extra work you've been doing around here."

"You're welcome." Truth be known, it made Sam feel useful—though Arielle tried to make him feel like a loser.

Once everyone sat down to eat, Grandpa said the prayer for their meal and passed the serving dishes, one at a time.

"So I think I told you I talked to a few of the guys yesterday after church, Charlotte. Looks like we got some meat coming to the restaurant."

Sam asked what was going on, and Charlotte filled him in on the Givenses' need for food inventory.

"So what do we have coming in?" Grandma asked.

"I'd have to look at my notebook, but if I remember correctly, we've got a couple of sides of beef, a couple of pigs, an abundance of chickens, and a goat or two."

Christopher scrunched his nose. "I sure wouldn't want to eat a goat."

"The Givenses may want the goats for milk; I don't know. We'll have to ask them," Grandpa said.

"That sounds like a great inventory," said Grandma. "Do you think any more will be donated?"

"I'm sure of it," Grandpa said, tearing off a bite of biscuit. "Once they heard that the Givenses were going through a tough time, they didn't hesitate to give." He smiled at Grandma. "Again, that's what I call Christianity in practice."

"I should say so. Melody and Russ will be greatly relieved to know that's taken care of."

"Yeah, Ashley says her dad has been really worried," Emily said. She turned to Grandma. "Are they still gonna make T-shirts to sell?"

"Yes. Should have them available early next week. Then we'll take orders."

"I want to get one," Emily said.

"I already ordered it for you," Grandma said.

Emily looked up with surprise.

"Well, why not? You've been working as hard as anyone there at the restaurant, serving and cleaning up. The least we can do is get you a T-shirt," Grandma said.

"Thanks, Grandma."

"You sure aren't having any problems eating this morning," Grandpa said to Christopher, who practically licked his plate clean.

"Um, yes, Grandpa."

"What does that mean?" Grandpa tried not to appear cross, but it was easy to see the frustration in his face. His cooking was passable, to Sam's way of thinking, but he was nowhere near ready for his own cooking show.

Christopher shrugged. Grandpa frowned. Grandma laughed.

"I think it means it's time to get upstairs and finish getting ready for school."

Before they could blink, Christopher darted out of the room with Toby on his heels, leaving everyone behind him laughing—everyone, that is, but Grandpa.

LATER THAT AFTERNOON, the server placed a cup of hot coffee in front of Charlotte and a glass of water in front of Melody Givens as they settled into their seats at Mel's Place.

The soothing scent of coffee swirled around her, and she lifted the cup for a sip. "So did you call them?"

"Yes. They've worked me in tomorrow. Surgery is at ten in the morning."

Charlotte's breath caught in her throat. Everything was

moving so quickly. She wanted to slow things down before they spun out of control.

"So I'm glad we're meeting. We can relieve my mind of some things before I'm, well, incapacitated." Melody smiled.

Charlotte nodded.

"We've discussed everything with the kids, so they know what's going on. They have their list of things to do to keep things together on the home front, and they know how to get in touch with Russ if anyone needs him for anything. How are things on this end?" Melody took a drink of her water.

Charlotte reminded her about the hospitality committee, how they were taking turns as cooks.

As they discussed all that the people were doing to help, fresh tears misted Melody's eyes. She pulled a tissue from her jeans pocket and shook her head.

"I still can't believe it."

Charlotte smiled. "It's like I've been saying, you are loved. Now, prepare a list of things we need to look after, just in case we've overlooked anything."

Melody stared at her cup and merely nodded.

"How are you feeling, you know, with all that's going on and everything?" Charlotte asked.

"I'm all right. Really, I am. No use fighting this. It is what it is, and a bad attitude isn't going to change it."

Charlotte shook her head. "You are amazing."

"What?"

"Your outlook on life in general."

"I'd really rather be positive about it all than negative. That does no one any good."

"You're right, of course. Still, it's only natural to feel concern and grieve the loss of your health."

"That's true. I'm just not one to grieve for long. I get up, wash my face, and carry on."

Charlotte erupted into a laugh. "That you do."

"Okay, so let's get down to business. I know you've covered the restaurant so far, but there obviously will be a lot more days ahead when I'll need help."

Charlotte held up her hand. "We have it covered, Melody, truly. You don't have to give it a thought. Things are taken care of until you say otherwise."

Melody shook her head. "I just can't believe you all are doing that."

"What's that worried look on your face?" Charlotte asked.

"It's just that, well, I'm worried about Esther. She will work herself to death if you let her."

"Not on my watch, she won't. I've made sure she doesn't put in so many hours."

Relief passed over Melody's face. "I'm so glad to hear that. I worry about her health; that's all." She tapped the pencil against her temple, and another shadow clouded her face. "Let's see, we need to keep an eye on the inventory, the food and meat supply. I'm a little nervous that our meat supply is getting low. I'll have Russ look at that when he gets a chance. We'll have to make an order soon."

"Don't you worry about the inventory; we'll keep watch on things."

Charlotte didn't want to spoil the surprise that was coming, so she kept silent a moment and scratched out some notes on her own pad of paper. "Now, what about meals? Are people signed up to bring you meals?"

"My goodness, Charlotte, they don't need to do that. Russ and the kids are certainly old enough to put a few meals on the table. They've had to do it before when I worked late."

"Yes, but they'll be under some strain themselves. Anything we can do to help ease the load will be a welcome relief, believe me."

"Thank you," Melody said in a near-whisper.

"Any dietary concerns we should know about?"

"Not that I can think of. The more chocolate, the better."

They laughed.

"Absolutely." Charlotte made more notes on her paper.

Just then a loud cheer went up in the kitchen. All the customers turned toward the commotion.

"We'd better go see what that's about," Melody said, leading the way to the kitchen.

When she and Charlotte arrived, there was a truck outside the back door with several men unloading large packages of what the driver said was beef.

"We heard you could use a little help, Mrs. Givens, so here we are." Frank Carter hoisted a large box of packaged meats from the truck with the help of Walt Freeman while Melody and the others stared on with disbelief.

"But what—who—where?"

"Don't you worry about that. You do plenty for this community. You donate coffee every year for the community lighting of the town's Christmas tree," Pastor Evans said.

Another man piped up. "Yeah, and I remember when my family just moved to town, didn't know a soul, and had two dollars to our name. We stopped in here, and you gave our entire family a free meal."

Tears rolled down Melody's face, and she covered her mouth with her hand.

"What about all the hot dogs and chips you donate to the youth group?" Jason Vink, the youth director at Bedford Community Church, reminded her.

Charlotte turned to her with a wide grin. "Looks to me like you'll just have to accept it as God's gift."

Tears filled the eyes of many standing there, including Charlotte's. There was nothing like God's people working together to help a sister and brother in need. Melody and Russ Givens loved this community, and now the community was loving them back.

The sight brought to mind a quote Charlotte remembered from a wedding: "When one weeps, the other tastes salt." That's what was happening here. This trial affected not only Melody and her family but the town as well.

Charlotte couldn't explain it, but somehow helping Melody like this—knowing Melody and Denise were good friends in high school—well, it made Charlotte feel as though she were helping Denise. Silly, she knew, but she couldn't help feeling as though Denise would be pleased that her mother was doing this for her friend.

Chapter Eighteen

The clack of Charlotte's and Hannah's shoes against the shiny tiled floor seemed loud enough to wake surgery patients. Charlotte slowed her pace to ease the sound, though it didn't seem to help all that much. She and Hannah exchanged a glance and took a deep breath before rounding the corner toward Melody's room. Their friend would be taken to surgery shortly.

Charlotte wished she knew the perfect words to help their sweet friend be at ease, to make her know everything would turn out all right. But Charlotte didn't have all the answers. She didn't know how it would turn out. She, of all people, knew that life didn't always turn out the way people planned.

The smell of antiseptic reached her. Nurses padded through the hallway, charts in hand, the day's agenda in place. A phone rang at the nurse's station. A doctor took determined steps past them, stethoscope dangling from his neck, and gave a morning greeting.

"You okay?" Hannah asked.

Charlotte nodded. "Just a little nervous for her, you know?"

"Yes, I know. Me too."

Pastor Evans's voice reached them before they arrived at the entrance to the room. Charlotte breathed a sigh of relief. He would know just what to say.

"Charlotte and Hannah, you're so sweet to come," Melody said, her cold fingers gently squeezing theirs.

"Of course we would come." Charlotte looked at Pastor Evans. "Morning, pastor."

He shoved the wire-rimmed glasses back up the bridge of his nose and lifted his trademark boyish grin. "Morning, ladies."

His wife, Nancy, stepped into the room.

"Hi, Nancy. We didn't see you out there," Hannah said.

Nancy gave Hannah and Charlotte a hug. "I ran down the hall to call Nicole from my cell phone. I wasn't sure if I could use it in here. She forgot her homework and needs me to bring it to the school. I told her she'd have to wait until the surgery was over. Tell me, when does responsibility kick in?"

Charlotte chuckled. "That's a tough one. Different for each kid, I think." Charlotte looked up at Ashley and Brett, Melody's children. "What do you think?"

Ashley smiled, and Brett just shrugged.

Charlotte smiled at her young friend, who lay on the hospital bed waiting for surgery and an unknown future. Melody's face, normally shiny and glowing with creamy foundation, colorful blush and lipstick, had been scrubbed clean and now looked as pale as the white gown she wore. Tape crisscrossed the back of her hand, holding an IV needle in place. A blood pressure cuff periodically tightened around her arm and clicked off numbers on an overhead screen.

"How are you doing, honey?" Charlotte knew she sounded motherly, but couldn't help it. Melody was practically like a daughter to her.

Melody fingered the light blanket draped over her. "As well as can be expected, considering they didn't allow me my morning coffee."

"That's so wrong," Hannah commiserated.

"Don't get her started," Melody's husband said with a grin.

Ashley rolled her eyes. "Here we go again."

Her brother Brett said nothing.

"How can they be so cruel?" Charlotte played along.

"It's not a sin, is it, pastor?" Melody asked, eyes sparkling with mischief.

"Not to my way of thinkin'," he said. "Enjoyed a cup this very morning myself."

Melody leaned in and whispered, for Charlotte's ears only, "Take my body parts if you must, but leave me my coffee."

Charlotte gasped. Sometimes Melody said the most shocking things, just the way Denise had done.

"Okay, Mrs. Givens, looks as though they're just about ready for you; an orderly will come in shortly to take you to pre-op."

The gentle smile on the woman's face brought calm to the room.

"Good. Then maybe I'll get my coffee."

The nurse grinned. "That's the hardest part, isn't it, honey?" She patted Melody's shoulder.

Melody nodded.

Reading the numbers on the machine, the nurse made a notation on her chart, rechecked the IV, and then patted Melody's hand. "You'll get your coffee soon, sweetie. I promise." She smiled brightly, her rubber soles squeaking with every step as she padded out of the room.

"Did you see that?" Melody said, "Now, there's a woman who's had her coffee."

Everyone laughed.

"Let's have a word of prayer with you before you go," Pastor Evans said.

He walked over to his wife, who was standing at the foot of the bed, and slipped his hand into hers. Russ lifted Melody's hand into his. Ashley walked to the other side and held her dad's free hand. Brett stood beside Ashley, Charlotte, and Hannah.

"Father, we believe that no matter what life may throw our way, we are never alone. We entrust our dear friend Melody to you. We ask that you would heal her and give the doctors wisdom in dealing with her care. And we leave the outcome to you, our all-knowing, all-wise God. Amen."

Charlotte choked back a tear. The last thing Melody needed was for Charlotte to crumble in front of her. Pastor was right. God would take care of her. Charlotte just hoped it would all turn out the way they wanted.

"HOW'D IT GO?" Bob asked when Charlotte stepped through the back door into the kitchen later that day.

The room smelled of fresh-brewed coffee. Hanging her

coat and scarf on the coat tree and pulling off her snow boots, she walked over to the cabinet and pulled out a mug.

"Everything went fine—"

Emily stepped into the kitchen, wide-eyed, eager for information.

Exhausted and emotionally spent, Charlotte dropped into a chair across from Bob at the table. Her legs ached from the extra walking she had done at the hospital. "They were able to perform the lumpectomy, avoiding the more radical surgery. They did have to take some lymph nodes though."

Bob nodded but said nothing.

"Is that bad?"

"No, honey. It just makes the healing process a little slower."

"Will she have to go through chemo?" Emily's worried expression touched Charlotte's heart.

"We don't know yet. They'll know more once they receive the pathology report. But the doctors are hoping for the best." Of course, time would tell.

Tears filled Emily's eyes. "At least there's hope."

Charlotte smiled. "Yes. There's always hope."

"Do you think it would be all right for me to call Ashley now?"

"They were staying at the hospital with Melody for a while, so you probably won't be able to reach her until tomorrow. They're keeping Melody overnight. She had some sort of drainage problem and blood pressure issues. Nothing serious, but they want to keep an eye on things. Ashley is planning to go to school tomorrow."

"She told you that?"

Charlotte nodded.

"Oh, I hope things turn out okay, Grandma." Emily gave her a quick hug.

"She's really worried," Bob said, looking at Charlotte while tilting his head in Emily's direction.

"I know. It's been hard on everybody."

"Hi, Grandma. Where ya been?" Christopher walked into the room with Toby at his side.

"At the hospital with Mrs. Givens."

"It took all day?"

"No, but I stayed there with the family."

"She okay?"

"We hope she'll be fine."

"That's good." Christopher stayed there. Waiting.

"Something on your mind, Christopher?" Bob asked.

"Well, I've been meaning to tell you—"

Just then the phone rang. "Excuse me," Charlotte said, walking over to the phone.

Pete came in and asked Bob for his help out in the barn.

"Charlotte, this is Russ Givens."

Charlotte's heart zipped to her throat. "Russ, what is it?"

"Everything is fine," he said. "I just forgot to ask you about the restaurant. Do we have cooks covering for us through the week?"

"We sure do," she said, so thankful she had taken charge of the situation so they could devote their energies to getting Melody better.

"I can't tell you how much we appreciate that. I'll be checking in the rest of the week, from time to time to make sure you don't need anything."

"Sounds good. Melody still resting and doing well?"

"Yes, she is. The kids are going home, but I'm staying the night here."

"Do the kids need a place to stay?"

"They're old enough to stay alone, I think."

She heard the hesitation in his voice.

"If they can keep their sibling arguments at bay." He chuckled.

"Well, Ashley is welcome to spend the night with us. I know Emily would love it. In fact, she can stay as long as she likes. Brett too, for that matter."

"I appreciate that, Charlotte, but I think it's good for them to share in this responsibility. They can help around the house and get things ready for when Melody gets home. Ashley has already made a list of things she wants to get done before her mother comes home. Brett, well, I've got to work on him a little more."

Charlotte laughed. "Well, if you change your mind, just let me know. In the meantime, don't worry about the restaurant. I'll let you know if we run into trouble; otherwise, don't give it another thought. Just keep your focus on your wife, and bring her safely home."

"Don't know what we would do without good friends like you, Charlotte. Thanks for all you're doing." With that, Russ clicked off.

While she was thinking about it, Charlotte figured she'd go ahead and call the cook scheduled to work tomorrow. Looking through her notebook, she found the name and number and immediately called her.

"Hello, Celia? This is Charlotte. Just checking to make

sure you're still able to cover cooking at Mel's Place tomorrow. I have you scheduled to work from six in the morning till noon, and then Hannah is gonna cover the afternoon shift. Does that still work for you?"

"Well, I planned to call you tonight, Charlotte. My son is coming into town tomorrow to stay for a few days. You know how busy he is. I have to take him when he can get here." She chuckled. "I haven't seen him in six months. I hope that doesn't put you in a bind if I stay with him."

"Oh, no, that's fine. It's important to spend time with family."

"Yes, and I miss him so much." Celia Potts's son lived seven hours away, so his visit would be a real treat for her.

They said their good-byes and Charlotte thought a moment. It was too late to ask someone else to help. Hannah was already scheduled to work in the afternoon. Charlotte decided she'd better plan to go in the morning herself. She knew the routine by now so it would be no problem.

She glanced at her notebook once again and looked through the names for the week. It was then she realized she had scheduled Celia to cook early shift all week because that was what Celia had requested. Looked like Charlotte would be covering the early shift and then some. The boys would be on their own once again for breakfast.

Christopher would not be happy about this.

Chapter Nineteen

"Mom, don't go! Please, don't go!" Emily shot up in bed, tears on her face, hands trembling, perspiration beading on the back of her neck. She took a deep breath.

Ashley's mom was doing all right, so why did she dream of her own mother? She thought on that a moment. Maybe since Ashley's mom was all right, Emily subconsciously thought she could get her own mother back. She let out a long sigh. No use worrying about it. She couldn't help what she dreamed.

Lying back down, she tried to get to sleep, but it eluded her. A glance at the clock said she had two more hours before she had to get up for school. She threw back the covers and pulled out her sketchpad. She hadn't worked much on ideas the past couple of days because she'd been so busy helping at the restaurant.

Grabbing a stack of the magazines she'd brought home from the library, she piled them beside her on the bed. With a plump here and there, she propped the pillows behind her so she could sit up in bed.

After browsing through a few of the magazines, she grabbed her pencil and began making long strokes on the page, feathering this way and that, until, after some time, she created a one-of-a-kind wedding dress design that pleased her. Key words being *pleased her*. Pleasing Miss Simons seemed to be another matter entirely.

A knock sounded at the door.

"Come in."

Grandma walked into her room. "What's the matter, honey? Can't you sleep?"

Grandma was dressed and obviously already up and doing chores. Emily had no clue how her Grandma did all that she did.

"I had a bad dream."

Grandma walked over to her and sat down on the bed beside Emily. "I understand," she said. And Emily knew that she did understand.

"Can you believe a girl at school told Ashley about her aunt who died over Christmas of breast cancer?"

"Oh, my!"

"Exactly. Why would she tell her that? So insensitive."

"Seems like people try to relate with stories of their own, and sometimes they just don't realize how it might affect someone else."

"I guess. But I told the girl privately she shouldn't talk about such things to Ashley. Her mom is going to be fine."

Grandma nodded and looked at the sketchpad. "Still working on wedding dress ideas?"

Emily sighed. "Yeah."

"You don't sound very happy about it."

"I love creating them. But I'm beginning to wonder if Miss Simons is ever going to like anything I design."

"Oh?" Grandma looked genuinely surprised, so that might be a good thing. At least Miss Simons hadn't said anything to Grandma—yet.

"She didn't like any of my first samples."

"Did she say that?"

"No. She just told me to keep working." Emily laughed.

Grandma brushed the hair from Emily's face. "Remember this. Just because they don't fit her tastes doesn't mean they aren't good. Everybody is different, and what one loves another might not. It's just human nature."

"Yeah, I get that. But I have to learn to please *somebody* or I won't be able to do this for a living."

Now Grandma laughed. "Well, I guess there's wisdom in that too." She rose to her feet. "I'd better get to the restaurant. There will be some hungry people wanting their breakfast soon." She turned to go.

"Grandma?"

She turned back to Emily. "Yes?"

"Will it ever get easier?"

"What's that, honey?"

"Living without my mom?"

"They tell me it will. We'll work through it together, okay?"

Emily nodded.

"Bye, honey." Grandma turned and walked out the door.

ONCE CHRISTOPHER DRESSED for school and ate breakfast, he dashed back upstairs to his room to check on the ants. They tirelessly dug tunnels through their little town. He watched how they worked together and let his mind wander.

Why had his dad left their family? Even though his dad had come to see them for the first time just last month, Christopher wasn't really sure yet if he could trust him to stay in their lives. Funny how ants could work and stay together, but people couldn't seem to.

Sometimes he wondered what a true family was all about. He used to think a family was a mom, a dad, and two or three kids. But lots of his friends only had one parent. One kid at school had seven brothers and sisters, a mom, a dad, and a grandma all living together. Christopher thought that might be kind of cool. There would always be someone around to play with.

And look at his family. No mom, no dad. Only Grandma, Grandpa, his sister, brother, and Uncle Pete. That was kind of a weird group living together.

Though his family might be a strange mix, he didn't want it to change. Not that he didn't want to see his dad, but he wasn't like a real dad since he never came around. Christopher hardly knew him, really. Grandpa was the closest thing to a dad he'd ever known, and Christopher was okay with that.

He hoped it wasn't wrong to feel that way.

"MY, MY, IS SCHOOL OUT for the day already?" Charlotte asked, when she walked up to Dana's table at the restaurant.

"Afraid so. Weren't you supposed to get off after the lunch crowd?"

"Supposed to. Hannah's working in the kitchen, and I told Esther to go home. She's been putting in long hours, and she's not exactly twenty." Charlotte winked. "Since

Pastor Evans gave that little talk about Christian love and how we might all pitch in to help the Givens family, we've had a steady flow of customers."

"That's good—I guess?"

"Yes, it's good."

"You look tired though. Have you been here awhile?"

Charlotte sighed. "Since six o'clock this morning."

"Oh my. You need to go home and rest, Charlotte."

"I know. I will soon. I had no idea how difficult it would be to keep people on schedule. Seems that last-minute things come up, and the buck stops with the supervisor, you know?"

Dana smiled. "Yes, I know. But you have to take care of yourself or you're no good to anyone."

"I know you're right. Hannah told me she'd start sharing the load when people back out; so hopefully, we'll get through it."

"You have a minute?" Dana asked.

Charlotte looked around at the thinning crowd. "Sure." She slipped into her seat across from Dana. "I'm heading home in a minute anyway. What's up? Wedding plans going okay?"

Dana sighed. "That's just it. I'm not sure what to do, and that's why I came over here. Bob told me you were still working, and it seemed a perfect time to talk with you alone."

Fear twisted Charlotte's heart. "Are you and Pete all right?"

"Oh, yes. Yes, we're fine."

Relief chased the fear away. "Oh, good. Anything else, we can work out."

"It's the dress."

"Oh?"

"Emily does a lovely job designing and sewing, no question about that, but, well, I'm not so sure we have the same tastes."

"I see."

"She prefers today's modern styles, while I guess I'm more of a traditionalist."

"Have you told her that?"

"Well, I've hinted, but I didn't want to hurt her feelings."

"How about if you bring in some examples from magazines to give her an idea of what you like?"

"That's a good idea. We've talked about it, but I haven't actually presented any pictures. That might put us more on the same page. Don't know why I didn't think of it."

Charlotte chuckled. "Maybe you've had a few other things on your mind."

"And you don't?"

Charlotte shrugged.

"Well, now I'm too excited to eat. I think I'll go see if I can get some magazines to pore through. Thanks, Charlotte." Without ordering, Dana got up, gave her a hug, and then turned and walked out the door.

Charlotte wondered if she was bad for business.

"WHAT ARE YOU GUYS DOING?" Sam asked Grandpa and Uncle Pete when he got home from school.

"I'm trying to teach your grandpa how to make a decent meatloaf," Uncle Pete said.

Somehow the words didn't match the man.

"*You're* teaching him?" Sam asked in disbelief.

"Hey, watch it. I've seen Dana make meatloaf before. There's nothing to it."

"I'm telling you, Pete, they said on TV to use dried breadcrumbs."

"And I'm telling you, crackers will work just fine."

It was plain to see that Grandpa didn't want anyone telling him what to do in his kitchen. Sam wondered if Grandma would ever be able to cook again.

"Ketchup. You need lots of ketchup," Uncle Pete said.

"Not lots, just some," Grandpa said. "That woman on the TV just put in a little."

"You need some onions too."

"Would you quit telling me how to cook?" Grandpa snapped.

"Are you making potatoes too?" Sam asked.

The two men turned and looked at him.

"Just asking. Grandma always adds potatoes and carrots."

Grandpa rubbed his jaw. "That's right. I'd forgotten that." He pulled a pot from the cupboard.

"What's that for?" Uncle Pete wanted to know.

"Boiling the potatoes."

"You don't boil the potatoes."

"That's what the lady on TV does."

"Not for meatloaf. You put them right in the pan with the meatloaf. It all cooks together."

"Then how come the lady on TV did it that way?"

"Was she making a meatloaf at the time?"

"No, but what's that got to do with it?"

Uncle Pete blew out a sigh. "Fine, make it your way. I'm outta here." He stomped to the back porch, pulled on his coat, yanked open the door, and then went outside.

Grandpa turned and frowned at Sam. "Now, you want to tell me how to cook too?"

"Nope. I'll leave that to you."

"Here. Make yourself useful and peel some potatoes. Then we'll set them on the stove to boil."

"Where's Emily?" They could sure use her help right about now.

"She's working on Dana's dress sketches."

With a sigh, Sam washed his hands at the sink, and then started on the potatoes.

Grandpa pulled some rubber gloves from the drawer and snapped them onto his hands. Sam knew Grandma used those for dishes, and since they didn't have any, Sam wondered what Grandpa was going to do.

He watched in horror as Grandpa plunged his hands into the meatloaf mixture and started kneading it into a loaf shape. He couldn't remember when he'd ever seen anything so disgusting. He finished the potatoes and put the pot on the stove, and then turned the heat on under the kettle.

Sam looked up to his grandpa and, in fact, considered him a very wise man. He wasn't so sure how his wisdom held up when it came to women, but he decided to take a chance.

"Arielle's still mad about the college thing," Sam said.

"Women are hard to please sometimes; that's for sure," Grandpa said.

Sam grabbed some dishes from the cupboard. "She wants me to do everything her way. Wants my future all mapped out—I suppose so she can give her approval."

Grandpa shrugged. "Women have their heads full of dreams. Men look at things realistically."

"Well, now I don't know if I agree with that or not."

Both Sam and Grandpa turned with a start to see Grandma standing in the kitchen doorway, smiling.

"Uh-oh, she caught us," Grandpa said, shoving the meatloaf—which resembled a shoebox rather than a loaf—into the oven.

"That looks good, Bob," she said. "You want any potatoes to go with that?"

"We've got potatoes on," he said, pulling the lid off the kettle of potatoes so she could see it.

"Oh, boiled potatoes. Okay."

The way she said it let Sam know Uncle Pete had been right about putting the potatoes in with the meatloaf. The look on Grandpa's face said now he knew it too. Sam decided this was a good time to slip away. Maybe he'd talk to Grandpa later about Arielle. Hopefully, he knew more about women than he did about cooking.

Chapter Twenty

Bill, what are you doing here this time of the evening?" Bob asked when his son stepped into the house.

"Had a meeting with some other attorneys in Bedford and thought I'd stop by before I went home."

"Well, we're glad you did. Come on in."

Charlotte stood in the hallway, drying her hands on a dishtowel and smiling at Bill. "Is the family with you?"

"Do you mean, specifically, baby Will?"

Charlotte laughed. "Of course not. I wanted to see the girls too."

He shook his head. "You grandmas are all alike."

"Want to stay for dinner? Your dad made meatloaf."

His eyebrows shot up. "That's got to be a first."

Charlotte smiled. "He's helping me out."

"It's tempting, but I have to head home. Just wanted to pop in and say hello."

"The least you can do is have a cookie." Charlotte just wasn't happy unless the people she loved were eating.

Bill followed her into the kitchen. "What's in the jar today?"

"Snickerdoodles," she said proudly.

"My favorite. You must have had a sixth sense or something that I was coming."

"Mothers have a way of knowing things," she said.

She checked on the meatloaf, releasing the scent of spices she'd secretly added when no one was looking.

"Wow, that does smell good."

"Not too late to change your mind."

He grinned. "Better not. Anna would have my head." He munched on a cookie and leaned against the counter. "Where are the kids?"

"They're upstairs working on their homework. I try to make sure they get a good start on it before dinner so they're not up all night." She closed the oven door and put the mitts back on the counter.

"I remember those days."

Charlotte chuckled. "I suppose you do."

"Listen, Mom. I want to talk to you about something," Bill said.

"Oh?"

Bob walked into the kitchen and grabbed a sugar-free cookie from the stash set aside for him. "Okay if I join you?"

"Sure," Bill said.

Bob settled in at the table near Bill.

"I was just wondering if Pete has mentioned anything to you about asking me to be the best man at his wedding."

"He hasn't mentioned it to me yet, but then you know Pete. He doesn't talk about details unless he's forced." She chuckled and then studied her older son.

"Yeah, I guess."

"Why do you ask?"

He shrugged. "Just wondered. Pete and Dana seemed sort of taken aback when Anna mentioned it. Like Anna, I had assumed he would ask me, and now I'm wondering if he will."

Charlotte could tell by the tone of his voice that it would bother him greatly if Pete didn't ask him. The idea surprised her—and bothered her. What if Pete didn't ask his brother?

"Pete will get around to it. Anna's comment most likely caught him off guard. Like I said, he doesn't think about details until he has to. I'm sure he just hasn't given it much thought till now."

"Yeah, you're probably right."

Bill walked over and kissed his mom on the cheek. "Thanks, Mom." He turned to Bob. "Dad."

The cookie jar only inches away, he reached in and grabbed another.

"Take some extra ones to the girls." Charlotte opened the drawer to get a plastic bag, but the box was gone. She turned to Bob. "Did you use all the plastic bags?"

"No. They're in that drawer over there," he said, pointing. "Why?"

"I moved them to make them more accessible when I need to wrap things and put them in the fridge."

Charlotte frowned. "I liked them just fine where they were."

Bill walked over and pulled out the plastic bags. "If you'll just give me what you think the girls need, I'll be on my way."

"Hey, Grandpa," Christopher practically skidded to a halt when he reached the kitchen. "A relative of my dad's contacted me on e-mail. He's like an in-law to a great-aunt or something. Anyway, this man has already done a lot of work on the family tree on my dad's side and has information to share. Isn't that cool?"

"That's cool," Bob said.

"Better be careful. You can't always trust strangers on the Internet," Bill said, ruffling the top of Christopher's head as he walked by. "See you later, Mom and Dad."

Fear jolted through Charlotte like an electric current. Suddenly the plastic bags didn't seem so important.

"SO THANKFUL we were able to get some other cooks to work at the restaurant today," Hannah said, sliding into her seat at Charlotte's kitchen table the next day.

"You and me both." Charlotte placed coffee in front of them.

"It's exhausting work to stand on your feet all day like that. I don't know how Melody does it."

"I sure wouldn't want to do it all the time. She may feel that way too when she's as old as we are," Charlotte said with a chuckle.

"Did you go to the hospital this morning?"

"No. I called her, and she said she was coming home this afternoon. So I'm taking dinner to her family tonight. I thought I'd see her for a few minutes then."

"Did she say how she was doing?"

"She seems to be getting along all right. She was disappointed that they didn't take the drain tube out. Seems she'll have to keep that in place for a few more days. Russ will have to help her with it. You know Melody. She's a doer. She doesn't want other people waiting on her.

"Yeah. I suppose most of us are that way."

"Especially us women."

They laughed together.

"So how are the boys getting along without you here to cook for them?"

"Can you believe Bob is actually taking up cooking?"

Hannah almost choked on her coffee. "You're kidding. Maybe I should send Frank over. He's been scratching around in the kitchen like a chicken in search of feed."

"I don't think I'd recommend sending him here. From what I've seen, Bob's not exactly Paula Deen."

Hannah laughed. "Got to give him an E for effort though."

"I suppose. But he's rearranged some of my kitchen drawers, so we're going to have it out pretty soon." Charlotte laughed ever so slightly.

"Oh my goodness, you mean to tell me that man doesn't realize you never mess with a woman's kitchen? It's like the unspoken cardinal rule."

"Exactly."

"Woe unto him once you get back in your kitchen for good. I'd like to be a little mouse that day." Hannah laughed with the idea of it all.

"No, I don't think you'd want to do that. It won't be pretty."

"What won't be pretty?" Bob asked when he walked into the kitchen.

"Oh, just girl talk; you wouldn't be interested," Charlotte said, sharing a mischievous glance with Hannah.

"Would you ladies like me to whip up some brownies for you?" Bob asked eagerly.

"Sounds great, but I've got to get back home before

Frank sends someone after me." Hannah rose from her seat, placed her mug in the sink, and headed for the door before Bob could pull in his next breath.

Charlotte stifled a laugh and waved good-bye. One thing that bothered her about Bob's new love for the kitchen: would he be willing to give it up once Charlotte's time at the diner came to an end?

EMILY DROPPED HER SCHOOL BAG by the stairway and walked to the kitchen for a drink of water.

"Well, hello," Grandma said.

"What are you doing home? I thought you'd be at the restaurant."

"A couple of other ladies from church offered to give Hannah and me a break, so I'm home today."

"Oh, great. You'll be cooking dinner?"

"Yes. How do chicken and noodles, mixed vegetables, mashed potatoes, and salad sound?"

"Fantastic—well, except for the chicken part. The veggies sound good."

"I'll set aside an extra plate of veggies for you."

"Thanks. I'll get my homework done and come back to help you," Emily said. She took a drink of water and turned to go.

"Oh, I almost forgot. Dana—Miss Simons—just dropped this off for you." Grandma handed her a manila envelope.

"What is it?"

"I think it might be some pictures of possible wedding dresses, to add to your flair for creativity, of course." Grandma handed her the packet.

"Thanks."

Emily wasn't sure how to feel about that. It obviously meant that Miss Simons was less than thrilled with what she'd seen of Emily's sketches thus far.

Taking the stairs two at a time, Emily dashed up to her room. She wanted to see just what kind of fashion Miss Simons preferred.

Once in the privacy of her room, she settled onto her bed and pulled the contents from the package Miss Simons had left for her. One by one she unfolded the magazine pages and looked at the full views of traditional wedding dresses that looked old enough to be out of fashion but not so old to be vintage and in fashion. Boring dresses, every last one of them.

Emily plunked her head back on a pillow and tried to sort through the whole idea. She knew Miss Simons wasn't the outgoing, flamboyant type, but she certainly didn't expect boring dresses. Not a single detail of any consequence on those dresses. Wedding gowns were supposed to make a statement, weren't they? "Hey, friends, this is the happiest day of my life. Can you tell?"

To Emily's way of thinking, these gowns said, "Hey, friends, thanks for coming. Coffee and donuts will be served following the lecture."

So if that was all Miss Simons wanted, why did she agree to let Emily help out? Why couldn't she just find one of these dresses to suit her at the store? They couldn't be that expensive because there wasn't anything to speak of adorning them. No frills.

Not that Emily preferred the frilly, poofy kind of dresses. She actually preferred a basic dress with unexpected tucks, swirls, and pearls here and there—sort of a built-in surprise. But obviously, Miss Simons didn't prefer that.

Emily sat up on her bed and picked up the photos of the dresses. It was time to get busy. The question was, how could she keep a boring dress boring for Miss Simons and still add enough of a surprise element to make Emily want her name associated with it?

EMILY AND ASHLEY disappeared through the door of Ashley's bedroom later that evening. "Don't go too far, Emily; we can't stay long," Charlotte called out to them.

"You shouldn't have brought dinner again, Charlotte. Russ can whip up something or go over to the diner."

"He has enough to do with keeping you healthy."

"I hate being pampered this way."

"Now's your time to enjoy the life of a princess." Charlotte looked around the room at all the flowers. "You certainly are loved."

Melody smiled. "The flowers are wonderful. But you want to know the truth? I wish Russ would scatter them around the living room for me to come out and enjoy. Seeing them clustered in the bedroom this way makes me feel I'm in a funeral home."

"Oh dear." Charlotte hadn't thought of that. She supposed Melody had more morbid thoughts on her mind of late.

Melody laughed. "No big deal, but still."

"I see what you mean."

"How's Russ doing?" Charlotte had noticed how tired he appeared lately and was a bit concerned about him.

"He's taking this awful hard. The thing is, he doesn't

have any close friends. You know Russ; he's sort of quiet, so it's hard for people to get close to him—and vice versa. So he's been bearing the weight of this alone."

Charlotte nodded but said nothing.

"He's appreciated the church folks and the townspeople so much, how they've pitched in to help us. Unbelievable, really. Still, I wish he could talk to someone, just sort of vent his feelings. He doesn't say much to me, and I know it's because he doesn't want me to know he's scared. But I see the fear in his eyes every time I look at him."

"You know, Pete thinks a lot of Russ. He's mentioned that a few times after he talked with Russ at church. What if Bob and Pete come out and check on him? Would that be all right?"

"That would be wonderful. Better still, how about you all come over and join us for dinner one night? Then it will be natural to all hang out together. Have Pete bring Dana too."

"You sure you're up to that?"

"What's the harm? We can pick up food from the diner, so I won't have to do any work. I don't do much around the house because Russ won't let me. And to be honest, I'm enjoying this side of him."

Charlotte laughed. "Good for you. Still, I insist on contributing to the meal. How about I do dessert?"

"Deal. Let's try it, say, Saturday evening."

"Sounds perfect."

"Six-thirty?"

"Six-thirty it is."

"Tell the boys not to say that I told you anything. Russ is so private about things."

"I understand."

"How's the restaurant holding together?" Melody rearranged her pillow, gently maneuvering her arm with the tube under it.

"Everything is going well. The town has really rallied around you, Melody. Lots of business, church ladies helping in the kitchen. Even the teen group got together this week and volunteered to take turns serving. The place is hoppin', I'm telling you."

Melody laughed. "Well, how do you like that! It runs better without me."

"I wouldn't go that far."

"It's amazing how the people have supported us through this. I never would have dreamed we had so many people around us who cared enough to do that."

"That's God's community in action."

"It sure is. I hope I can return the favor someday. You know, sort of a pay-it-forward kind of thing."

"I know exactly what you mean. Such a blessing to be a part of it all." Charlotte smiled. "Well, I don't want to wear you out, so I'm going home for now. If you need anything at all, have Russ call me and I'll be over."

"Thank you so much, Charlotte. For everything."

Charlotte waved good-bye and walked out of the bedroom in search of Emily, but not before she got a good glimpse of the haunting look in Melody's eyes before they drifted closed.

Chapter Twenty-One

After dinner that same evening, once the kids went into the family room and Pete and Bob finished their meals but still sat talking at the table, Charlotte stopped straightening the kitchen and joined them.

"I talked to Melody today, and she tells me Russ is going through a hard time with all that's going on. It seems he doesn't have a lot of guy friends he talks to regularly. He has acquaintances, but not close friends."

"Yeah?" Pete said.

"Yeah. I guess he could use some friends right now. She senses that he needs to talk to someone, just kind of vent a little, you know?"

Bob nodded.

She explained her talk with Melody and their plans to have Saturday night dinner together. "Would that work for you and Dana?" she asked Pete.

"Sure. We try to go out on Saturday night, and we don't have any specific plans for this Saturday. Why not?"

"Great. It would be nice if you could reach out to Russ, see if he'll open up at all."

"You mean have a heart-to-heart or something?" Bob asked nervously.

"Well, you don't have to get all mushy, but maybe let him know he can lean on the two of you if necessary," Charlotte explained. "Do you think you can do that?"

"I think we can manage that, Mom," Pete assured her, glancing at Bob.

"Sure, honey, we can do that," Bob agreed.

"Now, how about a piece of your delicious pie?" Pete said with a wide grin.

Charlotte didn't miss the way Bob glared at his son. No doubt a tad jealous that the family preferred her cooking to his.

After the men ate their pie and left the room to pursue television interests, and her kitchen sparkled clean, Charlotte turned to leave just as Emily walked into the room.

"Just wanted to say good night."

Charlotte gave her a quick hug. "Good night, honey."

"Grandma?"

"Yes."

"Ashley's really upset about this whole thing with her mom."

"I know."

"But she says her brother and her dad won't talk about it. They just come home and get busy with things. Her brother works on the computer, and her dad sits down to watch TV. Nobody ever talks about what's going on."

"I see."

"I know she needs her space, but she also needs them to talk. I mean, it's a scary thing and all."

"Yes, they do need to talk about it. Everyone handles pain differently though. They're choosing to ignore what's going on. It's not necessarily a good thing, but a lot of people do that."

Emily nodded. "I know. I just wish I knew how to help her."

"Maybe she should come over on Saturday. We're going over there Saturday evening for dinner. She could spend the day with you and you could put your cares aside and have a normal girls' day. If the weather holds up, you could take her riding. That is, if you can take a break from the dress designing."

Emily's eyes sparkled with excitement. "That's a great idea. Thanks. I really can't do much more on the dress until Miss Simons looks at the sketches I've drawn. She's going to have to make a decision soon or she'll be wearing jeans to her wedding." Emily laughed.

Charlotte sighed. "You're right; she's going to have to make a decision soon." Charlotte didn't want to think about that problem just now.

"I'll tell Ashley first thing when I see her at school tomorrow. G'night."

"Good night, Emily."

Charlotte made her way up the stairs to check on Christopher and Sam. She gave a gentle knock on Christopher's door. "Christopher?"

"Come on in, Grandma."

She walked into his room. It smelled of sneakers and dirty socks. A cough escaped her. "Just wanted to say good night." Another cough.

"Did I tell you that man, Great-Uncle Richard, is sending me family tree information in the next day or two?"

"You mentioned he had some information for you." Charlotte sat on his bed. "Christopher, you do know not to send out personal information over e-mail, right?"

"Oh, sure, I know that. I didn't even tell him where I lived, because he's sending the stuff over the Internet. We learned at school that you're not supposed to get into specifics with strangers. I'm very careful."

Though relief flooded through her, Charlotte still wondered if Christopher's idea of being careful and her idea of it were the same.

"It's not that I don't trust you, honey, but I want to see your e-mails before you send them, okay? Just to put my mind at rest, so I don't have to worry, okay?"

Christopher blew out a long, dramatic sigh. "Okay," he said, drawing out the word.

"Thank you. Now you have sweet dreams." She spotted a couple of clean shirts on the chair. She picked them up. "Christopher, I keep telling you, you need to put away your clothes right after they've been washed." She walked over to the closet to hang them.

"No, wait, Grandma. Don't go in there." Panic lined his voice.

She turned to him. "What's wrong?"

He hopped out of bed. "Oh, nothing. I just think I should do it. Learn responsibility and all."

She studied him a moment, and then turned toward the closet. "Nonsense. I'm already here." She opened the closet door and her foot bumped into something on the floor. She looked down. "What on earth?"

Picking it up, she spotted the ants. She whipped around to her grandson. "Christopher, what are you doing with this?"

"Well, see, Grandma, I'm learning about families and all, so when Dylan's mom told him he couldn't have the ant farm, we just couldn't toss it aside on the streets and let those poor ants die, could we? I know you would never do that. You help so many people, and I want to be just like you, Grandma, helping living things in need. So anyway, they're in my closet, but I'm taking good care of them. I watch over them every day, just like a family member would. Just like you taught me, Grandma, taking care of God's creatures, right?"

"Christopher Slater, hold on a minute!" Charlotte regretted the snap in her voice. But ants? In her house? Why, if they got loose, she'd spray every last one of them to their eternal reward!

He gently pried the ant farm from her hand, held it at eye level, and peered in. "Isn't it cool, Grandma?"

She had a word in mind and *cool* wasn't it.

"Do you honestly think it's the best idea to have an ant farm in the house?"

He looked up at her with big, worrisome eyes. "What else could we do? If we put them out in the cold, they'll die for sure."

She wanted to discuss with him the fact that these were insects, not house pets, but right now, she just didn't have the strength.

"See how they work in the tunnels. It's just amazing."

He was trying to make this look like an educational experience, but she was on to him.

"Put it away for now. But you can be sure of one thing, young man. You will have to find the ants a new home." She tried not to shiver. She did not appreciate insects. "In the meantime, you make sure they don't get loose. If they do, it's quite possible they could meet with an untimely death." One look at the horror on his face and the protective way he held the container almost made her wish she hadn't said that.

Almost.

"I'll take care of them," he said, backing away slowly, his gaze clamped on hers while he stumbled into the closet to tuck his charges safely away.

"See you in the morning," Charlotte said, closing the door behind her. She could be thankful for one thing—at least they weren't snakes.

CHRISTOPHER AND GRANDPA stood over a bowl, one dropping in ingredients, the other stirring, when Uncle Pete sauntered into the kitchen late Friday afternoon.

"So what's on the menu today?" Uncle Pete asked with a grin.

"I thought while your mom was out getting groceries, I'd throw on a batch of brownies and surprise her," Grandpa said.

"Sounds like a good plan," Uncle Pete said.

"And I'm helping," Christopher announced.

"Why? Do you think he needs it?" Uncle Pete laughed at his own joke. Grandpa didn't.

When Grandpa's head was turned, Christopher nodded enthusiastically toward Uncle Pete, who laughed some more.

Uncle Pete opened the refrigerator door and grabbed a handful of carrots from the bag.

"Did you get the seed ordered for the spring planting?" Grandpa asked.

"Sure did. Got the stalls cleaned out in the barn, fresh hay down, every creature fed and watered, Trudy milked, chickens plucked of their eggs. You name it, I've done it. I'll sure be glad when spring gets here. I'm bored to distraction."

"You could help your fiancée with the wedding plans—make yourself useful, you know."

Christopher hopped off the step stool and sat at the table with Uncle Pete, snitching one of his carrots when he wasn't looking and crunching down hard.

"You're starting to sound like Mom. Maybe this kitchen thing isn't good for you. Besides, I leave that wedding stuff to the women. They're having enough trouble just figuring out the dress."

Grandpa poured the brownie mixture into the pan and placed it in the oven.

"Can I lick the bowl, Grandpa?"

"I reckon."

Christopher chewed the last of his carrot and grabbed the bowl.

"I thought Emily was taking care of the dress."

"She was supposed to, but Dana and Emily can't come to an agreement over the design. I don't know why Dana doesn't just buy something and forget it. So much fuss over a few ruffles and some fancy material."

"You're sort of in the middle of it all, aren't you, Uncle Pete?" Christopher pointed out while licking chocolate from his fingers and leaving nary a speck in the bowl.

"Yeah, as a matter of fact, I am."

"Emily's not gonna like it one bit that Miss Simons is being so picky," Christopher said.

"Well, she'll have to get over it. Seems to me Dana ought to have the dress she wants."

"I'm just sayin' . . ."

Uncle Pete frowned at Christopher, making Christopher wonder if he should have saved some brownie residue for his uncle.

"Dana will have to tell Emily. She ought to have the dress she wants. Emily will have to respect that," Grandpa said. "By the way, Bill is wondering whether or not you'll ask him to be his best man."

"Of course I'm gonna ask him. Why wouldn't I?"

"Well, you didn't that night Anna brought it up."

"For one thing, it caught me off guard since I hadn't thought about the groomsmen yet, and secondly, I don't like Anna telling me what to do. I'll ask him soon enough."

They talked awhile longer about the matter, but Christopher got bored, so he got up from the table. The brownies were due out of the oven any minute, and he tried to linger long enough to get some but figured he could run back into the kitchen once the timer went off.

A car skidded into the driveway. Brakes screeched and tires crunched snow, coming to a sharp halt. Bob, Pete, and Christopher all rushed outside to see what had happened. When they got out there, they saw Sam's car and Toby nearby. Toby was fine, but Sam seemed pretty shaken.

"What happened?" Grandpa asked when he opened Sam's car door.

"Toby just darted out of nowhere. I didn't see her at all. I almost hit her."

"Well, you *didn't* hit her, right?" Grandpa helped Sam out of the car.

"I don't think so."

"Don't you know?" Uncle Pete asked. "Seems to me you would have felt a thump."

Christopher ran over to Toby, knelt down, and wrapped his arms around her.

"I don't know. It all happened so fast."

"You have something else on your mind besides driving?" Uncle Pete asked.

Christopher could tell Uncle Pete was upset too.

"No," Sam said defensively.

"You just seem upset."

"Of course, I'm upset! I almost hit Toby."

"Don't get all bent out of shape. We're just asking what happened."

Sam sighed. "Sorry, Uncle Pete. It just shook me up; that's all."

Grandpa checked Toby over, and then checked the car. "There's no harm done, so we may as well go back in the house. It's cold out here."

By the time they had gotten through all the commotion and were back in the house, the stench of burnt brownies greeted them. Grandpa's legs worked faster than Christopher had ever seen them move. They all ran into the smoke-filled kitchen, and Grandpa began barking orders.

"Quick, open those windows. Open the door. We have to air out this kitchen."

Uncle Pete ran over and opened each one.

"Get the room spray, Christopher; make it smell good in here." Christopher ran into the bathroom, grabbed the spray, and started spraying everywhere, all the while lamenting the brownies he would never eat.

"Sam, unplug that smoke alarm before it—"

Before Grandpa could finish what he was about to say, Grandma stood at the back door entrance, arms filled with groceries, frowning, nose scrunched in disapproval.

"What on earth happened?"

Before anyone could answer, the screech of the smoke alarm blasted through the stench of fog.

All eyes turned to Grandpa.

Busted.

Chapter Twenty-Two

That evening at the dinner table, Sam barely touched his chicken. The kitchen still smelled of burned brownies and air freshener.

After excusing himself from the table, he ran upstairs, grabbed the cordless telephone from the spare room, and took it into his room.

Staring at the phone, he told himself he had to call her. This had gone on long enough. It had been almost a week since he and Arielle went out for pizza and their date took a nosedive. She'd given him only glances and slight waves at school ever since. He didn't even know if they were still "going out." He needed to know where they stood.

Maybe he should go ahead and get those college brochures out and look over the degrees offered again, but he didn't like her telling him what to do.

The few bites of chicken he'd eaten rebelled in his stomach. Taking off his shoes, he stretched out on his bed and tried to get comfortable. He picked up the phone and punched in Arielle's number. It was all a misunderstanding. She'd be over it by now. Probably waiting by the phone for him to call. It did her good to stew a little. Maybe now she'd be happy to hear from him.

Disappointment kicked in when her mom answered and said that Arielle had gone out with some friends from school. She obviously wasn't waiting around for his call. Maybe he should go out for a little while too. Punching in more numbers, he waited again.

"Hey, Jake, what are you doing?"

"Who's this?"

"It's Sam, who'd you think?"

"Haven't heard from you in a while, dude. I wasn't sure."

"Whatever. What are you doing tonight?"

"Going to a movie with Kelsey. Oh, sorry. I forgot about you and Arielle."

"What are you talking about?"

"Didn't you guys break up?"

"Why do you say that?"

"I just thought . . . oh, never mind."

"No, tell me. What's going on?"

"Nothing, really. Just saw her at the mall a little while ago with Travis Henderson."

"Travis!" *Great. Just great.* The knot in his stomach expanded three inches. "Well, it's not like we're married."

"Right. I just hadn't seen her with other guys since you two—well, I didn't know."

"We're seeing other people. No big deal."

"Yeah, that's what she said."

"She did?" *Nice of her to let me know.*

"Hey, sorry to cut this short, but Kelsey's waiting on me, so I've got to go. Let's get together soon. Later, dude."

"Later."

Standing up, he walked over to the window and glanced out. "I'm so sick of this snow." He thumped across the room, kicking aside the clothes that were in his path. His stupid room was so boring. He couldn't wait to one day have a home of his own. He heard Arielle's voice in his head. Yeah, yeah, yeah, so he'd have to get a good job and make some money first.

Sam punched Arielle's numbers on the phone again. "Hello? Mrs. Friesen, do you know what time Arielle might be home?"

"Yes, she said she'd be home around ten o'clock."

"I know that's kind of late, but would you mind if I stopped by then just for a few minutes? I need to talk to her quickly about something."

"Well, I suppose that would be all right."

"Thanks a lot," Sam said. "I'll see you then."

"OH, I ALMOST FORGOT to show you guys." Charlotte rushed out of the family room, leaving Bob, Pete, Christopher, and Emily behind. She grabbed the T-shirt from her bag in the kitchen and came back. "Here it is," she said, whipping out the navy T-shirt and holding it in front of her.

The pink words on the front of the shirt read STIRRING UP A CURE. The back said MEL'S PLACE, along with the restaurant phone number.

"Oh, I love it," Emily said, running over to feel the material. "When will mine come in?"

"This is it," Charlotte said with a smile.

Emily clapped. "Thank you, Grandma. These are really cool."

"I thought they turned out nicely. And the proceeds go to the Givens family to help with medical expenses."

"You can't beat that," Bob said.

"How much are they? I'll get one for Dana," Pete said, pulling out his billfold.

"Twenty dollars. Men can wear them too, you know," Charlotte said.

"I don't look good in pink." Pete handed her a twenty.

"I don't either," Bob said in a stern voice, lest Charlotte get any ideas. "But I'll give you the twenty just the same."

"The shirt is blue. Only the words are pink," Charlotte said.

"I don't wear pink," Pete and Bob said simultaneously.

Charlotte sighed and shook her head while snatching the money from Bob and Pete. "We just got these in today, and we've sold a lot of them already. I can't believe how the town has come through for Melody and her family. It reinforces my faith in mankind."

Bob rubbed the stubble on his jaw. "I have to say it's been pretty amazing to see it. How's Melody doing?"

"She's all right. Her spirits are still up. You know Melody; she'd never show it if she was hurting in any way."

"Yeah, I know." Bob shook his head. "She sure is a wonder."

"She gets her drain tube out on Monday, so she's very happy about that. She's hoping she'll heal up quickly after that—providing there are no long-term problems," Charlotte said, preferring not to think about the other possibilities.

"Good. You working at the diner tomorrow?"

"Yeah. Emily and I are going in to work in the morning. You boys are on your own again for meals."

Christopher groaned. Bob shot him a look.

"What? I was clearing my throat," Christopher said.

Charlotte tried not to laugh. She knew Bob was doing the best he could. As far as she could tell, Bob had pretty good self-esteem where his cooking was concerned, despite Christopher's opinion. She suspected Pete's constant appetite kept Bob feeling pretty proud of himself.

Sam came bounding into the room with his coat on.

"Where are you going this late?" Bob asked.

"I was going to ask if it's all right if I run to Arielle's house for a few minutes. I won't stay long. Should be back no later than ten forty-five or eleven o'clock. Her mom said it was all right."

Bob hesitated and then said okay, which surprised Charlotte.

"Thanks, Grandpa." Sam practically ran out the back door before Bob could change his mind.

"What was that all about?" Charlotte asked.

Bob glanced at the others and then looked at Charlotte. "We'll talk later."

SAM PULLED THE SCARF UP closer to his neck as he walked to Arielle's front door. Darkness hovered over the neighborhood like a heavy blanket. The crunch of snow beneath his boots echoed through the silent air, emphasizing his feelings of loneliness. The moon ducked behind a heavy cloud, taking all the light from his path. He wondered if it was a sign. He took a deep breath, and it caught in his throat, causing him to cough. The cold air burned his lungs and his nose.

The door opened before he got there.

"Hi, Sam," Arielle said. "Come on in." She opened the door farther and allowed him to step inside. He shook the snow from his boots just outside the door and then pulled them off once he stepped inside.

The warmth of the room and the smell of something sweet, like pumpkin pie, invited him to stay—though the jury was still out on whether Arielle wanted him there.

"Here, let me have your coat."

He slipped his arms out of it and handed it to her. "Thanks."

In the hall closet, the clatter of hangers sounded as she hung up his coat. "Let's go into the living room." She led the way, and they settled on the sofa.

"So what's going on?" she asked.

"I think you know."

"Why don't you tell me?"

She was baiting him, which annoyed him immensely.

"What's going on with us?"

She shrugged. "I don't know what you mean, Sam." She stared at her nails, brushed something off her jeans, primped her hair, did everything but look at him.

"I think you do. You've been ignoring me at school."

"I have not." A spark flashed in her eyes when she turned to him. "You haven't bothered to talk to me."

"That's because I keep getting vibes that you don't want me around."

Silence.

"Is this all because I haven't picked out a college major, mapped out my future?"

"Still?"

"Still what?"

"Still haven't looked at the brochures, picked out a major?"

Though he really cared about Arielle, right now, he found it hard to relate to her. This little inquisition started to smother him.

"No, I still haven't. You know, Arielle, some people don't decide on a major until their sophomore year." Somehow saying that made him feel better. He didn't have to kowtow to her. He had a right to choose his own life, not be controlled by her.

"Look, Sam, I'm not trying to control you," she said, as though reading his mind. "I had just hoped we might go to school together and see where it leads. But honestly, I want a guy who shares my vision."

"And I want a girl who will let me be me." He couldn't help the tone of his voice. She just plain irritated him.

Her chin hiked up; her jaw set. "What is that supposed to mean?"

He sighed. "Listen, I don't want to fight with you. But I need you to give me some space. I'll figure things out. Give me time, will you?"

She sighed. "I had hoped things would be different—*could* be different—but obviously, I was wrong. I think it's best we don't see each other anymore, Sam. You're a great guy, and I've really enjoyed our friendship. But we obviously have different ideas about the future, and I think staying together would only bring us down."

Her words hit him like a hard punch in the gut.

Bring us down. In other words, she thinks I'm a big fat loser, and if she stays with me, I'll bring her down.

He wasn't about to let her know the blow her words had dealt him.

"If that's what you want."

"It's what I want." She stood to her feet, her resolve firmly in place.

Sam got up. "Good luck to you, Arielle." Their eyes met. For a fraction of a second, sorrow flickered in her eyes. She blinked it away, but he had seen it just as plain as the nose on her face.

"Good-bye, Sam."

Without another word, Sam pulled on his boots, coat, and scarf and then headed out into the icy night winds, his heart as cold as the limbs of the front-yard oak tree, layered with ice and just as brittle.

WHEN SAM GOT HOME, he stepped through the back door and shook the snow from his scarf.

"Started snowing again, huh?" Uncle Pete asked while munching on an oatmeal cookie.

"Yeah."

"You don't look so good," Uncle Pete pointed out.

"Thanks."

"Sit down and have a cookie with me."

Despite the gurgling in his stomach and the smell of sugar and cinnamon that permeated the kitchen, he said, "I'm not hungry."

Sam started to pass his uncle, but Uncle Pete grabbed his arm. "Sit down. Let's talk."

Sam reluctantly settled in the chair across from Uncle Pete.

"You want to tell me what's wrong?"

"Not really."

"Okay. Then have a cookie. I'll get you some milk." Uncle Pete got up and poured Sam a glass of milk and filled a plate with some cookies.

"Thanks." Sam sat there a minute, thinking how good the cookies tasted. Remembering that he'd had very little dinner, he took another.

"You not eating because of Dad's cooking?"

"That's some of it."

"What's the other some of it?"

"Arielle just broke up with me."

"Oh. Been there, done that. It stinks."

"Yeah, it does."

"But you'll see that life goes on, and you'll be just fine without her."

Sam explained the deal with the college major, the goals for the future, what it meant to Arielle, and her reaction to what she perceived as his lack of motivation.

"Well, the way I see it, it's your life. If you're not ready for college, don't let a girl push you into it."

Sam appreciated the validation from his uncle.

"On the other hand—"

Uh-oh, here it comes.

"—you don't want to use it as an excuse for shirking your responsibilities. You need to think through what you'd like to do with your life and pick the avenue that will take you to that goal. You do what's right for you and what works with your wallet."

"That's just it. Without a soccer scholarship, I don't know how I'd pay for it. It's easy for her to get all in an uproar. She doesn't have to worry about the money issue."

"Yeah, I see what you're saying. Don't give it another thought. Things will work out. They always do."

Sam and Uncle Pete got up from the table. After saying good night, Sam rinsed out his milk glass and went upstairs to bed, where the others had already gone.

There was one thing he couldn't get past. If everything was going to turn out all right, why did he feel so crummy?

Chapter Twenty-Three

Christopher's sneakered feet swished back and forth, skimming the carpet; his fingers drummed on the wooden desk—thumpity, thump, thump—as he waited for the e-mail attachment to open on the computer screen. The smell of sausage and biscuits traveled from the kitchen into the family room, making his stomach impatient. But he couldn't leave yet. He had to see what his dad's Great-Uncle Richard Slater, husband of Great-Aunt Ava Slater, had found in his research on the family tree.

Though this project was as massive as Christopher had feared, he had to admit it wasn't boring. He thought it was pretty cool to read about people in his family and what they had accomplished in their lives. Maybe one day someone would read something cool about him.

When the document appeared, Christopher scrolled through the screens one by one, learning more about his family than he ever dreamed he'd know.

Great-Uncle Richard said Christopher's great-grandfather, Samuel Matthew Slater, had been an army sergeant during World War II, and he had risked his life to save his battalion. During a fierce battle in the middle of a war zone, he had pulled every last one of his men to safety. He almost made it without injury, but as he hauled the last guy toward safety, his own leg was shattered by enemy fire; his comrade made it unharmed. Great-Grandpa Sam received a Purple Heart in June 1942.

Christopher didn't know what all that meant, but he was sure it must have been a good thing. He switched screens and looked up "Purple Heart" on Google.

"Wow, that's really cool," he said when he read the explanation of the honor.

"What's cool?" Sam asked when he walked up to the desk.

"This Purple Heart," Christopher said. He explained about the note and the news on Great-Grandpa Sam. "Hey, I wonder if you were named after him."

Sam grinned. "Could be, little brother. Do you think there's some big medal of honor in my future?"

"Maybe. You'd have to join the military first though."

"You boys ready to eat?" Grandma appeared at the family room entrance, a smile on her face, apron over her jeans, a smudge of flour on her cheek. Just the way Christopher loved to see her.

"Yeah, we're ready. I'm starving," Christopher said, jumping out of his chair. He jabbered to Grandma all the way to the kitchen, telling her what he'd discovered about the family. He looked around, but Sam hadn't followed them into the kitchen. Christopher hoped Sam didn't close out the information on the computer; he wanted to get back to it as soon as he could after breakfast.

He had a military hero in his family. And to think he had thought this project would be boring.

SAM READ THE INFORMATION on the screen. His eyes stopped a moment; then he re-read the information on Samuel Matthew Slater. Suddenly, his daydream took him to a faraway place where he heard enemy fire slashing through the air. Smoke billowed, the stench of it rising with the dust. Camouflaged men moved like shadows through a thick fog, screams pierced the air, and gunfire sprayed across the ground, plucking life from heroes.

Then one lone man emerged through the fog, smeared with dirt and grime, barely able to put one foot in front of the other, carrying a man to safety. Then he went back for another. And another. Until a group of men, scarred inside and out, huddled in safety behind a boulder while the hero went into shock from the shattered bones in his right leg. Engulfed in his daydream, Sam watched in expectation as the man turned around.

It was him.

"Sam, you coming for breakfast?" Grandma called out.

"Yeah, I'm coming." He got up from the chair and headed toward the kitchen, his thoughts still focused on what he'd just read.

Wars were a terrible thing, but something about his great-grandfather intrigued him. Why would a man willingly put himself in harm's way? There could be only one answer.

To make his life matter.

That's what Sam wanted. He wanted to do something worthwhile with his life. Not just make money—though that helped. He wanted his life to matter. His mom's life was cut short. What if his own life came to an early end? He had to do something that mattered.

With that thought on his mind, before Sam reached the breakfast table, he had made up his mind to check into the possibility of a future with the military.

SOON AFTER BREAKFAST, Charlotte dropped Emily off at the restaurant to cover for a server who would be an hour late for her shift. Then Charlotte went over to Melody's house to check on her.

"So how is my favorite patient?" Charlotte asked when she walked into Melody's living room. "I see you've been kicked out of the bedroom."

Melody laughed. "I've been up and around. Just decided to sit down and rest a while."

"That's a good idea. You don't want to overdo."

Sunlight slipped through the broad windows and sprayed across the living room carpet. Bouquets of flowers huddled in vases, perfuming the air with a sweet, gentle scent. Charlotte pulled in a long, pleasurable breath.

"It's nice in here."

"Yes, much cheerier than being cooped up in our bedroom."

"I brought you something," Charlotte said, lifting a small tray of veggies and dip.

"Mmm, looks yummy." Melody scooted herself upright, plumping the blue-and-yellow quilted pillow behind her and tugging on the soft, wool-blend blanket covering her.

"Good, healthy food for you. I was going to bring a dessert, but Christopher read to me from the Internet that veggies were the best foods to ward off cancer, so here we are."

Melody smiled at her. "That's so thoughtful, Charlotte. You are one in a million."

"Just want to be a good friend, that's all."

"Well, you certainly are that." Melody picked up a carrot and started munching. "Though, to be honest, I think a really good friend would have covered these with chocolate," she said, lifting the carrot.

Charlotte laughed. "I'm trying to make you a healthy eater."

"Do you see this body, Charlotte? It's used to getting its share of chocolate."

Charlotte waved her off. "Oh, you." She settled in a chair across from where Melody lay on the sofa and glanced around the room.

"Looks as though your flowers are still holding up well." Though a few petals dipped and a few stems sagged, the majority of the blooms still held their heads high.

"Yes, aren't they beautiful? They sure perk up my spirits."

"So do your spirits need perking up? How are you feeling?"

She chuckled. "Oh, I'm fine, really. I'll be so much better once I get this stupid drain tube taken out. It's such a bother." Gingerly, she eased herself into a better position on the sofa.

"It won't be long now." Charlotte looked around. "It's quiet in here. Where's the family?"

"Ashley is upstairs, and the guys went to the store for me. But they'll be right back. The truth is, they are driving me nuts. Ashley and I have a much easier time without them hovering over us."

The two shared a friendly laugh.

"Ashley has been such a trooper through all this." A shadow crossed Melody's face. "I fear it's been awfully hard on her."

Charlotte nodded.

"Russ and Brett have walked around the house like zombies, as though they don't know what to say or do, so they keep things quiet and stay pretty much to themselves. Makes me feel as though I'm in a morgue. Ashley spends time with me, plays games, talks and laughs with me. I don't know what I would have done without her."

"Women seem to have a better handle on emotional things, don't they?"

"That seems to be the case in this household."

"Are you sure it's all right to take her back home with me? I don't want to leave you with the guys if you'd rather Ashley stick around."

"Oh, no, no. I can handle them. Besides, Ashley needs to get out and have some fun with her friend. As I said, this has been a stressful time for her. I suspect Emily knows a little about that."

Charlotte's breath stuck in her throat. "Things will be better for you."

"Still, the threat of it hangs over Ashley." Melody fingered the blanket around her. "Hangs over all of us, really."

"I know. But we'll get you through this. You're not alone."

"That's so true. I'm just thankful that Ashley has Emily. I mean, Emily's been through a very hard adjustment, yet here she is, a shining example that life goes on and people survive."

Charlotte didn't like the way this conversation was headed at all.

"Thankfully, you're doing well, and honestly, I don't believe they would have let you come away with a lumpectomy if they'd thought you needed a full mastectomy, you know?"

"Yes, that's true. I'm hoping the tests won't prove otherwise. Not because I'm scared, mind you, but because I don't want my kids or my husband to go through that."

That was Melody. Always thinking of others.

"Are you keeping tabs on the restaurant?" Charlotte asked, hoping to lift her thoughts.

"Yes—as are you." Melody winked. "Can you believe the meat is still coming in?"

"Yes, I heard that. This town is amazing."

"I've always loved this town, but I will never look at it the same. You want me to call Ashley?" Melody asked.

"We can get her in a minute. It's almost time to pick up Emily so I'll stay long enough for her to get finished there, and then Ashley and I can pick her up together."

"Sounds good."

"How are you really feeling, Melody? I mean, spirit-wise and all that."

"I'm doing all right. Not that I don't have my moments of 'blue mood,' but I can't describe the peace that I've had through all this. It's truly amazing. I'm telling you, only God could do that."

Charlotte's thoughts turned inward and she wondered, momentarily, whether Denise's death in the car crash had been violent right up to the end or if she had experienced

God's peace as she slipped into eternity. Charlotte would never know, but she chose to believe her daughter had peace.

"That's wonderful, Mel."

"It really is. I want so much to explain it to others, but there really is no way to describe it. How can anyone have peace when their future is hanging in the balance? The possibility of not seeing my kids raised to adulthood looms large over me, yet God's peace is larger. Amazing."

"I'd say you've already experienced your miracle."

"Hey, Mrs. Stevenson." Ashley bounced into the room just as Russ's car pulled into the driveway.

"Looks like they're all coming at once," Melody said with a chuckle.

Russ and Brett walked through the front door.

"Hey, Charlotte. Either we're late for dinner or you're early." Russ laughed.

"Neither. I just came by to say hello to your wife and to kidnap your daughter for a while."

He grinned at Ashley. "That will be good for her. She's been working awful hard around here since . . ." He cleared his throat. "She's been working awful hard."

Charlotte and Melody exchanged a glance.

"I'm sure she has. Emily too. They need some girl time."

"I hate it that Emily's working so hard on account of me," Melody said, running a couple of fingers through her hair.

"Don't you give it another thought. It's what we want to do."

Melody nodded. "We're sure looking forward to you all coming over tonight."

"We're looking forward to being here." Charlotte hoped the men could encourage Russ. She watched as he and Brett carried groceries from the car into the kitchen.

"You ready to go?" Charlotte asked Ashley.

"Yep."

"Then we'd better get going. It will be time to come back before we know it."

Charlotte leaned over and kissed the top of Melody's head. "You behave yourself till we get back tonight."

"I'll try to . . . *Mom.*"

As Ashley and Charlotte headed out the door, Melody's statement lingered. It had been such a long time since she'd heard a woman's voice call her Mom.

Chapter Twenty-Four

Emily and Ashley went upstairs to hang out in Emily's room. Charlotte was pleased to see the two of them spending some quality time together.

Her home smelled of lemon wax from the morning dusting she'd done. She loved starting her weekends with a clean house. Something about going to church on Sunday knowing her house was in order just made the day go better for her.

A knock at the front door caused her to turn away from the kitchen and walk through the hallway. A cold breeze stirred when she opened it.

"Mrs. Stevenson?"

"Yes."

"Perhaps you remember me. I'm Misty Roberts, reporter for the *Bedford Leader*."

"Certainly."

"I'm doing an article for the paper about how the town has rallied around Melody Givens. I was told you were the perfect person to talk to about this."

"Well, wouldn't Melody be the better person? After all, it's her story."

"I will definitely get some input from her, but I wanted to have the perspective of some of the townsfolk who've seen all the behind-the-scenes stuff. Things not even Mrs. Givens knows."

Charlotte shrugged. "Well, I don't know that I can help all that much, but you're welcome to come in."

"Thank you." The woman stepped inside.

"Let me take your coat."

Miss Roberts shed her winter wraps and handed them to Charlotte.

She looked no more than fifteen, though Charlotte knew the young woman was through college so she had to be at least twenty-two or three. As she talked and moved, her brown hair, streaked with blonde highlights, gently brushed her shoulders. Large, inquisitive brown eyes searched Charlotte's own. Stylish high-heeled black boots complemented her black pantsuit, which she wore with a turquoise turtleneck and chunky gold necklace.

"It's so cold out there," she said, briskly rubbing her hands together.

"Can I get you some tea or coffee, hot chocolate?"

"Hot chocolate would be awesome," Miss Roberts said.

As they walked into the kitchen and Charlotte prepared their drinks, they discussed how long the reporter had been working at the *Leader*, why she had chosen journalism, and how much she enjoyed living in the small town of Bedford. Her hands moved and fluttered as she talked. Charlotte silently speculated that there wasn't a slacker cell in any part of the woman's body. She envied that kind of energy.

"Thank you so much," Miss Roberts said when Charlotte

placed a mug of steaming chocolate in front of her. "This will warm me up." After taking a quick sip from her cup, she pulled out a pad of paper and a pen. "So how long have you lived in Bedford?"

Charlotte slid into her chair. "All my life."

"I can see this is a caring community. Have you ever seen it reach out like this in the past?"

"Many times. People here love one another. We've grown up together, cheered at ball games together, applauded at school musicals, celebrated graduations, weddings, births, and grandchildren together. When one suffers, we all suffer."

Miss Roberts stopped writing and looked up at Charlotte. "That is truly awesome. Almost too good to be true."

"Well, I wouldn't know about that," Charlotte said with a chuckle.

"I'll discuss Mrs. Givens's illness with her, but maybe you can remind me how the town has come to her aid."

Charlotte thought a moment. "People from the church have—"

"What church?"

"Bedford Community Church."

The reporter scribbled notes.

"Anyway, our church's finest cooks have stepped up to the plate, so to speak, and offered their services to fill in for Melody, who generally does all the cooking at the diner."

"I see. And who headed that up?"

"What do you mean?"

"Who pulled those ladies together and set up a schedule?"

Just then Emily and Ashley walked into the room.

"She did," Ashley said, pointing.

"Well, I don't see that that matters one way or the other," Charlotte said.

Miss Roberts said nothing, just kept writing.

"The teen group from our church also has offered their services. The kids fill in as servers, covering for any staff members who get sick or need time off. I've been amazed at the kids' responsibility level. They've shown they are more dedicated than we ever thought possible," Charlotte said.

"That's really cool. Who headed that up?"

"She did," Ashley said with a grin, pointing to Emily.

"And you're Emily, right?"

Emily looked a little starstruck. Ashley nudged her in the side.

"Yes, Emily Slater. My brothers and I live here with our grandparents." She turned to Ashley. "Come on, let's go." Charlotte noted that Emily wasn't any more comfortable with the attention than she was.

Miss Roberts then turned to Ashley. "What's your name and how do you know the Givenses?

She and Emily laughed together. "I'm Ashley, their daughter."

The reporter looked as though she had struck gold. "Great! I'll have a few questions for you in a minute, so don't go away." She turned back to Charlotte. "Any other way in which the town has reached out to the Givens family?"

"Well, some of the area farmers have donated meat."

She stopped writing again and looked up. "Oh? I didn't know about that."

Charlotte took a sip from her drink and then nodded. "Packaged beef, pork, chickens, you name it."

"Is that right? Amazing. Who headed that up?"

"Her husband did," Ashley said, with a grin that implied she was proud to have so many answers.

Charlotte was beginning to wish Ashley would go home.

"So your whole family has been involved in this," the reporter said while writing something on her paper.

"Well, the Givenses are our friends," Charlotte said defensively, not appreciating at all the way this discussion was going. "This is about the good folks of Bedford and of course our dear friend, Melody. You see, Miss Roberts, there's a reason these folks are sacrificing for the Givens family. The Givenses have sacrificed for many themselves. They have offered food to the hungry, jobs to those in need, and they've donated plenty of food to the church-sponsored food pantry. They are caring folks, and people want to give back to them for the kindness they've shown to this community."

"Don't forget the T-shirts," Emily added.

"Oh, that's right. A worker at the restaurant has connections with a company in Harding that makes T-shirts. Anyway, we have T-shirts available that say 'Stirring Up a Cure,' and they're available for purchase by the public. The proceeds will go to the Givenses to help pay their medical bills."

"'Stirring Up a Cure.' I like that."

They talked a little longer about the Givens family. Miss Roberts asked Emily and Ashley a few questions and then pulled out a big camera and took a shot of the three of them together. Thanks to the flash, Charlotte could barely see to walk the reporter to the door.

Miss Roberts said thanks and headed into the afternoon sunshine. Charlotte had had an interview with the woman some time ago and she had done a good job of reporting. Hopefully, she would do a good job this time too.

Charlotte would just have to wait and see when the article surfaced.

"YOU SURE YOU don't want to go anywhere?" Emily asked Ashley when they plopped down on her bed, music blaring from the CD player.

With a sharp knock on the door, Grandma said, "You girls turn that music down."

Emily rolled her eyes, walked over and adjusted the volume, and then fell back onto the bed.

"That reporter was nice," Ashley said. "Why didn't your grandma want to take credit for anything?"

Emily took long strokes with the brush through her hair. "Oh, you know Grandma. She doesn't like the focus to be on her."

Ashley shrugged. "Well, she did head up everything, so she had to tell her."

"I guess."

Ashley grabbed a comb and tried to yank it through her auburn curls.

"Here, let me help you." Emily gently combed Ashley's curls. "Why don't you let me put your hair in an updo? I bet it would look really pretty."

"I don't know."

"Oh, come on. We're just going to your house tonight for dinner. It's not like anyone important will see you."

Ashley giggled. "Your family might disagree with that."

"Grandma said we should have a girls' day. How about I fix your hair, and then you can fix mine? We can paint our nails and work on our makeup, all that fun stuff."

"Okay," Ashley said, her eyes sparking with enthusiasm.

Emily gathered hair ribbons, bands, clips, nail polish, makeup, everything she could scrounge up in her bedroom, and placed them where they could go through them.

Ashley settled on a folding chair in the center of the room, and Emily stood behind her, working with her hair.

"Em, how do you do it?"

"Do what? Your hair?"

"No. How do you get along each day . . . without your mom?"

Emily stopped brushing and looked at her. "Some days I don't do so good." She walked over and turned off the music. Somehow it didn't seem appropriate to have it on just now.

"Were you close to her?"

"Yeah."

"My mom and I do everything together. Shop, eat, talk. I can't imagine ever being without her." Ashley teared up.

"I think she'll be all right, Ash. Her surgery wasn't as bad as they thought—I mean, she didn't have to have a full mastectomy, you know?"

"Yeah, I know. But still, I can't relax until we get the test results back."

"With my mom, I didn't even have a chance to say good-bye. A normal day in every way, then I come home and find out I'll never hear her say my name again. Not ever."

Sadness filled the air like a perfume.

"You know the thing I miss most about my mom?" Emily asked.

"What?"

"She made everything an adventure. Like one time Mom took me and my brothers on a picnic outside the city. On the way home that night, our car stalled in the middle of a country road. I was scared. My brothers were too. We didn't have a cell phone, and we didn't know where we were. But Mom made it an adventure. If she was scared, she didn't show it."

"What did she do?"

"She said we were gonna hike to the nearest house and get help. We climbed out of the car and walked down the road singing camp songs. Sam sang off-key and we started laughing. He did too. By the time we made it to the house, we were laughing and having fun."

"My mom likes to laugh too. She always looks at the bright side of things," Ashley said.

"Mom liked adventure. I guess that's why she was brave enough to run off with my dad and live in California instead of near her family. Sometimes I wonder if she had stayed around here how things would be today, you know?"

Ashley looked at the floor. "Yeah."

"But sometimes remembering her adventurous ways helps me get through things. When I'm feeling I can't do something, I think I can hear her voice telling me to move on, shoving me forward, to keep going, all that. Kind of weird, but that's what I do." Emily shrugged.

"That's what I need to think about. My mom makes me laugh all the time. I need to think of that when I'm feeling upset." Ashley looked up at Emily. "Thanks."

Emily laid the brush on her dresser and turned to look at Ashley. "I'll be with you, Ash. No matter what. I'll be your friend."

Ashley now unashamedly allowed the tears to flow down her face. Emily hugged her and allowed her own tears, pent up over the months for her own mother, to flow too.

When their emotions were spent they looked at each other and laughed.

"You're a mess," Ashley said.

"You are too. Good thing we're putting on fresh makeup."

Emily turned the music back on. Upbeat and happy music. Their normal high-school-girl chatter returned, and Emily felt lighter and happier than she'd felt in a long time.

Her friend had been through a lot. So had Emily. And the thing Emily was learning was that no matter how hard life got, it was easier to endure the hard times with friends.

Chapter Twenty-Five

Carrying a large chocolate cake, Charlotte and her family walked into Melody's house early Saturday evening.

"Ooh, that looks yummy," Melody said with an admiring glance at the cake as they headed for the kitchen.

"Smells pretty good in here too," Charlotte said, taking a whiff of the vegetable soup. She peeked into the pot on the table at the beefy tomato broth and cooked vegetables with garlic and onion. She took another breath. Heavenly.

While Charlotte and Melody visited for a moment, Ashley and Emily prepared the table, setting out bread bowls Esther had made at the diner. Ashley then added an enormous ceramic bowl containing crisp cold lettuce, tasty tomatoes, black olives, frozen peas, sliced boiled eggs, and crunchy croutons; frosted glasses of iced tea—hot coffee was ready for the cold-blooded ones—and decorative soup crackers completed the meal.

"This looks lovely, girls," Charlotte said.

Emily and Ashley let everyone know the meal was ready. Russ gave the blessing, and soon chatter abounded as they broke bread together.

Melody would not allow the conversation to migrate toward her illness but centered it instead on the kindness of the townspeople.

"I'm anxious to see what Misty Roberts comes up with for the paper," Emily said happily.

"Yeah, me too," Ashley added.

Charlotte looked at Melody. "Oh, I'd forgotten about that already. Did Ashley tell you about it?"

"Actually the reporter stopped by our house and talked to me too."

"Yeah." Russ scratched the back of his neck. "She even snapped a picture of me and my woman. Next thing you know, Hollywood will be calling."

A murmur of chuckles echoed around the table.

"She said it would be in Tuesday's paper. A human interest story."

"Wow, that's fast," Brett Givens said.

Pete looked at him and then at the others. "He talks."

Dana jabbed him in the side.

Pete grinned.

"Aw, people tease me all the time about that," Brett said with a shy grin. "Doesn't bother me."

"Don't pay attention to me; I like to poke fun," Pete said.

"That's for sure," Dana joined in.

"You're right about that being a fast turnaround on the article. I hope she takes her time and gets all the facts," Bob said.

"I'm sure it will be fine." Charlotte passed the salad bowl again.

Before the adults could work through their bowls of soup, Emily, Ashley and the boys had already excused themselves, with promises to come back later for cake. It seemed they were off to play video games or something.

"So, Dana, tell me about your wedding plans. How's all that going?"

"Still working on things. Currently trying to round up my bridesmaids. Not sure who I'm getting to sing yet. I need to get on that. And I still have to decide on my dress."

Charlotte noted the pink tinge that suddenly fanned Dana's cheeks.

"Yeah, you'll need to get that pretty soon. The wedding will be here before you know it," Melody said.

Dana glanced at Charlotte.

"It's like this. Emily is trying to design a dress, but they can't seem to agree on a style. And now Dana isn't sure what to do about it."

"I think that's our cue to escape to the other room for some guy talk," Bob said, scooting out his chair.

"Didn't mean to run you off," Melody said.

"No problem. We'll leave the wedding to you women," Pete said. "We'll expect some of that cake though, Mom, so don't get any ideas."

Charlotte shook her head and grinned. "That boy is always thinking about his stomach."

"I was so happy with my wedding dress. I got it from a designer in New York City. A once-in-a-lifetime deal, really." Melody's eyes took on a dreamy state. "Too bad it's over so quickly." She turned to Dana and Charlotte. "Ashley doesn't even like it, so no one will ever wear it again." Suddenly her eyes widened. "Do you want to see it?"

"Sure," Dana said.

Charlotte nodded.

They walked into a spare bedroom, where Melody opened the closet and pulled out a dress bag.

"Here, let me help you." Charlotte took the dress, laid it on the bed, pulled down the zipper, and then lifted the dress from the bag.

Dana gasped. "Oh, my! It's beautiful."

They listened as Melody talked about the soft folds, the satin material, the drape of the neck.

"Simple elegance," Dana said with a gush of admiration.

"That's exactly what I wanted, and it's what I got," Melody said.

"That's what I want too," Dana said with a sigh. "It's out there somewhere. I just have to find it."

"Well, if you don't find it, you can have this one."

Dana gasped. "You're serious?"

"Sure, why not? I don't have any further need for it. Like I said, Ashley doesn't like it."

"She might change her mind."

"You don't know Ashley very well, do you?" Melody laughed. "You take some time to think about it and just let me know if you want it. We're about the same height; with a few alterations, I'm sure it would fit you."

Charlotte marveled that Melody would be so generous. But then that was Melody. Then another thought occurred to her.

If Dana decided on Melody's dress, there was no telling how that would set with Emily.

JUST AS SAM WAS LEAVING church the next morning, he spotted Arielle alone in the parking lot. He'd been trying to talk to her all morning, but her friends were always around.

"Hey, Arielle, wait up."

She stopped and turned to him. "Hi, Sam."

The air was a bit awkward between them, but he knew once he told her about his decision to check out the military, she would be impressed. Finally, he was on to something.

They shared small talk at first, and then Sam went to the heart of why he'd stopped her. "I know you've got to get going. Me too. Grandma doesn't have to work at the restaurant today so she's 'excited'"—he gestured quotes—"to have us all together."

Arielle smiled. "That's good. I know she's been busy over there. My mom has helped out a time or two. I've done some serving. Haven't seen you there though."

"I helped clean a couple of times."

"That's good," she said.

For some reason it irritated him that she mentioned that. Did she think she was his warden or something? He'd never understand girls.

"Just wanted to tell you I've been thinking some about what you said, the future and all that."

The sparkle came back to her eyes. "Yeah?"

"Yeah. Christopher has been working on a family tree project, and can you believe he discovered that we have a distant relative—Samuel Matthew Slater—who won a Purple Heart for his bravery in the army in World War II? He rescued his buddies but got his leg shot up."

"Oh." Her face scrunched, and she didn't look at all impressed.

Sam couldn't be dissuaded. He practically rocked on his heels. "I'm thinking about joining."

Her eyes grew wide. The sparkle disappeared.

"Joining what?" she asked.

"The military. Not sure which branch yet." Maybe he'd let them fight over him.

"You're kidding."

The way she said it gave a hint that she wasn't as impressed as Sam had expected her to be.

"No, I'm not kidding. I like the idea of fighting for something I believe in."

"And where, Sam, does this sudden patriotism come from? Just knowing your distant relative was in the service? You made the decision that fast?"

"Well, no, it wasn't that fast—"

"I mean, it's one thing if you've had this burning desire all your life to join the military, move up in the ranks, and serve your country in a great capacity, but just to suddenly decide one afternoon when you heard you had a relative who won the Purple Heart?" She shook her head. "I don't get it."

He no longer rocked on his heels. The sense of accomplishment, pride in his decision, were all gone.

"Whatever you decide, good luck to you, Sam." With that, she turned and walked away.

Hot disappointment coiled in his stomach. Instead of looking up to him as a man with a purpose, Arielle saw him as a loser. Again.

AFTER SUNDAY LUNCH, Christopher settled in at the computer to work some more on his family tree project.

With a full belly, he'd rather lie down and flip through some of the old comic books he'd checked out from the library. He had no doubt that the smell of those chocolate chip cookies Grandma had in the oven would call out to him before he got through his e-mail.

He deleted the junk mail in search of more important mail with information on his family tree.

"Hey, Grandpa, your cousin sent some more pictures," Christopher said, clicking on the attachments and pulling up a picture of Luke Stevenson with his family on a picnic.

Bob adjusted his glasses and leaned in to the screen. "Well, will you look at that? Hey, Charlotte, come see Luke's family."

Grandma appeared in the hallway, apron still on, oven mitt in hand. "Better make it quick. I have to get those cookies out of the oven in a minute."

Grandpa motioned her over.

She inched in to see the screen. "What a nice-looking family. Look how big the kids are, and to think we've never even met them." She stood and stretched her back. "Isn't it amazing that, though we have never met them, we can keep up this way through the computer? My, my, it's something." The buzzer went off in the kitchen. "There's my cue."

"Let me know when you finish working on your school project, Christopher. I'd like to sit down and write my cousin an e-mail."

"Okay, Grandpa."

His grandpa walked away, and Christopher read through the next e-mail from Richard Slater, the guy who had done so much research on the Slater family tree. Most of the information he gave to Christopher wasn't all that helpful for his project because he needed documentation. But one piece of information Christopher enjoyed reading was that one of his ancestors had traveled with a circus. He thought that was pretty cool. Immediately, he wrote back and asked Great-Uncle Richard what Red Slater did in the circus. He wondered if his name was really Red or if it was a nickname. Christopher hoped he would get an answer soon.

"I'm done, Grandpa," he called out.

Christopher had no sooner left his seat than Grandpa filled it. Chocolate chip cookies were calling his name, and the smidgen of chocolate on the side of Grandpa's mouth said he'd already helped himself.

Christopher wondered if Grandma knew about that.

LOOPING THE THREAD through her embroidery piece, Charlotte thought how nice it was to have the kids in the family room with her and Bob, enjoying a quiet evening together. The corn burner in the corner of the room kept the area toasty warm, though the room smelled a bit like beer to Charlotte's way of thinking. She tugged the thread into place and snipped off the end with scissors before starting a new color.

She glanced at the floor, where Emily perched with her sketchpad, brushing long strokes with her pencil this way and that along the page. She had such talent. Charlotte wondered if that talent would find a way to Dana's wedding dress.

Christopher sat at the computer, working once again on his family tree project. Though she knew the computer offered lots of good things, it worried her for the kids to be on it for long periods of time. She'd heard horror stories about such things, and she aimed to keep an eye on it.

Farm bills piled beside Christopher on the desk reminded Charlotte of the "to-do list" she planned to work on first thing tomorrow morning. What a way to start a Monday. She groaned silently.

With a sigh, she poked the needle through the fabric once again to continue the coffee-cup design on the tea towel. She hoped Melody liked the embroidered towels. The colors would go well in her kitchen.

She glanced over at Sam and wondered what he was reading. He'd had his nose in the book for some time now. That wasn't like him. He normally didn't read unless he had to. She chuckled to herself.

Charlotte wondered what adventures awaited her grandchildren in the days ahead. They were growing so fast. They'd be out the door and on their own before she and Bob could blink.

Just like their own children.

"Emily, have you seen Ashley's mom's wedding dress?"

"Yeah, why?"

Charlotte shrugged. "Just wondered. She was talking about it last night at dinner and finally showed it to us. She got it in New York. Quite a fascinating story, really."

"Yeah, she told me about it."

"What did you think of her dress?"

"It was pretty, but kind of outdated nowadays. Why?"

Charlotte shrugged. "Dana seemed quite taken with it." She thought perhaps just mentioning it might soften the blow if Dana decided on that dress.

Emily scrunched her nose. "I sure wouldn't create a dress like that. It's too bland. No offense to Mrs. Givens, but I want my designs to be more progressive, you know?"

"I suppose." Charlotte didn't know, but why discuss it? Emily knew what she wanted to design, and Dana knew what she wanted in a dress. Time would tell if they could work things out between them.

"Do you kids have any homework?" Charlotte asked.

No one responded right away.

With a couple of clicks, Christopher turned away from the computer screen and looked at her. "I have my homework done, Grandma, but I think I'll get ready for bed."

She considered taking his temperature. Christopher getting ready to go to bed without being coerced?

"Are you feeling all right?" she asked.

"I'm fine." He smiled, and then she knew he was going up to check his ant farm. She could hardly wait to get that thing out of the house.

He practically skidded to a halt at the family room entrance. "Hey, Grandma, do you think you could take me to the library after school tomorrow? I want to check out some information on the circus—since we had a relative in one and all."

She smiled. "I think we can manage that."

Emily flopped her sketchpad to a close. "I think I'll go to bed too." She stood, stretched, and yawned. "I'm getting tired."

She walked over and gave Charlotte and Bob each a kiss good night.

"Good night, dear," Charlotte said. She glanced at Sam.

"Must be a good book."

He said nothing.

"Sam?"

He reluctantly pulled his gaze from the page. "Huh?"

"Good book?"

"Yeah. Fiction, military stuff. Got it at the library the other day."

She nodded. "Good to see you reading."

Sam glanced around. "Where did Christopher and Emily go?"

"They went upstairs to get ready for bed." He obviously had been very engrossed in his book.

"Guess I'll go too." He turned back around. "Oh, Grandma, I won't be home right after school."

"Going to the airport?"

"No, it's too cold. Not much going on there these days."

"You meeting Arielle?"

Bob got up from his chair. "Anybody want some popcorn?"

"You sure you should be eating this late at night, Bob?"

He frowned and sagged into his chair. "I guess not."

Sam started to leave.

"Sam, you didn't say where you're going," Charlotte pressed.

By now, she and Bob both were looking at him.

"Oh, I'm sorry. I thought I told you. I'll be stopping by the armed forces office in Harding."

"Whatever for?" she asked.

"I think I'm going to enlist."

Chapter Twenty-Six

Charlotte pulled back the covers on the bed and said in hushed tones, "What are we going to do about Sam?"

Standing at the bathroom sink, Bob tightened the floss between his fingers and said, "What do you mean?"

"Well, we can't let him go into the military instead of going to college." Her voice snapped more than she meant to, but she was upset and couldn't hide it.

Bob finished flossing and brushing and then walked back into the bedroom. "Charlotte, we can't control the kids. If nothing else, we learned that when Denise ran off." Bob slipped into his side of the bed, causing the boards and springs beneath him to protest.

He had to bring up Denise. She plumped a pillow with a little too much force and situated it on her place in bed.

"But it's such a big decision. It seems to have come out of nowhere," Charlotte said. He could be shipped overseas.

"You're right about that. I'm just saying, we can advise the kids and pray they make the right choices, but ultimately, it's his choice. We don't have the money to put him through four or five years of college without his help. And if he doesn't want to do it, we can't make him."

She slumped into bed. "Things were so much easier when the kids were young."

"Denise would want you to let him make the choice, Charlotte."

She knew he was right. They would just have to wait and see which way Sam went with this idea.

She rolled over and closed her eyes. Tears slipped beneath her lashes and moistened her pillow.

"WHERE YOU HEADED this fine Monday morning?" Charlotte asked the next day while she and Bob sat at the table sipping coffee after the kids left for school. She wasn't about to bring up Sam and the military thing again. She'd pray and pray and pray, and, hopefully, the boy would come to his senses.

"Thought I'd mosey over to the tractor supply and see what the boys are up to."

She still got a kick out of the fact that the farmers sat around with their coffee and jawed about crops, machinery, and weather. And they say women talk a lot.

"How about you?"

"Hannah and I are going over to the restaurant to work a while this afternoon. Looks like you'll have to prepare dinner for the family again. I'm sorry, Bob."

"No problem at all. I've managed to run an entire farm all these years; you don't think I'd let a little cooking set me back, do you?" He grinned.

Why point out his latest mishaps? He was doing the best he could, and she appreciated him for it. She just hoped he would easily surrender her kitchen back to her when she returned to full-time duty at the Stevenson household.

"Oh, that reminds me. I told Christopher I'd take him to the library after school. Would you mind doing that for me since I'll be at the restaurant? I'd forgotten I'd be there."

"Yeah, I can do that. Maybe I'll find some good cookbooks while I'm there." He winked.

Maybe he'd find a good meatloaf recipe and toss his old one. The upside to all this was that she'd needed to shed a few pounds. This just might be the very way to get them off.

WHILE CHRISTOPHER BROWSED through books on circus life, his grandpa snagged a few cookbooks from the shelf. Said he wanted to know more about spices and herbs, whatever that meant. Christopher was worried that his grandpa was settling into a job that better suited his grandma. He hoped Grandpa would realize the truth sooner or later.

Once they had their treasured reads, the two of them headed for home.

"Did you find what you wanted?" Grandpa asked.

Christopher looked over his books to make sure. "Yeah, I got some good stuff here." He glanced down at the books on the worn seat. "What did you get?"

"I got a couple of books on spices and herbs." He raised his eyebrows and gave a curt nod. "I'll be learning how to spice up our meals. Why, who knows? Maybe I'll get a part-time job as a cook at Mel's Place."

He laughed, but something in his manner told Christopher his grandpa was half serious. But who knew?

Maybe the herbs and spices, or whatever, would help Grandpa's cooking. Grandma said they should always hang on to hope.

Grandpa's truck made a hissing, chug-chug sound. Christopher wondered if Grandpa had been feeding his truck too.

"Tell me what you found out about the circus."

"It's kind of cool. They're like a real family."

"Is that so?"

"Yeah. It's not easy work though. Can you imagine being a lion trainer?"

"Is that what your relative was?"

"Don't know for sure. Richard didn't tell me yet."

"I see." Grandpa tapped the steering wheel while waiting at the light. No doubt, he was anxious to get home and start cooking. With any luck, Christopher could talk Grandma into bringing something home for him to eat.

They talked a little longer about circus life, and then Grandpa pulled the truck to a stop in the driveway.

Snow crunching beneath their boots, books in hand, they walked the shoveled path to the back door. Deer hoofprints dotted the backyard as though it had been patterned with a faint embossed stamp. Christopher wished he could have seen the deer.

Poplar branches bowed under the weight of a snowy covering. The apple trees, cold and barren, showed no evidence of having ever offered fruit for their dinner table. Gray birds plumped their feathers and roosted on frozen tree limbs. A blackbird cawed from a distance as it circled through the frigid air. It made Christopher cold just to look at it all.

Grandpa said Christopher would have to help him check on the animals in a little bit, but for now, Grandpa wanted to concentrate on getting his kitchen in order. Since he was cold, Christopher was glad he didn't have to check the animals right then.

He didn't think Grandma would like Grandpa's reference to "his" kitchen, but again, he figured he should keep this to himself.

With Toby at his feet, Christopher plopped onto the family room sofa and pulled books from his bag one by one while Grandpa clanged around in the kitchen. After looking through some books, Christopher decided to get a drink of water. When he and Toby got to the kitchen, Grandpa was still hard at work. Doing what, Christopher couldn't say. He just knew he wanted to get his drink and then get out of there.

He reached into the cupboard, but instead of the glasses, he found the bowls. He thought a moment and decided Grandma must have moved them. After he opened another cabinet, he found spices where the bowls should be. He turned to ask Grandpa if he knew anything about the mix-up, and one glance at the grin on Grandpa's face said he not only knew about it, but was also responsible for it.

He might only be in sixth grade, but one thing Christopher knew for sure: Grandma would not be happy about this.

SAM WALKED INTO THE OFFICE of the military recruiting office, heart hammering against his chest. The small room offered a couple of desks with men in uniform, simple chairs, and white walls. A bit sterile, but then Sam supposed that's the way it was in the military.

"May I help you, sir?" one of the uniformed men asked.

Sam walked over, introduced himself, and stated his reason for coming.

After the initial greeting, the man gave him some papers to fill out. It seemed they wanted to know if he had any criminal history, whether he abused drugs, and the current debt load he carried. After Sam filled out the paperwork, the recruiter launched into a rehearsed speech about the air force's programs and careers, emphasizing the opportunity to attend college while serving in the military and receiving generous vacation time. He said Sam would have to take a special test, and his test scores would give them an idea where to place him.

He also talked about the whole aspect of honor and serving one's country out of loyalty and all that. Sam admired guys who did that. It was no small thing to serve our country, and he would not make this decision lightly.

It sounded good enough—especially the education part —but Sam couldn't deny the twinge of uneasiness in his gut.

"I appreciate your time," he said to the man. "I want time to think about it, and I'll get back to you if I'm interested."

The officer handed Sam a card with his contact information. They shook hands and said good-bye.

All the way home, Sam thought about the possibilities. Yet something held him back. It didn't seem to fit for some reason. Maybe he just wasn't hero material.

He sighed. How long would he wander aimlessly through

life? Was that what his dad was doing? If that were true, Sam hoped he took after his mom's side of the family. Though right now, he had his doubts.

EMILY STAYED at the restaurant with Ashley and continued to help serve the customers while Hannah and Charlotte took the evening meal to the Givens home.

"So how's our friend doing today?" Hannah asked when she and Charlotte entered the Givenses' family room.

"Getting fat and sassy, that's what," Melody said. "I'm ready to come back to work, but they won't let me."

"Sit back and enjoy it," Charlotte said.

"Right. You may never get the chance to rest again, so enjoy it while you can," Hannah said. "We'll be right back. We have to put this in the kitchen."

Charlotte and Hannah placed the warm chicken-and-rice dinner plate on a towel on the countertop and then returned to Melody.

"No news today?"

"As a matter of fact, yes," she said.

Charlotte braced herself. She could see that Hannah did the same.

"They believe they got it all, but of course, they'll follow up with some spot chemo and radiation. Not as heavy as many have to go through but still . . . a bit of treatment." She smiled and then added, "Which I expected."

Tears sprang to Charlotte's eyes. "Though I'm sorry to see you have to go through the treatment, I'm so thankful they got it all, Melody." She reached over and gave her friend a quick kiss on the forehead. The relief washed over her in a way that surprised her. She knew she'd been concerned for her friend but hadn't realized just how much until that moment.

Hannah also kissed her head. "So thankful for you."

Right then and there in the Givenses' home, as the meandering scent of chicken and rice wafted into the room from the kitchen, Hannah and Charlotte lifted a prayer of thanks to heaven on behalf of Melody and her family. By the time their praise and thanks had ended, everyone in the room was crying—including Melody's husband, Russ, who had tiptoed in during the prayer.

"We're so thankful," he said, obvious relief in his eyes. "Don't know what I would do without my girl." His face glowed, and tears swam in his eyes as he shared a glance with his bride of sixteen years.

"Well, I'm just glad you don't have to know," Hannah said, dabbing her nose with a handkerchief.

Melody told them she was feeling better every day and the dinners could slow down, but Charlotte and Hannah insisted they continue to help for at least two more weeks.

Russ excused himself. He had to go pick up Brett from Chess Club. As soon as he left, Melody turned to Charlotte and Hannah.

"He's been much better since you all came over Saturday night," Melody said. "It helped him to talk with the guys. I don't know what they said, if anything, but his spirits have been much improved."

"It no doubt helped to hear your good news," Charlotte said.

"I'm sure that's some of it, but he was doing better even before that."

"Well, either way, I'm glad they connected."

"You know, Dana and I attended high school together," Melody said. "She seemed really sweet then, but we didn't hang out together so I didn't know her all that well. I hope to get to know her better in the future."

"She said the same thing about you," Charlotte offered. "She loved your dress too."

"Do you think she'll take it? It's obvious we have similar tastes."

"Time will tell."

They explained the dilemma to Hannah.

"Oh," Hannah said with a grimace. "That might be tricky."

"Emily will understand. I'm sure she'll want Dana to be happy with her dress, even if she doesn't make it," Charlotte said, praying all the while she knew her granddaughter as well as she thought she did.

Chapter Twenty-Seven

Later that same evening, Dylan and Christopher lay on their stomachs on the family room floor, chins shoved into the palms of their hands as they stared at the ants in their habitat. Grandma said during the day she'd rather keep the bugs out where she could keep an eye on them rather than up in Christopher's room where who knew what they were doing.

As they watched the little black bugs working through the tunnels, Dylan said, "I think it's pretty cool to learn all this stuff about our ancestors."

"Yeah, me too. It's kind of fun to learn about people who lived awhile ago—especially family members. I told you about the circus guy in our family. And we have a soldier named Samuel Matthew Slater who won a Purple Heart."

"Cool," Dylan sat up and looked at him. "No Indian chiefs in our family, but a few warriors. Plenty of hunters. One of my ancestors wrestled a bear."

"Wow, that's way cool!" Now Christopher sat up.

"Yeah. Hope I don't ever have to do that."

"Are you kidding? The closest you'll come to that is with your teddy bear," Christopher said in a teasing voice.

The two boys slugged each other and wrestled around on the carpet. Just then Christopher's foot hit the ant farm, knocking the top off. He saw it but knew he could get to it as soon as he finished clobbering his friend. But then Dylan took a playful punch and had the best of him, which required another tumble or two.

Christopher wasn't sure how long they tumbled on the family room floor, but happily when Grandpa's voice broke through the wrestling, he wasn't mad. It was merely time for dinner.

"I told you my grandpa doesn't cook so good, but right now I could eat a bear," Christopher said with a laugh.

"Me too."

"Yeah, then you wouldn't have to wrestle it." Christopher laughed again as they headed for the kitchen.

They found Grandpa standing by the stove, stirring something that smelled funny.

"Hi, boys."

"Hi, Mr. Stevenson," Dylan said.

"Better grab yourself a seat at the table."

Christopher dragged along behind Dylan, wondering if it was their last supper.

Once everyone was seated around the dinner table, Christopher started to relax. The meal didn't look too bad. Grandpa said it was stir-fry. Just looked like a bunch of vegetables and chicken all stirred together.

After their prayer, Christopher and Dylan shared a glance. The clock on the wall ticked. Toby shuffled out of the room. During dinnertime? Not a good sign. Uncle Pete was the first to pick up his fork. Then Sam, followed by

Emily, then Dylan and Christopher. Grandpa got up to put ice in his glass. Was he stalling?

Christopher watched as, around the table, they lifted their forks to their mouths. If they were brave enough to do it, he supposed he was too. He lifted his fork . . . He took the first bite just as the stir-fry was sliding onto the other diners' tongues too.

And that motion was quickly followed by frantic coughing, choking, and spitting. Tears ran down faces. Drinking glasses clanked against teeth. Chairs scooted across the floor. Feet stampeded toward the sink. Water glasses were refilled and emptied—until the fires were put out.

Christopher clamped his tongue between his fingers to see if it was still there. He doubted he'd ever talk again.

Grandpa looked at them as though they'd lost a marble or two. "What was that all about?"

Uncle Pete's eyes were as red as the alien Christopher had seen in a book at the library. It kind of scared him. Uncle Pete stomped over to a bottle on the counter, picked it up, read it, and held it out for Grandpa to see.

"Oh," Grandpa said.

"What is it?" Emily wanted to know. Her voice was raspy, like she had a bad cold or something.

"Tabasco sauce," Uncle Pete said, frowning at Grandpa.

Christopher wondered if Uncle Pete could still get grounded.

"That's another name for hot sauce," Sam said between coughs.

Dylan nodded at Christopher but said nothing. He probably couldn't move his tongue either. No doubt his parents would never let him come back and play.

Christopher's social life was ruined—in one bite.

Grandpa picked up the bottle again. "Guess I shouldn't have moved the spices and sauces around in the cupboard. I thought that was the soy sauce." He looked at everyone and gave a sheepish grin. "Sorry about that. I guess every cook has his share of mistakes."

No one smiled. No one spoke. Christopher wasn't even sure he heard anyone breathing.

"How about I give you the money and you go into Bedford and pick up some pizza?" Grandpa said to Sam.

That seemed to perk everyone's spirits immensely.

By the time they settled down to the pizza, Grandma had made it home. Grandpa had asked them kindly to keep his little fiasco to themselves. Christopher knew he'd be grounded for life if he said anything, so Grandma had no clue.

Yanking off her snow boots at the back door, Grandma said, "Smells like pizza in here. Don't tell me you were able to con your grandpa into buying pizza instead of cooking for you." She hung up her coat and walked into the kitchen with a smile. "I'm shocked."

"Every cook needs a day off now and then," Grandpa said.

"I'll remind you of that." Grandma gave him a peck on the cheek.

The family exchanged some friendly chitchat about their day. Just as the meal was ending and they were about to leave the kitchen, Emily got up to put her plate in the sink. "What's that doing in here?" Her voice was high-pitched, on the verge of a squeal.

"What is it?" Grandma asked, rushing to her side.

"A big, black ant. There's another one. And another. They're everywhere!" Emily shivered.

Hands on her hips, Grandma turned wide eyes to her grandson. "Christopher Slater."

All the air left his chest. Dylan turned two shades whiter. They made a beeline for the family room.

Watching where they stepped, the two boys scouted around the room catching the stray ants and carefully carrying them back to the ant farm. Then Christopher took it into the kitchen to gather the other escapees.

"Here's one!" Emily shouted, lifting a boot in the air, ready to smash it to smitherines.

"Grandma, don't let her do it," Christopher screamed.

Emily dropped the boot. Grandma whirled around.

"Christopher, we can't let them roam the kitchen."

"But they're family. You don't get rid of family just because they mess up. They don't know any better. It's my fault. I knocked the top off their container when Dylan and I were wrestling, and then I forgot to fix it. It won't ever happen again; I promise." He swallowed hard. Twice. He couldn't let Dylan see him cry.

"But . . ." Grandma's words seemed to bunch in her throat. "Well, you get them out of here. If I come back in and find even one, it's going outside or I'm going to smash it. Do you hear me? I will not have ants in my kitchen."

"Yes ma'am."

Grandma and Emily left the room. Christopher and Dylan scoured the room for ants. Christopher felt like the dad on *Honey, I Shrunk the Kids*. It wasn't an easy job. They found quite a few of the ants and returned them to the farm. He feared there were others roaming about, but he wasn't about to tell Grandma.

"Did you get them all?" Grandma asked when they exited the kitchen.

"I think so." Christopher just wanted to go to his room and be alone with his ants.

"I'm sorry, Christopher, but you know I can't allow you to keep these ants much longer. We'll have to find them another home."

"I know. Can I take them to my room for now, though?"

Grandma looked at him a moment. "Well, maybe you'd better."

Right then Dylan's mom pulled up, and the boys said good-bye. Christopher trudged up to his room alone. He wondered if the ants knew some of the others were missing—and that it was his fault.

"I'D BETTER GO CHECK on Christopher," Charlotte said to Bob in the family room.

"Okay," Bob said.

She walked up to his room and knocked on the door.

"Come in."

She walked inside and found him on the floor by his bed, his ant farm at his side.

"What are you doing?"

"Just thinking about the ants."

She settled on the floor beside him. "You really care about those ants, don't you?"

"They're like family."

"Oh?"

"Not all families are alike. Sometimes they're different than we imagine."

"That's true."

"Look at us. Most kids don't live with their grandparents, but here we are. And we're a family."

"True again."

"One of my friends at school is adopted. He's Korean. Doesn't look at all like his real family."

"I see."

"They're family though."

"That they are."

"So I figured the ants could be part of our family."

"Uh-huh."

"Families stick together and take care of each other. Just like you and Grandpa have taken care of me, Emily, and Sam."

Charlotte's heart lodged in her throat. "If I see any more ants that look as though they belong to your family, I'll put them in a jar or something and bring them up here to you."

"Thanks, Grandma." Christopher hugged her neck.

That was the least she could do—for family.

"HOW DID IT GO with Christopher last night?" Bob asked while he and Charlotte talked at the kitchen table the next morning.

"He's fine, but for some strange reason, he has attached himself to those ants, of all things."

"A strange family, to be sure."

"I told him as much, and he let me know that families are made up of many different variables. And then he mentioned how you and I took the kids in to live with us."

"Ouch. Tugging at the heartstrings," Bob said.

"Exactly."

"Sounds like this family tree project has stirred his thinking."

"I believe you're right. Wonder if it's made him miss his mom."

"Most likely," Charlotte said.

"Better let him keep his ants."

She chuckled. "You know, in all the excitement last night, I forgot to ask Sam how it went at the armed forces appointment. He wouldn't join on his own that fast, would he?"

Bob shook his head. "I talked to him before bed, and he told me the meeting went okay, but he hadn't made a decision one way or the other yet."

Charlotte sighed with relief. "There's still hope, then."

Bob gave her one of those Charlotte-you-need-to-let-it-go looks.

She said nothing further, just walked her mug over to the sink and whispered a word of thanks for one less thing to worry about—for now.

CHARLOTTE WALKED UP to the restaurant door, the smell of Salisbury steak and garlic potatoes, the Tuesday lunch special, tickling her nose before she stepped inside. Once she opened the door, everyone stopped what they were doing, looked at her, and cheered.

"What's this all about?" she asked.

One of the employees held up a newspaper. "You obviously haven't read the article yet. It's a human interest story on how a town takes care of its own. The reporter quoted you and all the nice things you had to say about the community. People from lots of surrounding communities have been calling all day, congratulating us, saying they would send donations to help with the Givenses' medical bills."

Charlotte's jaw dropped. "They did?"

"Yes. And we can thank you for that," Esther Showalter said, stepping into view. She wiped her hands on a dishtowel. "You gave the town a glowing review."

"And rightly so. You all have pitched in to help the Givens family."

"It's a win-win situation," one of the customers called out.

"And get this. Channel 21 from Grand Island is coming into town on Saturday to interview the lady who stole the hearts of the town and some of the townsfolk who have worked so hard to help this family," Esther said.

"Really?" Charlotte couldn't believe her ears. "Is Melody up for it?"

"She sure is," Melody walked out of the kitchen with a big smile on her face.

Hands on her hips, Charlotte looked her square in the eyes. "What are you doing here, young lady? You're supposed to be resting."

"Who can rest at a time like this? It's so exciting. Bedford is making a splash."

Everyone laughed.

"Where are they doing the interview?" Charlotte asked.

"Right here in the restaurant," Melody said. "So make sure you are here at one o'clock Saturday.

"Me? I don't need to be here."

"You most assuredly do," Melody said. "They specifically asked for you."

"Oh, good grief."

Another laugh rippled through the crowd.

Esther edged up to her and leaned toward her ear. "Remember, it's for a good cause."

Charlotte sighed. "Okay, I'll be here."

Chapter Twenty-Eight

Charlotte had managed to get home an hour before the kids got out of school. Bob was gone, so she had a little time to herself and planned to spend it with a cup of coffee. No sooner had she poured the dark liquid into a cup than the doorbell rang. When she answered it, Dana Simons stepped inside.

"Dana. Is everything all right?" It being a school day, Dana should have been at work.

"Everything is fine. I took a few days off to work on wedding plans."

"Come on in. I was having some coffee. Would you like some?"

"No, thank you."

They settled into chairs at the kitchen table.

"What can I do for you?" Charlotte asked.

"I wanted to let you know I've decided to accept Melody's generous offer of using her dress."

"That's great. Have you tried it on?"

"Yes, and it is perfect. Just what I've been looking for."

"That's wonderful, Dana."

"Well, sort of."

"What do you mean?"

"There's that little matter of telling Emily."

"Oh, dear." Charlotte bit her lower lip.

"Exactly. I don't want to hurt her feelings. She's worked so hard."

"That's true. But this is *your* wedding, and you should be absolutely thrilled with your dress."

"I know. And I am thrilled with Melody's dress. But I'm not sure if even having the dress I want is worth hurting my future niece's feelings."

"Oh, Emily's a big girl. She'll understand."

They talked a while about the wedding plans and Pete and Dana's plans for housing. Before they knew it, the kids were coming up the drive.

"Grandma, we're home," Emily yelled from the front door.

"Would you like me to tell her later?" Charlotte whispered.

With a worrisome frown, Dana said, "No. I won't put that on you. I'll tell her." She took a deep breath.

"Oh, hi," Emily said when she walked into the room. Sam and Christopher traipsed in after her, grabbed cookies from the jar—their afternoon ritual—and then went upstairs to unload their book bags.

Emily sauntered over to the cookie jar, and then stood there, as though she had something to say.

"Something wrong, Emily?" Charlotte asked.

"Could I talk to you and Miss Simons a moment?"

"Sure."

She sat down and looked straight at Dana. "You've been so kind to let me work on your wedding dress sketches that

I hate to say this." She tucked her hair nervously behind her ears. "It's like this. I think you're looking for a style that I just can't create—in a wedding dress."

"Oh?"

"I don't mean to sound all proud or anything. It's just that when I start designing wedding dresses, I'd like it to be in a direction—or brand, I guess—that people will be able to tell by looking that I've made it." She sighed. "I don't know if that makes sense."

"It makes perfect sense."

"And you like the more traditional look. My style is a bit more artsy—contemporary, eclectic? Whatever." She lifted a half smile.

"I understand completely."

"So you don't mind?"

"Don't mind what?" Dana asked.

"If I, well, back out of making your dress?"

Dana exchanged a glance with Charlotte.

"I still want us to be friends—I mean, we'll be family soon, and I don't want to mess things up for us . . ."

"Of course not, honey." Dana reached her hand across the table and patted Emily's. "That will work just fine. Perhaps you would be available to offer your expertise with the bridesmaids' dresses?"

She perked up. "Sure. If you really want me to. How many are you going to have?"

"Well, I've chosen my best friend from college, my cousin, and . . . I would love for you to be a bridesmaid as well."

Emily's jaw dropped. "Really?"

Dana nodded and smiled. "Really."

"That would be awesome. Thanks for asking me." Emily happily walked out of the room, barely in time to miss the chuckles that filled the kitchen.

Charlotte's heart warmed, knowing that in that moment a friendship was born.

THE NEXT DAY Charlotte leaned farther into the cabinet, her knees on the floor, the top of her head mere centimeters from receiving a good bonk. The kids would be home soon, and she had nothing started for dinner.

With all the busyness that had filled her hours in recent days, she struggled with midweek-itis, as she called it. By Wednesday, her creativity for meals had evaporated. It didn't help that she couldn't find any of her usual kitchen aids.

"Is it too much to ask to be able to find things in my own kitchen?" Heat flared in her stomach and spread to her fingertips. Set her near kindling, and she felt sure she could start a fire.

"What are you doing under there?" Hannah's voice called out.

Charlotte bonked her head as she tried to get out from the cupboard. "Ouch," she said, rubbing the top of her head.

"Sorry." Hannah pulled off her coat and settled at the kitchen table. "I knocked, but you didn't hear me so I walked on in. I hope that's all right."

Charlotte rubbed the slight bump on her head and frowned. "It's fine."

"What's going on here?"

Charlotte closed the cupboard door with more force than necessary and walked over to a chair across from Hannah. "Good thing you're here," she said. "I might have done something I would have regretted."

"Oh? Like what?"

Hannah was always one for juicy details.

"Like giving my husband a good tongue-lashing."

"Oh, it is good I came then." Hannah leaned back in her chair as though settling in for a good story.

"He has totally rearranged my kitchen. *My* kitchen, Hannah!"

Hannah's eyebrows shot straight up. "Oh, I see. That's dangerous territory, for sure."

"You'd better believe it." Charlotte took a minute to calm herself. It seemed that most of the steam went out of her when she released a long breath. "He's been so sweet to help cook and hold down the fort while I've been helping Melody." She looked up at Hannah. "He's taken over my kitchen, and I'm not sure I'll get it back."

"I thought the kids didn't like his cooking? I thought he burned the brownies, and all that."

"He did. But it hasn't fazed him in the least. You know Bob. He's not one to give up." Charlotte leaned her forehead against her hand. "I'm not sure what to do. Things may never be the same again."

Hannah chuckled. "I'm sure it's not as bad as all that."

"Well, if he's not planning to take over my kitchen, why would he totally reorganize everything? He has my spices in my can cupboard, my plates where the glasses ought to be." She threw her hands up. "I don't know where to find anything."

"Now that other people are helping out more at the restaurant, you're going to have to talk to him—either that or let him take over cooking." Hannah held up her hand. "Don't hit me. I'm just teasing."

"Very funny. This is serious, Hannah. I may never cook again."

"Well, I certainly hope that's not true," Bob said, joining them in the kitchen.

"Bob, I didn't hear you come in," Charlotte said, locking eyes with Hannah.

"That's because I wasn't gone. I was in the other room."

"I think I'd better be going," Hannah said, starting to rise from her chair.

"Don't leave on account of me," Bob said. "You girls go ahead with your visiting. I'm reading some recipes online that I thought we might want to try later, Charlotte. But what's this business about you not cooking?" Concern shadowed his face.

"Well, it's just that—"

"Are you saying you're not going to be cooking at the restaurant as much?"

Charlotte seized the moment. "Yes, yes, that's it."

He swiped his hand across his forehead. "Boy, am I glad to hear that."

"You are?" Charlotte asked.

"You are?" Hannah joined in.

They both turned and looked at Hannah.

"Just asking."

Charlotte turned back to Bob. "Why?"

"I hate cooking. I thought I would like it, but I don't. I only did it to help you. Everything I tried turned into a disaster. I struggled to keep my attitude positive through it all. I mean, you were working so hard, and I didn't want the kids to complain to you. In fact, I threatened to punish them till they were sixty-five if they did." He grinned.

"But I thought you liked looking up recipes and watching cooking shows."

"I do. I figure the recipes are another way I can help you out. Finding things I think we'll like to eat as a family. After all, I have the time to look up things; you don't."

"And watching cooking shows?"

"That was in the beginning. Before I actually started cooking. They made it look so easy. I don't watch them now. They just make me mad."

The women laughed.

"What about the redoing-the-kitchen thing?" Hannah asked, and then smacked her hand across her mouth. "It's none of my business," she mumbled.

This time it was Bob's and Charlotte's turn to laugh.

"I thought I was helping with that too. Watched a program the other day about getting your kitchen organized, so I rearranged things like they said—to help you. But I take it you don't like it?"

Charlotte warmed to his thoughtfulness. "Give me a little time to see if I can get used to it, okay?"

"You don't have to keep it that way. I was just trying to help make it a little more user-friendly."

She gave him a questioning look.

"Well, that's what they said on the program, anyway."

She and Hannah shared a glance and a grin.

"I'll be seeing you two lovebirds later," Hannah interjected, already wiggling into her coat. "Talk to you soon, Charlotte."

Charlotte and Bob said good-bye, and Hannah disappeared through the door.

Charlotte walked over to Bob and snuggled into his arms. "Did I ever tell you that you are the best husband ever?"

"Maybe once or twice," he said.

"Well, it's true."

They shared a kiss.

"The feeling is mutual," he said, giving her an enormous hug.

After a moment, Charlotte pulled away. "And Bob?"

He looked straight into her eyes. "Yes, honey?"

"Stay out of my kitchen."

Chapter Twenty-Nine

"How's our friend doing this blustery winter afternoon?" Charlotte called out as she and Hannah pulled off their boots and coats at the entryway of Melody's house. An icy, howling wind blasted the wooden structure, causing boards to creak and groan. The chill reached deep into Charlotte's bones. She wondered if she'd ever thaw.

A blazing fire on the hearth greeted them when they entered the family room, along with the sweet perfume of cinnamon wafting from flickering candles scattered about the room.

"Hmm, it smells delicious in here," Hannah said, pulling in a long breath of air.

"Maybe I should stop burning the food-scented candles. No wonder I want to eat all the time." Melody chuckled. "Speaking of eating, can I get you two anything, or did you already eat lunch?"

They walked over to her and gave her a friendly hug.

"We've eaten," Charlotte said. "What is all this?"

"Do you believe it?" Melody ran her hands through hundreds of envelopes surrounding her on the sofa. "It seems the newspaper has sparked people into action. I've only opened a few envelopes, but they're from people who want to wish me well. Some have even sent money. And they don't even know me. It's amazing."

"Goodness! The article just came out on Tuesday. They must have rushed right out and sent you their cards." Charlotte's gaze scanned the many envelopes.

Another groan from the house and a rattle of windows caught their attention.

"It sounds fierce out there," Melody said. "Glad I'm inside."

"It's so cold. I can hardly wait for spring," Charlotte said.

"Isn't it just like God to bring spring after winter? We're cooped up all season, forced indoors by inclement weather, and then suddenly it all stops. Trees bud, flowers bloom. We throw our doors open wide, tie back the curtains, raise the windows, and welcome the sunshine into our homes."

Melody and Charlotte stared at Hannah, impressed by her eloquence.

"Well, it's true." She pinned Melody with her gaze. "Spring always follows winter."

"Thank you, Hannah," Melody said.

"Don't thank me. I couldn't make the spring if I wanted to, but we know who can."

"Indeed we do," Charlotte joined in, remembering again just why she loved Hannah so much.

"Now, tell us about these," Hannah said, pointing to the envelopes. "Where are they from?"

"They're from Harding and Grand Island, mainly; some are from River Bend."

Melody stared at the pile and shook her head. "I've never seen anything like this."

"God provides," Charlotte said, and the others agreed.

"You want us to help you sort through the cards and pull out money, setting it aside and leaving the cards for you to read?" Hannah asked.

"Sure. That would be great. Here are some pens. If you would, please write the amount of the gift on their envelopes; then I'll have their addresses and the information right there when I send out thank-you notes."

"Good idea," Charlotte said. She and Hannah slid into seats near the sofa and began to tear through the envelopes with Melody.

"This one is from a colon cancer survivor. She sends you her prayers and a check for one hundred dollars," Hannah said, scrawling the amount on the envelope and setting it aside.

Melody's breath caught in her throat. "I can't imagine a stranger sending that kind of money to me."

"People who have been down the same road want to help. It's their way of giving back," Charlotte said.

"Yeah, I guess so." Melody opened one that appeared to have a letter with it.

Watching her read, Charlotte saw tears well up in her eyes and trail down her cheeks.

"Good letter?" Hannah asked.

Melody nodded. "Breast cancer survivor."

It was all she said, but it was enough.

"Another survivor here," Charlotte said, putting another check into the pile.

"Here's one from a woman who lost her mother; she

wants to give you a check in honor of her," Hannah said, waving the check. "Twenty-five dollars."

Melody shook her head, more tears spilling down her face.

"This one wants you to know that her entire church is praying for you."

"This is unique," Hannah said, holding up a card. "This is from a knitting group. They want you to know they are knitting chemo caps in your honor and will donate them to the American Cancer Society chapter in Grand Island. They enclosed this one for you." Hannah lifted a beautiful, cheery pink, yellow, white, and blue cap that looked bright with hope.

Melody brought her hands to her face. "It's too much. It's too much. These people don't even know me."

Charlotte and Hannah scooted in beside her on the sofa, one on either side.

"Melody, you give to so many. Would you not let the Lord bless you through others? It's their turn to give. You should accept it and not feel bad about it."

Melody patted her moistened face. "You're right. I know you're right. It's just so hard."

"It's easier to give, isn't it?" Hannah asked. "But God wants us to learn to be gracious givers *and* receivers. You didn't ask for this, but let him bless you in spite of the setback."

Melody nodded and pulled her lips together, attempting to keep her tears in check.

Hannah pulled on the chemo cap. "You know, some people don't lose their hair in treatment and you're not having a heavy dose, so you may not. But if you do, do you think the knitting group would make us matching hats?" Hannah fluttered her eyelashes, lightening the moment.

"Oh, I look terrible in those colors," Charlotte said. "I will settle for nothing less than bright green."

At that, Melody started laughing. "You two are terrible. And I love you to pieces."

They continued their journey through the cards and shared more laughs, tears, and hugs. The afternoon evaporated all too soon. When all was said and done, they had counted $725 in checks.

"Seven hundred and twenty-five dollars," Melody said, shaking her head in amazement. "It's a miracle."

"Spring is coming," Hannah said, tears in her eyes.

Hot tears sprang to Charlotte's own eyes, matching the emotion swimming on her friends' faces. They reached for one another's hands and held on tight. They'd weather this season together, one day at a time.

Spring was just around the corner.

MUSIC PLAYED SOFTLY behind Emily's door, and Christopher worked in his room, finishing up his family tree project. Sam thought it was the perfect time to talk to Grandma and Grandpa. Slowly, he descended the stairs, heading toward the family room, where he could hear Grandpa watching one of his game shows. He hoped Grandma wasn't in the kitchen baking something.

Once he stepped into the family room, he spotted Grandma at the desk, working on the farm bookkeeping. Maybe it wasn't such a great time to talk to them after all.

He started to turn and leave, but Grandma spotted him.

"Sam, do you need something?" she asked.

He took a deep breath. "I just wondered if I could talk to you and Grandpa—when you have a minute."

"Certainly. Bob?"

Grandpa turned off the television, and Grandma moved over to her rocking chair.

"Take a seat," she said, appearing eager to hear what he had to say.

That was one thing Sam appreciated about his grandparents. While some of his friends said their parents never listened to them, he realized his grandparents always seemed to have time when the kids wanted to talk. Always. They stopped whatever they were doing and made the time for them.

He cleared his throat. "You know I went to the recruiting office this week and talked to a recruiter."

They both nodded.

"I've been giving it a lot of thought. And well—" He wasn't sure, but he thought he saw his grandma scoot to the edge of her seat. Maybe they were eager to see him do something with his life. Maybe they would be disappointed with his decision. Arielle obviously thought he was a loser. It seemed he couldn't do anything right where she was concerned these days—unless he did exactly what she wanted him to do. Sometimes he didn't know what to do about anything anymore.

"I don't know how you'll feel about this, but I've decided not to join the military."

Grandma let out a sigh, and he wasn't sure what to make of it. Was it a sigh of relief or a sigh of disappointment?

"Well, that's fine, Sam. You need to do what you think best," Grandpa said, surprising him.

"Really?"

"Absolutely."

"What made you decide against it?" Grandma wanted to know.

"I'm not sure, really. It just didn't feel right. That probably doesn't make sense, but somehow I just knew."

Charlotte smiled. "It makes perfect sense."

"Then you're—" He looked from one to the other. "You're both okay with this? My decision, I mean?"

"Yes," they said simultaneously.

"Does Arielle have anything to do with this?" Grandma asked.

He shook his head. "Arielle and I aren't seeing each other anymore."

"Oh."

"It's all right, though. I was upset at first. She got mad at me for not having goals to her specifications. She wanted us to go to the same college. I'm still trying to sort through it all."

Grandma nodded.

"You know, my dad messed up big time." He could tell by their expressions that he'd surprised his grandparents by saying that. "I hope to make the right choices." With that, he got up and walked out of the room, hoping with everything in him that he did indeed make the right choices in the days ahead.

"LIKE I SAID, you've got to let them make the decisions on their own," Bob whispered to Charlotte when Sam left the room.

She nodded. "You were so right. I'm speechless. Absolutely speechless.

Bob grinned and walked over to her. "We're gonna make it. You'll see."

Charlotte swallowed hard to choke back her tears of thankfulness.

"The wind's died down," Bob said, glancing out the window. He turned back to her. "They say it's supposed to clear up by tomorrow. We'll have some sunshine and a decent warm front coming through for the weekend."

"Spring's coming."

"Well, it may be awhile yet—"

Charlotte cut him off. "But it's coming."

"Hey, Grandma and Grandpa, can I show you my family tree project?" Christopher walked into the room with his folder.

"Sure," they said.

"Let's all sit on the sofa," Charlotte said.

The three of them settled in, and Christopher turned the pages, pointing out his family members, with pictures dotting the pages here and there.

Charlotte was quite impressed with the information he had pulled together and the organized manner in which he had put his book in order, and she told him so.

Christopher sat a little taller in his seat. "Thanks."

"By the way, do you still have those ants in their container?" Grandma asked.

"Yeah, all present and accounted for."

She'd accept that, but she doubted that he really knew how many ants he had in that farm.

"You know, Grandma, I was thinkin'—"

Bob and Charlotte exchanged a glance and a grin.

"The ants work together to build a farm, just like we do. And what you said at supper about people giving Mrs. Givens money to help her get better, that's people working together too. Like family, right?"

"Right," she said.

Christopher grinned. "Well, I just wanted you to know I'm glad we're family."

"Me too," Bob and Charlotte responded together.

"Now, let's go get some ice cream," Bob said, leading the way to the kitchen while Charlotte watched with a lump in her throat, savoring the moment, and praising God . . . for family.

Chapter Thirty

Friday night Bob led the entire Stevenson-Slater clan in prayer for their evening meal. Charlotte thanked God for her many blessings, including those who had gathered around their table this evening.

At the final amen, Pete vigorously rubbed his hands together and said, "Let's eat."

Charlotte passed the enchiladas amid happy chatter. Baby Will whimpered. Anna adjusted the soft blanket around him, and his delicate eyelids drifted closed once again.

Once the chatter died down, Pete turned to Dana and said, "Do you think we should tell them?"

She grinned and nodded.

"Well, we've finally decided on our wedding party, providing everyone accepts our invitation."

The women around the table held their forks suspended in midair while the men kept eating.

"First off, I'd like to ask you, brother Bill, to be my best man."

Bill put the nacho chip he was holding back on his plate, grinned, and gave a hearty, "You bet I will."

Anna smiled and sat back in her seat, complete satisfaction clearly on her face.

"Great," Pete said. "I'm going to ask Brad Weber to stand up with me too." Then Pete turned to Sam. "I'd like to know if you'd be one of my groomsmen too, Sam."

Sam swallowed his bite with a notable gulp, and everyone laughed. "Really?"

"Well, sure." Pete's mouth split into a wide grin.

"Yeah, I'll do it," Sam said, a spark of appreciation in his eyes.

Christopher was inhaling his enchilada like there was no tomorrow. Charlotte had to stop herself from chuckling at the sight.

"Hey, slow down, little buddy." Pete gave Christopher a little nudge.

A bit startled, Christopher looked up. "What?"

Charlotte didn't miss the scowl on Bob's face at their grandson. Everyone knew Christopher had missed his grandma's cooking.

"Have you heard anything we've been saying?" Pete asked.

"You're just talking wedding stuff," Christopher said, obviously anxious to get back to his meal.

"How about you being a junior usher for me?" Pete asked.

Christopher's eyebrows raised, and he grinned. "Sure." Hesitation. "What's that?"

They all laughed, and Pete explained the importance of Christopher's position.

"I've already asked Emily to be one of my bridesmaids,"

Dana said. "My friend from college, Amber DeRuiter, will be my maid of honor. My cousin Michelle will complete my bridesmaids." She turned to Anna. "And of course we would love it if Jennifer and Madison could be our flower girls."

Anna clapped her hands together, and her eyes lit up like a sparkler in a Fourth of July parade. "That would be wonderful. What are your colors?" Clearly Anna's thoughts were off and running.

"Royal blue and silver," Dana said.

"Sounds lovely."

"One more thing," Dana said while she looked at Anna. "Would you be willing to help with the decorations? You're so good at that sort of thing."

Anna looked as though she'd just won an award. "I'd love to!"

"Good. We'll work on some ideas together soon."

With a pause in the conversation, Bob called out, "Well, now that we've got that settled, how about we have some of that apple pie?"

Charlotte laughed and headed for the apple pie on the counter.

The women spent the remainder of the evening dreaming of the wedding and making plans. The men chatted about work and sports, and the kids settled in for a family movie.

It all ended much too soon, as far as Charlotte was concerned.

Bob yawned as they prepared for bed later that night. "You know, that sure was a great meal tonight, Charlotte. Those enchiladas were something else," he said, patting his stomach.

She laughed. "Thank you." Charlotte put some folded laundry away. "It turned out to be such a nice day. It's always nice when all the kids are home."

Bob stuffed something in his drawer. "How's Mel today?"

"She's doing better every day. Now we'll just get her through the treatments, and we'll be back to normal again."

"She's been blessed."

"Yes, she has. She told Hannah and me that she was actually thankful it all happened. Seeing God's faithfulness encouraged her and strengthened her faith. Guess it did that for all of us, really. We tend to take it for granted sometimes."

"That we do," he said. "It will be interesting to see the turnout at the restaurant tomorrow."

"If the recent support is any indication, I'd say there will be plenty of people there. The Givenses are like family to so many."

Bob climbed into bed and then grabbed his Bible.

Charlotte washed her face while her thoughts turned to Christopher and what he had said about family. Then her thoughts turned to Denise and her high school days when she and Melody were cheerleaders together.

Yes, Melody is like one of our very own.

"LOOKS LIKE WORD certainly got out about the TV station coming today," Melody said, looking at the crowd spilling out of the restaurant onto the snow-covered lawn and street.

"At least the temperature is manageable," Charlotte said, thankful for the sunshine and a fairly warm winter's day.

"Well, you ready to go in?" Russ asked, turning to his wife in the car.

She turned to Charlotte, who nodded.

"Okay, let's do it."

Charlotte still didn't know why Melody had insisted on her riding with them to the restaurant. She called Charlotte the town's heartbeat, which Charlotte thought was ridiculous. Still, she wanted to support and encourage her friend, so she went along with her.

They climbed out of the car and headed up the walk to the restaurant as well-wishers, familiar and unfamiliar, patted Melody's back along the way, giving words of comfort and concern with every step.

Once inside, a camera crew waited in a corner of the restaurant that had been cleared to accommodate them.

Melody glanced around and noticed almost everyone had on a STIRRING UP A CURE T-shirt.

The camera crew came rushing up to Melody, the reporter speaking to her in a torrent of words. Quickly, they established some of the facts: they would do a short interview and then take comments from customers. They couldn't say exactly what would make it into the televised segment, but they'd gather more than enough film to cover the story. They'd also send her a copy of it.

Then the reporter stepped in front of the camera and said, "This is Linda Mayne with TV-15 Nebraska. It has been said the small town of Bedford's motto should be 'Family Matters,' because in this town, if you ask any one of its citizens, you will find out that everyone is family here.

"We have with us Melody Givens, owner of the popular mom-and-pop restaurant Mel's Place."

The camera shot to Melody and Russ and then back to the reporter.

"Melody, I understand you've recently had a bout with breast cancer."

"Yes."

"Your prognosis is good?"

"Yes, it is."

"And I also understand you've learned a lot more than just what it's like to have a serious illness. Is that right?"

"That's right."

"Tell us about that."

"I've learned that family means so much more than just blood relatives. Family consists of people who care about you, who stand by you when the going gets tough, and who love you, no matter what." Her voice grew weak, and Charlotte offered a quick prayer.

"How did you learn that?"

"Through this woman right here," Melody reached out and grabbed Charlotte's hand, pulling her to her side. "She organized cooks from Bedford Community Church to come to the restaurant and help out while I was undergoing treatment. Next thing I knew, the church youth group got involved and volunteered at the restaurant as servers. Business picked up as people learned of my illness and wanted to support us. That called for more people to help at the restaurant. At the same time, this lady and others brought food to my family. The restaurant's meat supply was low due to the increased demand, and we didn't know how we were going to pay for more to keep the restaurant going. Area farmers got together and donated packaged meat and delivered it to the restaurant.

"We've had an outpouring of love from people all over the area. And after a newspaper article on Tuesday, we've received cards and money from people in Bedford, Harding, Grand Island—all over. It's a miracle." Melody sniffed back her tears.

Next the reporter turned to Charlotte. "Was it hard, Mrs. Stevenson, to get people involved?"

"Not at all," Charlotte replied. "In fact, people came to me asking what they could do to help. They wanted to help in any way they could. Even the younger kids have helped by taking out the trash and passing out fliers that encouraged people to come and eat at Mel's Place."

"It's what families do," Christopher said, when some of the "younger kids" walked up to the group.

Charlotte was dumbfounded that he would say something to the reporter.

"What was that, young man?" The reporter lifted a wide smile and shifted the microphone over to Christopher.

"It's what families do. They help each other. It doesn't matter if we're related or not. We just do it, because . . . because . . ." Christopher looked around, and for a moment, Charlotte thought he had forgotten what he was talking about. Then he looked back at the reporter. "Because it's the right thing to do."

The crowd murmured in agreement.

"Well said, young man. What's your name?"

"Christopher Slater." He pointed at Charlotte and Bob. "They're my grandparents."

"Ah," the reporter said. "They're leaving a legacy behind."

"I don't know if they know about legacies, but they sure know about this family business," Christopher said.

Chuckles rippled through the crowd.

Emily and Sam walked up to stand beside Bob and Charlotte. "They sure do. And so do the Givenses," Emily said. "I've seen Mrs. Givens hand out food to people who were hungry."

Another person stepped through the crowd. "That's right. And when my family was down and out, somehow they knew. Mr. and Mrs. Givens dropped off meals for a week. Not a soul knew they did it, and they wouldn't let us tell anyone. Well, I'm sorry, Mr. and Mrs. Givens, but I just had to say something."

"And when all I had was debt and a two-year-old to raise on my own, they offered me a job at the restaurant," a young woman said. "I saved enough money while working here to get started at the community college in Grand Island."

"I know one thing for sure," said a gray-haired woman who stepped through the crowd. "There's no other town in all the world I'd rather live in than Bedford, Nebraska."

The crowd whistled and cheered.

"Mrs. Givens, we wish you all the best, and I'm sure you'll get it with the help of this great community."

"Thank you," Melody said.

Ms. Mayne smiled big for the camera and shrugged. "Well, there you have it, folks. If you're looking for a place to belong, this is the town for you. Family-friendly Bedford, Nebraska. Thanks for tuning in. This is Linda Mayne with TV-15."

After the camera was off, the crowd cheered again, and someone from the restaurant staff called out that there was free hot chocolate for everyone.

Charlotte glanced around the room a little later as those gathered enjoyed the warm refreshment as well as the warm fellowship. She spotted Emily and Dana deep in conversation, no doubt discussing bridesmaids' dresses. Pete and Russ Givens talked pleasantly, and Christopher sat with Dylan and his parents at a table, sipping hot chocolate. While Bill, Anna, and the girls talked to Hannah about baby Will, Bob talked with Frank.

Charlotte slipped on her coat before stepping into the cool air. She took in the scene around her, thanking God for her family, her friends, and the sweet town of Bedford, where being family meant more than just a name on a family tree. It was where hearts connected and lives were molded into honest citizens who truly cared about one another.

Tears filled Charlotte's eyes once more.

Bob stepped through the door and came up behind her. "What do you think?" he asked, putting his arms around her.

She turned and looked at him. "I think the reporter had it right. This truly is a great place to live."

Bob squeezed her tight. With the murmurs of friends and family spilling outside now and swirling on the light afternoon breeze, Charlotte leaned her head on her husband's shoulder, and together they looked around town.

Their town.

Bedford, Nebraska—where family matters.

About the Author

Diann Hunt is the author of three novellas and sixteen novels. Her books have finaled in the Holt Medallion and American Christian Fiction Writers Book of the Year contests. Her novel *RV There Yet?* was a 2006 Women of Faith pick, and in 2007 her novel, *Hot Tropics & Cold Feet* won the ACFW Book of the Year Award for the Lit category. Diann lives in Indiana with her husband of thirty-four years, where together they spoil their grandchildren ad nauseam.

A Note from the Editors

Guideposts, a nonprofit organization, touches millions of lives every day through products and services that inspire, encourage and uplift. Our magazines, books, prayer network and outreach programs help people connect their faith-filled values to their daily lives. To learn more, visit www.guideposts.com or www.guidepostsfoundation.org.

TABLE 1

Values of the Integrals $I_i(\rho)$, $i = 2,3,4$, Used in Evaluation of Multinormal Probabilities

ρ	$I_2(\rho)$	$I_3(\rho)$	$I_4(\rho)$
.00	.000000	.000000	.000000
.05	.001172	.000017	.000002
.10	.004404	.000117	.000022
.15	.009477	.000343	.000083
.20	.016067	.000712	.000203
.25	.024057	.001232	.000397
.30	.033375	.001907	.000673
.35	.043812	.002727	.001037
.40	.055459	.003706	.001495
.45	.068254	.004843	.002052
.50	.082247	.006152	.002714
.55	.097454	.007628	.003486
.60	.114012	.009291	.004379
.65	.132053	.011154	.005404
.70	.151813	.013243	.006580
.75	.173640	.015607	.007934
.80	.198120	.018306	.009506
.85	.226180	.021464	.011370
.90	.259820	.025310	.013668
.95	.303950	.030429	.016770
1.00	.411234	.043064	.024159

ere $c > 0$ and $\mathbf{B}$ is a real $m \times k$ matrix. If (35) holds, then $X_1,X_2,\ldots,X_m$ be represented by

$$c(Y_1,\ldots,Y_m) - (Z_1,\ldots,Z_k)\mathbf{B}'$$

h $Y_1,\ldots,Y_m,Z_1,\ldots,Z_k$ independent unit normal variables. Hence

$$\Pr\left[\bigcap_{j=1}^{m}(X_j < h_j)\right]$$

$$= \Pr\left[\bigcap_{j=1}^{m}\left(Y_j \le \left\{h_j + \sum_{i=1}^{k} b_{ji}Z_i\right\}c^{-1}\right)\right]$$

$$= (2\pi)^{-(1/2)k}\int_{-\infty}^{\infty}\cdots\int_{-\infty}^{\infty} e^{-\frac{1}{2}\sum_1^k z_i^2}\prod_{j=1}^{m}\Phi\left(c^{-1}\left\{h_j + \sum_{i=1}^{k} b_{ji}z_i\right\}\right)dz_1\cdots dz_k.$$

is a k-fold integral, so that it is very desirable to make k as small as ible.

[Note that since each $\rho_{\alpha\beta}$ is counted twice in j, j must be even. This ensures that $\prod_{k=1}^{m} A_{j_k}$ must be real. It also means that $(-1)^j$ can be omitted from (23).]

Unfortunately, these series converge very slowly unless all the ρ_{ij}'s are small. An approximate formula is presented in Section 4.4.

We now consider results that can be obtained by giving $\mathbf{R}$ special forms.

4.3. *Some Special Cases*

The matrix $\mathbf{R}$ may be specialized in a number of ways. Ihm [52] has obtained a general formula for $\Pr[(X_1,X_2,\ldots,X_m) \text{ in } \Omega]$ which applies when the *variance-covariance* matrix is of form $\mathbf{\Delta} + c^2\mathbf{11}'$ where Δ is a positive definite diagonal matrix and $\mathbf{1}' = (1,1,\ldots,1)$. This means that

$$\text{(24)}\qquad \operatorname{var}(X_j) = \delta_{jj} + c^2, \qquad \operatorname{cov}(X_i,X_j) = c^2.$$

Ihm showed that, if $E[\mathbf{X}'] = (0,0,\ldots,0)$,

$$\text{(25)}\quad \Pr[(X_1,X_2,\ldots,X_m) \text{ in } \Omega] = \frac{c}{\sqrt{2\pi}}\int_{-\infty}^{\infty} e^{-(1/2)c^2t^2}\int\cdots\int_{\Omega}[(2\pi)^{m/2}|\Delta|^{1/2}]^{-1} \times \exp\left[-\tfrac{1}{2}\sum_{j=1}^{m}\delta_{jj}^{-1}(y_j - t)^2\right]d\mathbf{y}\,dt.$$

Although this is a multiple integral of $(m + 1)$th order, which is greater than the order (m) of the original multinormal integral, the integral is in general of simpler form. If the correlations can be expressed in the form $\rho_{ij} = \lambda_i\lambda_j$, for all i and j, then $X_1,X_2,\ldots,X_m$ can be represented as

$$X_j = \lambda_j U_0 + \sqrt{1 - \lambda_j}\,U_j \qquad (j = 1,2,\ldots,m),$$

where $U_0,U_1,\ldots,U_m$ are independent unit normal variables. This representation greatly facilitates calculation of probabilities. The inequality $(X_j \le h_j)$ is equivalent to

$$U_j \le (h_j - \lambda_j U_0)/\sqrt{1 - \lambda_j},$$

hence

$$\text{(26)}\qquad \Pr\left[\bigcap_{j=1}^{m}(X_j \le h_j)\right] = \int_{-\infty}^{\infty} Z(u_0)\prod_{j=1}^{m}\Phi\left(\frac{h_j - \lambda_j u_0}{\sqrt{(1 - \lambda_j)}}\right)du_0$$

(Dunnett and Sobel [34]).

For the special case $\rho_{ij} = \lambda_i/\lambda_j$, for all $i \le j$, Curnow and Dunnett [24] have found reduction formulas for $m = 3, 4, 5$.

If all the correlations are equal and positive ($\rho_{ij} = \rho > 0$ for all i,j), then we have the representation

$$X_j = \sqrt{\rho}U_0 + \sqrt{1-\rho}U_j \qquad (j = 1,2,\ldots,m) \tag{27}$$

obtained by putting $\lambda_j = \sqrt{\rho}$. The inequality $X_j \le h_j$ is equivalent to $U_j \le (h_j - \sqrt{\rho}U_0)/\sqrt{1-\rho}$, and

$$\Pr\left[\bigcap_{j=1}^{m}(X_j \le h_j)\right] = \int_{-\infty}^{\infty} Z(u_0)\prod_{j=1}^{m}\Phi\left(\frac{h_j - \sqrt{\rho}u_0}{\sqrt{1-\rho}}\right)du_0. \tag{28}$$

In the general case this must still be evaluated by numerical quadrature, but the reduction to a single integral makes the calculation much simpler. If also $h_1 = h_2 = \cdots = h_m = h$, we have

$$\Pr[\max(X_1,\ldots,X_m) \le h] = \int_{-\infty}^{\infty} Z(u_0)\left[\Phi\left(\frac{h - \sqrt{\rho}u_0}{\sqrt{1-\rho}}\right)\right]^m du_0. \tag{29}$$

This formula has been obtained in a number of equivalent forms by Das [25], Dunnett [32], Dunnett and Sobel [34], Gupta [47], Ihm [52], Moran [90], Ruben [100], and Stuart [117], among others. Steck and Owen [116] have shown that this formula is valid for negative ρ as well, even though the integrand on the right-hand side is complex. These authors also obtain a useful recurrence relation (valid for ρ positive or negative). Denoting the probability in (25) by $F(h \mid \rho,m)$ they show that

$$F(h \mid \rho,m) = \sum_{j=1}^{m}(-1)^{j+1}\binom{m}{j}F(\alpha h \mid \rho',j)F(h \mid \rho,m-j), \tag{30}$$

where

$$\alpha = \left[\frac{1-\rho}{\{1+(m-1)\rho\}\{1+(m-2)\rho\}}\right]^{1/2}$$

and

$$\rho' = -\rho\{1+(m-2)\rho\}^{-1}.$$

When $\rho_{ij} = \rho$ for all i,j *and* $h = 0$ a number of simplifications are possible. We denote $\Phi_m(\mathbf{O};\mathbf{R})$ in this case by $L_m(\rho)$ for convenience.

Sampford (quoted by Moran [90]) showed that if $\rho > 0$, then

$$L_m(\rho) = \frac{1}{\sqrt{\pi}}\int_{-\infty}^{\infty} e^{-t^2}[1 - \Phi(at)]^m\,dt, \tag{31}$$

where $a = 2\rho/(1-\rho)$. Although the integral must be evaluated by quadrature, accurate values are easily obtained from simple summation formulas.

From Plackett's formula (15), putting $\rho_{ij} = \rho$ for all i,j a[…] obtain

$$\frac{\partial L_m(\rho)}{\partial\rho} = \frac{m(m-1)}{4\pi(1-\rho^2)^{1/2}}L_{m-2}\left(\frac{\rho}{1+2\rho}\right), \tag{32}$$

from which (noting that $L_m(0) = 2^{-m}$), we have

$$L_m(\rho) = (\tfrac{1}{2})^m + \frac{m(m-1)}{4\pi}\cdot\int_0^r L_{m-2}\left(\frac{r}{1+2r}\right)(1 - \ldots \tag{33}$$

(Ruben [100]). Using the known values of $L_2(\rho)$ and $L_3(\rho)$ […] Section 4) we find

(33)′

$$L_m(\rho) = 2^{-m}\left[1 + \frac{m^{(2)}}{\pi}\sin^{-1}\rho + \frac{m^{(4)}}{\pi^2}\int_0^\rho \frac{\sin^{-1}[r_1/(1+2\ldots}{(1-r_1^2)^{1/2}}\right.$$

$$+ \frac{m^{(6)}}{\pi^3}\int_0^\rho\int_0^{r_2/(1+2r_2)}\frac{\sin^{-1}[r_1/(1+2r_1)]}{(1-r_1^2)^{1/2}}\frac{dr_1\,dr_2}{(1-r_2^2)^{1/\ldots}}$$

The $(j+1)$th term in the series on the right is

$$\frac{m^{(2j)}}{\pi^j}I_j(\rho),$$

where

$$I_j(\rho) = \int_0^\rho\int_0^{r_j/(1+2r_j)}\cdots\int_0^{r_2/(1+2r_2)}\frac{\sin^{-1}[r_1/(1+2r_1)]}{(1-r_1^2)^{1/2}}$$

Bacon [10] gives a table of values of $I_2(\rho)$, $I_3(\rho)$, and I_4[…]

David and Six [28] have shown that when $\rho_{ij} = \frac{1}{2}$ fo[…]

$$\Pr\left[\bigcap_{t=1}^{u}(X_t \le 0)\bigcap_{t=u+1}^{m}(X_t > 0)\right] = (m+1)^{-1} \tag{34}$$

They also give tables of the probability that u or fewe[…] positive when $\rho_{ij} = \rho$, to three decimal places f[…] $m = 12, 14, 16, 20, 24, 36, 48, 96$ for various values[…]

Das [25] reduced the evaluation of L to an integral[…] of $m + k$ *independent* normal variables, where k need[…] plicity of smallest eigenvalue of $\mathbf{R}$) (Marsaglia [82]).

To perform the reduction it is necessary to expres[…]

$$\mathbf{R} = c^2\mathbf{I}_m + \mathbf{BB}', \tag{35}$$

Webster [130] has extended Das's method, replacing (35) by

$$\mathbf{R} = \mathbf{D}_{c^2} + \mathbf{B}\mathbf{B}'$$

with $\mathbf{D}_{c^2}$ a diagonal matrix with diagonal elements $c_1^2, c_2^2, \ldots, c_m^2$. By appropriate choice of values of the c_j's, it may be possible to obtain a smaller value for k.

For the particular case when all correlations are equal to the least possible common value $[-(m-1)^{-1}]$, so that the distribution is singular, Bland and Owen [18] have utilized the recurrence relation [see (73), Chapter 1]:

$$\Pr\left[\bigcap_{j=1}^{m}(X_j \leq x)\right] = \sum_{k=0}^{m-1}(-1)^{k+1}\binom{m}{k}\Pr\left[\bigcap_{j=1}^{m-k}(X_j \leq x)\right].$$

4.4. *Approximations*

Because of the difficulties of exact evaluation of multinormal probabilities, reasonably accurate approximate formulas would be valuable. The only general formulas presently available are due to Bacon [10]. He obtained, on empirical grounds, the formula

$$\begin{aligned}(36)\quad \Pr\left[\bigcap_{j=1}^{m}(X_j > 0)\right] &= (\tfrac{1}{2})^m\Big[1 + 2\sum\theta_{ij} + 4\sum\theta_{ij}\theta_{kl}(1 + \textstyle\sum^*\theta_{uv})^{-1} \\ &\quad + 8\sum\theta_{ij}\theta_{kl}\theta_{rs}(1 + \tfrac{1}{3}\textstyle\sum^*\theta_{uv})^{-1}(1 + \tfrac{2}{3}\textstyle\sum^*\theta_{u'v'})^{-1} + \cdots \\ &\quad + 2^m\sum\theta_{ij}\cdots\theta_{rs}\left(1 + \frac{2}{m(m-1)}\textstyle\sum^*\theta_{uv}\right)^{-1}\cdots \\ &\quad \times\left(1 + \frac{2(m-1)}{m(m-1)}\textstyle\sum^*\theta_{u'v'}\right)^{-1}\Big],\end{aligned}$$

where $\theta_{ij} = \pi^{-1}\sin^{-1}\rho_{ij}$; the summations $\sum$ are over $i \neq j, k \neq l$, $(i,j) \neq (k,l)$, and so on, and the summations $\sum^*$ are over subscript pairs that do not appear in the corresponding numerator. Error bounds are not available, but some numerical examples, given in [10], indicate an accuracy of about 0.002 for values of the probability in the range 0.1 to 0.2.

(For the special cases $m = 2, 3, 4$ there are better approximate formulas. The case $m = 4$ will be discussed in Section 5; the cases $m = 2, 3$ are the subjects of Chapter 36.)

Bacon also obtained the following formula for the equally correlated case:

$$(37)\quad \Pr\left[\bigcap_{j=1}^{m}(X_j \le 0)\right] \doteq 1 + \sum_{j=1}^{[(1/2)m]} \frac{m^{(2j)}}{j!} \frac{\theta^j}{(1+4\theta)(1+8\theta)\cdots(1+4[j-1]\theta)} (\tfrac{1}{2})^m,$$

where $\theta = \pi^{-1}\sin^{-1}\rho$. This approximation is exact for $\rho = 0, \frac{1}{2}$, and 1.

The orthant probability $\Phi_m(\mathbf{O};\mathbf{R})$ can be expressed in terms of multinormal integrals with $(m-1)$ variables, provided that m is odd. The relationship is obtained by an ingenious use of Boole's formula, due to David [26] (see also Schläfli [105]). We have

$$\Phi_m(\mathbf{O};\mathbf{R}) = \Pr\left[\bigcap_{j=1}^{m}(X_j \le 0)\right] = 1 - \Pr\left[\bigcup_{j=1}^{m}(X_j > 0)\right] = 1 - \Pr\left[\bigcup_{j=1}^{m}(X_j \le 0)\right]$$

(noting that probabilities and correlations are unchanged by replacing each X_j by $-X_j$).

Using Boole's formula (Chapter 1, Section 4)

$$(38)\quad \Phi_m(\mathbf{O};\mathbf{R}) = 1 - \sum_{j=1}^{m}\Pr[X_j \le 0] + \sum_{j<j'}^{m}\sum^{m}\Pr[(X_j \le 0)\cap(X_{j'} \le 0)] - \cdots + (-1)^m \Pr\left[\bigcap_{j=1}^{m}(X_j \le 0)\right].$$

If m is odd, then (38) is equivalent to

$$(38)'\quad \Phi_m(\mathbf{O};\mathbf{R}) = \frac{1}{2}\left\{-\frac{m}{2} + 1 + \sum_{j<j'}\sum \Pr[(X_j \le 0)\cap(X_{j'} \le 0)] - \cdots + \sum_{j_1<j_2<\cdots<j_{m-1}}\sum \Pr\left[\bigcap_{i=1}^{m-1}(X_{j_i} \le 0)\right]\right\}$$

(noting that $\Pr[X_j \le 0] = \frac{1}{2}$ and $\Pr[\bigcap_{j=1}^{m}(X_j \le 0)] = \Phi_m(\mathbf{O};\mathbf{R})$). In the special case when $\rho_{ij} = \rho$ for all i,j, $\Pr[(X_j \le 0) \cap (X_{j'} \le 0)]$ has the same value, $L_2(\rho)$ for all j,j' and so on, and (38)′ becomes

$$(39)\quad L_m(\rho) = \frac{1}{2}\left\{-\frac{m}{2} + 1 + \binom{m}{2}L_2(\rho) - \binom{m}{3}L_3(\rho) + \cdots + \binom{m}{m-1}L_{m-1}(\rho)\right\}.$$

Unfortunately there is no such simple formula when m is even.

When the common value, ρ, of the ρ_{ij}'s is equal to $\frac{1}{2}$ we have the simple result [a special case of (34)]:

$$L_m(\tfrac{1}{2}) = (m+1)^{-1} \tag{40}$$

(Moran [89]). The orthant probability has the same value when

$$\mathbf{R}^{-1} = \begin{pmatrix} 1 & \frac{1}{2} & 0 & \cdot & \cdot & \cdots & 0 & 0 \\ \frac{1}{2} & 1 & \frac{1}{2} & \cdot & \cdot & \cdots & 0 & 0 \\ 0 & \frac{1}{2} & 1 & \cdot & \cdot & \cdots & 0 & 0 \\ \cdot & \cdot & \cdot & \cdot & \cdot & \cdots & \cdot & \cdot \\ 0 & 0 & 0 & \cdot & \cdot & \cdots & 1 & \frac{1}{2} \\ 0 & 0 & 0 & \cdot & \cdot & \cdots & \frac{1}{2} & 1 \end{pmatrix}$$

(Anis and Lloyd [9]).

5. Quadrivariate Normal Orthant Probabilities

While it is possible to compute integrals of bivariate and trivariate normal density functions with some facility, using auxiliary tables to be described in Chapter 36, this is not yet the case for quadrivariate normal densities. If such integrals can be calculated, calculation of integrals of five-variate normal integrals is straightforward, using (38)′. We present here some methods of calculation and approximation that can be helpful, and also give a summary of available tables.

Moran [90] hás evaluated the first few items in Kendall's [62] series (23) for the case $m = 4$, obtaining

$$\Phi(\mathbf{O};\mathbf{R}) = \frac{1}{16} + \frac{1}{8\pi}\sum \rho_{ij} + \frac{1}{4\pi^2}\sum \rho_{ij}\rho_{ij'} - \cdots. \tag{41}$$

Cheng [20] has obtained the following formulas for orthant probabilities when the correlation matrix has certain specific forms. If $\rho_{12} = \rho_{34} = \alpha$ and all four other correlations are equal to β, with $-\frac{1}{3} < \alpha < 1$ and $|\beta| \leq 1$, then, denoting the orthant probability by $L(\alpha,\beta)$ we have

$$L(\alpha,\beta) = L(\alpha,0) + \int_0^\beta \frac{\partial L(\alpha,b)}{\partial b}\,db \tag{42.1}$$

and

$$\frac{\partial L(\alpha,b)}{\partial b} = \alpha\left[\frac{\partial}{\partial \rho_{13}} + \frac{\partial}{\partial \rho_{14}} + \frac{\partial}{\partial \rho_{23}} + \frac{\partial}{\partial \rho_{24}}\right]L(\alpha,b). \tag{42.2}$$

Using formula (15) we find

$$(43)\quad L(\alpha,\beta) = \frac{1}{16} + \frac{1}{4\pi}[\sin^{-1}\alpha + 2\sin(\alpha\beta)] + \frac{1}{4\pi^2}[\sin^{-1}\alpha]^2 - \pi^{-2}\int_0^{\alpha\beta}(1-t^2)^{-1/2}\sin^{-1}\{g(t)\}\,dt,$$

where $g(t) = t[1 - 2(1+\alpha)^{-1}][1 - 2t^2(1+\alpha)^{-1}]^{-1}$. Cheng shows how to evaluate the final term in (43), in terms of the *dilogarithmic function* $Li_2(z)$ defined by

$$(44.1)\qquad Li_2(z) = -\int_0^z v^{-1}\log(1-v)\,dv.$$

The z may be real or complex. If $z = re^{i\theta}$ with r,θ real then the real part of $Li_2(z)$ is

$$(44.2)\qquad -\tfrac{1}{2}\int_0^z v^{-1}\log(1 - 2v\cos\theta + v^2)\,dv,$$

which is denoted by $Li_2(r,\theta)$.

Lewin [75] gives tables of $Li_2(z)$ to five decimal places for $z =$ 0.00(0.01)1.00, and of $Li_2(r,\theta)$ to six decimal places for $r =$ 0.00(0.01)1.00; $\theta = 0°(5°)180°$. (Of course, $Li_2(r,0) = Li_2(r)$, so that the latter table includes the former.) In order to evaluate $Li_2(z)$ for values of z between -1 and 0, the equation

$$(45)\qquad Li_2(-z) = \tfrac{1}{2}Li_2(z^2) - Li_2(z) \qquad (z > 0)$$

can be used. Note that for $|z| \le 1$,

$$(46)\qquad Li_2(z) = \sum_{j=1}^{\infty} j^{-2}z^j.$$

In particular, $Li_2(1) = \tfrac{1}{6}\pi^2$, $Li_2(\tfrac{1}{2}) = \tfrac{1}{12}\pi^2 - \tfrac{1}{2}(\log 2)^2$.

In terms of this function we have

$$(47)\quad L(\alpha,\beta) = \frac{1}{16} + \frac{1}{4\pi}[\sin^{-1}\alpha + 2\sin^{-1}(\alpha\beta)] + \frac{1}{4\pi^2}[\{\sin^{-1}\alpha\}^2 - 2\{\sin^{-1}(\alpha\beta)\}^2] + \frac{1}{\pi^2}[2Li_2(f,\cos^{-1}(\alpha\beta)) - Li_2(f^2,\cos^{-1}\alpha) + \tfrac{1}{2}Li_2(-f^2)],$$

where

$$f = (2\alpha\beta)^{-1}[1 + \alpha - \sqrt{(1+\alpha)^2 - 4\alpha^2\beta^2}]$$

with $f = 0$ when $\alpha = 0$ or $\beta = 0$.

For the equally correlated case, $\beta = 1$, and $\alpha = \rho$; hence

$$(48)\quad L(\alpha,1) = \frac{1}{16} + \frac{3}{4\pi}\sin^{-1}\rho - \frac{1}{4\pi^2}(\sin^{-1}\rho)^2 + \frac{1}{\pi^2}[2Li_2(f,\cos^{-1}\rho) - Li_2(f^2,\cos^{-1}\rho) + \tfrac{1}{2}Li_2(-f^2)],$$

where

$$f = (2\rho)^{-1}[1 + \rho - \sqrt{(1-\rho)(1+3\rho)}] \qquad \text{for} \quad -\tfrac{1}{3} \leq \rho \leq 1.$$

The corresponding value for the five-variate orthant probability, with all correlations equal to ρ, is easily obtained from the recurrence relation (39). It is

$$(49)\quad \frac{1}{32} + \frac{5}{8\pi}(\sin^{-1}\rho)\left[1 - \frac{1}{\pi}\sin^{-1}\rho\right] + \frac{5}{2\pi^2}[2Li_2(f,\cos^{-1}\rho) - Li_2(f^2,\cos^{-1}\rho) + \tfrac{1}{2}Li_2(-f^2)],$$

with f as in (48).

For the case $\rho_{12} = \rho_{34} = \alpha$; $\rho_{13} = \rho_{24} = \beta$; $\rho_{14} = \rho_{23} = \alpha\beta$ (with $|\alpha| \leq 1$, $|\beta| \leq 1$) the orthant probability is

$$(50)\quad \frac{1}{16} + \frac{1}{4\pi}[\sin^{-1}\alpha + \sin^{-1}\beta + \sin^{-1}(\alpha\beta)] + \frac{1}{4\pi^2}[(\sin^{-1}\alpha)^2 + (\sin^{-1}\beta)^2 - \{\sin^{-1}(\alpha\beta)\}^2]$$

(Cheng [20]). Note that this expression does not include dilogarithmic functions but only easily evaluated inverse sine functions.

For the case $\rho_{12} = \alpha$; $\rho_{13} = \rho_{24} = \beta$; $\rho_{14} = \rho_{23} = \alpha\beta$; $\rho_{34} = \alpha\beta^2$ (with $|\alpha| \leq 1$, $|\beta| \leq 1$) the orthant probability has the more complicated expression

$$(51)\quad \frac{1}{16} + \frac{1}{4\pi}[\tfrac{1}{2}\sin^{-1}\alpha + \sin^{-1}\beta + \sin^{-1}(\alpha\beta) + \tfrac{1}{2}\sin^{-1}(\alpha\beta^2)] + \frac{1}{4\pi^2}[(\sin^{-1}\beta)^2 - \tfrac{1}{2}(\sin^{-1}(\alpha\beta^2))^2 + 2Li_2(f,\cos^{-1}(\alpha\beta^2)) - Li_2(f^2,\cos^{-1}(2\beta^2-1)) + \tfrac{1}{2}Li_2(-f^2)]$$

with $f = \alpha^{-1}[1 - \sqrt{1-\alpha^2}]$ ($= 0$ if $\alpha = 0$).

For the case $\rho_{12} = \rho_{13} = \rho_{24} = \rho_{34} = \rho$; $\rho_{14} = \rho_{23} = 0$ (with $|\rho| < \frac{1}{2}$) the orthant probability is

$$\frac{1}{16} + \frac{\sin^{-1}\rho}{2\pi}\left[1 - \frac{\sin^{-1}\rho}{\pi}\right] + \frac{1}{\pi^2}\left[2Li_2(f, \cos^{-1}\rho) + \tfrac{1}{2}Li_2(-f^2) - \tfrac{1}{4}Li_2(-f^4)\right] \tag{52}$$

with $f = (2\rho)^{-1}[1 - \sqrt{1 - 4\rho^2}]$.

David and Mallows [27] give series expansions for certain of these expressions. Abrahamson [2] has shown that the orthant probability for the general quadrivariate normal probability can be expressed as a linear function of six orthant probabilities of the kind obtained with $\rho_{13} = \rho_{14} = \rho_{24} = 0$ (i.e., only ρ_{12}, ρ_{23}, and ρ_{34} nonzero).

Unfortunately, closed expressions for such orthant probabilities are not at present available, though Cheng has shown that for the special case when $\rho_{12} = \rho_{34}$ the orthant probability is

$$\frac{1}{16} + \frac{1}{4\pi}\left[\sin^{-1}\rho_{12} + \tfrac{1}{2}\sin^{-1}\rho_{23}\right] + \frac{1}{4\pi^2}\left[(\sin^{-1}\rho_{13})^2 - \tfrac{1}{2}(\sin^{-1}\rho_{23})^2\right] + \frac{1}{4\pi^2}\left[2Li_2(f, \cos^{-1}\rho_{23}) - Li_2(f^2, \cos^{-1}(1 - 2\rho_{12}^2)) + \tfrac{1}{2}Li_2(-f^2)\right] \tag{53}$$

with $f = \beta^{-1}[1 - \sqrt{1 - \beta^2}]$ ($= 0$ if $\beta = 0$), where $\beta = \rho_{23}/(1 - \rho_{12}^2)$.

Approximate expressions derived by McFadden [83, 84] and Sondhi [114] give 5 decimal accuracy for the orthant probability when all six simple correlations are equal to ρ. For $0 \le \rho \le \frac{1}{2}$, the formula to use is

$$\frac{1}{16} + \frac{1}{4\pi}\phi + \frac{1}{4\pi^2}\,\frac{\phi^2(3 + 5\phi)}{(1 + \phi)(1 + 2\phi)} \tag{54.1}$$

where $\phi = \sin^{-1}\rho$ (McFadden [83]). For $\frac{1}{2} < \rho < 1$, the formula is

$$\frac{1}{2} - \frac{3\phi'}{2\pi^2}\left(\tfrac{1}{2}\pi + \sin^{-1}\tfrac{1}{3}\right) + \frac{3\phi'^3}{\pi^2\sqrt{8}}\left(\frac{1}{36} + \phi'^2\,\frac{(ac - b^2)\phi'^2 - ab}{c\phi'^2 - b}\right) \tag{54.2}$$

where $\phi' = \cos^{-1}\rho$,

$$a = (1/5!)\cdot\left(\tfrac{23}{48}\right) = 0.00399306,$$

$$b = (1/7!)\cdot\left(\tfrac{3727}{1152}\right) = 0.00064191,$$

$$c = (1/9!)\cdot\left(\tfrac{3320309}{82944}\right) = 0.00011031,$$

so that (54.2) can be calculated as

(54.3) $\frac{1}{2} - 0.275\phi' + 0.003\phi'^3 + 0.000028\phi'^5(\phi'^2 - 90.20)(\phi'^2 - 5.82)^{-1}$

(Sondhi [114]).

The range of values $-\frac{1}{3} \leq \rho < 0$ can be covered by using the relation

$$L_4\left(-\frac{\rho}{1+2\rho}\right) + L_4(\rho) = \frac{1}{8} + \frac{3}{4\pi}\left[\sin^{-1}\rho - \sin^{-1}\left(\frac{\rho}{1+2\rho}\right)\right] + \frac{3}{2\pi^2}\sin^{-1}\rho\,\sin^{-1}\left(\frac{\rho}{1+2\rho}\right). \tag{55}$$

These expressions are considerably better approximations than the general formulas of Section 4.4 (though the latter can be employed for $m > 4$). They can be used in conjunction with (38)′ to give approximations for $L_5(\rho)$.

Poznyakov [96a] has obtained the exact formula

$$L_4(\rho) = \frac{1}{16} + \frac{3}{4\pi}\sin^{-1}\rho + \frac{3}{2\pi^2}\int_0^\rho (1-u^2)^{-1/2}\sin^{-1}[u/(1+2u)]\,du.$$

David and Mallows [27] have given formulas for quadrivariate orthant probabilities in a number of special cases, each involving, at most, univariate integrals needing evaluation by quadrature. We give a few examples.

ρ_{12}	ρ_{13}	ρ_{14}	ρ_{23}	ρ_{24}	ρ_{34}	$\Pr\left[\bigcap_{j=1}^{4}(X_j \leq 0)\right]$
ρ	0	0	0	0	ρ	$\left(\frac{1}{4} + \frac{1}{2\pi}\sin^{-1}\rho\right)^2$
ρ	0	0	0	0	$\frac{1}{2}\rho$	$\left(\frac{1}{4} + \frac{1}{2\pi}\sin^{-1}\frac{1}{2}\rho\right)\left(\frac{1}{4} + \frac{1}{2\pi}\sin^{-1}\rho\right)$
ρ	$\frac{1}{2}$	0	0	0	ρ	$\frac{1}{12} + \frac{1}{4\pi}\sin^{-1}\rho + \frac{1}{2\pi^2}I_1$
ρ	0	0	ρ	0	ρ	$\frac{1}{16} + \frac{3}{8\pi}\sin^{-1}\rho + \frac{1}{4\pi^2}(2I_2 + I_3)$
ρ	0	ρ	ρ	0	ρ	$\frac{1}{16} + \frac{1}{2\pi}\sin^{-1}\rho + \frac{1}{\pi^2}I_4$
ρ	$\frac{1}{2}$	0	0	$\frac{1}{2}$	ρ	$\frac{1}{9} + \frac{1}{4\pi}\sin^{-1}\rho + \frac{1}{2\pi^2}I_5$

ρ_{12}	ρ_{13}	ρ_{14}	ρ_{23}	ρ_{24}	ρ_{34}	$\Pr\left[\bigcap_{j=1}^{4}(X_j \le 0)\right]$
ρ	$-\frac{1}{2}$	$-\rho$	0	0	ρ	$\frac{1}{24} + \frac{1}{8\pi}\sin^{-1}\rho + \frac{1}{4\pi^2}I_1$
ρ	$-\frac{1}{2}$	0	$-\rho$	$\frac{1}{2}$	ρ	$\frac{1}{18} + \frac{1}{8\pi}\sin^{-1}\rho + \frac{1}{4\pi^2}I_5$
ρ	0	ρ	$-\rho$	$-\frac{1}{2}$	ρ	$\frac{1}{24} + \frac{1}{4\pi}\sin^{-1}\rho$
ρ	$\frac{1}{2}$	$\frac{1}{2}\rho$	$\frac{1}{2}\rho$	$\frac{1}{2}$	ρ	$\frac{1}{9} + \frac{1}{4\pi}(\sin^{-1}\rho + \sin^{-1}\frac{1}{2}\rho) + \frac{1}{4\pi^2}\{(\sin^{-1}\rho)^2 - (\sin^{-1}\frac{1}{2}\rho)^2\}$
$\frac{1}{2}\rho$	$-\frac{1}{2}$	$\frac{1}{2}\rho$	$-\rho$	$-\frac{1}{2}$	$\frac{1}{2}\rho$	$\frac{1}{36} + \frac{1}{8\pi}(3\sin^{-1}\frac{1}{2}\rho - \sin^{-1}\rho) + \frac{1}{8\pi^2}\{(\sin^{-1}\frac{1}{2}\rho)^2 - (\sin^{-1}\rho)^2\}$
ρ	$-\frac{1}{2}$	$\frac{1}{2}\rho$	$-\frac{1}{2}\rho$	$\frac{1}{2}$	$\frac{1}{2}\rho$	$\frac{1}{18} + \frac{1}{8\pi}(\sin^{-1}\rho + \sin^{-1}\frac{1}{2}\rho) + \frac{1}{8\pi^2}\{(\sin^{-1}\rho)^2 - (\sin^{-1}\frac{1}{2}\rho)^2\}$
ρ	$-\frac{1}{2}$	$-\frac{1}{2}\rho$	$-\frac{1}{2}\rho$	$-\frac{1}{2}$	ρ	$\frac{1}{36} + \frac{1}{4\pi}(\sin^{-1}\rho - \sin^{-1}\frac{1}{2}\rho) + \frac{1}{4\pi^2}\{(\sin^{-1}\rho)^2 - (\sin^{-1}\frac{1}{2}\rho)^2\}$

$$I_j = \int_0^{\sin^{-1}\rho} \sin^{-1}(g_j(t))\,dt$$

with

$$g_1(t) = \frac{\sin 2t}{\sqrt{(1 + 2\cos 2t)}}; \qquad g_2(t) = \frac{\sin 2t}{2\sqrt{(\cos 2t)}};$$

$$g_3(t) = \frac{3\sin t - \sin 3t}{4\cos 2t}; \qquad g_4(t) = \frac{\sin t}{\cos 2t};$$

$$g_5(t) = \frac{3 + 2\cos 2t}{1 + 2\cos 2t}.$$

6. Characterizations

Fréchet [40] showed that if $X_1, X_2, \ldots, X_m$ are random variables, and the distribution of $\sum_{j=1}^{m} a_j X_j$ is normal for *any* set of real numbers $a_1, a_2, \ldots, a_m$ (not all zero), then the joint distribution of $X_1, X_2, \ldots, X_m$ must be multinormal. This property has been used by Rao [98] as a *definition* of multinormal distributions.

Basu [12] showed that if $\mathbf{X}'_1, \ldots, \mathbf{X}'_n$ are independent $1 \times m$ vectors, there are two sets of n constants $a_1, \ldots, a_n; b_1, \ldots, b_n$ such that the vectors $\sum a_j \mathbf{X}_j$ and $\sum b_j \mathbf{X}_j$ are mutually independent; the distribution of all $\mathbf{X}_i$'s for which $a_i b_i \neq 0$ must then be multivariate normal.

This is a generalization of the Darmois-Skitovitch theorem for the univariate case (see Chapter 13, Section 4). Ghurye and Olkin [43] have demonstrated another generalization of this theorem. They show that if there exist two sets of nonsingular $m \times m$ matrices $\mathbf{A}_1, \mathbf{A}_2, \ldots, \mathbf{A}_n; \mathbf{B}_1, \mathbf{B}_2, \ldots, \mathbf{B}_n$ such that

$$\sum_{j=1}^{n} \mathbf{A}_j \mathbf{X}_j \qquad \text{and} \qquad \sum_{j=1}^{n} \mathbf{B}_j \mathbf{X}_j$$

are mutually independent, then each $\mathbf{X}_j$ has a multinormal distribution.

Lukacs [78] and Laha [73] have shown that if $X_1, X_2, \ldots, X_m$ have a finite variance-covariance matrix $\mathbf{V}$ and $\mathbf{X}'_j \equiv (X_{1j}, \ldots, X_{mj})$ $(j = 1, \ldots, n)$ are independent vectors each having the same distribution as $(X_1, X_2, \ldots, X_m)$, then if there is a fixed $m \times n$ matrix $\mathbf{A}$ such that

$$E[(X_1, X_2, \ldots, X_m)'\mathbf{A}(X_1, X_2, \ldots, X_m) \mid \mathbf{T}] = \mathbf{V},$$

where

$$\mathbf{T} = \left(\sum_{j=1}^{n} X_{1j}, \sum_{j=1}^{n} X_{2j}, \ldots, \sum_{j=1}^{n} X_{mj}\right),$$

then the common distribution must be multinormal. This is a generalization of a univariate result due to Geary [41] and Laha [72]. A simplified proof has been given by Basu [12].

Invariance under linear combination can be used in characterizing multinormal distributions. As before, let $\mathbf{X}'_1, \ldots, \mathbf{X}'_n$ be n independent $1 \times m$ random vectors, with a common distribution. Furthermore, suppose that $\mathbf{B}_1, \mathbf{B}_2, \ldots, \mathbf{B}_n$ are symmetric nonsingular $m \times m$ matrices and $\mathbf{b}$ a vector such that $\left(\sum_{j=1}^{n} \mathbf{X}'_j \mathbf{B}_j + \mathbf{b}\right)$ has the same distribution as each of the $\mathbf{X}$'s. Then

(i) if $\sum_{j=1}^{n} \mathbf{B}_j^2 - \mathbf{I}$ is positive definite, each $\mathbf{X}_j$ is equal to a constant vector with probability 1; (ii) if $\sum_{j=1}^{n} \mathbf{B}_j^2 - \mathbf{I}$ is positive semidefinite and $\left|\sum_{j=1}^{n} \mathbf{B}_j^2 - \mathbf{I}\right| = 0$, each $\mathbf{X}_j$ has a multinormal distribution, with variance-covariance matrix $\mathbf{V}$ satisfying the equation

$$\mathbf{V} = \sum_{j=1}^{n} \mathbf{B}_j \mathbf{V} \mathbf{B}_j.$$

(Eaton [35]. Shimizu [108] established a similar result, assuming $\mathbf{X}_j'$ to have finite first and second moments.) In the univariate case, if the conditional distribution of W, given $(W + Z)$ is normal, then both W and Z are normally distributed (e.g., Patil and Seshadri [94]). A multivariate extension, due to Seshadri [107], is natural, but requires more complicated conditions. Suppose that $\mathbf{W}$ and $\mathbf{Z}$ are independent $m \times 1$ random vectors each with a continuous density that is not zero when $\mathbf{W} = \mathbf{0}$ (or $\mathbf{Z} = \mathbf{0}$). The $\mathbf{C}$ and $\mathbf{V}$ are nonsingular $m \times m$ matrices, $\mathbf{V}$ is symmetrical and positive definite, and $\mathbf{V}^{-1}\mathbf{C}$ is symmetrical, satisfying either (i) $\mathbf{V}^{-1}(\mathbf{I} - \mathbf{C})$ is positive definite or (ii) the eigenvalues of $\mathbf{C}$ lie in the open interval 0 to 1. Then if the conditional distribution of $\mathbf{W}$ given $\mathbf{W} + \mathbf{Z} = \mathbf{K}$ is multinormal with expected value vector $\mathbf{CK}'$ and variance-covariance matrix $\mathbf{V}$, both $\mathbf{W}$ and $\mathbf{Z}$ have multinormal distributions.

Fisk [38] has shown that multinormal distributions can be characterized by linear regression, and homogeneity of conditional *distribution* (not just homoscedasticity) subject only to the requirement of finiteness of each absolute first moment. More precisely, if $\mathbf{X}_1, \mathbf{X}_2$ are nondegenerate random vectors with all absolute first moments finite, and the conditional distribution of $\mathbf{X}_j$, given $\mathbf{X}_k (j,k,1,2; j \neq k)$ depends on $\mathbf{X}_k$ only through the conditional expected value

$$E[\mathbf{X}_j \mid \mathbf{X}_k] = \mathbf{A}_j + \mathbf{B}_j \mathbf{X}_k,$$

where each row and column of $\mathbf{B}_j$ contains at least one nonzero element, and $\mathbf{B}_1\mathbf{B}_2 \neq \mathbf{I}$, $\mathbf{B}_2\mathbf{B}_1 \neq \mathbf{I}$, then the joint distribution of $\mathbf{X}_1, \mathbf{X}_2$ is multinormal. Fisk [38] also gives a generalization of this result to k sets of variables. Kagan et al. [61] have shown that the condition

$$E[\bar{\mathbf{X}} \mid \mathbf{X}_2 - \mathbf{X}_1, \ldots, \mathbf{X}_k - \mathbf{X}_1] \quad \text{constant}$$

suffices to ensure multinormality.

Khatri [68a] has shown that the conditioning set $(\mathbf{X}_2 - \mathbf{X}_1, \ldots, \mathbf{X}_k - \mathbf{X}_1)$ may be replaced by two or more linear sets of functions of the $\mathbf{X}$'s, subject to certain conditions on the coefficients.

Bildikar and Patil [14] have obtained the following characterizations. An m-variate exponential-type distribution (see Chapter 34, Section 6) is multinormal if and only if (i) all cumulants of order 3 are zero or (ii) the regression of one variable on the remaining $(m - 1)$ variables is linear, *and* every pair of these $(m - 1)$ variables has a bivariate normal joint distribution.

Anderson [7] has shown that if (i) the joint density function $p_{\mathbf{X}}(\mathbf{x} \mid \boldsymbol{\theta})$, with $\boldsymbol{\theta}' = (\theta_1, \ldots, \theta_m)$, is such that

$$\int_{-\infty}^{\infty} \frac{\partial p_{\mathbf{X}}(\mathbf{x} \mid \boldsymbol{\theta})}{\partial \theta_j} \, d\mathbf{x} = \frac{\partial}{\partial \theta_j} \int_{-\infty}^{\infty} p_{\mathbf{X}}(\mathbf{x} \mid \boldsymbol{\theta}) \, d\mathbf{x} = 0 \qquad \text{for all } j$$

and (ii) $E[\mathbf{X}] = \mathbf{M}(\boldsymbol{\theta})$ with the Jacobian $\partial \mathbf{M}/\partial \boldsymbol{\theta}$ nonsingular, then $\mathbf{X}$ has a multinormal distribution if and only if

$$p_{\mathbf{X}}(\mathbf{x} \mid \boldsymbol{\theta}) = \exp[\mathbf{x}'\mathbf{B}\mathbf{M}(\boldsymbol{\theta}) + S(\mathbf{x}) + Q(\boldsymbol{\theta})],$$

where $\mathbf{B}$ is a $m \times m$ matrix not depending on $\boldsymbol{\theta}$ or $\mathbf{x}$.

The relation (14) (Section 4.1) used by Plackett in obtaining a computational formula for the integral of a standardized multinormal density function can be extended to general multinormal density functions. For such functions we have

$$\text{(56.1)} \qquad \frac{\partial p}{\partial \sigma_{rs}} = \frac{\partial^2 p}{\partial x_r \, \partial x_s} \qquad (r \neq s),$$

$$\text{(56.2)} \qquad \frac{\partial p}{\partial \sigma_{rr}} = \frac{1}{2} \frac{\partial^2 p}{\partial x_r^2},$$

where σ_{rs}, the covariance between X_r and X_s, is the r,sth element of $\mathbf{V}$. Patil and Boswell [93] showed that the relations (56.1) and (56.2) suffice to ensure that $X_1, X_2, \ldots, X_n$ have a joint multinormal distribution.

The multinormal distribution can also be characterized by the property of "radial symmetry" of the joint distribution of $\mathbf{X}_1, \ldots, \mathbf{X}_n$ where each $\mathbf{X}_j$ (with $m \leq n$ elements) has the same distribution, and the $\mathbf{X}_j$'s are mutually independent. If the joint distribution is a function only of elements of the matrix $\mathbf{X}\mathbf{X}'$ where $\mathbf{X} = (\mathbf{X}_1, \mathbf{X}_2, \ldots, \mathbf{X}_n)$, then the common distribution of the $\mathbf{X}_j$'s is multinormal. A proof, on the assumption that the distribution has a continuous density function, is given by Kendall and Stuart [64]. Proofs requiring only the existence of a density have been given by James [54] and Thomas [123].

Zinger and Linnik [136] have shown that a limited kind of symmetry suffices to characterize multinormality. In fact if $X_1, \ldots, X_m$ have a continuous density function and identical marginal distributions, then equality of density at three points (a) $(x_1, x_2, \ldots, x_m)$, (b) obtained from (a) by replacing (x_4, x_5, x_6) by (x_1, x_2, x_3), and (c) obtained from (a) by replacing (x_1, x_2, x_3) by (x_4, x_5, x_6) with $x_1^r + x_2^r + x_3^r = x_4^r + x_5^r + x_6^r$ $(r = 1,2)$, ensures multinormality. Clearly this applies only when $m \geq 6$.

The property of maximum entropy for specified variance-covariance matrix, mentioned at the end of Section 2 also characterizes multinormal distributions.

7. Estimation

7.1. *Point-Estimates of Parameters*

The parameters of the marginal (normal) distributions of each X_j may be estimated, using the observed values of X_j alone, by any of the methods described in Chapter 13.

Given a random sample, representable as observed values of n independent random vectors $\mathbf{X}_t = (X_{1t}, X_{2t}, \ldots, X_{mt})$ $(t = 1, \ldots, n)$ with

$$p_{\mathbf{X}_t}(\mathbf{x}_t) = \frac{|\mathbf{V}|^{-1/2}}{(2\pi)^{(1/2)m}} \exp[-\tfrac{1}{2}(\mathbf{x}_t - \boldsymbol{\xi})'\mathbf{V}^{-1}(\mathbf{x}_t - \boldsymbol{\xi})], \tag{57}$$

the maximum likelihood estimators are

$$\hat{\boldsymbol{\xi}} = \bar{\mathbf{X}} = n^{-1} \sum_{t=1}^{n} \mathbf{X}_t; \qquad \hat{\mathbf{V}} = n^{-1}\mathbf{S} \tag{58.1}$$

with

$$S_{ij} = \sum_{t=1}^{n} (X_{ti} - \bar{X}_i)(X_{tj} - \bar{X}_j).$$

Many, more or less arbitrary, criteria have been set up to measure the overall inaccuracy of sets of estimators ($\tilde{\boldsymbol{\xi}}$) of the expected value vector ($\boldsymbol{\xi}$). Among these we may note;

(a) The determinant of the variance-covariance matrix of $\tilde{\boldsymbol{\xi}}$.
(b) The expected value of $(\tilde{\boldsymbol{\xi}} - \boldsymbol{\xi})'\mathbf{V}^{-1}(\tilde{\boldsymbol{\xi}} - \boldsymbol{\xi})$.

James and Stein [55] have shown that if criterion (b) is used and there is available a matrix $\mathbf{S}$ independent of $\bar{\mathbf{X}}$ and having a Wishart distribution (see Chapter 38) with parameters ν $(> m - 3)$,$\mathbf{V}$, then the vector

$$\left(1 - \frac{m-2}{\nu - m + 3} \frac{1}{n\bar{\mathbf{X}}'\mathbf{S}^{-1}\bar{\mathbf{X}}}\right)\bar{\mathbf{X}}$$

has a smaller value of (b) than $\bar{\mathbf{X}}$.

In fact, for this vector, the value of (b) is

$$\left\{m - \frac{\nu - m + 1}{\nu - m + 3}(m-2)^2 E[(m - 2 + 2\phi)^{-1}]\right\}n^{-1}$$

where ϕ has a Poisson distribution with expected value $\frac{n}{2}\,\boldsymbol{\xi}'\mathbf{V}^{-1}\boldsymbol{\xi}$; while the value for $\bar{\mathbf{X}}$ is just m/n.

(In many cases $\mathbf{S}$ may be taken as the matrix of sums of squares and products for sample means. Then $\nu = n - 1$.)

If it is known that $\mathbf{V}$ is of form $\mathbf{I}\sigma^2$—that is, the variates are independent and all have the same variance—then in place of $\mathbf{S}$ we may use a statistic T distributed as $\chi^2_\nu\sigma^2/n$. In this case Baranchik [11] has shown that any estimator of the form

$$\left(1 - g\left(\frac{\bar{\mathbf{X}}'\bar{\mathbf{X}}}{T}\right)\cdot\frac{T}{\bar{\mathbf{X}}'\bar{\mathbf{X}}}\right)\bar{\mathbf{X}}$$

has a smaller value of (b) than $\bar{\mathbf{X}}$, provided $g(\cdot)$ is a positive monotonic nondecreasing function which is less than $2(m-2)/(\nu+2)$.

The maximum likelihood estimator of the variance of X_{jt} is

$$\hat{\sigma}^2_{jj} = v_{jj} = n^{-1}S_{jj} \tag{58.2}$$

and of the correlation between X_{it} and X_{jt}:

$$\hat{\rho}_{ij} = \frac{v_{ij}}{\sqrt{(v_{ii}v_{jj})}} = \frac{S_{ij}}{\sqrt{(S_{ii}S_{jj})}}. \tag{58.3}$$

This is the ordinary sample product moment correlation. The distribution of such statistics has been discussed in Chapter 32; the joint distribution of several such statistics will be considered in Chapters 38 and 39. Here we note a correction to reduce the bias in $\hat{\rho}_{ij}$ as an estimator of ρ_{ij}, suggested by Olkin and Pratt [91]. This consists of using the modified estimator

$$\hat{\rho}_{ij}\left\{1 + \frac{1-\hat{\rho}^2_{ij}}{2(n-4)}\right\}. \tag{59}$$

Olkin and Pratt [91] also give a table of corrective multipliers to apply to $\hat{\rho}_{ij}$. This is reproduced as our Table 2. The corrected estimator is the minimum variance unbiased estimator of ρ_{ij}.

Tallis [122] has studied estimation of parameters of multinormal distributions from grouped data. He found that the univariate formulas

$$\text{sample variance} - \tfrac{1}{12}\,(\text{group width})^2$$

can be used for each variate, and the sample covariances do not need correction. He found that the variance of an estimated correlation (ρ) is increased by approximately

$$(12n)^{-1}(1-\rho^4)$$
$$\times\ (\text{sum of squares of standardized group widths of the two variates}).$$

TABLE 2

Corrective Multipliers for $\hat{\rho}_{ij}$

	$\hat{\rho}_{ij}$										
n	0	.1	.2	.3	.4	.5	.6	.7	.8	.9	1.0
3	∞	10.000	5.000	3.333	2.500	2.000	1.667	1.429	1.250	1.111	1
5	1.571	1.478	1.398	1.327	1.265	1.209	1.159	1.114	1.073	1.035	1
7	1.178	1.173	1.161	1.144	1.125	1.105	1.083	1.062	1.041	1.020	1
9	1.104	1.103	1.098	1.090	1.080	1.068	1.056	1.042	1.028	1.014	1
11	1.074	1.073	1.070	1.065	1.058	1.050	1.042	1.032	1.022	1.011	1
13	1.057	1.056	1.054	1.050	1.046	1.040	1.033	1.026	1.018	1.009	1
15	1.046	1.046	1.044	1.041	1.038	1.033	1.027	1.021	1.015	1.008	1
17	1.039	1.039	1.037	1.035	1.032	1.028	1.023	1.018	1.013	1.006	1
19	1.034	1.033	1.032	1.030	1.028	1.024	1.020	1.016	1.011	1.006	1
21	1.030	1.029	1.028	1.027	1.024	1.022	1.018	1.014	1.010	1.005	1
23	1.027	1.026	1.025	1.024	1.022	1.019	1.016	1.013	1.009	1.005	1
25	1.024	1.024	1.023	1.022	1.020	1.018	1.015	1.012	1.008	1.004	1
27	1.022	1.022	1.021	1.020	1.018	1.016	1.014	1.011	1.007	1.004	1
29	1.020	1.020	1.019	1.018	1.017	1.017	1.012	1.010	1.007	1.004	1
31	1.019	1.018	1.018	1.017	1.015	1.014	1.012	1.009	1.006	1.003	1
∞	1	1	1	1	1	1	1	1	1	1	1

Problems of estimation peculiar to multivariate distributions arise when the sets of observations on some individuals are incomplete. We shall give a fairly detailed account of ways of dealing with this problem for the bivariate normal distribution in Chapter 36 (Section 6.1(x)). In the general multinormal case there is a wide variety of possible patterns and complete analysis would be lengthy. We, therefore, list only the following useful references to this topic: Anderson [8], Afifi and Elashoff [3], Lord [76], and Trawinski and Bargmann [126].

If it is known that

(i) all variances (σ^2) are the same,
(ii) all correlations (ρ) are the same,

then there is an orthogonal transformation

$$\mathbf{X} = \mathbf{Y}\boldsymbol{\Gamma} \qquad (\boldsymbol{\Gamma}\boldsymbol{\Gamma}' = \mathbf{I})$$

such that $Y_1, \ldots, Y_m$ are mutually independent and

$$\operatorname{var}(Y_1) = \{1 + (m-1)\rho\}\sigma^2; \qquad \operatorname{var}(Y_j) = (1-\rho)\sigma^2 \qquad (j \geq 2).$$

Applying this transformation to $\mathbf{X}_1, \ldots, \mathbf{X}_n$ we obtain $\mathbf{Y}_1, \ldots, \mathbf{Y}_n$. The ratio

$$(n-1)^{-1}\sum_{j=1}^{n}(Y_{1j} - \bar{Y}_1)^2 \quad \text{to} \quad (m-1)^{-1}(n-1)^{-1}\sum_{i=2}^{m}\sum_{j=1}^{n}(Y_{ij} - \bar{Y}_i)^2$$

is distributed as (F with $(n-1),(m-1)(n-1)$ degrees of freedom) multiplied by $\{[1 + (m-1)\rho]/(1-\rho)\}$. Since

$$(n-1)^{-1}\sum_{j=1}^{n}(Y_{1j} - \bar{Y}_1)^2 = S^2\{1 + (m-1)R\}$$

and

$$(m-1)^{-1}(n-1)^{-1}\sum_{i=2}^{m}\sum_{j=1}^{n}(Y_{ij} - \bar{Y}_i)^2 = S^2(1-R)$$

with

$$S^2 = \{m(n-1)\}^{-1}\sum_{i=1}^{m}\sum_{j=1}^{n}(X_{ij} - \bar{X}_i)^2$$

and

$$R = \{m(m-1)(n-1)S^2\}^{-1}\sum_{i\neq k}\sum\sum_{j=1}^{n}(X_{ij} - \bar{X}_i)(X_{kj} - \bar{X}_k),$$

we have

$$\frac{(1-\rho)\{1 + (m-1)R\}}{(1-R)\{1 + (m-1)\rho\}}$$

distributed as $F_{n-1,(m-1)(n-1)}$. Confidence intervals for ρ with $100\alpha\%$ confidence coefficient are thus given by

$$1 - m(1-R)F^*_{1-\alpha_1}\{1 + (m-1)[R + (1-R)F^*_{1-\alpha_1}]\}^{-1}$$

and

$$1 - m(1-R)F^*_{\alpha_2}\{1 + (m-1)[R + (1-R)F^*_{\alpha_2}]\}^{-1}$$

with

$$F^*_\varepsilon = F_{n-1,(m-1)(n-1),\varepsilon} \qquad \text{and} \qquad \alpha_1 + \alpha_2 = \alpha.$$

(Geisser [42].) Confidence regions for $\boldsymbol{\xi}$ can be derived by noting that

$$\frac{n(\bar{Y}_1 - \eta_1)^2}{S^2\{1 + (m-1)R\}} \qquad \text{and} \qquad \frac{n\sum_{i=2}^{m}(\bar{Y}_i - \eta_i)^2}{(m-1)S^2(1-R)},$$

where $\boldsymbol{\eta} = \boldsymbol{\xi}\boldsymbol{\Gamma}'$ are independently distributed as $F_{1,n-1}$ and $F_{m-1,(m-1)(n-1)}$, respectively.

We take note of formulas for maximum likelihood estimators in the highly symmetrical case when it is known that, in addition to (i) and (ii),

(iii) all expected values (ξ) are the same.

The formulas (given by Kusunori [71]) are:

$$\hat{\xi} = \bar{X} = (mn)^{-1}\sum_{i=1}^{m}\sum_{j=1}^{n} X_{ij},$$

$$\hat{\sigma}^2 = S^2 = (mn)^{-1}\sum_{i=1}^{m}\sum_{j=1}^{n}(X_{ij} - \bar{X})^2, \tag{60}$$

$$\hat{\rho} = [m(m-1)nS^2]^{-1}\sum_{i<i'}\sum\sum_{j=1}^{n}(X_{ij} - \bar{X})(X_{i'j} - \bar{X}).$$

Doktorov [30] has given the following expression for the maximum likelihood estimator of σ_1, when the values of all the correlations and all other standard deviations $\sigma_2, \sigma_3, \ldots, \sigma_m$ are known:

$$\hat{\sigma}_1 = \tfrac{1}{2}\left(\sum_{j=2}^{m}\rho^{1j}\hat{v}_{ij}\sigma_j^{-1} + \left(\sum_{j=2}^{m}\rho^{1j}\hat{v}_{1j}\sigma_j^{-1}\right)^2 + 4\rho^{11}\hat{v}_{11}\right), \tag{61}$$

where

$$(\rho^{ij}) = \mathbf{R}^{-1} \qquad \text{and} \qquad \hat{v}_{ij} = n^{-1}\sum_{k=1}^{n}(X_{ik} - \bar{X}_i)(X_{jk} - \bar{X}_j).$$

For n large,

$$n\,\text{var}(\hat{\sigma}_1) \doteqdot \sigma_1^2(1 + \rho^{11})^{-1}.$$

Further special cases are discussed by Styan in [118].

Sometimes it is desired to estimate particular functions of the parameters. In particular we may wish to estimate

$$P(\Omega) = (2\pi)^{-m/2}|\mathbf{V}|^{-1/2}\int\cdots\int_{\Omega}\exp[-\tfrac{1}{2}(\mathbf{x}-\boldsymbol{\xi})'\mathbf{V}^{-1}(\mathbf{x}-\boldsymbol{\xi})]\,d\mathbf{x}.$$

Lumel'skii [80] has shown that the minimum variance unbiased estimator of $P(\Omega)$, based on a random sample of size $n(>m)$ is

$$(62)\quad P(\Omega) = [\pi(n-1)]^{-m/2}|\mathbf{V}|^{-1/2}\Gamma(\tfrac{1}{2}(n-1))\{\Gamma(\tfrac{1}{2}(n-m-1)\}^{-1} \times \int\cdots\int_{\Omega}\{f(\mathbf{x})\}^{(1/2)(n-m-3)}\,d\mathbf{x}$$

where

$$f(\mathbf{x}) = \begin{cases} 1-(n-1)^{-1}(\mathbf{x}-\bar{\mathbf{X}})'\mathbf{V}^{-1}(\mathbf{x}-\bar{\mathbf{X}}) \\ \quad \text{if } \mathbf{V} \text{ is positive definite and } (\mathbf{x}-\bar{\mathbf{X}})'\mathbf{V}^{-1}(\mathbf{x}-\bar{\mathbf{X}}) < (n-1)^{-1}, \\ 0 \quad \text{otherwise.} \end{cases}$$

(This may be regarded as a generalization of (63) of Chapter 13.) (See also Kabe [60].)

We finally note that Ghurye and Olkin [44] have obtained formulas for minimum variance estimators of multinormal *density functions* [i.e., of (3)] under various conditions. Some of their results are summarized in the following Table 3 (page 68).

Lumel'skii and Sapozhnikov [81] have also given these formulas for cases (i), (ii), and (iv).

7.2. *Tolerance Regions*

The density function (1) is a decreasing function of $(\mathbf{x}-\boldsymbol{\xi})'\mathbf{V}^{-1}(\mathbf{x}-\boldsymbol{\xi})$. The region R_β with smallest "volume" that contains a specified proportion, say β, of the distribution is therefore

$$(\mathbf{X}-\boldsymbol{\xi})'\mathbf{V}^{-1}(\mathbf{X}-\boldsymbol{\xi}) \le \chi^2_{m,\beta}$$

It is sometimes desired to "estimate" R_β, in some sense.

It is natural to construct a "tolerance region" from a given set of $r(>m)$ random sample values $\mathbf{X}_1,\ldots,\mathbf{X}_n$ of the form

$$(63)\qquad (\mathbf{X}-\bar{\mathbf{X}})'\hat{\mathbf{V}}^{-1}(\mathbf{X}-\bar{\mathbf{X}}) \le K,$$

where $\bar{\mathbf{X}} = n^{-1}\sum_{j=1}^{n}\mathbf{X}_n$ and $\hat{\mathbf{V}}$ is an independent Wishart matrix with $(n-1)$ degrees of freedom and the same variance-covariance matrix as each X_j.

TABLE 3

Known parameters	Estimator
(i) $\boldsymbol{\xi} = \boldsymbol{\xi}_0$	$(2\pi)^{-(1/2)m}[K_{n-1-m}/K_{n-1}]\,\lvert\mathbf{S}\rvert^{-\frac{1}{2}(n-m-2)} \times \lvert\mathbf{S} - (\mathbf{x} - \boldsymbol{\xi}_0)(\mathbf{x} - \boldsymbol{\xi}_0)'\rvert^{\frac{1}{2}(n-m-3)}$
(ii) $\mathbf{V} = \mathbf{V}_0$	$(2\pi)^{-(1/2)m}\,\lvert\mathbf{V}_0\rvert^{-1/2}(1 - n^{-1})^{-(1/2)m} \times \exp\left[-\frac{n}{2(n-1)}(\mathbf{x} - \bar{\mathbf{X}})'\mathbf{V}_0^{-1}(\mathbf{x} - \bar{\mathbf{X}})\right]$
(iii) $\mathbf{V} = \sigma^2\mathbf{V}_0$ (σ unknown)	$(2\pi)^{-(1/2)m}2^{(1/2)m}\Gamma(\frac{1}{2}(n-1)m)[\Gamma(\frac{1}{2}(n-2)m)]^{-1} \times [\text{tr}\mathbf{V}_0^{-1}\mathbf{S}]^{-\frac{1}{2}[(n-1)m-2]} \times \lvert\mathbf{S} - n(\mathbf{x} - \bar{\mathbf{X}})\mathbf{V}_0^{-1}(\mathbf{x} - \bar{\mathbf{X}})'\rvert^{\frac{1}{2}[(n-2)m-2]}$
(iv) None	$(2\pi)^{-(1/2)m}[K_{n-1-m}/K_{n-1}](1 - n^{-1})^{-(1/2)m} \times \lvert\mathbf{S}\rvert^{-\frac{1}{2}(n-m-2)} \times \left\lvert\mathbf{S} - \frac{n-1}{n}(\mathbf{x} - \bar{\mathbf{X}})(\mathbf{x} - \bar{\mathbf{X}})'\right\rvert^{\frac{1}{2}(n-m-3)}$

Notes.

1. $K_\nu = [2^{(1/2)m\nu}\pi^{(1/4)m(m-1)}\prod_{j=1}^{m}\Gamma(\frac{1}{2}(\nu - j + 1))]^{-1}$.

2. When a matrix of form $\mathbf{S} - \mathbf{A}$ is not positive definite, its determinant is to be replaced by zero.

The constant K is to be chosen so that

$$\Pr[\Pr[(\mathbf{X} - \bar{\mathbf{X}})'\hat{\mathbf{V}}^{-1}(\mathbf{X} - \bar{\mathbf{X}}) \le K] \ge \beta] = \gamma. \tag{64}$$

The value of K depends on n, β, and γ (and, of course, on m). Although we can quite simply make the *expected value* of the inner probability in (64) equal to specified value, say α, by taking

$$K = m(n^2 - 1)n^{-1}(n - m)^{-1}F_{m,n-m,\alpha} \tag{65}$$

(Fraser and Guttman [39]), the solution of (64) for K is difficult. Guttman [48] has approximated to K by finding approximations to the mean and variance of

$$P = \Pr[(\mathbf{X} - \bar{\mathbf{X}})'\hat{\mathbf{V}}^{-1}(\mathbf{X} - \bar{\mathbf{X}}) \le K]$$

and then fitting a beta distribution (Chapter 24) with the same mean, variance, and range of variation (0 to 1). He gives tables of approximate values of K to four decimal places for $m = 2(1)4$; $n = 100(20)1000, \infty$; $\beta, \gamma = 0.75$, 0.90, 0.95, and 0.99. (The $n = \infty$ value is $K = \chi^2_{m,\beta}$). The accuracy of the values should increase with n. Comparison with Wald and Wolfowitz' approximation (Chapter 13, Section 6.3) for the univariate

($m = 1$) case confirmed this, and appeared to indicate a satisfactory absolute level of accuracy. A few values from the tables in [48] are reproduced in Table 4.

It is of interest to note the formulas for mean and variance of $\hat{P}$ used by Guttman:

$$E[\hat{P}] = \Pr[\chi_m^2 \leq K] - K^{(1/2)m}[2^{(1/2)m}\Gamma(\tfrac{1}{2}m)]^{-1}e^{-(1/2)K}n^{-1} + o(n^{-1}), \tag{66.1}$$

$$\operatorname{var}(\hat{P}) = K^m[2^{m-1}m\{\Gamma(\tfrac{1}{2}m)\}^2]^{-1}e^{-K}n^{-1} + o(n^{-1}). \tag{66.2}$$

John [58] has considered construction of a region of form (63) which shall include *all* of R_β with specified probability δ. He gives two approximate formulas for K:

$$\left[\sqrt{\frac{(n-1)\chi^2_{m,\beta}}{n-m-2}} + \sqrt{\frac{(n-1)mF_{m,n-m,\delta}}{n(n-m)F_{m,n-m,\delta}}}\right]^2, \tag{67.1}$$

$$\left[\sqrt{\frac{(n-1)\chi^2_{m,\beta}}{\lambda_{m,0.5}}} + \sqrt{\frac{(n-1)mF_{m,n-m,\delta}}{n(n-m)}}\right]^2, \tag{67.2}$$

where, in (67.2), $\lambda_{m,0.5}$ is the median of the distribution of the smallest

TABLE 4

Approximate Values of K

β				0.95		
γ		0.75			0.90	
n/m	2	3	4	2	3	4
100	6.3737	8.2290	9.9296	6.7582	8.6300	10.3460
400	6.1889	8.0267	9.7122	6.3775	8.2253	9.9196
∞	5.9915	7.8147	9.4877	5.9915	7.8147	9.4877
β				0.99		
100	9.7329	11.8881	13.8403	10.2901	12.4404	14.3949
400	9.4977	11.6381	13.5771	9.7798	11.9195	13.8608
∞	9.2103	11.3449	13.2767	9.2103	11.3449	13.2767

Note. Interpolation with respect to $n^{-1/2}$ gives very useful results.

canonical root of a Wishart matrix (see Chapter 38) with variance-covariance matrix $\mathbf{I}_m$ and $(n - 1)$ degrees of freedom.

Of these two formulas (67.2) is the more accurate, but (67.1) does not require knowledge of $\lambda_{m,0.5}$.

8. Truncated Multinormal Distributions

If the variables $X_1, \ldots, X_p$ $(p < m)$ are truncated (in any way), but the remaining variables $X_{p+1}, \ldots, X_m$ are not, the conditional joint distribution of $X_{p+1}, \ldots, X_m$ given any set (or subset) of $X_1, \ldots, X_p$ (or the specified subset) is as shown in Section 3. From this, it is possible to derive convenient formulas for the expected values, variances, and covariances of $X_{p+1}, \ldots, X_m$ in the truncated distribution.

Subject to the conditions that (i) regression of $X_1, \ldots, X_p$ on $X_{p+1}, \ldots, X_m$ is linear and (ii) the conditional distribution of $X_1, \ldots, X_p$ given $X_{p+1}, \ldots, X_m$ is of the same form (apart from a change in location), Aitken [4] showed that for a *general* (not necessarily multinormal) distribution with expected value vector $\mathbf{O}$ and variance-covariance matrix

$$\mathbf{V} = \begin{pmatrix} \mathbf{V}_{11} & \mathbf{V}_{12} \\ \mathbf{V}_{21} & \mathbf{V}_{22} \end{pmatrix}$$

(where $\mathbf{V}_{11}$ is the $p \times p$ variance-covariance matrix of $X_1, \ldots, X_p$), the expected value vector and variance-covariance matrix under a *general selection* on $X_1, X_2, \ldots, X_p$ can be expressed in the form

$$(\boldsymbol{\xi}_1', \; \boldsymbol{\xi}_1'\mathbf{V}_{11}^{-1}\mathbf{V}_{12}) \tag{68.1}$$

and

$$\begin{pmatrix} \mathbf{U}_{11} & \mathbf{U}_{11}\mathbf{V}_{11}^{-1}\mathbf{V}_{12} \\ \mathbf{V}_{21}\mathbf{V}_{11}^{-1}\mathbf{U}_{11} & \mathbf{V}_{22} - \mathbf{V}_{21}(\mathbf{V}_{11}^{-1} - \mathbf{V}_{11}^{-1}\mathbf{U}_{11}\mathbf{V}_{11}^{-1})\mathbf{V}_{12} \end{pmatrix}, \tag{68.2}$$

where $\boldsymbol{\xi}_1', \mathbf{U}_{11}$ are the expected value vector and variance-covariance matrix of $X_1, \ldots, X_p$ after selection. These formulas had been obtained, for special cases of selection from a multinormal distribution by Pearson [95].

Lawley [74] later pointed out that the *identity* of conditional distributions is not essential for formulas (68.1) and (68.2) to hold. All that is necessary is linearity of regression and homoscedasticity of the array variance-covariance matrices. Of course, it is necessary to evaluate $\mathbf{U}_{11}$ and $\boldsymbol{\xi}_1$ for the truncated variables.

For the special case when truncation is of type $X_j \geq h_j$ $(j = 1, \ldots, m)$—that is, values of X_j less than h_j are excluded—explicit, though complicated, formulas were obtained by Birnbaum et al. [17]. Tallis [119] later gave an alternative derivation.

Note that truncation of functionally independent linear functions of the X's, such as

$$\sum_{j=1}^{m} a_j X_j \geq d,$$

can be reduced to cases of the form $X_j > h_j$ by appropriate transformation of variables.

An unusual type of truncation ("elliptical" truncation), which leads to remarkably simple formulas, has been described by Tallis [120]. Taking the standardized form of distribution, it is supposed that values of $\mathbf{X}$ are restricted by the condition

$$a \leq \mathbf{X}'\mathbf{R}^{-1}\mathbf{X} \leq b \qquad (0 \leq a < b). \tag{69}$$

Remembering that $\mathbf{X}'\mathbf{R}^{-1}\mathbf{X}$ is distributed as χ^2 with m degrees of freedom, we obtain the following formula for the moment generating function of $\mathbf{X}$:

$$\phi_{\mathbf{X}}(\mathbf{t}) = \{\Pr[a \leq \chi_m^2 \leq b]\}^{-1}(2\pi)^{-(1/2)m}\,|\mathbf{R}|^{-1/2}\int \exp[-\tfrac{1}{2}\mathbf{x}'\mathbf{R}^{-1}\mathbf{x} + \mathbf{t}'\mathbf{x}]\,d\mathbf{x},$$

where the integral is over the region defined by (69). Making the transformation (see Section 2) $\mathbf{z}' = \mathbf{x}'\mathbf{H}'$ with $\mathbf{H}'\mathbf{H} = \mathbf{R}^{-1}$, we obtain

$$\phi_{\mathbf{X}}(\mathbf{t}) = \{\Pr[a \leq \chi_m^2 \leq b]\}^{-1}(2\pi)^{-(1/2)m} \times e^{(1/2)\mathbf{t}'\mathbf{R}\mathbf{t}}\int \exp[-\tfrac{1}{2}(\mathbf{z} - \mathbf{H}\mathbf{t})'(\mathbf{z} - \mathbf{H}\mathbf{t})]\,d\mathbf{z}, \tag{70}$$

the integral now being over the region

$$a \leq \mathbf{z}'\mathbf{z} \leq b.$$

$\left(\text{note that } \mathbf{z}'\mathbf{z} = \sum_{j=1}^{m} z_j^2\right).$

If the variables $\mathbf{Z}' = \mathbf{X}'\mathbf{H}'$ were to have joint density function

$$p_{\mathbf{Z}}(\mathbf{z}') = (2\pi)^{-(1/2)m}\exp[-\tfrac{1}{2}(\mathbf{z} - \mathbf{H}\mathbf{t})'(\mathbf{z} - \mathbf{H}\mathbf{t})],$$

then $\mathbf{Z}'\mathbf{Z}$ would have a $\chi_m'^2(\mathbf{t}'\mathbf{R}\mathbf{t})$ distribution (see Chapter 28). Hence (70) can be expressed as

$$\begin{aligned} \phi_{\mathbf{X}}(\mathbf{t}) &= \{\Pr[a < \chi_m^2 < b]\}^{-1} e^{(1/2)\mathbf{t}'\mathbf{R}\mathbf{t}} \Pr[a \leq \chi_m'^2(\mathbf{t}'\mathbf{R}\mathbf{t}) \leq b] \\ &= \frac{1}{\Pr[a \leq \chi_m^2 \leq b]} \sum_{j=0}^{\infty} \frac{(\frac{1}{2}\mathbf{t}'\mathbf{R}\mathbf{t})^j}{j!} \Pr[a \leq \chi_{m+2j}^2 \leq b] \end{aligned} \tag{71}$$

[see equation (2), Chapter 28].

From (71) it follows that

(i) the expected value vector, and indeed all moments and product-moments of odd order, of **X** are zero,
(ii) the variance-covariance vector of **X** is $c\mathbf{R}$ with

$$c = \{\Pr[a \le \chi^2_{m+2} \le b]\}/\{\Pr[a \le \chi^2_m \le b]\},$$

(iii) moments and product-moments of even order ($2k$) are obtained from the corresponding values for the complete (untruncated) standardized multinormal distribution by multiplying by the factor

$$\{\Pr[a \le \chi^2_{m+2k} \le b]\}/\{\Pr[a \le \chi^2_m \le b]\}.$$

From (ii) we note that if a and b be chosen so that

$$\Pr[a \le \chi^2_{m+2} \le b] = \Pr[a \le \chi^2_m \le b]$$

then the truncated distribution has the *same* expected value vector and variance-covariance matrix as the untruncated distribution.

Tallis [120] also discusses combination of elliptical truncation with "radial" truncation in which the angles made by the radius vector to the origin with coordinate axes are truncated. In [121] the same author considers truncation by sets of inequalities of form $\sum_{j=1}^{m} \alpha_{t_j} X_j > \alpha_t$. (See also Yoneda [134].)

A special kind of truncation is considered by Beattie [13]. It is desired to truncate two variables (X_1,X_2) out of m, from below in such a way that

(i) a specified proportion, P, of the original distribution is retained and
(ii) a certain linear function $\sum_{j=1}^{m} w_j E[X_j]$ is maximized.

Supposing that only values $X_1 \ge a_1, X_2 \ge a_2$ are retained, Beattie finds the following results. Put

$$A_1 = (1 - \rho_{12}^2)^{-1/2}(a_2 - \rho_{12}a_1); \qquad A_2 = (1 - \rho^2)^{-1/2}(a_1 - \rho_{12}a_2)$$

so that for the truncated distribution

$$E[X_1] = \{Z(a_1)[1 - \Phi(A_1)] + \rho_{12}Z(a_2)[1 - \Phi(A_2)]\}P^{-1}, \tag{72.1}$$

$$E[X_2] = \{\rho_{12}Z(a_1)[1 - \Phi(A_1)] + Z(a_2)[1 - \Phi(A_2)]\}P^{-1}, \tag{72.2}$$

$$E[X_j] = \rho_{j1\cdot 2}E[X_1] + \rho_{j2\cdot 1}E[X_2] \qquad (j = 3,\ldots,m). \tag{72.3}$$

From (72) it is clear that

$$\sum_{j=1}^{m} w_j E[X_j] = \sum_{j=1}^{2} \alpha_j Z(a_j)[1 - \Phi(A_j)]$$

with

$$\alpha_1 = w_1 + \rho_{12}w_2 + (\rho_{j1\cdot 2} + \rho_{12}\rho_{j2\cdot 1})\sum_{j=3}^{m} w_j,$$

$$\alpha_2 = \rho_{12}w_1 + w_2 + (\rho_{j2\cdot 1} + \rho_{12}\rho_{j1\cdot 2})\sum_{j=3}^{m} w_j.$$

9. Mixtures of Multinormal Distributions

If the joint distribution of $X_1, \ldots, X_m$ is a mixture of k multinormal distributions with weights $\{a_j\}$ then the joint distribution of any subset of the X's is a mixture of k multinormal distributions with the same weights. (See Chapter 34, Section 1.)

For mixtures of univariate normal distributions we have (in Chapter 13, Section 7.2) described methods of estimation based on moments. Day [29] has found that these methods are not greatly inferior to maximum likelihood, at least for the case of two components with equal variances. The situation is quite different for two-component mixtures of bivariate (and even more for multivariate) normal distributions with common variance-covariance matrix.

For the population density

$$p_{\mathbf{X}}(\mathbf{x}) = (2\pi)^{-(1/2)m}\, |\mathbf{V}|^{-1/2}\{\omega \exp[-\tfrac{1}{2}(\mathbf{x} - \boldsymbol{\xi}_1)'\mathbf{V}^{-1}(\mathbf{x} - \boldsymbol{\xi}_1)] + (1 - \omega)\exp[-\tfrac{1}{2}(\mathbf{x} - \boldsymbol{\xi}_2)'\mathbf{V}^{-1}(\mathbf{x} - \boldsymbol{\xi}_2)]\}$$

the expected value vector is

$$\bar{\boldsymbol{\xi}} = \omega\boldsymbol{\xi}_1 + (1 - \omega)\boldsymbol{\xi}_2 \tag{73.1}$$

and the variance covariance matrix is

$$\mathbf{V} + \omega(1 - \omega)(\boldsymbol{\xi}_1 - \boldsymbol{\xi}_2)(\boldsymbol{\xi}_1 - \boldsymbol{\xi}_2)' = \mathbf{V} + \omega(1 - \omega)^{-1}(\boldsymbol{\xi}_1 - \bar{\boldsymbol{\xi}})(\boldsymbol{\xi}_1 - \bar{\boldsymbol{\xi}})'. \tag{73.2}$$

The total number of parameters ω, $\boldsymbol{\xi}_1$, $\boldsymbol{\xi}_2$, and $\mathbf{V}$ is

$$1 + 2m + \tfrac{1}{2}m(m + 1) = \tfrac{1}{2}(m^2 + 5m + 2).$$

Equating sample first and second moments to corresponding population values gives only

$$m + \tfrac{1}{2}m(m + 1) = \tfrac{1}{2}(m^2 + 3m)$$

equations, so that further $(m + 1)$ equations are needed. Equating third sample moments of each marginal distribution to the corresponding population values

(74) $E[(X_j - \xi_j)^3] = \omega(1 - 2\omega)(1 - \omega)^{-2}(\xi_j - \xi_j)^3 \qquad j = 1,2,\ldots,m$

provides m equations.

The choice of the final equation appears to be somewhat arbitrary. Day [29] gives an equation based on a certain symmetrical function of third and fourth moments and product moments. We shall not present this here, as he found the moment estimators to be much inferior to maximum likelihood estimators. Day [29] gave an ingenious method of organizing the iterative calculation of maximum likelihood estimators. The equations for these estimators can be arranged to give (i) the $\frac{1}{2}(m^2 + 3m)$ equations obtained by equating first and second moments with the corresponding population values and (ii)

$$(75)\quad \begin{cases} \hat{\mathbf{a}} = \dfrac{\hat{\mathbf{V}}^{-1}(\hat{\boldsymbol{\xi}}_1 - \hat{\boldsymbol{\xi}}_2)}{1 - \hat{\omega}(1 - \hat{\omega})(\hat{\boldsymbol{\xi}}_1 - \hat{\boldsymbol{\xi}}_2)'\hat{\mathbf{V}}^{-1}(\hat{\boldsymbol{\xi}}_1 - \hat{\boldsymbol{\xi}}_2)}, \\ \hat{b} = -\frac{1}{2}\hat{\mathbf{a}}'(\hat{\boldsymbol{\xi}}_1 + \hat{\boldsymbol{\xi}}_2) + \log[(1 - \hat{\omega})/\hat{\omega}], \end{cases}$$

where $\mathbf{a} = \mathbf{V}^{-1}(\boldsymbol{\xi}_2 - \boldsymbol{\xi}_1)$, $b = \frac{1}{2}(\boldsymbol{\xi}_1\mathbf{V}^{-1}\boldsymbol{\xi}_1' - \boldsymbol{\xi}_2\mathbf{V}^{-1}\boldsymbol{\xi}_2') + \log[(1 - \omega)/\omega]$, and $\hat{\mathbf{V}}$ is the matrix of sample variances and covariances.

A computer program for maximum likelihood fitting of multinormal mixtures with common variance-covariance matrix is described by Wolfe [132]. (He also describes a program for the case when there is no common variance-covariance matrix, but see the remarks in Section 10 of Chapter 34.)

Note that if (X, Y) be distributed as a mixture of standardized bivariate normals (with different ρ's), X and Y each have marginal unit normal distributions. If there are two components with $\rho_1 = -\rho_2$, X and Y are also uncorrelated, but they are not independent. (See also Chapter 42, Section 7.)

10. Complex Multinormal Distributions

It is possible to regard the joint distribution of $2m$ (real) random variables $\mathbf{X}' = (X_1,\ldots,X_m)$; $\mathbf{Y}' = (Y_1,\ldots,Y_m)$ as representing the joint distribution of m complex variables

$$Z_j = X_j + iY_j \qquad (j = 1,2,\ldots,m;\ i = \sqrt{-1}).$$

While such a concept may suggest new problems, and enable some results to be expressed in a new form, it is clear that any distributional properties of the Z's are equivalent to properties of the real random variables $\mathbf{X}'$ and $\mathbf{Y}'$. There is nothing essentially new involved.

If $\mathbf{X}'$ and $\mathbf{Y}'$ have a joint multinormal distribution then the Z's may be said to have a joint *complex multinormal distribution*. Wooding [133] showed that in the special case when

$$\text{(76)}\qquad \begin{aligned} \text{var}(X_j) = \text{var}(Y_j) = \sigma_j^2; \qquad \text{corr}(X_j,Y_j) = 0 \qquad & (j = 1,\ldots,m) \\ \text{corr}(X_j,X_k) = \text{corr}(Y_j,Y_k) = \tfrac{1}{2}\alpha_{jk} \qquad & \\ \text{corr}(X_k,Y_j) = -\text{corr}(X_j,Y_k) = \tfrac{1}{2}\beta_{jk} \qquad & (j \neq k) \end{aligned}$$

the joint density of $\mathbf{X}'$ and $\mathbf{Y}'$ can be written as

(77)

$$p_{\mathbf{X}',\mathbf{Y}'}(\mathbf{x}',\mathbf{y}') = \pi^{-m}\,|\mathbf{V}|^{-1}\exp[-(\mathbf{x} - i\mathbf{y} - \boldsymbol{\xi} + i\boldsymbol{\eta})'\mathbf{V}^{-1}(\mathbf{x} + i\mathbf{y} - \boldsymbol{\xi} - i\boldsymbol{\eta})],$$

where $\boldsymbol{\xi} = E[\mathbf{X}]$; $\boldsymbol{\eta} = E[\mathbf{Y}]$ and

$$\mathbf{V} = E[(\mathbf{X} + i\mathbf{Y})(\mathbf{X} - i\mathbf{Y})'].$$

Writing, $\mathbf{z} = \mathbf{x} + i\mathbf{y}$, the right-hand side of (77) can be expressed in the form

$$\text{(78)}\qquad \pi^{-m}\,|\mathbf{V}|^{-1}\exp[-(\tilde{\mathbf{z}} - \tilde{\boldsymbol{\zeta}})'\mathbf{V}^{-1}(\mathbf{z} - \boldsymbol{\zeta})],$$

where $\boldsymbol{\zeta} = \boldsymbol{\xi} + i\boldsymbol{\eta}$ and a tilde over a symbol means "conjugate complement of" (e.g., $\tilde{\mathbf{z}} = \mathbf{x} - i\mathbf{y}$). (The $\boldsymbol{\zeta}$ may be regarded as the "expected value" of $\mathbf{Z}$.) Since (78) depends on $\mathbf{x}$ and $\mathbf{y}$ only through $\mathbf{z}$ and $\tilde{\mathbf{z}}$, it may be regarded (in a formal sense) as the joint density function $p_{\mathbf{Z}}(\mathbf{z})$ of the complex variables $Z_1,Z_2,\ldots,Z_m$. It is not, in general, possible to obtain an expression for $p_{\mathbf{X},\mathbf{Y}}(\mathbf{x},\mathbf{y})$ depending only on $\mathbf{z}$ and $\tilde{\mathbf{z}}$; this is a consequence of the special form assumed for the covariance matrix.

Goodman [45] initiated further developments of the theory of this special kind of complex multinormal distribution (see also Khatri [66]). Some results of these developments appear at appropriate places in later chapters. Useful surveys of the theory are given by Miller [86] and Young [135].

REFERENCES

[1] Abbe, Elizabeth N. (1964). *Experimental Comparison of Monte Carlo Sampling Techniques to Evaluate the Multivariate Normal Integral*, Technical Research Note No. 28, U.S. Army Behavioral Science Research Laboratory.

[2] Abrahamson, I. G. (1964). Orthant probabilities for the quadrivariate normal distribution, *Annals of Mathematical Statistics*, **35,** 1685–1703.

[3] Afifi, A. A. and Elashoff, R. M. (1966–1969). Missing observations in multivariate statistics, *Journal of the American Statistical Association*, **61,** 595–604; **62,** 10–29, **64,** 337–358, 359–365.

[4] Aitken, A. C. (1934). Note on selection from a multivariate normal population, *Proceedings of the Edinburgh Mathematical Society, Series 2*, **4,** 106–110.

[5] Anderson, D. E. (1968). *The Characterization of Multivariate Normal Integrals and the Distribution of Linear Combinations of Order Statistics from the Multivariate Normal Distribution*, Ph.D. thesis, South Methodist University, Dallas, Texas.

[6] Anderson, D. E. (1970). A technique for reducing multivariate normal integrals, *Proceedings, Symposium on Empirical Bayes Estimation, Lubbock, Texas*, 212–217.

[7] Anderson, Mary R. (1971). A characterization of the multivariate normal distribution, *Annals of Mathematical Statistics*, **42,** 824–827.

[8] Anderson, T. W. (1957). Maximum likelihood estimates for a multivariate normal distribution when some observations are missing, *Journal of the American Statistical Association*, **52,** 200–203.

[9] Anis, A. A. and Lloyd, E. H. (1953). On the range of partial sums of a finite number of independent normal variates, *Biometrika*, **40,** 35–42.

[10] Bacon, R. H. (1963). Approximations to multivariate normal orthant probabilities, *Annals of Mathematical Statistics*, **34,** 191–198.

[11] Baranchik, A. J. (1970). A family of minimax estimators of the mean of a multivariate normal distribution, *Annals of Mathematical Statistics*, **41,** 642–645.

[12] Basu, D. (1956). A note on the multivariate extension of some theorems related to the univariate normal distribution, *Sankhyā*, **17,** 221–224.

[13] Beattie, A. W. (1962). Truncation in two variables to maximize a function of the means of a normal multivariate distribution, *Australian Journal of Statistics*, **4,** 1–3.

[14] Bildikar, Sheela and Patil, G. P. (1968). Multivariate exponential-type distributions, *Annals of Mathematical Statistics*, **39,** 1316–1326.

[15] Birnbaum, Z. W. (1950). Effect of linear truncation on a multivariate population, *Annals of Mathematical Statistics*, **21,** 272–279.

[16] Birnbaum, Z. W. and Meyer, P. L. (1953). On the effect of truncation

in some or all coordinates of a multinormal population, *Journal of the Indian Society for Agricultural Statistics*, **5,** 17–28.

[17] Birnbaum, Z. W., Paulson, E. and Andrews, F. C. (1950). On the effect of selection performed on some coordinates of a multi-dimensional population, *Psychometrika*, **15,** 191–204.

[18] Bland, R. P. and Owen, D. B. (1966). A note on singular normal distributions, *Annals of the Institute of Statistical Mathematics, Tokyo*, **18,** 113–116.

[19] Brown, J. L. (1968). On the expansion of the bivariate Gaussian probability density using results of nonlinear theorems, *IEEE Transactions on Information Theory*, **14,** 158–159.

[20] Cheng, M. C. (1969). The orthant probabilities of four Gaussian variates, *Annals of Mathematical Statistics*, **40,** 152–161.

[21] Childs, D. R. (1967). Reduction of the multivariate normal integral to characteristic form, *Biometrika*, **54,** 293–299.

[22] Cohen, A. C. (1957). Restriction and selection in multinormal distributions, *Annals of Mathematical Statistics*, **28,** 731–741

[23] Coxeter, H. S. M. (1935). The functions of Schläfli and Lobatschefsky, *Quarterly Journal of Mathematics*, **6,** 13–29.

[24] Curnow, R. N. and Dunnett, C. W. (1962). The numerical evaluation of certain multivariate normal integrals, *Annals of Mathematical Statistics*, **33,** 571–579.

[25] Das, S. C. (1956). The numerical evaluation of a class of integrals, II, *Proceedings of the Cambridge Philosophical Society*, **52,** 442–448.

[26] David, F. N. (1953). A note on the evaluation of the multivariate normal integral, *Biometrika*, **40,** 458–459.

[27] David, F. N. and Mallows, C. L. (1961). The variance of Spearman's rho in normal samples, *Biometrika*, **48,** 19–28.

[28] David, H. A. and Six, F. B. (1971). Sign distribution of standard multinormal variables with equal positive correlation, *Review of the International Statistical Institute*, **39,** 1–3.

[29] Day, N. E. (1969). Estimating the components of a mixture of normal distributions, *Biometrika*, **56,** 463–474.

[30] Doktorov, B. Z. (1969). On some estimates of a multivariate normal distribution, *Teoriya Veroyatnostei i ee Primeneniya*, **14,** 552–554. (In Russian.) English translation pp. 526–528.

[31] Dunn, Olive J. (1958). Estimation of the means of dependent variables, *Annals of Mathematical Statistics*, **29,** 1095–1111.

[32] Dunnett, C. W. (1955). Statistical need for new tables involving the multivariate normal distribution, *Presented at a Meeting of the Institute of Mathematical Statistics*, New York.

[33] Dunnett, C. W. and Lamm, R. A. (1960). Some tables of the multivariate normal probability integral with correlation coefficients 1/3, *Mathematical Tables and Aids to Computation*, **14,** 290–291. (Abstract.)

[34] Dunnett, C. W. and Sobel, M. (1955). Approximations to the probability integral and certain percentage points of a multivariate analogue of Student's *t*-distribution, *Biometrika*, **42**, 258–260.

[35] Eaton, M. L. (1966). Characterization of distributions by the identical distribution of linear forms, *Journal of Applied Probability*, **3**, 481–494.

[36] Escoufier, Y. (1967). Calculs de probabilités par une methode de Monte Carlo pour une variable p-normale, *Revue de Statistique Appliquée*, **15**, No. 4, 5–15.

[37] Finney, D. J. (1962). Cumulants of truncated multinormal distributions, *Journal of the Royal Statistical Society, Series B*, **24**, 535–536.

[38] Fisk, P. R. (1970). A note on a characterization of the multivariate normal distribution, *Annals of Mathematical Statistics*, **41**, 486–494.

[39] Fraser, D. A. S. and Guttman, I. (1956). Tolerance regions, *Annals of Mathematical Statistics*, **27**, 162–179.

[40] Fréchet, M. (1951). Généralizations de la loi de probabilité de Laplace, *Annales de l'Institut Henri Poincaré*, **13**, 1–29.

[41] Geary, R. C. (1933). A general expression for the moments of certain symmetrical functions of normal samples, *Biometrika*, **25**, 184–186.

[42] Geisser, S. (1964). Estimation in the uniform covariance case, *Journal of the Royal Statistical Society, Series B*, **26**, 477–483.

[43] Ghurye, S. G. and Olkin, I. (1962). A characterization of the multivariate normal distribution, *Annals of Mathematical Statistics*, **33**, 533–541.

[44] Ghurye, S. G. and Olkin, I. (1969). Unbiased estimation of some multivariate probability densities and related functions, *Annals of Mathematical Statistics*, **40**, 1261–1271.

[45] Goodman, N. R. (1963). Statistical analysis based on a certain multivariate complex Gaussian distribution (an introduction), *Annals of Mathematical Statistics*, **34**, 152–177.

[46] Gupta, S. D. (1969). A note on some inequalities for multivariate normal distribution, *Bulletin of the Calcutta Statistical Association*, **18**, 179–180.

[47] Gupta, S. S. (1963). Bibliography on the multivariate normal integrals and related topics, *Annals of Mathematical Statistics*, **34**, 829–838.

[48] Guttman, I. (1970). Construction of β-content tolerance regions at confidence level δ for large samples from the k-variate normal distribution, *Annals of Mathematical Statistics*, **41**, 376–400.

[49] Hannan, J. F. and Tate, R. F. (1965). Estimation of the parameters for a multivariate normal distribution when one variable is dichotomized, *Biometrika*, **52**, 664–668.

[50] Hocking, R. R. and Smith, W. B. (1968). Estimation of parameters in the multivariate normal distribution with missing observations, *Journal of the American Statistical Association*, **63**, 159–173.

[51] Hotelling, H. (1948). Fitting generalized truncated normal distributions, *Annals of Mathematical Statistics*, **19**, 596 (Abstract).

[52] Ihm, P. (1959). Numerical evaluation of certain multivariate normal integrals, *Sankhyā*, **21,** 363–366.

[53] Ihm, P. (1961). A further contribution to the numerical evaluation of certain multivariate integrals, *Sankhyā*, *Series A*, **23,** 205–206.

[54] James, A. T. (1954) Normal multivariate analysis and the orthogonal group, *Annals of Mathematical Statistics*, **25,** 40–75.

[55] James, W. and Stein, C. (1955). Estimation with quadratic loss, *Third Berkeley Symposium on Mathematical Statistics and Probability*, **1,** 361–379.

[56] Jogdeo, K. (1970). A simple proof of an inequality for multivariate normal probabilities of rectangles, *Annals of Mathematical Statistics*, **41,** 1357–1359.

[57] John, S. (1959). On the evaluation of the probability integral of a multivariate normal distribution, *Sankhyā*, **21,** 376–370.

[58] John, S. (1968). A central tolerance region for the multivariate normal distribution, *Journal of the Royal Statistical Society*, *Series B*, **30,** 599–601.

[59] John, S. (1966). On the evaluation of probabilities of convex polyhedra under multivariate normal and t-distributions, *Journal of the Royal Statistical Society*, *Series B*, **28,** 366–369.

[60] Kabe, D. G. (1968). Minimum variance unbiased estimate of a coverage probability, *Operations Research*, **16,** 1016–1020.

[61] Kagan, A. M., Linnik, Yu. V. and Rao, C. R. (1965). On a characterization of the normal law based on a property of the sample average, *Sankhyā*, *Series A*, **27,** 405–406.

[62] Kendall, M. G. (1941). Proof of relations connected with tetrachoric series and its generalization, *Biometrika*, **32,** 196–198.

[63] Kendall, M. G. (1954). Two problems in sets of measurements, *Biometrika*, **41,** 560–564.

[64] Kendall, M. G. and Stuart, A. (1963). *The Advanced Theory of Statistics*, Vol. 1, 2nd ed., London: Griffin.

[65] Kendall, M. G. and Stuart, A. (1966). *The Advanced Theory of Statistics*, Vol. 3, 1st ed., London: Griffin.

[66] Khatri, C. G. (1965). Classical statistical analysis based on a certain multivariate complex Gaussian distribution, *Annals of Mathematical Statistics*, **36,** 98–114.

[67] Khatri, C. G. (1965). Joint estimation of the parameters of multivariate normal distributions, *Journal of the Indian Statistical Association*, **1,** 125–133.

[68] Khatri, C. G. (1967). On certain inequalities for normal distributions and their applications to simultaneous confidence bounds, *Annals of Mathematical Statistics*, **38,** 1853–1867.

[68a] Khatri, C. G. (1971). On characterization of gamma and multivariate normal distributions by solving some functional equations in vector variables, *Journal of Multivariate Analysis*, **1,** 70–89.

[69] Kibble, W. F. (1945). An extension of a theorem of Mehler on Hermite polynomials, *Proceedings of the Cambridge Philosophical Society*, **41,** 12–15.

[70] Kudô, A. (1958). On the distribution of the maximum value of an equally correlated sample from a normal population, *Sankhyā*, **20,** 309–316.

[71] Kusunori, K. (1967). On the estimates of the unknown parameters in the multivariate distribution with the intraclass correlation, *Technological Reports, Kansas University 1967*, No. 9, 101–108.

[72] Laha, R. G. (1953). On an extension of Geary's theorem, *Biometrika*, **40,** 228–229.

[73] Laha, R. G. (1955). On a characterization of the multivariate normal distribution, *Sankhyā*, **14,** 376–368.

[74] Lawley, D. N. (1943). A note on Karl Pearson's selection formulae, *Proceedings of the Royal Society of Edinburgh*, **62,** 28–30.

[75] Lewin, L. (1958). *Dilogarithms and Associated Functions*, London: Macdonald.

[76] Lord, F. M. (1955). Estimation of parameters from incomplete data, *Journal of the American Statistical Association*, **50,** 870–876.

[77] Lukacs, E. (1942). A characterization of the normal distribution, *Annals of Mathematical Statistics*, **13,** 91–93.

[78] Lukacs, E. (1956). Characterization of populations by properties of suitable statistics, *Proceedings of the 3rd Berkeley Symposium on Mathematical Statistics and Probability*, **2,** 195–214.

[79] Lukacs, E. and Laha, R. G. (1964). *Applications of Characteristic Functions*, London: Griffin.

[80] Lumel'skii, Ya. P. (1968). Unbiased sufficient estimations of probability for the multivariate normal distribution, *Vestnik Moskovskogo Universiteta*, No. 6, 14–17. (In Russian.)

[81] Lumel'skii, Ya. P. and Sapozhnikov, P. N. (1969). Unbiased estimates of density functions, *Theory of Probability and its Applications*, **14,** 357–364.

[82] Marsaglia, G. (1963). Expressing the normal distribution with covariance matrix $A + B$ in terms of one with covariance matrix A, *Biometrika*, **50,** 535–538.

[83] McFadden, J. A. (1956). An approximation for the symmetric, quadrivariate normal integral, *Biometrika*, **43,** 206–207.

[84] McFadden, J. A. (1960). Two expansions for the quadrivariate normal integral, *Biometrika*, **47,** 325–333.

[85] Mehler, F. G. (1866). Über die Entwicklung einer Funktion von beliebig vielen Variablen nach Laplace'schen Funktionen höherer Ordnung, *Journal für die reine und angewandte Mathematik*, **66,** 161–176.

[86] Miller, K. S. (1964). *Multidimensional Gaussian Distributions*, New York: John Wiley and Sons, Inc.

[87] Miller, K. S. and Sackrowitz, H. (1965). Distributions associated with the quadrivariate normal, *Journal of the Industrial Mathematics Society*, **15,** No. 2, 1–15.

[88] Mises, R. von (1954). Numerische Berechnung mehrdimensionaler Integrale, *Zeitschrift für Angewandte Mathematik und Mechanik*, **34,** 201–210.

[89] Moran, P. A. P. (1948). Rank correlation and product moment correlation, *Biometrika*, **35,** 203–206.

[90] Moran, P. A. P. (1956). The numerical evaluation of a class of integrals, *Proceedings of the Cambridge Philosophical Society*, **52,** 230–233.

[91] Olkin, I. and Pratt, J. W. (1958). Unbiased estimation of certain correlation coefficients, *Annals of Mathematical Statistics*, **29,** 201–211.

[92] Olkin, I. and Roy, S. N. (1954). On multivariate distribution theory, *Annals of Mathematical Statistics*, **25,** 329–339.

[93] Patil, G. P. and Boswell, M. T. (1970). A characteristic property of the multivariate normal distribution and some of its applications, *Annals of Mathematical Statistics*, **41,** 1970–1977.

[94] Patil, G. P. and Seshadri, V. (1964). Characterization theorems for some univariate probability distributions, *Journal of the Royal Statistical Society, Series B*, **26,** 286–292.

[95] Pearson, K. (1903). Mathematical contributions to the theory of evolution—XI. On the influence of natural selection on the variability and correlation of organs, *Philosophical Transactions of the Royal Society of London, Series A*, **200,** 1–66.

[96] Plackett, R. L. (1954). A reduction formula for normal multivariate integrals, *Biometrika*, **41,** 351–360.

[96a] Poznyakov, V. V. (1971). On one representation of the multidimensional normal distribution function, *Ukrainian Mathematical Journal*, **23,** 562–566.

[97] Quenouille, M. H. (1950). The evaluation of probabilities in a normal multivariate distribution with special reference to correlation ratio, *Proceedings of the Edinburgh Mathematical Society*, **8,** 95–100.

[98] Rao, C. R. (1965). *Linear Statistical Inference and Applications*, New York: John Wiley & Sons, Inc.

[99] Rao, C. R. (1969). On vector variables with a linear structure and a characterization of the multivariate normal distribution, *Bulletin of the International Statistical Institute*, **42,** 1207–1212.

[100] Ruben, H. (1961). On the numerical evaluation of a class of multivariate normal integrals, *Proceedings of the Royal Society of Edinburgh*, **65,** 272–281.

[101] Ruben, H. (1962). An asymptotic expansion for a class of multivariate normal integrals, *Journal of the Australian Mathematical Society*, **2,** 253–264.

[102] Ruben, H. (1964). An asymptotic expansion for the multivariate normal distribution and Mill's ratio, *Journal of Research, National Bureau of Standards*, **68B,** 3–11.

[103] Rukhin, A. L. (1967). The complex normal law and the admissibility of the sample mean as an estimator of a location parameter, *Teoriya Veroyatnostei i ee Primeneniya*, **12,** 762–764. (In Russian.) (English translation, 695–697.)

[104] Savage, R. (1962). Mill's ratio for multivariate normal distributions, *Journal of Research, National Bureau of Standards*, **66B,** 93–96.

[105] Schläfli, L. (1858). On the multiple integral . . . , *Quarterly Journal of Pure and Applied Mathematics*, **2**, 269–301; **3**, 54–68; 97–108.

[106] Scott, A. (1967). A note on conservative confidence regions for the means of a multivariate normal, *Annals of Mathematical Statistics*, **38**, 278–280.

[107] Seshadri, V. (1966). A characteristic property of the multivariate normal distribution, *Annals of Mathematical Statistics*, **37**, 1829–1831.

[108] Shimizu, R. (1962). Characterization of the normal distribution, II, *Annals of the Institute of Statistical Mathematics, Tokyo*, **14**, 173–178.

[109] Šidák, Z. (1967). Rectangular confidence regions for the means of multivariate normal distributions, *Journal of the American Statistical Association*, **62**, 626–633.

[110] Šidák, Z. (1968). On multivariate normal probabilities of rectangles: their dependence on correlations, *Annals of Mathematical Statistics*, **39**, 1425–1434.

[111] Singh, N. (1960). Estimation of parameters of a multivariate population from truncated and censored samples, *Journal of the Royal Statistical Society, Series B*, **22**, 307–311.

[112] Slepian, D. (1962). The one sided barrier problem for Gaussian noise, *Bell System Technical Journal*, **41**, 463–501.

[113] Smith, W. B. and Hocking, R. R. (1968). A simple method for obtaining the information matrix for a multivariate normal distribution, *American Statistician*, **22**, No. 1, 18–19.

[114] Sondhi, M. M. (1961). A note on the quadrivariate normal integral, *Biometrika*, **48**, 201–203.

[115] Steck, G. P. (1958). A table for computing trivariate normal probabilities, *Annals of Mathematical Statistics*, **29**, 780–800.

[116] Steck, G. P. and Owen, P. B. (1962). A note on the equicorrelated multivariate normal distribution, *Biometrika*, **49**, 269–271.

[117] Stuart, A. (1958). Equally correlated variates and the multinormal integral, *Journal of the Royal Statistical Society, Series B*, **20**, 373–378.

[118] Styan, G. P. H. (1968). Inference in multivariate normal populations with structure—Part I: Inference on variance when correlations are known, *Technical Report No. 1*, School of Aerospace Medicine, Brooks A.F.B., Texas.

[119] Tallis, G. M. (1961). The moment generating function of the truncated multinormal distribution, *Journal of the Royal Statistical Society, Series B*, **23**, 233–239.

[120] Tallis, G. M. (1963). Elliptical and radial truncation in normal populations, *Annals of Mathematical Statistics*, **34**, 940–944.

[121] Tallis, G. M. (1965). Plane truncation in normal populations, *Journal of the Royal Statistical Society, Series B*, **27**, 301–307.

[122] Tallis, G. M. (1967). Approximate maximum likelihood estimates from grouped data, *Technometrics*, **9**, 599–606.

[123] Thomas, D. H. (1970). *A Cauchy Type Functional Equation and a Characterization of the Multivariate Normal Distribution*, Report GMR-1003, General Motors Corporation.

[124] Todhunter, J. (1869). On the method of least squares, *Transactions of the Cambridge Philosophical Society*, **11,** 219–238.

[125] Tong, Y. L. (1970). Some probability inequalities of multivariate normal and multivariate *t*, *Journal of the American Statistical Association*, **65,** 1243–1247.

[126] Trawinski, Irene and Bargmann, R. E. (1964). Maximum likelihood estimation with incomplete multivariate data, *Annals of Mathematical Statistics*, **35,** 647–658.

[127] Vaart, H. R. van der (1953). The content of certain spherical polyhedra for any number of dimensions, *Experientia*, **9,** 88–89.

[128] Vaart, H. R. van der (1955). The content of some classes of non-Euclidean polyhedra for any number of dimensions, with several applications, I, II, *Proceedings of the Royal Academy of Sciences, Amsterdam, Series A*, **58,** 199–221.

[129] Watterson, G. A. (1959). Linear estimation in censored samples from multivariate normal populations, *Annals of Mathematical Statistics*, **30,** 814–825.

[130] Webster, J. T. (1970). On the application of the method of Das in normal integral, *Biometrika*, **57,** 657–660.

[131] Weiss, Marie C. (1966). Determination d'une variable de Gauss a plusieurs dimensions a l'aide de la function caractéristique, *Journal de la Société de Statistique de Paris*, **107,** 135–136.

[132] Wolfe, J. H. (1970). Pattern clustering by multivariate mixture analysis, *Multivariate Behavioral Research*, **5,** 329–350.

[133] Wooding, R. A. (1956). The multivariate distribution of complex normal variables, *Biometrika*, **43,** 212–215.

[134] Yoneda, K. (1961). Some estimations of the parameters of multinormal populations from linearly truncated samples, *Yokohama Mathematical Journal*, **9,** 149–161.

[135] Young, J. C. (1971). *Some Inference Problems Associated with the Complex Multivariate Normal Distribution*, Technical Report No. 102, Department of Statistics, Southern Methodist University, Dallas, Texas.

[136] Zinger, A. A. and Linnik, Yu. V. (1964). A characteristic property of the normal distribution, *Theory of Probability and its Applications*, **9,** 624–626.

36

Bivariate and Trivariate Normal Distributions

1. Definitions and Applications

In this chapter we make frequent use of results obtained in Chapter 35. Our attention is concentrated on the details of work that has been done on multinormal distributions with two or three variables, and not on general multinormal distributions.

When there are just two variables, X_1,X_2, (1) of Chapter 35 becomes

$$(1)\quad p(x_1,x_2) = [2\pi\sqrt{1-\rho^2}]^{-1}\exp\left[-\frac{1}{2(1-\rho^2)}\left\{\left(\frac{x_1-\xi_1}{\sigma_1}\right)^2 - 2\rho\left(\frac{x_1-\xi_1}{\sigma_1}\right)\left(\frac{x_2-\xi_2}{\sigma_2}\right) + \left(\frac{x_2-\xi_2}{\sigma_2}\right)^2\right\}\right],$$

where $E[X_j] = \xi_j$, $\text{var}(X_j) = \sigma_j^2$ $(j = 1,2)$, and the correlation between X_1 and X_2 is ρ. This is the bivariate normal or *binormal* distribution. Other names are *Gaussian*, *Laplace-Gauss*, and *Bravais* [13].

It is possible to regard the bivariate normal as a "univariate" complex normal distribution (Chapter 35, Section 10) but this does not possess any advantages for our present interest.

For many purposes it is sufficient to study the standardized distribution, obtained by putting $\xi_1 = \xi_2 = 0$; $\sigma_1 = \sigma_2 = 1$ in (1):

$$(2)\quad p(x_1,x_2) = [2\pi\sqrt{1-\rho^2}]^{-1}\exp\left[-\frac{1}{2(1-\rho^2)}(x_1^2 - 2\rho x_1x_2 + x_2^2)\right].$$

If in (1) we have $\sigma_1 = \sigma_2$ and $\rho = 0$, it is called a *circular normal* density function. This should not be confused with the circular normal distribution described in Section 3.1 of Chapter 33. If $\rho = 0$ but $\sigma_1 \neq \sigma_2$, the name *elliptical normal* is sometimes used.

The *standardized trivariate normal* or *trinormal* probability density function of three random variables X_1, X_2, X_3 depends on the correlation coefficients $\rho_{23}, \rho_{13}, \rho_{12}$ and can be written as

$$(3) \qquad p_{X_1,X_2,X_3}(x_1,x_2,x_3) = (2\pi)^{-3/2}\Delta^{-1/2}\exp\left[-\tfrac{1}{2}\sum_{i=1}^{3}\sum_{j=1}^{3}A_{ij}x_ix_j\right],$$

where

$$\Delta = 1 - \rho_{23}^2 - \rho_{13}^2 - \rho_{12}^2 + 2\rho_{23}\rho_{13}\rho_{12},$$

$$A_{11} = (1 - \rho_{23}^2)\Delta^{-1}; \qquad A_{22} = (1 - \rho_{13}^2)\Delta^{-1}; \qquad A_{33} = (1 - \rho_{12}^2)\Delta^{-1},$$

$$A_{12} = A_{21} = (\rho_{13}\rho_{23} - \rho_{12})\Delta^{-1}; \qquad A_{13} = A_{31} = (\rho_{12}\rho_{23} - \rho_{13})\Delta^{-1};$$

$$A_{23} = A_{32} = (\rho_{12}\rho_{13} - \rho_{23})\Delta^{-1}.$$

If all ρ's are zero and all σ's equal, the distribution is sometimes called *spherical normal*; if all ρ's are zero but σ's are not equal, the name *ellipsoidal normal* has been used.

Bivariate and trivariate normal distributions are used in a wide variety of applications. Among the oldest are applications in artillery fire control. To a first approximation deviations from a target on a plane (for land artillery) are described by bivariate normal distributions. For aerial targets, trivariate normal distributions are appropriate.

Multivariate normal distributions are very commonly employed as approximations to joint distributions, even when the marginal distributions are not exactly normal, as pointed out in Chapter 34. Although the theoretical framework thus constructed is useful as a basis for construction of tests and estimation procedures, it is only for the bivariate and (though to a lesser extent) trivariate normal distributions that it is easy to form a picture of the distribution. Study of these distributions is of special value in forming ideas of the effect of truncation, applied to one or two of a number of multinormal variables.

2. Historical Remarks

Although the joint distribution of normal variables was considered occasionally as early as the beginning of the nineteenth century (Adrian [1], Bravais [13], Plana [86], and Helmert [44]), it was not until the last quarter of that century that it became a subject of systematic study.

The main impetus came from the work of Schols [96] and especially of Galton, from 1877 onward [36, 37], at whose suggestion Dickson [27] demonstrated a possible genesis for the bivariate normal distribution as the vector combination of independent normally distributed components on *oblique* axes. Subsequently, around 1900, Pearson [80, 81] applied the bivariate normal distribution to biometric data. He also initiated work on tabulation of values of integral probabilities for bivariate normal distributions. Later work on tabulation of special values has been associated with development of techniques for selection among (univariate) normal populations with regard to their expected values (see, e.g., Dunnett [29] and Somerville [105]).

Accounts of the earlier history of the bivariate normal distribution have been given by Czuber [23] and Pearson [82]. A briefer, but broader account, has been given by Anderson [9].

3. Properties and Moments

For the standardized bivariate normal distribution (2) the conditional distribution of X_2, given X_1, is normal with expected values ρX_1 and variance $(1 - \rho^2)$ [conversely, that of X_1, given X_2, is normal with expected value ρX_2 and variance $(1 - \rho^2)$]. This is reflected in the fact that $p(x_1,x_2)$ in (2) can be written

$$Z(x_1)Z([x_2 - \rho x_1][1 - \rho^2]^{-1/2})(1 - \rho^2)^{-1/2} \tag{4.1}$$

or

$$Z(x_2)Z([x_1 - \rho x_2][1 - \rho^2]^{-1/2})(1 - \rho^2)^{-1/2}, \tag{4.2}$$

where $Z(x) = (2\pi)^{-1/2} \exp(-\frac{1}{2}x^2)$.

We may note here the characterization of the bivariate normal distributions, in terms of exponential-type distribution (see Chapter 34, Section 6), obtained by Bildikar and Patil (in reference [9] of Chapter 34). If X_1 and X_2 have a bivariate exponential-type distribution, that distribution is bivariate normal if and only if

(a) the regression of one variable or the other is linear and

(b) the marginal distribution of one of the variables is normal. Condition (b) may be replaced by the requirement that $(X_1 + X_2)$ have a normal distribution.

For the standardized trivariate normal distribution (3), the regression of any variate on the other two is linear, with constant array variance. The distribution of X_3, given X_1 and X_2 for example, is normal with expected value $\rho_{13.2}X_1 + \rho_{23.1}X_2$ and variance $(1 - R^2_{3.12})$, where $\rho_{ij.k}$ means partial correlation between X_i and X_j given X_k and $R^2_{3.12}$ is the multiple correlation of X_3

on X_1 and X_2 as defined in Chapter 32. The joint distribution of X_1 and X_2, given X_3, is bivariate normal with marginal expected values $\rho_{13}X_3, \rho_{23}X_3$, with variances $(1 - \rho_{13}^2)$ and $(1 - \rho_{23}^2)$, and with the correlation coefficient

$$\rho_{12.3} = \frac{\rho_{12} - \rho_{13}\rho_{23}}{\sqrt{(1 - \rho_{13}^2)(1 - \rho_{23}^2)}}. \tag{5}$$

The parameter $\rho_{12.3}$ is the *partial correlation* between X_1 and X_2, given X_3. The partial correlations $\rho_{23.1}$ and $\rho_{13.2}$ are defined similarly.

As special cases of the result stated at the end of Section 2, Chapter 35, the statistics

$$\frac{1}{1 - \rho^2}(X_1^2 - 2\rho X_1 X_2 + X_2^2) \qquad \text{[for distribution (2)]}$$

and

$$\sum_{i=1}^{3}\sum_{j=1}^{3} A_{ij}X_iX_j \qquad \text{[for distribution (3)]}$$

have chi-square distributions with 2,3 degrees of freedom respectively. This makes it easy to construct elliptical or ellipsoidal contours, within which specified proportions of the distributions lie. In the bivariate case, since $\Pr[\chi_2^2 < K] = 1 - e^{-K/2}$, the ellipse containing $100\alpha\%$ of the distribution has the simple equation

$$x_1^2 - 2\rho x_1 x_2 + x_2^2 = -2(1 - \rho^2)\log(1 - \alpha). \tag{6}$$

For the general bivariate distribution (1) the corresponding ellipse has equation

$$\left(\frac{x_1 - \xi_1}{\sigma_1}\right)^2 - 2\rho\left(\frac{x_1 - \xi_1}{\sigma_1}\right)\left(\frac{x_2 - \xi_2}{\sigma_2}\right) + \left(\frac{x_2 - \xi_2}{\sigma_2}\right)^2 = -2(1 - \rho^2)\log(1 - \alpha). \tag{7}$$

(Several such ellipses are shown in Figure 1*a*.) The major axis of the ellipse makes an angle $\theta = \frac{1}{2}\tan^{-1}[2\rho\sigma_1\sigma_2/(\sigma_1^2 - \sigma_2^2)]$ with the x_1-axis. Note that this angle is 45° if $\sigma_1 = \sigma_2$ and $\rho > 0$, whatever the numerical value of ρ. If $\rho = 0$ and $\sigma_1 = \sigma_2$ (i.e., the variables are independent and have equal variances), then (7) is the equation of a circle. The corresponding distribution is called circular normal (but should not be confused with the distribution described in Section 3.1 of Chapter 33). Some perspective drawings of the density function (2) are shown in Fig. 1*b*. The value of $p(x_1,x_2)$ is measured in the vertical direction.

For bivariate normal distributions, zero correlation implies independence. This is, of course, not so in general. Examples of dependent normal variables

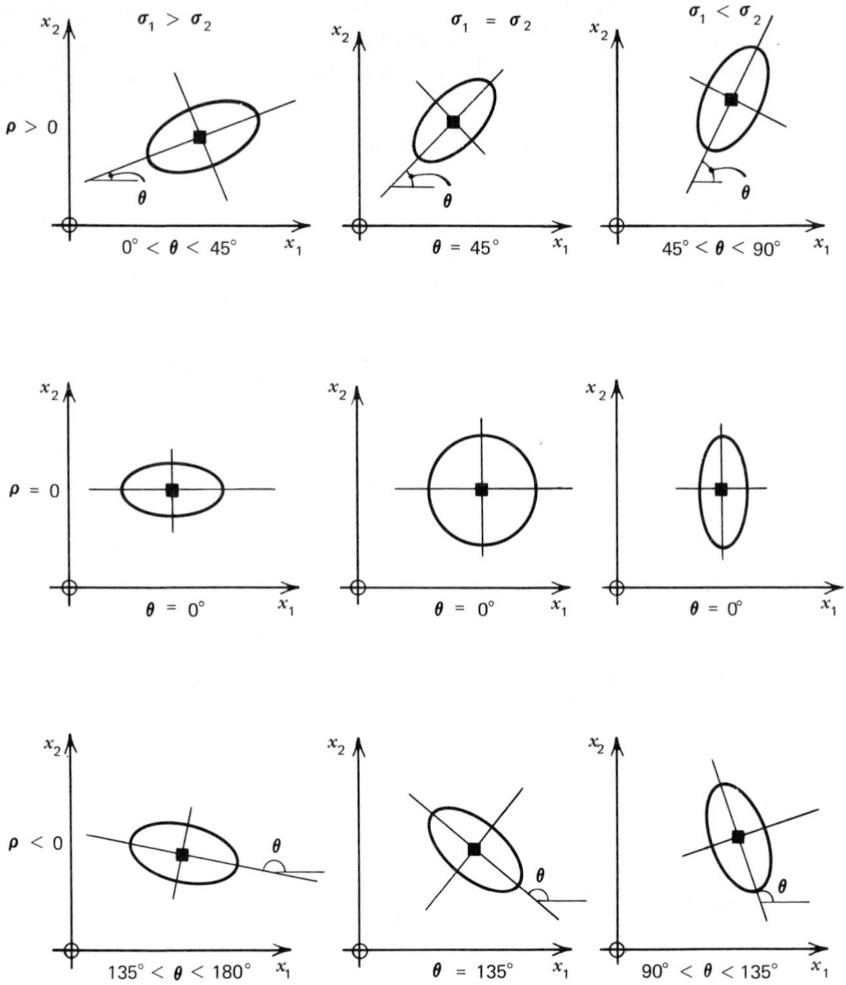

FIGURE 1*a*

Contours of equal density of bivariate normal distributions. (The expected value point, or centroid (ξ_1,ξ_2) *is denoted by* ■.)

with zero correlation are numerous. (See Chapter 42, Section 7; also Pitman [85].)

We have already noted (Section 2 of Chapter 35) that all cumulants, of order higher than 2, of *any* multivariate normal distribution are zero. This is true, in particular, of binormal and trinormal distributions, and it is therefore easy to evaluate the moments of these distributions. For the standardized

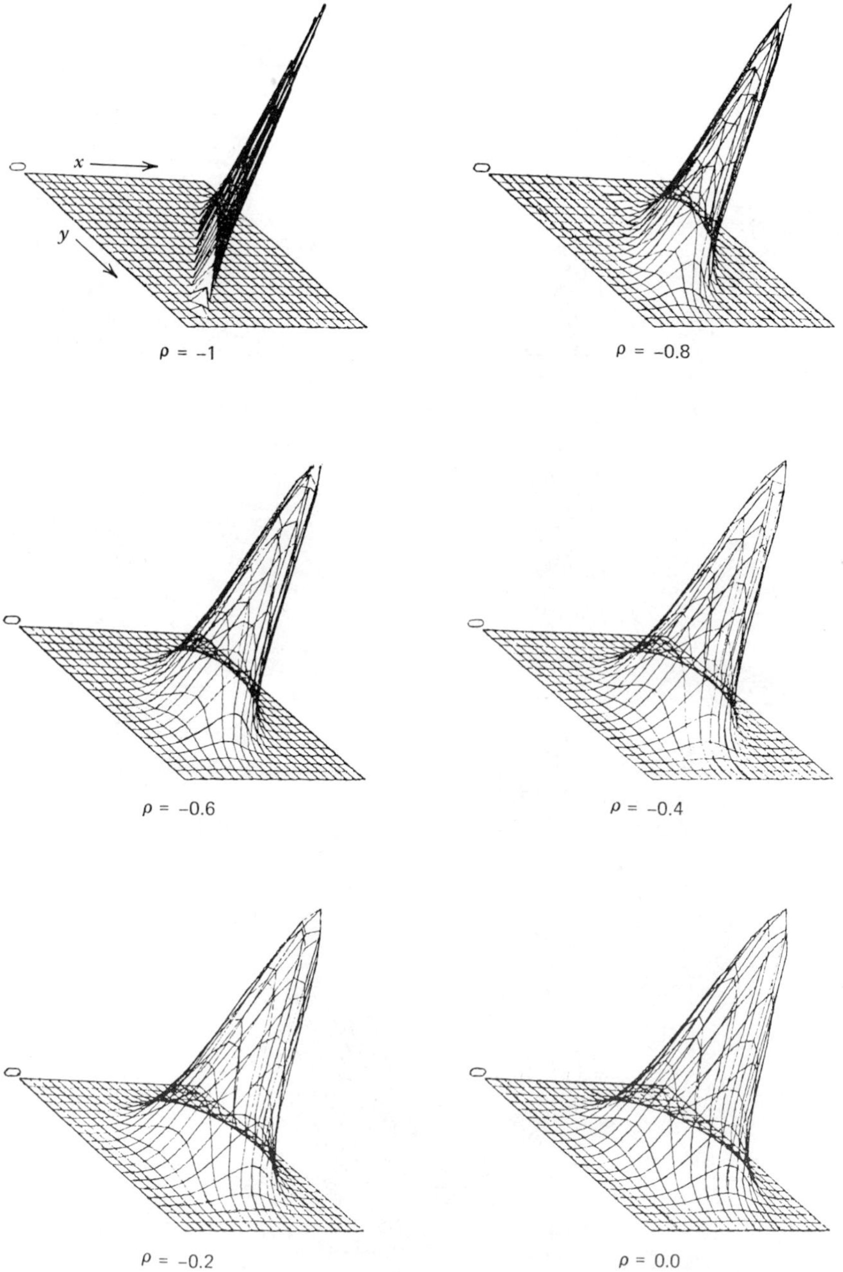

FIGURE 1*b*

Perspective drawings of standardized bivariate normal density function.

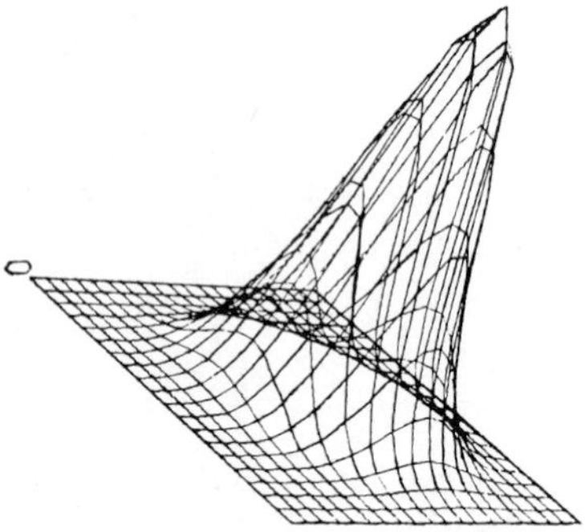

$\rho = +0.2$

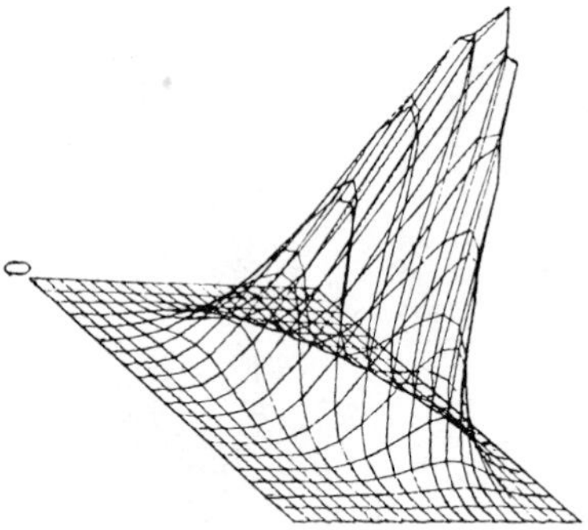

$\rho = +0.4$

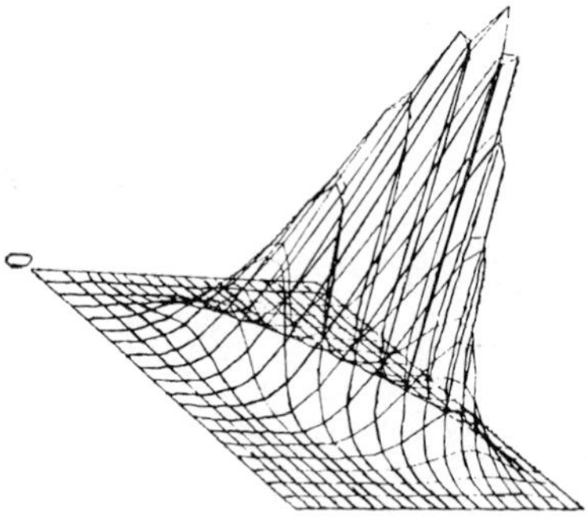

$\rho = +0.6$

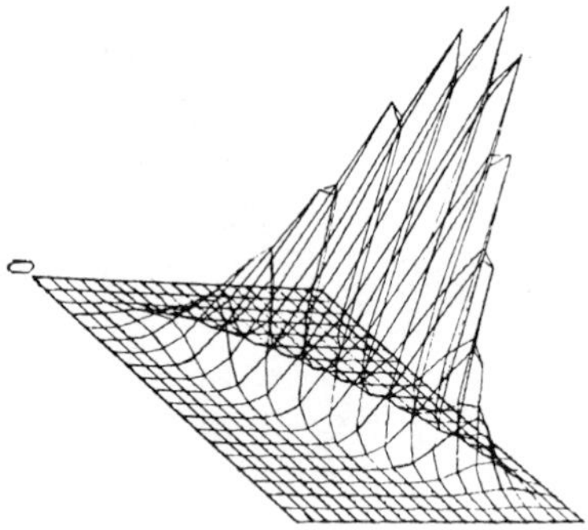

$\rho = +0.8$

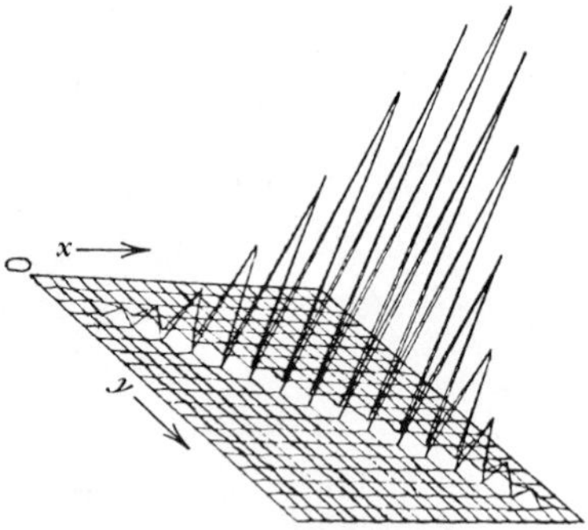

$\rho = +1$

FIGURE 1*b* (*Contd.*)

distribution (2) we have

$$\begin{aligned}
&\mu_{21} = \mu_{12} = 0;\\
(8)\quad &\mu_{31} = \mu_{13} = 3\rho; \qquad \mu_{22} = 1 + 2\rho^2;\\
&\mu_{41} = \mu_{14} = 0; \qquad \mu_{32} = \mu_{23} = 0;\\
&\mu_{51} = \mu_{15} = 15\rho; \qquad \mu_{42} = \mu_{24} = 3(1 + 4\rho^2); \qquad \mu_{33} = 3\rho(3 + 2\rho^2).
\end{aligned}$$

Generally

$$(9.1)\qquad \mu_{2r,2s} = \frac{(2r)!(2s)!}{2^{r+s}} \sum_{j=0}^{t} \frac{(2\rho)^{2j}}{(r-j)!(s-j)!(2j)!}$$

$$(9.2)\qquad \mu_{2r+1,2s+1} = \frac{(2r+1)!(2s+1)!}{2^{r+s}} \times \sum_{j=0}^{t} \frac{(2\rho)^{2j}}{(r-j)!(s-j)!(2j+1)!}$$

$$t = \min(r,s)$$

$$(9.3)\qquad \mu_{r,s} = 0 \quad \text{if} \quad r + s = \text{odd}.$$

The following recurrence relation exists (Kendall and Stuart [55]):

$$(10)\qquad \mu_{rs} = (r + s - 1)\rho\mu_{r-1,s-1} + (r-1)(s-1)(1-\rho^2)\mu_{r-2,s-2}.$$

Pearson and Young [84] give tables of μ_{rs} to nine decimal places for $r,s \leq 10$; $\rho = 0.00(0.05)1.00$.

The joint moment generating function of X_1 and X_2 is

$$(11)\qquad E[e^{t_1X_1+t_2X_2}] = \exp[-\tfrac{1}{2}(t_1^2 + 2\rho t_1t_2 + t_2^2)].$$

Absolute moments are not so easily evaluated. It can be shown (Kamat [51] and Nabeya [69]) that

$$(12)\qquad \nu_{rs} = E[|X_1^rX_2^s|] = \pi^{-1}\, 2^{\frac{1}{2}(r+s)}\Gamma\left(\frac{r+1}{2}\right)\Gamma\left(\frac{s+1}{2}\right)F(-\tfrac{1}{2}r,-\tfrac{1}{2}s;\tfrac{1}{2};\rho^2).$$

($F(\cdot)$ is the hypergeometric function

$$F(\alpha,\beta;\gamma;z) = 1 + \frac{\alpha\beta}{1!\gamma}z + \frac{\alpha(\alpha+1)\beta(\beta+1)}{2!\gamma(\gamma+1)}z^2 + \cdots.)$$

For small r and s, the hypergeometric and gamma functions can be evaluated in terms of more elementary functions, giving:

$$(13)\quad \begin{cases} \nu_{11} = 2\pi^{-1}(\sqrt{1-\rho^2} + \rho\sin^{-1}\rho); \\ \nu_{12} = \nu_{21} = \sqrt{(2/\pi)}\,(1+\rho^2); \\ \nu_{13} = \nu_{31} = 2\pi^{-1}\{\sqrt{1-\rho^2}\,(2+\rho^2) + 3\rho\sin^{-1}\rho\}; \qquad \nu_{22} = 1 + 2\rho^2; \\ \nu_{14} = \nu_{41} = \sqrt{(2/\pi)}\,(3 + 6\rho^2 - \rho^4); \quad \nu_{23} = \nu_{32} = 2\sqrt{(2/\pi)}(1+3\rho^2); \\ \nu_{15} = \nu_{51} = 2\pi^{-1}\{\sqrt{1-\rho^2}\,(8 + 9\rho^2 - 2\rho^4) + 15\rho\sin^{-1}\rho\}; \\ \qquad\qquad \nu_{24} = \nu_{42} = 3(1+4\rho^2); \\ \nu_{33} = 2\pi^{-1}\{\sqrt{1-\rho^2}\,(4 + 11\rho^2) + 3\rho(3+2\rho^2)\sin^{-1}\rho\}. \end{cases}$$

Nabeya gives values of ν_{rs} for $r + s \leq 12$. The incomplete moments

$$\left([r,s] = \int_0^\infty\int_0^\infty x_1^r x_2^s p(x_1,x_2)\,dx_1\,dx_2\right)$$

have been evaluated by Kamat [52]. We have

$$(14)\quad [r,s] = 2^{\frac{1}{2}(r+s)-2}\pi^{-1}\left\{\Gamma\left(\frac{r+1}{2}\right)\Gamma\left(\frac{s+1}{2}\right)F(-\tfrac{1}{2}r,-\tfrac{1}{2}s;\tfrac{1}{2};\rho^2)\right.$$
$$\left. + 2\rho\Gamma\left(\frac{r}{2}+1\right)\Gamma\left(\frac{s}{2}+1\right)F(-\tfrac{1}{2}(r-1),-\tfrac{1}{2}(s-1);\tfrac{3}{2};\rho\,).\right.$$

The value of $[0,0] = \Pr[(X_1 > 0) \cap (X_2 > 0)]$ was shown to be

$$\frac{1}{4} + \frac{1}{2\pi}\sin^{-1}\rho$$

by Sheppard [98] (see also [99]). Other special values are

$$[1,0] = \tfrac{1}{4}\sqrt{(2/\pi)}\,(1+\rho);$$

$$(15)\quad \begin{cases} [2,0] = \tfrac{1}{4} + \tfrac{1}{2}\pi^{-1}[\sin^{-1}\rho + \rho\sqrt{1-\rho^2}]; \\ [1,1] = \tfrac{1}{2}\pi^{-1}[\rho(\tfrac{1}{2}\pi + \sin^{-1}\rho) + \sqrt{1-\rho^2}]; \\ [3,0] = \tfrac{1}{4}\sqrt{(2/\pi)}\cdot(1+\rho)^2(2-\rho); \qquad [2,1] = \tfrac{1}{4}\sqrt{(2/\pi)}\,(1+\rho)^2; \\ [4,0] = \tfrac{1}{2}\pi^{-1}[3(\tfrac{1}{2}\pi + \sin^{-1}\rho) + (5\rho - 2\rho^3)\sqrt{1-\rho^2}]; \\ [3,1] = \tfrac{1}{2}\pi^{-1}[3\rho(\tfrac{1}{2}\pi + \sin^{-1}\rho) + (2+\rho^2)\sqrt{1-\rho^2}]; \\ [2,2] = \tfrac{1}{2}\pi^{-1}[(1+2\rho^2)(\tfrac{1}{2}\pi + \sin^{-1}\rho) + 3\rho\sqrt{1-\rho^2}]. \end{cases}$$

Kamat gives tables of $[r,s]$ to six decimal places for $r + s \leq 4$; $\rho = -0.9(0.1)1.0$.

For the standardized trivariate normal distribution, Nabeya [70] gives the following values for absolute product moments:

$$(\nu_{rst} = E[|X_1^r X_2^s X_3^t|]),$$

(16) $$\nu_{111} = (2/\pi)^{3/2}(\Delta^{1/2} + \Sigma^*(\rho_{23} + \rho_{12}\rho_{13})\sin^{-1}\rho_{23.1})$$

(where Σ^* stands for a cyclic sum),

$$\nu_{211} = 2\pi^{-1}[(\rho_{23} + 2\rho_{12}\rho_{13})\sin^{-1}\rho_{23} + (1 + \rho_{12}^2 + \rho_{13}^2)\sqrt{1 - \rho_{23}^2}].$$

Kamat [53] gave the following values for incomplete moments:

$$[r,s,t] = (2\pi)^{-3/2}\Delta^{-1/2}\int_0^\infty\int_0^\infty\int_0^\infty x_1^r x_2^s x_3^t \exp\left[-\tfrac{1}{2}\sum_{i=1}^3\sum_{j=1}^3 A_{ij}x_i x_j\right] dx_1\,dx_2\,dx_3;$$

(17)
$$\begin{cases}
[1,0,0] = (2\pi)^{-3/2}\{\tfrac{1}{2}\pi + \sin^{-1}\rho_{23.1} + \rho_{12}(\tfrac{1}{2}\pi + \sin^{-1}\rho_{13.2}) \\
\qquad\qquad + \rho_{13}(\tfrac{1}{2}\pi + \sin^{-1}\rho_{12.3})\}; \\
[2,0,0] = (4\pi)^{-1}\left\{\tfrac{1}{2}\pi + \sum_{i<j}^{3}\sin^{-1}\rho_{ij} + \Delta\rho_{23}\sqrt{1 - \rho_{23}^2} + (2\rho_{12}\rho_{13} - \rho_{23})\right. \\
\qquad\qquad \left.\times\sqrt{1 - \rho_{23}^2} + \rho_{12}\sqrt{1 - \rho_{12}^2} + \rho_{13}\sqrt{1 - \rho_{13}^2}\right\}; \\
[1,1,0] = (4\pi)^{-1}\left\{\rho_{12}\left(\tfrac{1}{2}\pi + \sum_{i<j}^{3}\sin^{-1}\rho_{ij}\right)\right. \\
\qquad\qquad \left. + \sqrt{1 - \rho_{12}^2} + \rho_{13}\sqrt{1 - \rho_{13}^2} + \rho_{23}\sqrt{1 - \rho_{23}^2}\right\}; \\
[1,1,1] = (2\pi)^{-3/2}[\Delta^{1/2} + \Sigma^*(\rho_{23} + \rho_{12}\rho_{13})(\tfrac{1}{2}\pi + \sin^{-1}\rho_{23.1})].
\end{cases}$$

(Kamat [53] gives formulas for $[r,s,t]$ for all r,s,t with $r + s + t \leq 3$.)

Further formulas will be found in Haldane [42].

4. Bivariate Normal Integral—Tables and Approximations

The joint cumulative distribution of random variables Y_1, Y_2 having the joint standardized bivariate normal density (2) is

(18) $$\Phi(h,k;\rho) = (2\pi\sqrt{1 - \rho^2})^{-1} \times \int_{-\infty}^{h}\int_{-\infty}^{k}\exp\left[-\frac{1}{2(1 - \rho^2)}(x_1^2 - 2\rho x_1 x_2 + x_2^2)\right] dx_2\,dx_1.$$

A more commonly tabulated quantity is

$$(19)\quad L(h,k;\rho) = (2\pi\sqrt{1-\rho^2})^{-1} \times \int_h^\infty \int_k^\infty \exp\left[-\frac{1}{2(1-\rho^2)}(x_1^2 - 2\rho x_1 x_2 + x_2^2)\right] dx_2\, dx_1.$$

The functions $\Phi(\cdot)$ and $L(\cdot)$ are related by the equation

$$(20)\qquad \Phi(h,k;\rho) = 1 - L(h,-\infty;\rho) - L(-\infty,k;\rho) + L(h,k;\rho).$$

Note also that

$$(21)\qquad \Phi(h,\infty;\rho) = \Phi(h); \qquad \Phi(\infty,k;\rho) = \Phi(k),$$

where

$$\Phi(y) \equiv (\sqrt{2\pi})^{-1} \int_{-\infty}^{y} e^{-(1/2)t^2}\, dt.$$

Further relations between the L and Φ functions are:

$$(22.1)\qquad L(h,k;\rho) = L(k,h;\rho);$$

$$(22.2)\qquad L(-h,k;\rho) + L(h,k;-\rho) = 1 - \Phi(k);$$

$$(22.3)\qquad L(-h,-k;\rho) - L(h,k;\rho) = 1 - \Phi(h) - \Phi(k);$$

$$(22.4)\qquad L(h,k;0) = (1 - \Phi(h))(1 - \Phi(k));$$

$$(22.5)\qquad L(h,k;1) = \Phi(\max(h,k));$$

$$(22.6)\qquad L(h,k;-1) = \begin{cases} 0 & (h + k \geq 0); \\ 1 - \Phi(h) - \Phi(k) & (h + k \leq 0). \end{cases}$$

Using (4) we have

$$(23)\qquad L(h,k;\rho) = \frac{1}{2\pi}\int_h^\infty Z(x_1) \int_{(k-\rho x_1)/\sqrt{(1-\rho^2)}}^{\infty} Z(x_2)\, dx_2\, dx_1.$$

For $h > 0, k > 0, \rho > 0$, this is the integral of the circular normal probability density $(2\pi)^{-1}\exp[-\frac{1}{2}(x_1^2 + x_2^2)]$ over the shaded region shown in Fig. 2. The slope of the line AB is $-\rho/\sqrt{1-\rho^2}$; the angle between AB and the x_2-axis is

$$\cot^{-1}\left(\frac{-\rho}{\sqrt{(1-\rho^2)}}\right) = \frac{\pi}{2} + \sin^{-1}\rho.$$

If $h = k = 0$ then A coincides with O and, from the symmetry of the circular

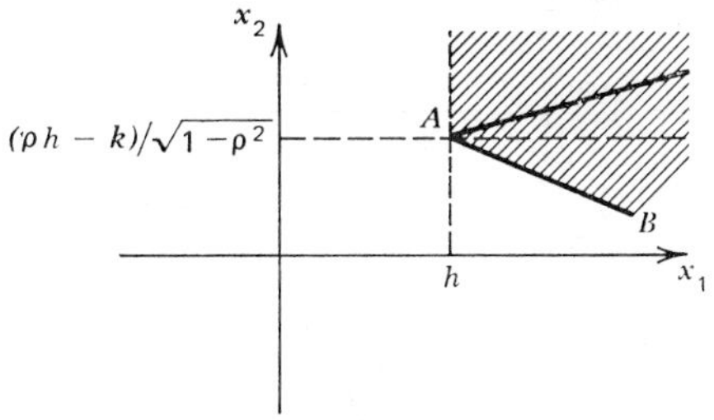

FIGURE 2

normal distribution,

$$L(0,0;\rho) = \frac{1}{2\pi}\left(\frac{\pi}{2} + \sin^{-1}\rho\right) = \frac{1}{4} + \frac{1}{2\pi}\sin^{-1}\rho, \tag{24}$$

a result obtained by Sheppard [98]. Sheppard [99] gave values to seven decimal places of $L(U_{0.75},U_{0.75};\rho)$ for $\pi^{-1}\cos^{-1}\rho = 0.00(0.01)0.80$. ($U_{0.75} = 0.67749$.)

An extensive set of tables of $L(h,k;\rho)$ were published by Karl Pearson in [83] in 1931. These collected together tables published at various times from 1910 onward by Everitt [32], Elderton et al. [31], and Lee [60, 61]. They give $L(h,k;\rho)$ for $h,k = 0.0(0.1)2.6$ to six decimal places for $\rho = 0(0.05)1$ and to seven decimal places for $-\rho = 0(0.05)1$. In 1959, these tables were extended, in [72], to give $L(h,k;\rho)$ for $h,k = 0(0.1)4.0$ to six decimal places for $\rho = 0(0.05)0.95(0.01)1.00$ and to seven decimal places for $-\rho = 0(0.05)0.95(0.01)1.00$. Tables for the special cases $\rho = 1/\sqrt{2}$ and $\rho = \frac{1}{3}$ have been given by Dunnett [28] and Dunnett and Lamm [30] respectively.

Pólya [87] has obtained the inequalities

$$1 - \Phi(h) - \frac{1-\rho^2}{\rho h - k} Z(k)\left\{1 - \Phi\left(\frac{h-\rho k}{\sqrt{1-\rho^2}}\right)\right\} < L(h,k;\rho) < 1 - \Phi(h) \tag{25}$$

(for $0 < \rho < 1$; $\rho h - k > 0$). Since $\rho h - k > 0$, it follows that $h - \rho k > 0$ if $h > 0$ and so (25) is of form $1 - \Phi(h) - \Delta < L(h,k;\rho) < 1 - \Phi(h)$ with $0 < \Delta < (2\sqrt{2\pi})^{-1}(1-\rho^2)(\rho h - k)^{-1}$. Inequalities (25) were used for checking purposes on the calculations for [72].

Tables of $L(h,k;\rho)$ are of necessity rather bulky, since there are three arguments. Zelen and Severo [122] pointed out that since

$$L(h,k;\rho) = L(h,0;\rho(h,k)) + L(k,0;\rho(k,h)) - \tfrac{1}{2}(1-\delta_{hk}), \tag{26}$$

where

$$\rho(h,k) = \frac{(\rho h - k)f(h)}{\sqrt{h^2 - 2\rho hk + k^2}};$$

$$f(h) = \begin{cases} 1 & \text{if } h > 0, \\ -1 & \text{if } h < 0, \end{cases}$$

$$\delta_{hk} = \begin{cases} 0 & \text{if } Sg(h)Sg(k) = 1, \\ 1 & \text{otherwise,} \end{cases}$$

with

$$Sg(h) = 1 \quad \text{if } h \geq 0,$$
$$Sg(h) = -1 \quad \text{if } h < 0,$$

it is possible to evaluate $L(h,k;\rho)$ from a table with $k = 0$, hence having only two arguments. In **[122]** and also in **[123]** there are charts from which values of $L(h,0;\rho)$ can be read off, thus giving a rapid way of obtaining approximate values of $L(h,k;\rho)$.

We have already noted [see (23)] that $L(h,k;\rho)$ can be expressed as an integral of the standardized circular normal distribution over a certain region. Sheppard **[99]** in 1900 suggested that tabulation of the two-argument function

(27) $$V(h,k) = \int_0^h Z(x_1) \int_0^{kx_1/h} Z(x_2)\, dx_2\, dx_1$$

would be useful, since

(28) $$L(h,k;\rho) = V\left(h, \frac{k - \rho h}{\sqrt{1-\rho^2}}\right) + V\left(k, \frac{h - \rho k}{\sqrt{1-\rho^2}}\right) + 1 - \tfrac{1}{2}(\Phi(h) + \Phi(k)) - \frac{\cos^{-1}\rho}{2\pi}.$$

The quantity $V(h,k)$ is (for $h > 0$, $k > 0$) the integral of the standardized circular normal distribution over a triangle with vertices at the origin (O) and the points H,P with coordinates $(h,0),(h,k)$ respectively (see Figure 3).

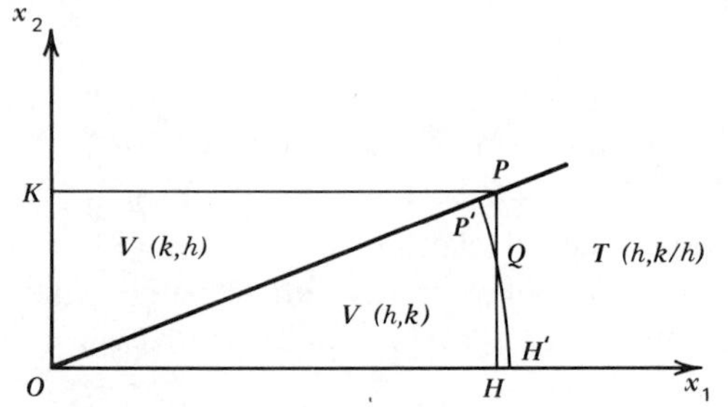

FIGURE 3

Similarly $V(k,h)$ is the integral over the triangle OKP. Since the integral over the rectangle $OHPK$ is simply $\Pr[(0 < X_1 < h) \cap (0 < X_2 < k)]$ we have

$$V(h,k) + V(k,h) = (\Phi(h) - \tfrac{1}{2})(\Phi(k) - \tfrac{1}{2}). \tag{29}$$

For other values of h and k, $V(h,k)$ is defined by

$$V(h,-k) = -V(h,k) = V(-h,k); \tag{30}$$

hence $V(-h,-k) = V(h,k)$.

It was not until 1943 that Nicholson [73] put Sheppard's suggestion into effect. He gave tables of $V(h,k)$ to six decimal places for $h,k = 0.0(0.1)3.1,\infty$. (Note that $V(h,\infty) = \Phi(h) - \tfrac{1}{2}; V(\infty,k) = 0$.) He used the formula

$$V(h,k) = (2\pi)^{-1}\Big[\lambda(1 - e^{-m}) - \tfrac{1}{3}\lambda^3(1 - e^{-m} - me^{-m}) + \tfrac{1}{5}\lambda^5\Big(1 - e^{-m} - me^{-m} - \frac{m^2}{2!}e^{-m}\Big) - \cdots\Big] \tag{31}$$

with $\lambda = k/h < 1$; $m = \tfrac{1}{2}h^2$, in his calculation. For $\lambda > 1$, (29) can be used.

Interpolation is facilitated if the variables are taken to be h and $\lambda(= k/h)$ instead of h and k. Tables were published in 1959 in [72], giving $V(h,\lambda h)$ to seven decimal places for $\lambda = 0.1(0.1)1.0$; $h = 0.00(0.01)4.00(0.2)4.60(0.1)5.6, \infty$; and also $V(\lambda h,h)$ to seven decimal places for $\lambda = 0.1(0.1)1.0$; $h = 0.00(0.01)4.00(0.02)5.60,\infty$. Note that $V(\infty,\lambda\cdot\infty) = \lim_{h\to\infty} V(h,\lambda h) = \tfrac{1}{2}\pi \tan^{-1}\lambda$. For $h \geq 5.6$ and $0.1 \leq \lambda \leq 1$, $V(h,\lambda h)$ agrees with $V(\infty,\lambda\cdot\infty)$ to seven decimal places. The same agreement is not found between $V(\lambda h,h)$ and $V(\lambda\cdot\infty,\infty) = \lim_{h\to\infty} V(\lambda h,h) = 2\pi\cot^{-1}\lambda$, but the approximation

$$V(\lambda h,h) \doteqdot \frac{1}{2\pi}\cot^{-1}\lambda - \tfrac{1}{2}\{1 - \Phi(\lambda h)\} \tag{32}$$

holds with an error less than $\tfrac{1}{2}\times 10^{-7}$ for $h \geq 5.6$. For small values of h (up to about 0.8) and $\lambda \leq 1$ the simple approximation

$$V(h,\lambda h) \doteqdot \frac{\lambda h^2}{4\pi}[1 - \tfrac{1}{4}h^2(1 + \tfrac{1}{3}\lambda^2)] \tag{33}$$

gives useful results.

Cadwell [15] has obtained another useful approximation to $V(h,k)$ for $k/h = \lambda$ small by replacing the boundary PH by the circular arc $P'H'$ (see Fig. 3) with center at O and radius so chosen that $P'QP$ and $H'QH$ have equal areas (Q is the point of intersection of $P'H'$ and PH). The resulting approximation is

$$V(h,\lambda h) \doteqdot (2\pi)^{-1}\tan^{-1}\lambda\Big[1 - \exp\Big(-\frac{\tfrac{1}{2}h^2\lambda}{\tan^{-1}\lambda}\Big)\Big]. \tag{34}$$

This is always less than $V(h,\lambda h)$; the maximum error (for $\lambda < 1$) is 0.0015; generally accuracy is much better. If the correction $0.04h^4(\lambda - \frac{3}{4})$ is added to the exponent the error is always less than 0.0005. For $\lambda > 1$, the relation (29) can be used.

Owen [75] has tabled values of the integral of (2) over the remainder of the sector POH (i.e., the part to the right of the line PH in Fig. 3). For $h > 0$, $k > 0$, we see that the integral over the whole sector is (by the symmetry of the circular normal distribution) $(1/2\pi)\tan^{-1}(k/h)$, hence the quantity tabulated by Owen is $(1/2\pi)\tan^{-1}(k/h) - V(h,k)$. He regards this as a function $T(h,k/h)$ of h and k/h. The function thus is

$$(35) \qquad T(h,\lambda) = \frac{1}{2\pi}\int_h^\infty Z(x_1)\int_{\lambda x_1}^\infty Z(x_2)\,dx_2\,dx_1.$$

This can be expressed as the single integral

$$(35)' \qquad T(h,\lambda) = \frac{1}{2\pi}\int_0^\lambda (1+x^2)^{-1}\exp[-\tfrac{1}{2}h^2(1+x^2)]\,dx.$$

Owen showed that

$$(35)'' \qquad T(h,\lambda) = \frac{1}{2\pi}\left[\tan^{-1}\lambda - \sum_{j=0}^{\infty} c_j\lambda^{2j+1}\right]$$

with

$$c_j = \frac{(-1)^j}{2j+1}\left[1 - e^{-(1/2)h^2}\sum_{i=0}^{j}\frac{(\frac{1}{2}h^2)^i}{i!}\right].$$

For small values of h and λ convergence is rapid, and the formula is useful for computing $T(h,\lambda)$. Owen has given values of $T(h,\lambda)$ to six decimal places for $h = 0(0.01)2.00(0.02)3.00$; $\lambda = 0.25(0.25)1.00$* in [75], and for $h = 0(0.05)4.75$; $\lambda = 0(0.25)1.00,\infty$ in [76]. (See also Owen and Wiesen [77].) Smirnov and Bol'shev [102] have given tables of $T(h,\lambda)$ to seven decimal places for

(i) $h = 0(0.01)3.00$; $\lambda = 0(0.01)1.00$
(ii) $h = 3.00(0.05)4.00$; $\lambda = 0.05(0.05)1.00$
(iii) $h = 4.0(0.1)5.2$; $\lambda = 0.1(0.1)1.0$

and also of $T(h,1)$ for $h = 0(0.001)3.000(0.005)4.000(0.01)5.00(0.1)6.0$, and of $T(0,\lambda) = \frac{1}{2}\pi^{-1}\tan^{-1}\lambda$ for $\lambda = 0.000(0.001)1.000$.

Amos [7] and Sowden and Ashford [107] have given instructive comparisons of time taken to compute the bivariate normal integral $L(h,k;\rho)$ on electronic computers, using various formulas. Amos recommends formula (28) [with (35)′] as being generally preferable. Sowden and Ashford agree with this conclusion for $0.2 \le \rho \le 0.95$, and also $-0.7 \le \rho \le -0.4$ if

*Also for $h = 0(0.25)3.00$; $\lambda = 0(0.01)1.00$, and for $h = 3.00(0.05)4.00(0.1)4.7$; $\lambda = 0.1(0.1)1.0$.

$|h - k| < 1$ or either of h,k exceeds 1. For other situations they recommend direct quadrature using the formula

$$L(h,k;\rho) = \int_{-\infty}^{\infty} Z(t)\Phi\left(\frac{c_1t - h}{\sqrt{(1 - c_1^2)}}\right)\Phi\left(\frac{c_2t - k}{\sqrt{(1 - c_2^2)}}\right) dt, \tag{36}$$

which can be obtained by noting that X_1 and X_2 with distribution (1) can be represented as

$$X_i = c_iT + \sqrt{1 - c_i^2}\, U_i$$

with T, U_1 and U_2 mutually independent unit normal variables, $0 \leq c_i^2 \leq 1$ $(i = 1,2)$, $c_1c_2 = \rho$. Subject to these limitations c_1 and c_2 can be chosen arbitrarily. A good choice, suggested in [107], is to take $c_1 = c_2 = \sqrt{\rho}$ if $\rho > 0$ and $c_1 = -c_2 = \sqrt{-\rho}$ if $\rho < 0$. The first few terms of the series (73.1) below may be used as an approximation to $L(h_1,k_1;\rho)$, when ρ is small.

Expansions for $\Phi(h_1,h_2;\rho)$, of similar form to (73.1) have been used by Bofinger and Bofinger [12] to obtain series expansions (in powers of ρ) for the correlation between $\max(X_{11},\ldots,X_{1n})$ and $\max(X_{21},\ldots,X_{2n})$, where (X_{1j},X_{2j}) $(j = 1,\ldots,n)$ are independent vectors with a common bivariate normal distribution. They give a table of coefficients of ρ, ρ^2, ρ^3, ρ^4, and ρ^5 in this series, to five decimal places for $n = 2(1)50$.

The integral of (2) over any convex polygon can be expressed as the sum or difference of integrals over a number of triangles, each having one vertex at the origin. Any one of these can be expressed as the integral of the joint distribution of two *independent* unit normal variables ovei a triangular region of the same kind (see Fig. 4*a*). By suitable further transformation the region of integration can be arranged to be as in Fig. 4*b*. Such integrals can be evaluated from tables of $V(h,k)$. In the case shown the required integral is

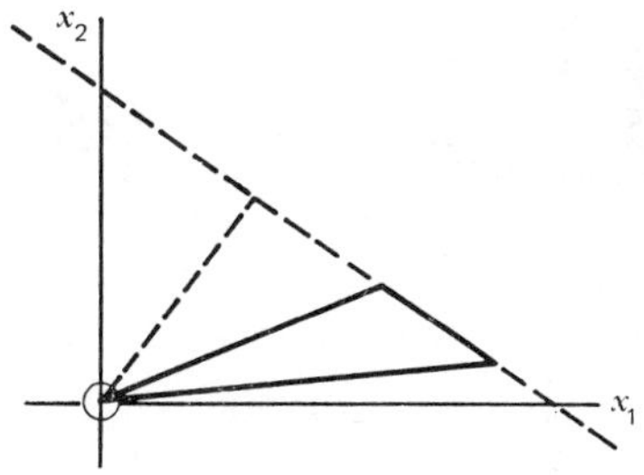

FIGURE 4*a*

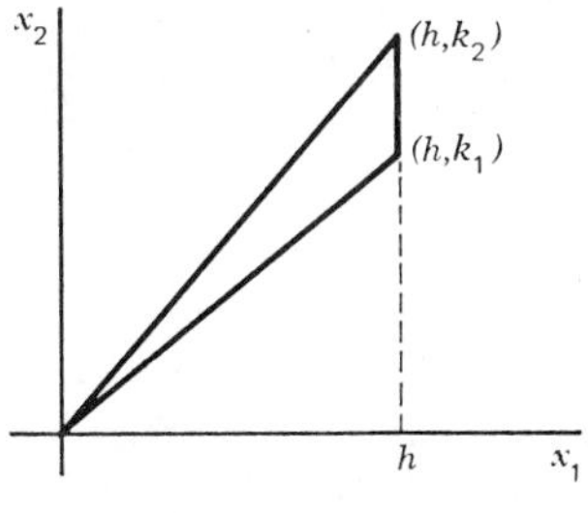

FIGURE 4*b*

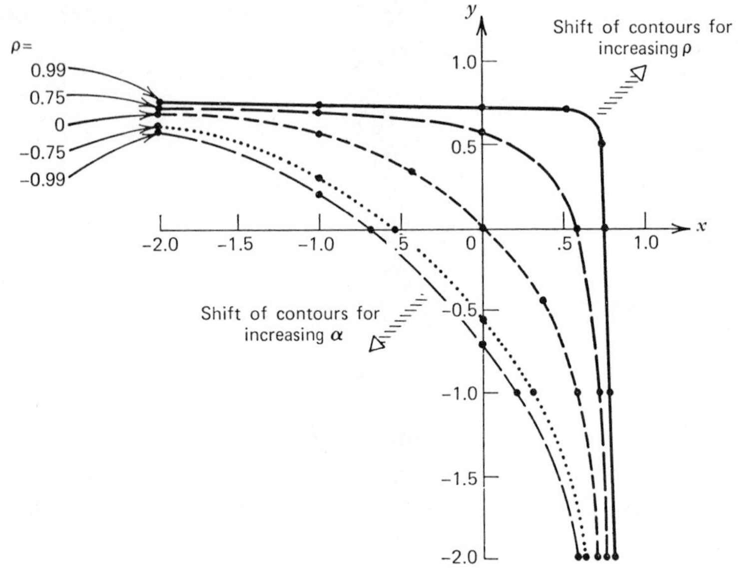

FIGURE 5

Equidistributional contours ($L(x,y;\rho) = \alpha$) *for the standard bivariate normal distribution with* $\alpha = 0.25$.

$V(h,k_2) - V(h,k_1)$. In general, some care is needed to keep the signs of the various terms correct.

Integrals over circles and ellipses are in fact probability integrals of positive definite quadratic forms in normal variables and, as such, have been discussed in Chapters 28 and 29.

Tihansky [112] has described construction of "equidistributional contours"—loci of points (x,y) such that $L(x,y;\rho) = \alpha$. Figure 5 (from [112]) shows such contours for $\alpha = 0.25$, $\rho = 0, \pm 0.75, \pm 0.99$.

Burington and May [14] have shown how two-way normal probability paper (with each scale as described in Section 5, Chapter 13) can be used as a basis for graphical quadrature of circular normal distributions over arbitrary regions.

Tables of random normal deviates (see Chapter 13, Section 1) can be used to construct tables of correlated random normal deviates. One way of doing this, described by Wold [119] is to use *independent* unit normal variates U_1, U_2 and calculate $Y_1 = U_1$, $Y_2 = \rho U_1 + \sqrt{1 - \rho^2}\, U_2$. Then Y_1, Y_2 are unit normal variates with correlation ρ. Fieller et al. [34] and Iyer and Simha [49] have published tables constructed by this method.

5. Trivariate Normal Integral

As in the case of the bivariate normal integral, we confine ourselves to the consideration of standardized distributions, with expected value vector (0,0,0) and variance-covariance matrix

$$\begin{pmatrix} 1 & \rho_{12} & \rho_{13} \\ \rho_{12} & 1 & \rho_{23} \\ \rho_{13} & \rho_{23} & 1 \end{pmatrix}$$

Analogously to $\Phi(h,k;\rho)$ and $L(h,k;\rho)$ we have

(37.1) $\Phi(h_1,h_2,h_3;\rho_{23},\rho_{13},\rho_{12}) = \Pr[(X_1 < h_1) \cap (X_2 < h_2) \cap (X_3 < h_3)]$

and

(37.2) $L(h_1,h_2,h_3;\rho_{23},\rho_{13},\rho_{12}) = \Pr[(X_1 > h_1) \cap (X_2 > h_2) \cap (X_3 > h_3)]$.

Equation (24) generalizes to

(38) $$\Phi(0,0,0;\rho_{23},\rho_{13},\rho_{12}) = L(0,0,0;\rho_{23},\rho_{13},\rho_{12}).$$

Ruben [93] has given a table of $\frac{1}{2} - \frac{3}{4}\pi \cos^{-1}\rho$ (corresponding to $\rho_{23} = \rho_{13} = \rho_{12} = \rho$) to eight decimal places for $\rho^{-1} = 2(1)11$ (his $\bar{V}_{n,n}(x) = \bar{u}_n(x)$ for $n = 3$). Tables of $\Phi(h,h,h;\frac{1}{2},\frac{1}{2},\frac{1}{2})$ have been published by (i) Teichroew [111] to five decimal places for $h\sqrt{2} = 0(0.01)6.09$ and (ii) Somerville [105] to four decimal places for $h = 0(0.1)2.0(0.5)3.0$. There are also unpublished tables by Owen (reported in [108]) of $\Phi(h,h,h;\rho,\rho,\rho)$ for (a) $\rho = (1 + \sqrt{3})^{-1}$, $\frac{1}{4}$; $h = 0(0.1)3.0(0.5)8.0$; and (b) $\rho = 0(0.1)0.9$; $h = 0(0.2)1.0$.

Steck [108] has expressed the trivariate integral Φ in terms of a function $S(h,a,b)$ defined (for $h,a,b > 0$) as

(39) $$\frac{1}{4\pi}\tan^{-1}\frac{b}{\sqrt{(1 + a^2 + a^2b^2)}} + \Pr[(0 < U_1 < U_2 + bU_3) \cap (0 < U_2 < h) \cap (U_3 > aU_2)],$$

where U_1, U_2, and U_3 are independent unit normal variables. For negative values of h,a, or $b,S(h,a,b)$ is defined through the formulas

(40.1) $S(h,-a,b) = S(h,a,b)$;

(40.2) $S(h,a,-b) = -S(h,a,b)$;

(40.3) $$S(-h,a,b) = \frac{1}{2\pi}\tan^{-1}\frac{b}{\sqrt{(1 + a^2 + a^2b^2)}} - S(h,a,b).$$

Also

$$(41.1)\qquad S(0,a,b) = \tfrac{1}{2}S(\infty,a,b) = \frac{1}{4\pi}\tan^{-1}\frac{b}{\sqrt{(1+a^2+a^2b^2)}};$$

$$(41.2)\qquad S(h,0,b) = \frac{1}{2\pi}\Phi(h)\tan^{-1} b;$$

$$(41.3)\qquad S(h,a,0) = 0 = S(h,\infty,b);$$

$$(41.4)\qquad S(h,a,\infty) = \begin{cases} \tfrac{1}{2}[\tfrac{1}{2}\Phi(h) + T(h,|a|)] - \dfrac{1}{2\pi}\tan^{-1}|a| & (h \geq 0), \\ \tfrac{1}{2}[\tfrac{1}{2}\Phi(h) - T(h,|a|)] \quad (h < 0). \end{cases}$$

The formulas for $\Phi(h_1,h_2,h_3;\rho_{23},\rho_{13},\rho_{12})$ are:

(i) $h_1,h_2,h_3 \geq 0$ (or $h_1,h_2,h_3 \leq 0$)

$$(42.1)\qquad \Phi(h_1,h_2,h_3;\rho_{23},\rho_{13},\rho_{12}) = \sum_{j=1}^{3}(1-\tfrac{1}{2}\delta_{a_jc_j})\Phi(h_j) + \tfrac{1}{4}\sum_{i<j}^{3}\sum^{3}\delta_{h_ih_j}$$
$$+\frac{1}{2}\left[\sum_{i<j}^{3}\sum^{3} L(h_i,h_j;\rho_{ij}) - 3\right]$$
$$-\sum_{j=1}^{3}[S(h_j,a_j,b_j) + S(h_j,c_j,d_j)],$$

where

$$a_1 = \frac{h_2 - h_1\rho_{12}}{h_1\sqrt{1-\rho_{12}^2}};\qquad a_2 = \frac{h_3 - h_2\rho_{23}}{h_2\sqrt{1-\rho_{23}^2}};\qquad a_3 = \frac{h_1 - h_3\rho_{13}}{h_3\sqrt{1-\rho_{13}^2}};$$

$$c_1 = \frac{h_3 - h_1\rho_{13}}{h_1\sqrt{1-\rho_{13}^2}};\qquad c_2 = \frac{h_1 - h_2\rho_{12}}{h_2\sqrt{1-\rho_{12}^2}};\qquad c_3 = \frac{h_2 - h_3\rho_{23}}{h_3\sqrt{1-\rho_{23}^2}};$$

$$b_1 = \sqrt{(1-\rho_{12}^2)(1-\rho_{13}^2)}\,(c_1a_1^{-1} - \rho_{23.1})\,\Delta^{-1/2};$$

$$d_1 = \sqrt{(1-\rho_{12}^2)(1-\rho_{13}^2)}\,(a_1c_1^{-1} - \rho_{23.1})\,\Delta^{-1/2};$$

and so on; and δ_{hk} is as defined in (26).

(ii) $h_1,h_2 \geq 0$; $h_3 < 0$ (or $h_1,h_2 \leq 0$, $h_3 > 0$)

$$(42.2)\qquad \Phi(h_1,h_2,h_3;\rho_{23},\rho_{13},\rho_{12}) = L(h_1,h_2;\rho_{12}) + \Phi(h_1) + \Phi(h_2) - 1$$
$$- \Phi(h_1,h_2,-h_3;-\rho_{23},\rho_{13},\rho_{12}).$$

Two other similar formulas can be obtained by permuting the variates.

Steck [108] gives tables of $S(h,a,b)$ to seven decimal places for $a = 0.0(0.1)2.0(0.2)5.0(0.5)8.0$; $b = 0.1(0.1)1.0$, and h increasing from zero by intervals of 0.1 to an upper limit such that beyond this limit

$$(43)\quad S(h,a,b) \doteqdot \frac{1}{2\pi}\,\Phi(h\sqrt{(1+a^2+\tfrac{1}{4}a^2b_2)})\tan^{-1}\left(\frac{b}{\sqrt{(1+a^2+a^2b^2)}}\right)$$

with an error less than 5×10^{-5}. For values of b greater than 1, the formulas

$$(44.1)\quad S(h,a,b) = [\Phi(h) - \tfrac{1}{2}]T(ah,b) - [\Phi(hab) - \tfrac{1}{2}]T(ah,a^{-1}) + S(hab,b^{-1},a^{-1}) \qquad (\text{for } a > 1)$$

or

$$(44.2)\quad S(h,a,b) = \tfrac{1}{4}\Phi(h) + [\Phi(hab) - \tfrac{1}{2}]T(h,a) - S(hab,(ab)^{-1},a) - S(h,ab,b^{-1}) \qquad (\text{for } a < 1)$$

may be used.

6. Estimation

6.1 *Bivariate Normal Distribution*

The likelihood function of n independent pairs of random variables $(X_{11},X_{21}),(X_{12},X_{22})\cdots(X_{1n}\,X_{2n})$ each having the same joint bivariate normal distribution with parameters $\xi_1,\xi_2;\sigma_1,\sigma_2;$ and ρ, is

$$(45)\quad \left(\frac{1}{2\pi\sqrt{1-\rho^2}}\right)^n \exp\left[-\frac{1}{2(1-\rho^2)}\left\{\frac{\sum_{j=1}^{n}(X_{1j}-\xi_1)^2}{\sigma_1^2} - 2\rho\frac{\sum_{j=1}^{n}(X_{1j}-\xi_1)(X_{2j}-\xi_2)}{\sigma_1\sigma_2} + \frac{\sum_{j=1}^{n}(X_{2j}-\xi_2)^2}{\sigma_2^2}\right\}\right]$$

$$= \left(\frac{1}{2\pi\sqrt{1-\rho^2}}\right)^n \exp\left[-\frac{n}{2(1-\rho^2)} \times \left\{\frac{(\bar{X}_1-\xi_1)^2}{\sigma_1^2} - 2\rho\frac{(\bar{X}_1-\xi_1)(X_2-\xi_2)}{\sigma_1\sigma_2} + \frac{(\bar{X}_2-\xi_2)^2}{\sigma_2^2}\right\}\right] \times \exp\left[-\frac{n}{2(1-\rho^2)}\left\{\frac{S_1^2}{\sigma_1^2} - 2R\frac{S_1S_2}{\sigma_1\sigma_2} + \frac{S_2^2}{\sigma_2^2}\right\}\right],$$

where

$$\bar{X}_t = \sum_{j=1}^{n} X_{tj}; \qquad S_t^2 = n^{-1}\sum_{j=1}^{n}(X_{tj} - \bar{X}_t)^2 \ (t = 1,2)$$

$$RS_1S_2 = n^{-1}\sum_{j=1}^{n}(X_{1j} - \bar{X}_1)(X_{2j} - \bar{X}_2).$$

The maximum likelihood estimators of the parameters are

$$(46) \qquad \hat{\xi}_1 = \bar{X}_1; \qquad \hat{\xi}_2 = \bar{X}_2; \qquad \hat{\sigma}_1 = S_1; \qquad \hat{\sigma}_2 = S_2; \qquad \hat{\rho} = R.$$

The two sets of variables $(\hat{\xi}_1,\hat{\xi}_2)$ and $(\hat{\sigma}_1,\hat{\sigma}_2,\hat{\rho})$ are mutually independent. The set $\hat{\xi}_1,\hat{\xi}_2,\hat{\sigma}_1,\hat{\sigma}_2,\hat{\rho}$ is jointly sufficient for $\xi_1,\xi_2,\sigma_1,\sigma_2,\rho$. We have

$$(47.1) \qquad n \operatorname{var}(\hat{\xi}_t) = \sigma_t^2 \qquad (t = 1,2)$$

and

$$(47.2) \qquad n \operatorname{var}(\hat{\sigma}_t^2) = 2\sigma_t^4(1 - n^{-1}) \qquad (t = 1,2).$$

For large n we have

$$(47.3) \qquad n \operatorname{var}(\hat{\rho}) \doteqdot (1 - \rho^2)^2;$$

$$(47.4) \qquad \operatorname{corr}(\hat{\sigma}_1^2,\hat{\sigma}_2^2) \doteqdot \rho^2;$$

$$(47.5) \qquad \operatorname{corr}(\hat{\sigma}_t^2,\hat{\rho}) \doteqdot \rho/\sqrt{2} \qquad (t = 1,2).$$

Formulas (47.1) and (47.3) have already been encountered in Chapters 13 (page 59) and 32 (equation (12)).

Note that the estimators of ξ_1, ξ_2, σ_1, and σ_2 are those that would be obtained by using only the observed values of the appropriate variables. We have already described the distributions of $\hat{\xi}_t$ (in Chapter 13), $\hat{\sigma}_t$ (in Chapter 17), and $\hat{\rho}$ (in Chapter 32).

If the values of some of the parameters are known, different estimators of the remaining parameters are obtained. We now set out, briefly, some special cases.

(i) *One mean, say* ξ_1, *known.* The maximum likelihood estimators are now

$$(48) \qquad \begin{cases} \hat{\xi}_2 = \bar{X}_2 - (\hat{\rho}\hat{\sigma}_2/\hat{\sigma}_1)(\bar{X}_1 - \xi_1), \\ \hat{\sigma}_1 = \left[n^{-1}\sum_{j=1}^{n}(X_{1j} - \xi_1)^2\right]^{1/2}; \qquad \hat{\sigma}_2 = \left[n^{-1}\sum_{j=1}^{n}(X_{2j} - \bar{X}_2)^2\right]^{1/2}, \\ \hat{\rho} = \left[n^{-1}\sum_{j=1}^{n}(X_{1j} - \xi_1)(X_{2j} - \bar{X}_2)\right](\hat{\sigma}_1\hat{\sigma}_2)^{-1}. \end{cases}$$

The estimators $\hat{\sigma}_1,\hat{\sigma}_2,\hat{\rho}$ may be obtained from (46) by replacing $\bar{X}_1$ by ξ_1, but $\hat{\xi}_2$ cannot be obtained in this way.

(ii) ξ_1 *and* ξ_2 *known.* Maximum likelihood estimators of σ_1, σ_2, and ρ are obtained by replacing $\bar{X}_1$ by ξ_1 and $\bar{X}_2$ by ξ_2 in the corresponding formulas in (46). The three estimators so obtained are jointly sufficient for σ_1, σ_2, and ρ. For large n, the variances and correlations of $\hat{\sigma}_1^2$, $\hat{\sigma}_2^2$, and $\hat{\rho}$ are the same as in the case when no parameters are known [(see equations (47)].

(iii) *ξ_1 and σ_1 known.* The maximum likelihood estimators are now

(49.1) $$\hat{\xi}_2 = \bar{X}_2 - (RS_2/S_1)(\bar{X}_1 - \xi_1)$$

(49.2) $$\hat{\sigma}_2^2 = S_2^2(1 - R^2 + R^2\sigma_1^2/S_1^2)$$

(49.3) $$\hat{\rho} = (R\sigma_1/S_1)(1 - R^2 + R^2\sigma_1^2/S_1^2)^{-1/2}.$$

(iv) *ξ_1, σ_1, and ρ known.* The maximum likelihood estimator of σ_2 is (with $\rho > 0$)

(50.1) $$\hat{\sigma}_2 = \frac{[(\rho S_{12}'/\sigma_1)^2 + 4n(1 - \rho^2)S_{22}]^{1/2} - \rho S_{12}'/\sigma_1}{2n(1 - \rho^2)}$$

where

$$S_{12}' = \sum_{j=1}^{n}(X_{1j} - \xi_1)(X_{2j} - \bar{X}_2);$$

$$S_{22} = \sum_{j=1}^{n}(X_{2j} - \bar{X})^2.$$

The maximum likelihood estimator of ξ_2 is

(50.2) $$\hat{\xi}_2 = \bar{X}_2 - (\rho\hat{\sigma}_2/\sigma_1)(\bar{X}_1 - \xi_1).$$

(Note that if $\rho = 0$ the estimators $\hat{\xi}_2$, $\hat{\sigma}_2$ become $\bar{X}_2$, $\sqrt{S_{22}/n}$ respectively, based on observations of X_2 only.)

(v) *$\xi_1,\sigma_1,\xi_2,\sigma_2$ known.* The maximum likelihood estimator of ρ is a solution of the cubic equation

(51) $$\sigma_1^2\sigma_2^2 n\hat{\rho}(1 - \hat{\rho}^2) + \sigma_1\sigma_2(1 + \hat{\rho}^2)\sum_{j=1}^{n}(X_{1j} - \xi_1)(X_{2j} - \xi_2) - \hat{\rho}\left[\sigma_2^2\sum_{j=1}^{n}(X_{1j} - \xi_1)^2 + \sigma_1^2\sum_{j=1}^{n}(X_{2j} - \xi_2)^2\right] = 0.$$

Kendall and Stuart [55] show that the probability that this equation has only one real root between -1 and $+1$ tends to 1 as n tends to infinity. Since the left-hand side of (51) is positive for $\hat{\rho} = -1$ and negative for $\hat{\rho} = 1$ there must always be a real root between -1 and $+1$.

In any particular case, however, there may be three roots between -1 and $+1$. That root should be chosen for which the likelihood function (45) is greatest.

It is convenient to introduce the symbols

$$r = \frac{n^{-1}\sum_{j=1}^{n}(X_{1j} - \xi_1)(X_{2j} - \xi_2)}{\sigma_1\sigma_2},$$

$$r_t = n^{-1}\sum_{j=1}^{n}(X_{tj} - \xi_t)^2/\sigma_t^2 \qquad (t = 1,2).$$

Madansky [64] has shown that provided

$$r^2 < 3(r_1 + r_2 - 1)$$

(note that this will usually be true, since we expect r_1,r_2 to be about 1 and r^2 to be less than 1, on the average), we have

(52.1) $$\hat{\rho} = \tfrac{2}{3}\{3(r_1 + r_2 - 1) - r^2\}^{1/2} \sinh[\tfrac{1}{3} \sinh^{-1} C] + \tfrac{1}{3}r,$$

where

$$C = \frac{36r + 2r^3 - 9(r_1 + r_2)r}{2[3(r_1 + r_2 - 1) - r^2]^{1/2}}.$$

In the (unusual) case $r^2 > 3(r_1 + r_2 - 1)$ we have

(52.2) If $|C| \geq 1$:

$$\hat{\rho} = \tfrac{2}{3}\{r^2 - 3(r_1 + r_2 - 1)\}^{1/2} \cosh[\tfrac{1}{3} \cosh^{-1} C] + \tfrac{1}{3}r.$$

(52.3) If $|C| \leq 1$,

$$\hat{\rho} = \tfrac{2}{3}\{r^2 - 3(r_1 + r_2 - 1)\}^{1/2} \cos\left(\frac{4\pi}{3} + \tfrac{1}{3}\cos^{-1} C\right) + \tfrac{1}{3}r$$

(see Nadler [71]).

For many practical purposes the following method of calculation can be used. Put

$$\hat{\rho}_1 = \left[\frac{1}{n}\sum_{j=1}^{n}(X_{1j} - \xi_1)(X_{2j} - \xi_2)\right](\sigma_1\sigma_2)^{-1}.$$

Then

$$\hat{\rho} = \hat{\rho}_1 + \hat{\varepsilon},$$

where

$$\hat{\varepsilon} = \frac{\hat{\rho}_1}{1 + \hat{\rho}_1^2}\left[2 - \frac{\tilde{\sigma}_1^2}{\sigma_1^2} - \frac{\tilde{\sigma}_2^2}{\sigma_2^2}\right]$$

with

$$\tilde{\sigma}_t^2 = n^{-1}\sum_{j=1}^{n}(X_{tj} - \xi_t)^2 \qquad (t = 1,2).$$

(vi) $\sigma_1 = \sigma_2$ (*but common value unknown*). DeLury [25] has shown that the intraclass correlation coefficient $2RS_1S_2(S_1^2 + S_2^2)^{-1}$ is slightly more efficient than R as an estimator of ρ in this case. The common value of σ_1 and σ_2 is estimated by $[\tfrac{1}{2}(S_1^2 + S_2^2)]^{1/2}$; ξ_1,ξ_2 are estimated by $\bar{X}_1,\bar{X}_2$ respectively.

Ahsanullah [3] has studied the properties of an estimation procedure in which it is first tested whether $\xi_1 = \xi_2$. The estimate of ξ_1 employed is $\bar{X}_1$ or that appropriate to item (vii) according to the result of the test.

(vii) $\xi_1 = \xi_2, \sigma_1 = \sigma_2$ (*common values unknown*). The ρ can be estimated by

$$(53) \qquad \left\{2\sum_{j=1}^{n}(X_{1j} - \hat{\xi})(X_{2j} - \hat{\xi})\right\}\left\{\sum_{j=1}^{n}(X_{1j} - \hat{\xi})^2 + \sum_{j=1}^{n}(X_{2j} - \hat{\xi})^2\right\}^{-1}.$$

The common value of ξ_1 and ξ_2 is estimated by $\frac{1}{2}(\bar{X}_1 + \bar{X}_2) = \hat{\xi}$; that of σ_1 and σ_2 by

$$\left[\tfrac{1}{2}n^{-1}\left\{\sum_{t=1}^{2}\sum_{j=1}^{n}(X_{tj} - \hat{\xi})^2\right\}\right]^{1/2}.$$

(viii) $\sigma_1^2\sigma_2^2(1 - \rho^2)^2 = \theta^2$ (*known*). Press [88] has considered this case. He shows that the maximum likelihood estimator of ρ is

$$(54) \qquad \hat{\rho} = -\tfrac{1}{2}n\theta S_{12}^{-1} + \operatorname{sgn}(S_{12})\sqrt{1 + \tfrac{1}{4}(n\theta S_{12}^{-1})^2},$$

where

$$S_{12} = \sum_{j=1}^{n}(X_{1j} - \bar{X}_1)(X_{2j} - \bar{X}_2)$$

$$\operatorname{sgn}(S_{12}) = \begin{cases} 1 & \text{if } S_{12} > 0, \\ 0 & \text{if } S_{12} = 0, \\ -1 & \text{if } S_{12} < 0. \end{cases}$$

(ix) $\xi_1 = \xi_2$ (*but common value unknown*). Rastogi and Rohatgi [90] show that the weighted mean of $\bar{X}_1$ and $\bar{X}_2$,

$$(55) \qquad \alpha\bar{X}_1 + (1 - \alpha)\bar{X}_2$$

with

$$\alpha = (S_2^2 - S_{12})(S_1^2 + S_2^2 - 2S_{12})^{-1}$$

is an unbiased estimator of the common value of ξ_1 and ξ_2, with variance

$$(56) \qquad \frac{n-2}{n(n-3)}\,\frac{\sigma_1^2\sigma_2^2(1-\rho^2)}{\sigma_1^2 + 2\rho\sigma_1\sigma_2 + \sigma_2^2}.$$

(x) *Missing Observations.* We have already noted (in Section 7.1 of Chapter 35) that multivariate data may be lacking values of certain variates for some individuals in a random sample. Many different patterns of data are possible, and methods of estimation need to be related to the actual data pattern. General methods have been developed by Afifi and Elashoff [2] (who also give a useful list of references), Smith [103], Hocking and Smith [46, 104], Trawinski and Bargmann [113], and Kleinbaum [57]. Here we consider in detail only the bivariate case, where the variety of possible patterns is limited. We will also describe the general method proposed by Hocking and Smith.

Suppose there are n_{12} observations on both X_1 and X_2; n_1 on X_1 alone and n_2 on X_2 alone. A rational method of solution is to start by estimating ρ from the n_{12} observations on both X_1 and X_2, because these are the only data providing information on ρ. Then $\xi_1,\sigma_1^2,\xi_2,\sigma_2^2$ are estimated by the sample means and variances of the whole available data ($(n_1 + n_{12})$ observations for $\xi_1,\sigma_1;(n_2 + n_{12})$ for ξ_2,σ_2). Although unsophisticated, this procedure is good enough for many practical problems. However, it does suffer from the defect that one does not use the information available on ξ_1, σ_1, ξ_2, and σ_2 in the $(n_1 + n_2)$ observations where one variate is missing, in the estimation of ρ. If one attempts to do this using the estimator

$$\rho^* = \frac{\sum (X_{1j} - \xi_1)(X_{2j} - \xi_2)}{[\sum (X_{1j} - \xi_1)^2]^{1/2}[\sum (X_{2j} - \xi_2)^2]^{1/2}} \tag{57}$$

(where summations are over the n_{12} observations on both X_1 and X_2 and ξ_j is the arithmetic mean of all $(n_j + n_{12})$ observations on X_j), it is possible that a value of $|\rho^*|$ in excess of 1 may be obtained. The possible increase of accuracy in the estimator of ρ must be judged against the possibility of obtaining such a value of ρ^*. We are inclined not to use ρ^* unless n_1,n_2 are large compared with n_{12}. Then one can use the estimators of ξ_1 and σ_1, ξ_2 and σ_2 from the sets of n_1,n_2 observations respectively as if they were the actual values, and estimate ρ from the n_{12} observations using the method of Madansky **[64]**. (See item (v) above.)

The maximum likelihood equations for estimators of ξ_1, σ_1, ξ_2, σ_2, and ρ are

$$\frac{n_j(\bar{X}_j - \hat{\xi}_j) + (1 + \hat{\rho}^2)^{-1}n_{12}(\bar{X}'_j - \hat{\xi}_j)}{\hat{\sigma}_j^2} = \frac{n_{12}\hat{\rho}}{1 - \hat{\rho}^2} \cdot \frac{\bar{X}'_{j'} - \hat{\xi}_{j'}}{\hat{\sigma}_1\hat{\sigma}_2}, \tag{58.1}$$

$$n_j + n_{12} = \frac{\hat{S}_{jj} + (1 - \hat{\rho}^2)^{-1}\hat{S}'_{jj}}{\hat{\sigma}_j^2} - \frac{\hat{\rho}}{(1 - \hat{\rho}^2)} \cdot \frac{\hat{P}'}{\hat{\sigma}_1\hat{\sigma}_2} \tag{58.2}$$

$$(j = 1,2; j' = 3 - j),$$

$$n_{12}\hat{\rho} = \frac{\hat{\rho}}{1 - \hat{\rho}^2}\left(\frac{\hat{S}'_{11}}{\hat{\sigma}_1^2} + \frac{\hat{S}'_{22}}{\hat{\sigma}_2^2}\right) - \frac{1 + \hat{\rho}^2}{1 - \hat{\rho}^2}\frac{\hat{P}'}{\hat{\sigma}_1\hat{\sigma}_2}, \tag{58.3}$$

where $\bar{X}_j,\hat{S}_{jj}$ = mean X_j, and sum of squares $(X_j - \hat{\xi}_j)^2$, for n_j observations on X_j alone; $\bar{X}'_j,\hat{S}'_{jj}$ = mean X_j, and sum of squares $(X_j - \hat{\xi}_j)^2$, for n_{12} observations on both X_1 and X_2; and $\hat{P}'$ = sum of products $(X_1 - \hat{\xi}_1)(X_2 - \hat{\xi}_2)$ for n_{12} observations on both X_1 and X_2.

In deriving equations (58) we have used the likelihood function

$$(2\pi\sigma_1\sigma_2\sqrt{(1 - \rho^2)})^{-n_{12}}(\sqrt{2\pi}\,\sigma_1)^{-n_1}(\sqrt{2\pi}\,\sigma_2)^{-n_2}$$
$$\times \exp\left[-\frac{1}{2(1 - \rho^2)}\left(\frac{S'_{11}}{\sigma_1^2} - \frac{2\rho P'}{\sigma_1\sigma_2} + \frac{S'_{22}}{\sigma_2^2}\right) - \frac{S_{11}}{2\sigma_1^2} - \frac{S_{22}}{2\sigma_2^2}\right]$$

(in an obvious notation).

Solution of these five simultaneous equations is not simple. For the special case $n_2 = 0$, Anderson [8] has obtained explicit formulas for the maximum likelihood estimators:

$$
\begin{aligned}
\hat{\xi}_1 &= (n_1\bar{X}_1 + n_{12}\bar{X}_1')/(n_1 + n_{12}),\\
\hat{\sigma}_1^2 &= (S_{11} + S_{11}')/(n_1 + n_{12}),\\
\hat{\xi}_2 &= X_2' + (P'/S_{11}')(\bar{X}_1 - \bar{X}_1'),\\
\hat{\sigma}_2^2 &= n_{12}^{-1}S_{22}' + (P'/S_{11}')^2[\hat{\sigma}_1^2 - S_{11}'/n_{12}],\\
\hat{\rho} &= (P'/S_{11}')(\hat{\sigma}_1/\hat{\sigma}_2).
\end{aligned}
\tag{59}
$$

These estimators are obtained expeditiously by writing the likelihood function as a product of the likelihood of the X_1's with the conditional likelihood function of the X_2's given the X_1's. A similar method can be used when the pattern of data allows, but this is not always the case.

If n_1, n_2, and n_{12} are large with $p_1 = n_1/n$, $p_2 = n_2/n$, $p_{12} = n_{12}/n$, where $n = n_1 + n_2 + n_{12}$, then $\sqrt{n}$ times the maximum likelihood estimators of $\sigma_1^2, \rho\sigma_1\sigma_2, \sigma_2^2$ should have limiting variance-covariance matrix

$$
cp_{12}\begin{pmatrix} 2\sigma_1^4 & 2\rho\sigma_1^3\sigma_2 & 2\rho^2\sigma_1^2\sigma_2^2\\ 2\rho\sigma_1^3\sigma_2 & (1+\rho^2)\sigma_1^2\sigma_2^2 & 2\rho\sigma_1\sigma_2^3\\ 2\rho^2\sigma_1^2\sigma_2^2 & 2\rho\sigma_1\sigma_2^3 & 2\sigma_2^4 \end{pmatrix} + c(1-\rho^2)
$$
$$
\times \begin{pmatrix} 2p_2(1+\rho^2)\sigma_1^4 & 2p_2\rho\sigma_1^3\sigma_2 & 0\\ 2p_2\rho\sigma_1^3\sigma_2 & [1 - p_{12} + p_1p_2(1-\rho^2)/p_{12}]\sigma_1^3\sigma_2^2 & 2p_1\sigma_1\sigma_2^3\\ 0 & 2p_1\sigma_1\sigma_2^3 & 2p_1(1+\rho^2)\sigma_2^4 \end{pmatrix}
$$

where $c = [p_{12} + p_1p_2(1-\rho^4)]^{-1}$. (Nadler [71], Wilks [117].)

Hocking and Smith [46, 104] have proposed a system of estimators that can be applied in many general situations to estimation of parameters of m-variate multinormal populations from data with missing observations. The steps in this method can be described as follows:

(i) Group the data according to the sets of variables for which values are available.

(ii) For each set of data estimate all the parameters (means, variances, and covariances of the available variables). It is suggested that "best unbiased estimation" be used.

(iii) Starting with the group for which full data are available (if any; otherwise the fullest data), modify the estimators by adding linear functions of difference between estimators of the same parameter from this group and all other groups where such estimators are available. (Means are treated separately from variances and covariances.)

TABLE 1

Set of Observations	Estimators of ξ_1	σ_1^2	ξ_2	σ_2^2	$\rho\sigma_1\sigma_2$
n_{12} (on X_1 and X_2)	$\bar{X}_1'$	$\dfrac{S_{11}'}{n_{12}-1}$	$\bar{X}_2'$	$\dfrac{S_{22}'}{n_{12}-1}$	$\dfrac{}{n_{12}-1}$
n_1 (on X_1)	$\bar{X}_1$	$\dfrac{S_{11}}{n_1-1}$	—	—	—
n_2 (on X_2)	—	—	$\bar{X}_2$	$\dfrac{S_{22}}{n_2-1}$	—

Application of this method to the bivariate case has been described by Smith [103]. The first estimators are shown in Table 1. The estimators in the first line are then "improved" by adding linear multipliers of $(\bar{X}_1' - \bar{X}_1)$ (for ξ_1 and ξ_2) and of $((n_{12}-1)^{-1}S_{11}' - (n_1-1)S_{11})$ (for σ_1^2, σ_2^2, and $\rho\sigma_1\sigma_2$). These are in turn "improved" by introducing linear terms involving $\bar{X}_2$ and $(n_2-1)^{-1}S_{22}$. The coefficients of the linear adjusting functions should be chosen to minimize the variance of the resultant estimators. They would be functions of the unknown parameters, and we have to use estimators of these parameters to calculate the coefficients.*

It is also possible to estimate ρ from broadly grouped data according to the scheme shown in Fig. 6. n_1,n_2,n_3,n_4 denote the number of observations falling into the cells where they are placed. Given these data (only) the maximum likelihood estimator, $\hat{\rho}$, of ρ is the solution of the equation:

$$\frac{n_1+n_3}{n_1+n_2+n_3+n_4} = \frac{L(h,0;\hat{\rho})}{1-\Phi(h)}.$$

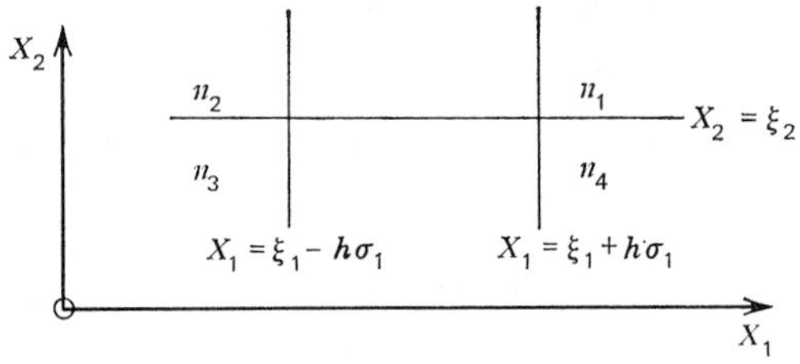

FIGURE 6

* J. N. Srivastava and M. K. Zaatar (Report ARL 72–0032 (1972), Aerospace Research Laboratories, U.S. Air Force) have found empirical evidence in favor of the simple estimators $\tilde{\sigma}_j^2 = S_{jj}n_j^{-1}$, $\tilde{\rho} = P'(S_{11}S_{22}')^{-\frac{1}{2}}$.

For large n,

$$n \operatorname{var}(\hat{\rho}) \doteqdot \frac{L(h,0;\rho)[1 - \Phi(h) - L(h,0;\rho)]}{2(1 - \Phi(h))[\partial L(h,0;\rho)/\partial \rho]^2}$$

$(\partial L(h,0;\rho)/\partial \rho = [2\pi\sqrt{1 - \rho^2}]^{-1} \exp[-\frac{1}{2}h^2(1 - \rho^2)^{-1}])$ (Mosteller [68]). Table 2 gives values of h which minimize this function for a few values of ρ, and corresponding approximate values of $n \operatorname{var}(\hat{\rho})$.

TABLE 2

Optimal Values of h

ρ	Optimal values h	$\Phi(h)$	n var $(\hat{\rho})$ (approximate)
0.0	0.61	0.73	1.94
0.2	0.61	0.73	1.82
0.4	0.60	0.73	1.47
0.6	0.58	0.72	0.96
0.8	0.48	0.68	0.39

Note. The maximum value is not very critical. For example, if we take $h = 0.60$ when $\rho = 0.8$, then n var $(\hat{\rho}) = 0.40$.

6.2. *Trivariate Normal Distribution*

We shall not discuss a wide range of special situations, as we did for bivariate normal distributions. There are in general nine parameters to be estimated, three means, three standard deviations, and three correlation coefficients. When no parameters are known, estimators are the same as in case (i) of Section 6.1. The maximum likelihood estimator of the multiple correlation of X_1 with X_2 and X_3,

$$R^2 = (\rho_{12}^2 + \rho_{13}^2 - 2\rho_{12}\rho_{13}\rho_{23})/(1 - \rho_{23}^2)$$

is, of course,

$$\hat{R}^2 = (\hat{\rho}_{12}^2 + \hat{\rho}_{13}^2 - 2\hat{\rho}_{12}\hat{\rho}_{13}\hat{\rho}_{23})/(1 - \hat{\rho}_{23}^2). \tag{60.1}$$

Olkin and Pratt [74] suggest the adjusted estimator

$$\hat{R}^2 - 2(n - 1)^{-1}(1 - \hat{R}^2)^{-2}, \tag{60.2}$$

which has bias of order n^{-2} (while $\hat{R}^2$ has bias of order n^{-1}).

In cases when values of some of the expected values and variances are known, formulas for maximum likelihood estimators of correlation coefficients are the same as for the bivariate distribution of the two variates concerned.

If $E[X_1] = \xi_1$ and $E[X_2] = \xi_2$ (but no other parameters are known) then the maximum likelihood estimator of ξ_3 is

$$\hat{\xi}_3 = \bar{X}_3 - (\hat{\rho}_{13.2}\hat{\sigma}_3/\hat{\sigma}_1')(\bar{X}_1 - \xi_1) - (\hat{\rho}_{23.1}\hat{\sigma}_3/\hat{\sigma}_2')(\bar{X}_2 - \xi_2), \tag{61}$$

where $\hat{\rho}_{13.2} = (\hat{\rho}_{13}' - \hat{\rho}_{12}'\hat{\rho}_{23}')(1 - \hat{\rho}_{12}'^2)^{-1/2}(1 - \hat{\rho}_{23}'^2)^{-1/2}$, with a similar formula for $\rho_{23.1}$, and primes denote that X_1,X_2 are replaced by ξ_1,ξ_2 respectively in $\hat{\sigma}_1,\hat{\sigma}_2,\hat{\rho}_{12},\hat{\rho}_{13},\hat{\rho}_{23}$. Cases when additional parameters are known give modifications of (61) analogous to these for the bivariate case.

7. Truncated Bivariate and Trivariate Normal Distributions

In the following discussion we are using the standardized distributions (2) or (3). Extension to the general case (by using new variables $\xi_t + \sigma_t X_t$) is straightforward.

The most common form of truncation of a bivariate normal distribution is single truncation (from above or below) with respect to one of the variables. If we select so that only values of X_1 that exceed h are used, the resulting joint distribution has density function

$$p_{X_1,X_2}(x_1,x_2) = [1 - \Phi(h)]^{-1} \exp\left[-\frac{1}{2(1-\rho^2)}(x_1^2 - 2\rho x_1 x_2 + x_2^2)\right] \quad (x_1 > h). \tag{62}$$

Using the fact that the conditional distribution of X_2, given X_1, is normal with expected value ρX_1 and standard deviation $(1 - \rho^2)^{\frac{1}{2}}$, we have

$$E[X_2] = E[E[X_2 \mid X_1]] = \rho E[X_1], \tag{63.1}$$

$$E[X_1X_2] = E[X_1E[X_2 \mid X_1]] = \rho E[X_1^2], \tag{63.2}$$

$$E[X_2^2] = E[E[X_2^2 \mid X_1]] = E[\rho^2 X_1^2 + 1 - \rho^2] = \rho^2 E[X_1^2] + 1 - \rho^2. \tag{63.3}$$

Hence $\text{var}(X_2) = \rho^2 \text{var}(X_1) + 1 - \rho^2$,

$$\text{cov}(X_1,X_2) = \rho \,\text{var}(X_1),$$

and

$$\text{corr}(X_1,X_2) = \rho\sqrt{\text{var}(X_1)/\text{var}(X_2)} = \rho\left[\rho^2 + \frac{1-\rho^2}{\text{var}(X_1)}\right]^{-1/2}. \tag{64}$$

(Note that (64) applies to *any* form of truncation of X_1, provided X_2 is not truncated.) From (80) of Chapter 13 we have

$$\text{var}(X_1) = 1 + \frac{hZ(h)}{1 - \Phi(h)} - \left\{\frac{Z(h)}{1 - \Phi(h)}\right\}^2.$$

Some values of $\text{var}(X_1)$ are given in Table 10 of Chapter 13. Since $\text{var}(X_1) \le 1$

it follows that

$$|\mathrm{corr}(X_1,X_2)| \leq |\rho|.$$

Thus we would expect the correlation in the truncated population to be numerically less than that in the original population. Table 3 gives a few numerical values (see also Aitkin [4]).

TABLE 3

Correlation in Truncated Bivariate Normal Population

Degree of truncation $\Phi(h)$	Original correlation ρ 0.25	0.5	0.75	0.9
0.1	0.213	0.438	0.691	0.867
0.2	0.193	0.403	0.655	0.845
0.3	0.178	0.376	0.623	0.823
0.4	0.165	0.351	0.593	0.802
0.5	0.154	0.329	0.564	0.780
0.6	0.143	0.307	0.535	0.755
0.7	0.132	0.285	0.504	0.728
0.8	0.120	0.261	0.468	0.695
0.9	0.106	0.231	0.423	0.647

Thus if individuals are chosen on the basis of their X_1-values, with a view to controlling their X_2-values, the observed results tend to be "disappointing" in the sense that the observed correlation between X_1 and X_2 is less than that in the original population. This does not mean (though it is sometimes taken to do so) that the accuracy of prediction of X_2, given X_1, is any less; it is, in fact, the same. It is also worth noting that, while the regression of X_2 on X_1 is linear, that of X_1 on X_2 is, in the truncated population,

$$(65) \quad E[X_1 \mid X_2] = \rho X_2 + \frac{Z[(h - \rho X_2)/(\sqrt{1-\rho^2})]}{1 - \Phi[(h - \rho X_2)/(\sqrt{1-\rho^2})]} \cdot \sqrt{1-\rho^2}.$$

If both X_1 and X_2 are truncated from below ($X_1 > h, X_2 > k$), then the moments (μ'_{rs}) are given by

$$(66.1) \quad L(h,k;\rho)\mu'_{10} = Z(h)\{1 - \Phi(A)\} + \rho Z(k)\{1 - \Phi(B)\}$$

$$(66.2) \quad L(h,k;\rho)\mu'_{20} = hZ(h)\{1 - \Phi(A)\} + \rho^2 kZ(k)\{1 - \Phi(B)\} + \rho(1-\rho^2)^{\frac{1}{2}}Z(h,k;\rho) + L(h,k;\rho)$$

$$(66.3) \quad L(h,k;\rho)\mu'_{11} = \rho[hZ(h)\{1 - \Phi(A)\} + kZ(k)\{1 - \Phi(B)\} + L(h,k;\rho)] + (1-\rho^2)Z(h,k;\rho)$$

where

$$A = \frac{k - \rho h^2}{\sqrt{1 - \rho^2}}; \qquad B = \frac{h - \rho k^2}{\sqrt{1 - \rho^2}};$$

$$Z(h,k;\rho) = \frac{1}{2\pi\sqrt{1 - \rho^2}} \exp\left[- \frac{1}{2(1 - \rho^2)} (h^2 - 2\rho hk + k^2)\right].$$

(Formulas for μ'_{0r} are obtained from those for μ'_{r0} by interchanging h and k, A and B.)

From (66) we have

$$\begin{aligned}(67)\quad & (h + k)\rho^2 - \{(h + k)\mu'_{11} - hk(\mu'_{10} + \mu'_{01})\}\rho \\ & \qquad - (h + k) - hk(\mu'_{10} + \mu'_{01}) + k\mu'_{20} + h\mu'_{02} = 0\end{aligned}$$

(Rosenbaum [92]).

Cases where both variables are truncated (either singly or doubly) have been considered by Des Raj [26], Shah and Parikh [97], and Regier and Hamdan [91]. Supposing the retained ranges of values are

$$h_1 < X_1 < k_1; \qquad h_2 < X_2 < k_2,$$

Shah and Parikh obtained several recurrence relations among the product moments $\mu'_{r,s} = E[X_1^r X_2^s]$. Among these, we quote

$$\begin{aligned}(68.1)\quad & \mu'_{r,s} - (r - 1)(1 - \rho^2)\mu'_{r-2,s} - \rho\mu'_{r-1,s+1} \\ & = P^{-1}(1 - \rho^2)[h_1^{r-1}Z(h_1)G_s(h_2,k_2,h_1\rho;\sqrt{1 - \rho^2}) \\ & \qquad - k_1^{r-1}Z(k_1)G_s(h_2,k_2,k_1\rho;\sqrt{1 - \rho^2})] \qquad (r \geq 2, s \geq 2),\end{aligned}$$

where

$$P = \int_{h_1}^{h_2}\int_{k_1}^{k_2} Z(0,0;1,1;\rho)\, dx_1\, dx_2$$

and

$$G_s(a_1,a_2,b;c) = c^{-1}\int_{a_1}^{a_2} x^s Z\left(\frac{x - b}{c}\right) dx.$$

Also

$$\begin{aligned}(68.2)\quad & \mu'_{r-1,s+1} - s(1 - \rho^2)\mu'_{r-1,s-1} - \rho\mu'_{r,s} \\ & = P^{-1}(1 - \rho^2)[h_2^s Z(h_2)G_{r-1}(h_1,k_1,h_2\rho;\sqrt{1 - \rho^2}) \\ & \qquad - k_2^s Z(k_2)G_{r-1}(h_1,k_1,k_2\rho;\sqrt{1 - \rho^2})].\end{aligned}$$

For the case when both variates are singly truncated from below at the *same* (standardized) point (so that the retained values are $X_1 > a$, $X_2 > a$), Regier and Hamdan [91] give values of the correlation coefficient (ρ') as a function of a and the pretruncation correlation coefficient (ρ) to three decimal places for $\pm a = 0.0(0.1)1.1(0.2)1.5(0.5)2.5$; $\rho = 0.05(0.05)0.95$.

Use of tables of $L(h,k;\rho)$ to evaluate $\Pr[X_1 - X_2 > 0]$ when X_1,X_2 are independent and one is truncated has been described by Lipow and Eidemiller [62] for single truncation and (in a very similar manner) by Parikh and Sheth [78] for double truncation.

If truncation of a single variable (selection of $X_1 \geq h$) is applied to a trivariate normal population, then since the conditional joint distribution of X_2 and X_3, given X_1, is bivariate normal with parameters $\rho_{12}X_1,\rho_{13}X_1,\sqrt{1-\rho_{12}^2},\sqrt{1-\rho_{13}^2},\rho_{23.1}$, we have the following results. As in the bivariate case, for $t = 2,3$,

$$E[X_t] = \rho_{1t}E[X_1]; \qquad E[X_t^2] = \rho_{1t}^2 E[X_1^2] + 1 - \rho_{1t}^2;$$

$$\operatorname{var}(X_t) = \rho_{1t}^2 \operatorname{var}(X_1) + 1 - \rho_{1t}^2;$$

$$\operatorname{corr}(X_1,X_t) = \rho_{1t}\left[\rho_{1t}^2 + \frac{1-\rho_{1t}^2}{\operatorname{var}(X_1)}\right]^{-1/2}.$$

Also,

$$\begin{aligned} E[X_2X_3] &= E[E[X_2X_3 \mid X_1]] \\ &= E[\rho_{23.1}\sqrt{(1-\rho_{12}^2)(1-\rho_{13}^2)} + \rho_{12}\rho_{13}X_1^2] \\ &= \rho_{12}\rho_{13}E[X_1^2] + \rho_{23} - \rho_{12}\rho_{13}. \end{aligned}$$

Hence

$$\operatorname{cov}(X_2,X_3) = \rho_{12}\rho_{13}\operatorname{var}(X_1) + \rho_{23} - \rho_{12}\rho_{13} \tag{69.1}$$

and

$$\operatorname{corr}(X_2,X_3) = \frac{\rho_{23} - \rho_{12}\rho_{13}\left(\dfrac{1}{\operatorname{var}(X_1)} - 1\right)}{\sqrt{\left(\rho_{12}^2 + \dfrac{1-\rho_{12}^2}{\operatorname{var}(X_1)}\right)\left(\rho_{13}^2 + \dfrac{1-\rho_{13}^2}{\operatorname{var}(X_1)}\right)}}. \tag{69.2}$$

If truncation is by selection only of values X_1,X_2 such that $\alpha_1X_1 + \alpha_2X_2 > h$, the problem reduces to that of bivariate normal with single truncation of one variable, discussed at the beginning of this section. This is because $(\alpha_1X_1 + \alpha_2X_2)$ and X_3 have (before truncation) a bivariate normal distribution. If there is a further truncation, $\alpha_1'X_1 + \alpha_2'X_2 > h'$ say, then by transformation to new variables we obtain truncations of the form $Z > h$, $Z' > h'$. (See also Birnbaum [11] and Young and Weiler [120].)

We shall now no longer suppose that we are discussing standardized distributions and shall discuss, briefly, the estimation of parameters for truncated bivariate and trivariate normal distributions. For the case when each of the two variates X_1,X_2 is truncated from below ($X_1 \geq h_1, X_2 \geq h_2$) Rosenbaum [92] has given a method of estimating $h_1,h_2,\xi_1,\xi_2,\sigma_1,\sigma_2$, and ρ by using equations (66) and (67), which relate to the standardized variables $(X_1 - \xi_1)/\sigma_1,(X_2 - \xi_2)/\sigma_2$ with $h = (h_1 - \xi_1)/\sigma_1$, $k = (h_2 - \xi_2)/\sigma_2$. Approximate values of $\hat{h}$, $\hat{k}$, and $\hat{\rho}$ are used to evaluate $\hat{\mu}'_{rs}$. These, in turn, are used to calculate

(70.1) $$\hat{\sigma}_1 = [S_{11}(\hat{\mu}'_{20} - \hat{\mu}'^{2}_{10})^{-1}]^{1/2};$$

(70.2) $$\hat{\sigma}_2 = [S_{22}(\hat{\mu}'_{02} - \hat{\mu}'^{2}_{01})^{-1}]^{1/2};$$

(70.3) $$\hat{\xi}_1 = \bar{X}_1 - \hat{\mu}'_{10}\hat{\sigma}_1;$$

(70.4) $$\hat{\xi}_2 = \bar{X}_2 - \hat{\mu}'_{01}\hat{\sigma}_2.$$

From these values, new values of $\hat{h}$ and $\hat{k}$ can be obtained. Finally, a new value for $\hat{\rho}$ is obtained by solving (67) (with all quantities replaced by estimates) and a new cycle of calculation started.

Maximum likelihood equations for the cases when both variables are singly or doubly truncated (and for linear truncation) are given by Nath [71a], who also gives formulas from which the asymptotic variances and covariances of the maximum likelihood estimators can be calculated.

Jaiswal and Khatri [50] have given moment estimators applicable when only one of the two variables is truncated. As high moments are needed, the estimators are likely to be variable.

Votaw et al. [114] have described a method of calculating maximum likelihood estimators for some parameters of a trivariate normal distribution with one variable truncated from below ($X_1 \geq h_1$) when the parameters $\xi_1,\xi_2,\sigma_1,\sigma_2,\rho_{12}$, and h_1 are known. The parameters to be estimated are ξ_3, σ_3,ρ_{13}, and ρ_{23}, that is, those relating to the third variable, X_3.

Elliptical truncation (Tallis [109]) has been discussed in Chapter 35, Section 8. For the case of standardized bivariate normal distribution, Tallis gave a table enabling one to choose a region

$$a_1 < (1 - \rho^2)^{-1}(X_1^2 - 2\rho X_1X_2 + X_2^2) < a_2$$

such that the variance-covariance matrix of the truncated distribution equals that of the original distribution. This table, reproduced in Table 4, gives appropriate pairs of values a_1 and a_2 for each of a number of different degrees of truncation (q). (Values of a_1 and a_2 are obtained as solutions of the equations

(71) $$\Pr[a_1 < \chi_4^2 < a_2] = \Pr[a_1 < \chi_2^2 < a_2] = 1 - q,$$

TABLE 4

Constants for Elliptical Truncation of Bivariate Normal

q	a_1	a_2	q	a_1	a_2
0.1	0.171	8.632	0.6	1.068	3.361
0.2	0.335	6.161	0.7	1.277	2.956
0.3	0.506	5.144	0.8	1.500	2.601
0.4	0.684	4.411	0.9	1.740	2.285
0.5	0.871	3.836			

that is,

$$a_1 e^{-(1/2)a_1} = a_2 e^{-(1/2)a_2} \quad \text{and} \quad e^{-(1/2)a_1} - e^{-(1/2)a_2} = 1 - q.)$$

8. Dichotomized Variables

When data are grouped, calculations can be made as if all observations in a group were at one specific point in the group. Subsequently corrections may be applied. In many practical cases these corrections are of relatively small importance.

When the grouping is very coarse, however, the situation is different. In this section we consider the coarsest possible grouping in which one, or both, of the variables is dichotomized, that is, divided into two groups $X \leq x_0$, $X > x_0$.

8.1. *Tetrachoric Correlation*

When both X_1 and X_2 are dichotomized, the available data can be represented in the form of a 2 × 2 table (Fig. 7). The symbols a, b, c, and d stand

	$X_1 \leqslant x_{10}$	$X_2 > x_{10}$
$X_2 > x_{20}$	c	d
$X_2 \leqslant x_{20}$	a	b

FIGURE 7

for the frequencies of observations, in a sample of size n, of the events

$$a\colon\ (X_1 \le x_{10}) \cap (X_2 \le x_{20}),$$
$$b\colon\ (X_1 > x_{10}) \cap (X_2 \le x_{20}),$$
$$c\colon\ (X_1 \le x_{10}) \cap (X_2 > x_{20}),$$
$$d\colon\ (X_1 > x_{10}) \cap (X_2 > x_{20}).$$

Evidently $a + b + c + d = n$. Although there are only three distinct observations, and at least five unknown parameters (seven if, as is commonly the case, x_{10} and x_{20} are unknown), it is possible to construct useful estimators of ρ. The method now to be described was originally constructed by Pearson [80] in 1901.

The observed proportion of X_1's less than x_{10} is $(a + c)/n$, and we estimate $h_1 = (x_{10} - \xi_1)/\sigma_1$ by $\hat{h}_1$, which satisfies the equation

$$\Phi(\tilde{h}_1) = (a + c)/n. \tag{72.1}$$

Similarly, $h_2 = (x_{20} - \xi_2)/\sigma_2$ is estimated by $\hat{h}_2$, where

$$\Phi(\tilde{h}_2) = (a + b)/n. \tag{72.2}$$

Then ρ is estimated by $\tilde{\rho}$, where

$$L(\tilde{h}_1,\tilde{h}_2;\tilde{\rho}) = d/n. \tag{72.3}$$

The resulting estimator is called the *tetrachoric correlation*, because it is based on the *tetrachoric* (four-entry) table in Fig. 7. Recently, Hamdan [43] has shown that this is the maximum likelihood estimator of ρ, for the given data. Equation (72.3) may be solved by an iterative process, using the tables of $L(h_1,h_2;\rho)$ described in Section 4.

Before these tables were available, approximate analytic methods of solution were devised. Pearson [80] obtained the expansion

$$\begin{aligned} (73.1)\quad & L(h_1,h_2;\rho) \\ &= \Phi(h_1)\Phi(h_2) + Z(h_1)Z(h_2)\left[\rho + \frac{\rho^2}{2!}h_1h_2 + \frac{\rho^3}{3!}(h_1^2 - 1)(h_2^2 - 1) + \cdots\right] \\ &= \sum_{j=0}^{\infty} \tau_j(h_1)\tau_j(h_2)\rho^j, \end{aligned}$$

where

$$\tau_j(h) = \frac{(-1)^{j-1}}{\sqrt{j!}}\frac{d^{j-1}Z(h)}{dh^{j-1}} \qquad (j \ge 1)$$

and

$$\tau_0(h) = \Phi(h).$$

The $\tau_j(h)$ is called the jth *tetrachoric function*. It is a multiple of the $(j-1)$th Hermite polynomial (for $j \geq 1$). Lee [60] has given tables of $\tau_j(h)$ to seven decimal places for $j = 0(1)19$; $h = 0.0(0.1)4.0$. These tables are included in [83]. (Note that (73.1) can be obtained by integration of Mehler's series expansion (see Chapter 35, Section 4.2):

$$Z(x_1,x_2;\rho) = Z(x_1)Z(x_2)\left[1 + \rho H_1(x_1)H_1(x_2) + \frac{\rho^2}{2!}H_2(x_1)H_2(x_2) + \cdots\right].$$

The fact that $|\tau_j(h)| < 1$ makes possible a rough assessment of the convergence of the series in (73.1). For values of $|h_1|$ and $|h_2|$ less than 1, another series, also obtained by Pearson, gives rather better convergence. This series is an expansion in powers of $\theta = \sin^{-1}\rho$ and starts

$$(73.2)\quad L(h_1,h_2;\rho) = \Phi(h_1)\Phi(h_2) + Z(h_1)Z(h_2)\left[\theta + \frac{\theta^2}{2!}h_1h_2 + \frac{\theta^3}{3!}(h_1^2 + h_2^2 - h_1^2h_2^2) + \frac{\theta^4}{4!}h_1h_2\{5 - 3(h_1^2 + h_2^2) + h_1^2h_2^2\} + \cdots\right].$$

It will be appreciated that solution of either (73.1) or (73.2) for ρ is usually troublesome. A number of approximations, which are simple to compute, have been suggested.

Using the values of $\Phi(\tilde{h}_1)$ and $\Phi(\tilde{h}_2)$ from (72.1) and (72.2) in (73.1) we find

$$(74.1)\quad R_1 = \frac{ad - bc}{n^2Z(\tilde{h}_1)Z(\tilde{h}_2)} = \tilde{\rho} + \frac{\tilde{\rho}^2}{2!}\tilde{h}_1\tilde{h}_2 + \frac{\tilde{\rho}^3}{3!}(\tilde{h}_1^2 - 1)(\tilde{h}_2^2 - 1) + \cdots.$$

The jth term in the series is $(\tilde{\rho}^j/j!)H_{j-1}(\tilde{h}_1)H_{j-1}(\tilde{h}_2)$. This suggests that if $\tilde{\rho}$ is small then $\tilde{\rho} \doteqdot R_1$; this approximate formula was given by Pearson [80]. Yule [121] had previously (in 1897) suggested the estimator

$$(74.2)\qquad R_2 = (ad - bc)/(ad + bc).$$

Further estimators suggested by Pearson [81] include

$$(74.3)\qquad R_3 = \cos[\pi(1 + ad/bc)^{-1}],$$

$$(74.4)\qquad R_4 = \sin\left[(\pi/2)\left\{1 + \frac{2bc}{ad - bc}\frac{n}{b + c}\right\}^{-1}\right]\qquad (ad \geq bc),$$

and

$$(74.5)\qquad R_5 = \sin\left[(\pi/2)\left\{1 + \frac{4abcdn^2}{(ad - bc)^2(a + d)(b + c)}\right\}^{-1/2}\right].$$

Pearson made a number of numerical comparisons among these formulas. His work was extended in 1966 by Castellan [17] who found that an estimator proposed by Camp [16] in 1931 gave results generally considerably closer to $\hat{\rho}$. This estimator is constructed as follows. First arrange (by changing signs of variables, if necessary) that $a + c \geq b + d$. Then calculate $\tilde{h}_2^-$, $\tilde{h}_2^+$ from

$$\Phi(\tilde{h}_2^-) = a/(a + c); \qquad \Phi(\tilde{h}_2^+) = b/(b + d) \tag{75}$$

and

$$M = \frac{(a + c)(b + d)}{n^2} \frac{\tilde{h}_2^- + \tilde{h}_2^+}{Z(\tilde{h}_1)}.$$

The estimator is then

$$R_6 = M(1 + \theta^2 M)^{-1}, \tag{74.6}$$

where θ can be found by interpolation in the following table:

$$(a + c)/n = 0.50\ 0.55\ 0.60\ 0.65\ 0.70\ 0.75\ 0.80\ 0.85\ 0.90$$
$$\theta = 0.64\ 0.63\ 0.63\ 0.63\ 0.62\ 0.61\ 0.60\ 0.58\ 0.56.$$

For many purposes it suffices to take $\theta = \frac{5}{8}$. Note that a different value of R_6 is obtained, in general, if X_1 and X_2 are interchanged.

The approximate standard deviation of $\hat{\rho}$ (and of each of the R's insofar as they approximate to $\hat{\rho}$) for large n is

$$\frac{1}{\sqrt{n}} \frac{\sqrt{\Phi(h_1)[1 - \Phi(h_1)]\Phi(h_2)[1 - \Phi(h_2)]}}{Z(h_1)Z(h_2)} \tag{76}$$

(Pearson [80].) This is often estimated by

$$\frac{1}{n^{5/2}} \frac{\sqrt{(a + b)(c + d)(a + c)(b + d)}}{Z(\hat{h}_1)Z(\hat{h}_2)}.$$

8.2. *Biserial Correlation*

If only one of the two variables, say X_2, is dichotomized, we may regard the available data as represented by n independent pairs of random variables (X_{1j}, Y_j), where

$$Y_j = \begin{cases} 1 & \text{if } X_{2j} > x_{20}, \\ 0 & \text{if } X_{2j} \leq x_{20}. \end{cases}$$

The correlation between X_{1j} and Y_j, say ρ', is related to ρ by the formula

$$\rho' = \rho Z(h_2)[\Phi(h_2)\{1 - \Phi(h_2)\}]^{-1/2} \tag{77}$$

(where $h_2 = (x_{20} - \xi_2)/\sigma_2$).

It is natural to take, as an estimator of ρ, the statistic

$$\rho^* = (\text{sample correlation between } X_1 \text{ and } Y) \frac{\sqrt{\Phi(\hat{h}_2)[1 - \Phi(\hat{h}_2)]}}{Z(\hat{h}_2)},$$

where $\Phi(\hat{h}_2) = \bar{Y} = n^{-1} \sum_{j=1}^{n} Y_j$ = proportion of X_2's greater than x_{20}. Since

$$\sum_{j=1}^{n}(Y_j - \bar{Y})^2 = n\Phi(\hat{h}_2)[1 - \Phi(\hat{h}_2)],$$

it follows that

$$\rho^* = \frac{n^{-1}\sum_{j=1}^{n}(X_{1j} - \bar{X}_1)(Y_j - \bar{Y})}{Z(\hat{h}_2)\left[n^{-1}\sum_{j=1}^{n}(X_{1j} - \bar{X}_1)^2\right]^{1/2}}. \tag{78}$$

This formula was obtained by Pearson **[81]** and termed by him the *biserial correlation coefficient*. As $n \to \infty$, $E[\rho^*] \to \rho$. Soper **[106]** showed that for n large

$$n \operatorname{var}(\rho^*) \doteqdot \rho^4 + (h_2^2\rho^2 - 1)\frac{\Phi(h_2)[1 - \Phi(h_2)]}{[Z(h_2)]^2} + \rho^2\left\{\frac{(2\Phi(h_2) - 1)h_2}{Z(h_2)} - \frac{5}{2}\right\}. \tag{79}$$

Tate **[110]** gives values of the square root of the right-hand side of (79) to three decimal places for $\rho = 0.0(0.1)1.0$; $\Phi(h_2) = 0.05(0.05)0.50$. (Note that the value is unchanged if the sign of ρ or h_2 is reversed.)

Maximum likelihood estimation of the parameters ρ, h_2, ξ_1, and σ_1 has been studied by Tate **[110]**. The ξ_1 and σ_1^2, are estimated by $\bar{X}_1$ and $n^{-1} \sum_{j=1}^{n} (X_{1j} - \bar{X}_1)^2 = S^2$ respectively. Then $\hat{\rho}$ and $\hat{h}_2$, the maximum likelihood estimators of ρ and h_2 respectively, have to satisfy the equations

$$\Sigma^+(X'_{1j} - \hat{\rho}\hat{h}_2)\left[\mathfrak{R}\left(\frac{\hat{h}_2 - \hat{\rho}X'_{1j}}{\sqrt{1 - \hat{\rho}^2}}\right)\right]^{-1} = \Sigma^-(X'_{1j} - \hat{\rho}\hat{h}_2)\left[\mathfrak{R}\left(-\frac{\hat{h}_2 - \hat{\rho}X'_{1j}}{\sqrt{1 - \hat{\rho}^2}}\right)\right]^{-1}, \tag{80.1}$$

$$\Sigma^+\left[\mathfrak{R}\left(\frac{\hat{h}_2 - \hat{\rho}X'_{1j}}{\sqrt{1 - \hat{\rho}^2}}\right)\right]^{-1} = \Sigma^-\left[\mathfrak{R}\left(\frac{\hat{h}_2 - \hat{\rho}X'_{1j}}{-\sqrt{1 - \hat{\rho}^2}}\right)\right]^{-1}, \tag{80.2}$$

where Σ^+ denotes summation over j for $Y_j = 1$ and Σ^- denotes summation over j for $Y_j = 0$; $X'_{1j} = \dfrac{X_{1j} - \bar{X}_1}{S}$; and $\mathfrak{R}(u) = \dfrac{1 - \Phi(u)}{Z(u)}$ is Mills' ratio (see Chapter 33, Section 7).

Tate [110] has constructed an iterative method of solving (80.1) and (80.2) for $\hat{\rho}$ and $\hat{h}_2$. He suggests taking the biserial correlation ρ^* and h^* as initial values. For large n,

$$(81.1)\quad n\,\text{var}(\hat{h}_2) \doteqdot \frac{(1-\rho^2)(\psi_2 - 2\rho h_2\psi_1 + \rho^2 h_2\psi_0)}{\psi_0\psi_2 - \psi_1^2} + \rho^2(\rho^2 h_2^2 + 2),$$

$$(81.2)\quad n\,\text{var}(\hat{\rho}) \doteqdot \frac{(1-\rho^2)^3\psi_0}{\psi_0\psi_2 - \psi_1^2} + \rho^2(1-\rho^2)^2,$$

where

$$\psi_r = \int_{-\infty}^{\infty} t^r Z(t)\left[\mathcal{R}\left(\frac{h_2 - \rho t}{\sqrt{1-\rho^2}}\right)\mathcal{R}\left(-\frac{h_2-\rho t}{\sqrt{1-\rho^2}}\right)\right]^{-1} dt.$$

Prince and Tate [89] give values of the right-hand sides of (81.1) and (81.2) and of ψ_0,ψ_1, and ψ_2 to five decimal places for $h_2 = 0(0.1)0.8(0.05)1.60(0.025)1.65$ and various values of ρ. Note that (81.1) and (81.2) are unchanged by reversal of sign of ρ or h_2;ψ_r is unchanged by reversal of sign of ρ, but is multiplied by $(-1)^r$ if the sign of h_2 is changed.

Birnbaum [10] has discussed the situation arising when X_1 is truncated.

9. Related Distributions

Distributions obtained by simple transformations of multinormal variables have been discussed in Chapter 34.

Mixtures of bivariate normal distributions were described in 1916 by Åkesson [6] and in 1923 by Charlier and Wicksell [18], but little further work has been published using such distributions. Hyrenius [48], in 1952, used a mixture of bivariate normal distributions as a specimen nonnormal distribution in assessing the effects of nonnormality on distributions of sample arithmetic means, variances, and covariances. A special case was described by Charnley [19] in 1941.

The relative accuracy of moment estimators for mixtures of univariate distributions is exploited in the following practical method of fitting a two-component mixture of bivariate normal distributions with common variance-covariance matrix (Day [24]). Denoting the variates by X and Y, each marginal distribution is fitted separately by a two-component mixture of normal distributions, each with common variance, using the method of moments. Call the fitted values of ω (the proportion of first component) for the two cases $\hat{\omega}_x,\hat{\omega}_y$. These should be estimators of the same value ω. (In fact, substantial difference between $\hat{\omega}_x$ and $\hat{\omega}_y$ can be taken as indication that the mixture of two bivariate normal distributions is inappropriate.)

Take $\tilde{\omega} = \frac{1}{2}(\hat{\omega}_x + \hat{\omega}_y)$ and then fit each marginal distribution to make first three sample and population moments agree. Denote the fitted parameters for $X,\tilde{\xi}_1,\tilde{\xi}_2,\tilde{\sigma}_x$; and for $Y,\tilde{\eta}_1,\tilde{\eta}_2,\tilde{\sigma}_y$. Then ρ is estimated by equating the sample covariance between X and Y to

$$\tilde{\rho}\tilde{\sigma}_x\tilde{\sigma}_y + \tilde{\omega}(1 - \tilde{\omega})(\tilde{\xi}_1 - \tilde{\xi}_2)(\tilde{\eta}_1 - \tilde{\eta}_2).$$

Some, or all, of the variates in a multinormal distribution may be replaced by their absolute values. This produces a joint distribution with some, or all of the marginal distributions folded normal (see Chapter 13, Section 7.3). If the expected values of the original variables are zero, the marginal distributions are half normal. In particular we have the *bivariate half normal* distribution

$$\text{(82)}\quad p_{X_1,X_2}(x_1,x_2) = 2[\pi\sigma_1\sigma_2\sqrt{1-\rho^2}]^{-1} \times \left[\exp\left\{-\frac{(x_1/\sigma_1)^2 + (x_2/\sigma_2)^2}{2(1-\rho^2)}\right\}\right]\cosh\left[\frac{\rho x_1 x_2}{(1-\rho^2)\sigma_1\sigma_2}\right] \qquad (0 < x_1; 0 < x_2).$$

The X_1 and X_2 each have half normal distributions. The conditional distribution of X_2 given X_1 is folded normal, being the distribution of the absolute value of a normal variable with expected value $|\rho|\, X_1$ and variance $(1 - \rho^2)$. The regression function of X_2 on X_1 is

$$\text{(83)}\qquad E[X_2 \mid X_1] = |\rho| X_1 + 2Z\left(\frac{\rho X_1}{\sqrt{1-\rho^2}}\right).$$

The distribution of ratios of variables having a joint bivariate normal distribution has attracted some attention. If X_1,X_2 have joint density (1), then

$$\text{(84)}\qquad \Pr[X_1/X_2 \le g] = \Pr[(U_1\sigma_1 + \xi_1)/(U_2\sigma_2 + \xi_2) \le g] = \Pr[(U_1 + \xi_1\sigma_1^{-1})/(U_2 + \xi_2\sigma_2^{-1}) \le g\sigma_2\sigma_1^{-1}],$$

where U_1,U_2 have a joint standardized bivariate normal distribution. We therefore need consider only the distribution of $(U_1 + \delta_1)/(U_2 + \delta_2)$, and it can always be arranged to have δ_1 and δ_2 nonnegative. (For a contrary opinion, see Hinkley [45].)

Fieller [33] obtained an expression for the cumulative distribution of the ratio, effectively in the form

$$\text{(85.1)}\quad \Pr[(U_1 + \delta_1)/(U_2 + \delta_2) \le g] = L(\varepsilon,-\delta_2;\rho') + L(-\varepsilon,\delta_2;\rho')$$

with

$$\varepsilon = (\delta_1 - \delta_2 g)(g^2 - 2\rho g + 1)^{-1/2};$$
$$\rho' = (g - \rho)(g^2 - 2\rho g + 1)^{-1/2}.$$

An equivalent expression is

$$(85.2)\quad 1 - \frac{\cos^{-1}\rho'}{\pi} - 2\left[V\left(\varepsilon, \frac{\delta_2 + \rho'\varepsilon}{\sqrt{(1-\rho'^2)}}\right) + V\left(\delta_2, \frac{\varepsilon + \rho'\delta_2}{\sqrt{(1-\rho'^2)}}\right)\right].$$

(The $L(\cdot), V(\cdot)$ are defined in (19), (27) respectively). If δ_2 is large, so that $\Pr[U_2 + \delta_2 < 0]$ is negligible, an approximate formula is easily obtained. We have (Geary [39]):

$$\begin{aligned}(86)\quad \Pr[(U_1 + \delta_1)/(U_2 + \delta_2) \le g] &= \Pr[U_1 + \delta_1 \le g(U_2 + \delta_2)] \\ &= \Pr[U_1 - gU_2 \le g\delta_2 - \delta_1] \\ &= \Phi((g\delta_2 - \delta_1)(g^2 - 2\rho g + 1)^{-1/2}).\end{aligned}$$

Hinkley [45] has investigated the accuracy of this approximation. He suggests adding the correction $\pm\Phi(-\delta_2)$; the sign being the same as that of $(\delta_1 - \rho\delta_2)$.

A paper by Marsaglia [67] includes a number of graphs of the density function, which can be bimodal. In the special case $\delta_1 = \delta_2 = 0$, we have a Cauchy distribution (Chapter 16).

REFERENCES

[1] Adrian, R. (1808). Research concerning the probabilities of errors which happen in making observations, etc., *The Analyst of Mathematics*, **1,** 93–109.

[2] Afifi, A. A. and Elashoff, R. M. (1966–1969). Missing observations in multivariate analysis, *Journal of the American Statistical Association*, **61,** 595–604; **62,** 10–29; **64,** 337–358, 359–365.

[3] Ahsanullah, M. (1970). On the estimation of means in a bivariate normal distribution with equal marginal variance (abstract), *Annals of Mathematical Statistics*, **41,** 1155–1156.

[4] Aitkin, M. A. (1964). Correlation in a singly truncated bivariate normal distribution, *Psychometrika*, **29,** 263–270.

[5] Aitkin, M. A. and Hume, M. W. (1966). Correlation in a singly truncated bivariate normal distribution, III. Correlation between ranks and variate-values, *Biometrika*, **53,** 278–281.

[6] Åkesson, O. A. (1916). On the dissection of correlation surfaces, *Arkiv för Matematik, Astronomi och Fysik*, **11,** No. 16, 1–18.

[7] Amos, D. E. (1969). On computation of the bivariate normal distribution, *Mathematics of Computation*, **23,** 655–659.

[8] Anderson, T. W. (1957). Maximum likelihood estimates for a multivariate normal distribution when some observations are missing, *Journal of the American Statistical Association*, **52,** 200–203.

[9] Anderson, T. W. (1958). *An Introduction to Multivariate Statistical Analysis*, New York: John Wiley and Sons, Inc.

[10] Birnbaum, Z. W. (1950). On the effect of cutting score when selection is performed against a dichotomized criterion, *Psychometrika*, **15,** 385–389.

[11] Birnbaum, Z. W. (1950). Effect of linear truncation on a multinormal population, *Annals of Mathematical Statistics*, **21,** 272–279.

[12] Bofinger, Eve and Bofinger, V. J. (1965). The correlation of maxima in samples drawn from a bivariate normal distribution, *Australian Journal of Statistics*, **7,** 57–61.

[13] Bravais, A. (1846). Analyse mathématique sur la probabilité des erreurs de situation d'un point, *Mémoires presentés à l'Académie Royale des Sciences, Paris*, **9,** 255–332. (English translation, 1958; White Sands Proving Ground, New Mexico.)

[14] Burington, R. S. and May, D. C. (1970). *Handbook of Probability and Statistics with Tables*, 2nd ed., pp. 144–147, New York: McGraw-Hill.

[15] Cadwell, J. H. (1951). The bivariate normal integral, *Biometrika*, **38,** 475–479.

[16] Camp, B. H. (1931). *The Mathematical Parts of Elementary Statistics*, New York: D. C. Heath.

[17] Castellan, N. J. (1966). On the estimation of the tetrachoric correlation coefficient, *Psychometrika*, **31,** 67–73.

[18] Charlier, C. V. L. and Wicksell, S. D. (1923). On the dissection of frequency functions, *Arkiv för Matematik, Astronomi och Fysik*, **18,** No. 6.

[19] Charnley, F. (1941). Some properties of a composite, bivariate distribution in which the means of the component normal distributions are linearly related, *Canadian Journal of Research*, **19,** 139–151.

[20] Chew, V. (1964). *Confidence, prediction and tolerance regions, Technical Memo No. 64–9*, RCA System Analysis, U.S. Air Force, Patrick Air Force Base, Florida.

[21] Cohen, A. C. (1955). Restriction and selection in samples from bivariate normal distributions, *Journal of the American Statistical Association*, **50,** 884–893.

[22] Cohen, A. C. (1959). Simplified estimators for the normal distribution when samples are singly censored or truncated, *Technometrics*, **1,** 217–237.

[23] Czuber, E. (1891). *Theorie der Beobachtungsfehler*, Leipzig: Teubner.

[24] Day, N. E. (1969). Estimating the components of a mixture of normal distributions, *Biometrika*, **56,** 463–474.

[25] DeLury, D. B. (1938). Note on correlations, *Annals of Mathematical Statistics*, **9,** 149–151.

[26] Des Raj (1953). On estimating the parameters of bivariate normal populations from doubly and singly linearly truncated samples, *Sankhyā*, **12,** 277–290.

[27] Dickson, I. D. H. (1886). Appendix to "Family likeness in stature," by F. Galton, *Proceedings of the Royal Society of London*, **40,** 63–73.

[28] Dunnett, C. W. (1958). *Tables of the Bivariate Normal Distribution with Correlation* $1/\sqrt{2}$, Deposited in UMT file (abstract in *Mathematics of Computation* **14** (1960), 79).

[29] Dunnett, C. W. (1960). On selecting the largest of k normal population means, *Journal of the Royal Statistical Society, Series B*, **22,** 1–30.

[30] Dunnett, C. W. and Lamm, R. A. (1960). *Some tables of the multivariate normal probability integral with correlation coefficient 1/3*, Deposited in UMF file (abstract in *Mathematics of Computation*, **14,** 290–291).

[31] Elderton, Ethel M., Moul, Margaret, Fieller, E. C., Pretorius, S. J. and Church, A. E. R. (1930). On the remaining tables for determining the volumes of a bivariate normal surface, *Biometrika*, **22,** 13–35. (Introduction by K. Pearson, 1–12.)

[32] Everitt, P. F. (1912). Supplementary tables for finding the correlation coefficient from tetrachoric groupings, *Biometrika*, **8,** 385–395.

[33] Fieller, E. C. (1932). The distribution of the index in a normal bivariate population, *Biometrika*, **24,** 428–440.

[34] Fieller, E. C., Lewis, T. and Pearson, E. S. (1956). *Correlated Random Normal Deviates*, Tracts for Computers, **26,** Cambridge University Press.

[35] Fisher, R. A. (1929). Moments and product moments of sampling distributions, *Proceedings of the London Mathematical Society, Series 2*, **30,** 199–238.

[36] Galton, F. (1877). *Typical Laws of Heredity in Man*, Address to Royal Institution of Great Britain.

[37] Galton, F. (1888). Co-relations and their measurement chiefly from anthropometric data, *Proceedings of the Royal Society of London*, **45**, 134–145.

[38] Gauss, C. F. (1823). *Theoria Combinationis Observationum Erroribus Minimis Obnoxiae*, Göttingen.

[39] Geary, R. C. (1930). The frequency distribution of the quotient of two normal variates, *Journal of the Royal Statistical Society, Series A*, **93**, 442–446.

[40] Grundy, P. M., Healy, M. J. R. and Rees, D. H. (1956). Economic choice of the amount of experimentation, *Journal of the Royal Statistical Society, Series B*, **18**, 32–49.

[41] Gupta, S. S. (1963). Bibliography on the multivariate normal integrals and related topics, *Annals of Mathematical Statistics*, **34**, 829–838.

[42] Haldane, J. B. S. (1942). Moments of the distributions of powers and products of normal variates, *Biometrika*, **32**, 226–242.

[43] Hamdan, M. A. (1970). The equivalence of tetrachoric and maximum likelihood estimates of ρ in 2×2 tables, *Biometrika*, **57**, 212–215.

[44] Helmert, F. R. (1868). Studien über rationelle Vermessungen, im Gebiete der höheren Geodäsie, *Zeitschrift für Mathematik und Physik*, **13**, 73–129.

[45] Hinkley, D. V. (1969). On the ratio of two correlated normal random variables, *Biometrika*, **56**, 635–639.

[46] Hocking, R. R. and Smith, W. B. (1968). Estimation of parameters in the multivariate normal distribution with missing observations, *Journal of the American Statistical Association*, **63**, 159–173.

[47] Hughes, H. M. (1949). Estimation of the variance of the bivariate normal distribution, *University of California at Berkeley, Publications in Statistics*, **1**, 37–52.

[48] Hyrenius, H. (1952). Sampling from bivariate non-normal universes by means of compound normal distributions, *Biometrika*, **39**, 238–246.

[49] Iyer, P. V. K. and Simha, P. S. (1967). *Tables of Bivariate Random Normal Deviates*, Defense Science Laboratory, Delhi, India.

[50] Jaiswal, M. C. and Khatri, C. G. (1967). Estimation of parameters for the selected samples from bivariate normal populations, *Metron*, **26**, Nos. 3–4, 1–8.

[51] Kamat, A. R. (1953). Incomplete and absolute moments of the multivariate normal distribution with some applications, *Biometrika*, **40**, 20–34.

[52] Kamat, A. R. (1958). Hypergeometric expansions for incomplete moments of the bivariate normal distribution, *Sankhyā*, **20**, 317–320.

[53] Kamat, A. R. (1958). Incomplete moments of the trivariate normal distribution, *Sankhyā*, **20**, 321–322.

[54] Kendall, M. G. (1941). Proof of relations connected with the tetrachoric series and its generalization, *Biometrika*, **32**, 196–198.

[55] Kendall, M. G. and Stuart, A. (1963). *The Advanced Theory of Statistics*, **1**, London: Griffin.

[56] Khatri, C. G. and Waiswal, M. C. (1963). Estimation of parameters of a truncated bivariate normal distribution, *Journal of the American Statistical Association*, **58**, 519–526.

[57] Kleinbaum, D. (1969). *Estimation and hypothesis testing for generalized multivariate linear models*, Ph.D. thesis, University of North Carolina, Chapel Hill.

[58] Lancaster, H. O. (1959). Zero correlation and independence, *Australian Journal of Statistics*, **1**, 53–56.

[59] Laplace, P. S. (1810). Mémoire sur les intégrales définies, et leur application aux probabilités, *Mémoires de l'Institut Impérial de France*, 279–347.

[60] Lee, Alice (1917). Further supplementary tables for determining high (tetrachoric) correlations from tetrachoric groupings, *Biometrika*, **11**, 287–291.

[61] Lee, Alice (1927). Supplementary tables for determining correlation from tetrachoric groupings (tetrachoric correlations), *Biometrika*, **19**, 354–404.

[62] Lipow, M. and Eidemiller, R. L. (1964). Application of the bivariate normal distribution to a stress vs strength problem in reliability analysis, *Technometrics*, **6**, 325–328.

[63] Lukatzkaya, M. L. (1965). Some properties of random variables with a generalized normal distribution, *Nauchnye Trudy Novosibirsk. U-ta*, **5**, 57–71. (In Russian.)

[64] Madansky, A. (1958). *On the maximum likelihood estimate of the correlation coefficient*, Report No. P-1355, RAND Corporation, Santa Monica, California.

[65] Mallows, C. L. (1958). *An approximate formula for bivariate normal probabilities*, Technical Report No. 30. Statistical Techniques Research Group, Princeton University.

[66] Maritz, J. S. (1953). Estimation of the correlation coefficient in the case of a bivariate normal population when one of the variables is dichotomized, *Psychometrika*, **18**, 97–110.

[67] Marsaglia, G. (1965). Ratios of normal variables and ratios of sums of uniform variables, *Journal of the American Statistical Association*, **60**, 193–204.

[68] Mosteller, F. (1946). On some useful "inefficient" statistics, *Annals of Mathematical Statistics*, **17**, 377–408.

[69] Nabeya, S. (1951). Absolute moments in 2-dimensional normal distribution, *Annals of the Institute of Statistical Mathematics, Tokyo*, **3**, 2–6.

[70] Nabeya, S. (1952). Absolute moments in 3-dimensional normal distribution, *Annals of the Institute of Statistical Mathematics, Tokyo*, **4**, 15–20.

[71] Nadler, J. (1967). Bivariate samples with missing values, *Technometrics*, **9**, 679–682.

[71a] Nath, G. B. (1971). Estimation in truncated bivariate normal distributions, *Applied Statistics,* **20,** 313–319.

[72] National Bureau of Standards (1959). *Tables of the Bivariate Normal Distribution Function and Related Functions*, Applied Mathematics Series, **50**.

[73] Nicholson, C. (1943). The probability integral for two variables, *Biometrika*, **33,** 59–72.

[74] Olkin, I. and Pratt, J. W. (1958). Unbiased estimation of certain correlation coefficients, *Annals of Mathematical Statistics*, **29,** 201–211.

[75] Owen, D. B. (1956). Tables for computing bivariate normal probabilities, *Annals of Mathematical Statistics*, **27,** 1075–1090.

[76] Owen, D. B. (1957). *The bivariate normal probability distribution*, Research Report SC 3831-TR, Sandia Corporation.

[77] Owen, D. B. and Wiesen, J. M. (1959). A method of computing bivariate normal probabilities with an application to handling errors in testing and measuring, *Bell System Technical Journal*, **38,** 553–572.

[78] Parikh, N. T. and Sheth, R. J. (1966). Applications of bivariate normal distribution; to a stress vs. strength problem in reliability analysis, *Journal of the Indian Statistical Association*, **4,** 105–107.

[79] Paulson, E. (1942). A note on the estimation of some mean values for a bivariate distribution, *Annals of Mathematical Statistics*, **13,** 440–445.

[80] Pearson, K. (1901). Mathematical contributions to the theory of evolution—VII. On the correlation of characters not quantitatively measurable, *Philosophical Transactions of the Royal Society of London, Series A*, **195,** 1–47.

[81] Pearson, K. (1903). Mathematical contributions to the theory of evolution—XI. On the influence of natural selection on the variability and correlation of organs, *Philosophical Transactions of the Royal Society of London, Series A*, **200,** 1–66.

[82] Pearson, K. (1920). Notes on the history of correlation, *Biometrika*, **13,** 25–45.

[83] Pearson, K. (1931). *Tables for Statisticians and Biometricians*, **2,** Cambridge University Press.

[84] Pearson, K. and Young, A. W. (1918). On the product-moments of various orders of the normal correlation surface of two variates, *Biometrika*, **12,** 86–92.

[85] Pitman, E. J. G. (1939). A note on normal correlation, *Biometrika*, **31,** 9–12.

[86] Plana, G. A. A. (1813). Mémoire sur divers problèmes de probabilité, *Mémoires de l'Académie Impériale de Turin*, **20,** 355–408.

[87] Pólya, G. (1949). Remarks on computing the probability integral in one and two dimensions, *Proceedings of the 1st Berkeley Symposium in Mathematical Statistics and Probability*, 63–78.

[88] Press, S. J. (1965). *Correlation in a bivariate normal distribution when the conditional variances are known*, RAND Corporation.

[89] Prince, J. and Tate, R. F. (1966). Accuracy of maximum likelihood estimates of correlation for a biserial model, *Psychometrika*, **31,** 85–92.

[90] Rastogi, S. C. and Rohatgi, V. K. (1972). On unbiased estimation of the common mean of a bivariate normal distribution, *Journal of the American Statistical Association*, **67**.

[91] Regier, Mary H. and Hamdan, M. A. (1971). Correlation in a bivariate normal distribution with truncation in both variables, *Australian Journal of Statistics*, **13,** 77–82.

[92] Rosenbaum, S. (1961). Moments of a truncated bivariate normal distribution, *Journal of the Royal Statistical Society, Series B*, **23,** 405–408.

[93] Ruben, H. (1954). On the moments of order statistics in samples from normal populations, *Biometrika*, **41,** 200–227. (Correction: **41,** ix.)

[94] Ruben, H. (1961). Probability content of regions under spherical normal distributions. III: The bivariate normal integral. *Annals of Mathematical Statistics*, **32,** 171–186.

[95] Ruben, H. (1960). On the numerical evaluation of a class of multivariate normal integrals, *Proceedings of the Royal Society of Edinburgh*, **65**A**,** 272–281.

[96] Schols, C. M. (1875). Over de theorie der fouten in de ruimte en in het platte vlak, *Verhandelingen van de Koninklijke Akademie van Wetenschappen*, **15.** (English translation, 1958; White Sands Proving Ground, New Mexico.)

[97] Shah, S. M. and Parikh, N. T. (1964). Moments of singly and doubly truncated standard bivariate normal distribution, *Vidya* (*Gujarat University*), **7,** 82–91.

[98] Sheppard, W. F. (1899). On the application of the theory of error to cases of normal distribution and normal correlation, *Philosophical Transactions of the Royal Society of London, Series A*, **192,** 101–167.

[99] Sheppard, W. F. (1900). On the calculation of the double integral expressing normal correlation, *Transactions of the Cambridge Philosophical Society*, **19,** 23–66.

[100] Sheppard, W. F. (1898). On the geometric treatment of the 'normal curve' of statistics with special reference to correlation and to the theory of errors, *Proceedings of the Royal Society of London*, **62,** 170–173.

[101] Singh, N. (1960). Estimation of parameters of a multivariate normal population from truncated and censored samples, *Journal of the Royal Statistical Society, Series B*, **22,** 307–311.

[102] Smirnov, N. V. and Bol'shev, L. N. (1962). *Tables for Evaluating a Function of a Bivariate Normal Distribution*, Izdatel'stvo Akademii Nauk SSSR, Moscow.

[103] Smith, W. B. (1968). Bivariate samples with missing values, *Technometrics*, **10,** 867–868.

[104] Smith, W. B. and Hocking, R. R. (1968). A simple method for obtaining the information matrix for a multivariate normal distribution, *American Statistician*, **22,** No. 1, 18–20.

[105] Somerville, P. N. (1954). Some problems of optimum sampling, *Biometrika*, **41,** 420–429.

[106] Soper, H. E. (1915). On the probable error for the bi-serial expression for the correlation coefficient, *Biometrika*, **10,** 384–390.

[107] Sowden, R. R. and Ashford, J. R. (1969). Computation of the bivariate normal integral, *Applied Statistics*, **18,** 169–180.

[108] Steck, G. P. (1958). A table for computing trivariate normal probabilities, *Annals of Mathematical Statistics*, **29,** 780–800.

[109] Tallis, G. M. (1963). Elliptical and radial truncation in normal populations, *Annals of Mathematical Statistics*, **34,** 940–944.

[110] Tate, R. F. (1955). The theory of correlation between two continuous variables when one variable is dichotomized, *Biometrika*, **42,** 205–216.

[111] Teichroew, D. (1955). *Probabilities associated with order statistics in samples from two normal populations with equal variances*, Chemical Corps Engineering Agency, Army Chemical Center, Maryland.

[112] Tihansky, D. P. (1970). *Properties of the bivariate normal cumulative distribution*, Rand Corporation Report P4400, Santa Monica, California.

[113] Trawinski, Irene and Bargmann, R. E. (1964). Maximum likelihood estimation with incomplete multivariate data, *Annals of Mathematical Statistics*, **35,** 647–657.

[114] Votaw, D. F., Rafferty, J. A., and Deemer, W. L. (1950). Estimation of parameters in a truncated trivariate normal distribution, *Psychometrika*, **15,** 339–347.

[115] Weiler, H. (1959). Mean and standard deviations of a truncated normal bivariate distribution, *Australian Journal of Statistics*, **1,** 73–81.

[116] Welsh, G. S. (1955). A tabular method of obtaining tetrachoric *r* with median-cut variables, *Psychometrika*, **20,** 83–85.

[117] Wilks, S. S. (1932). Moments and distributions of estimates of population parameters from fragmentary samples, *Annals of Mathematical Statistics*, **3,** 163–195.

[118] Williams, J. M. and Weiler, H. (1964). Further charts for the means of truncated normal bivariate distributions, *Australian Journal of Statistics*, **6,** 117–129.

[119] Wold, H. (1948). *Random Normal Deviates*, Tracts for Computers, **35,** Cambridge University Press.

[120] Young, S. S. Y. and Weiler, H. (1960). Selection for two correlated traits by independent culling levels, *Journal of Genetics*, **57,** 329–338.

[121] Yule, G. U. (1897). On the theory of correlation, *Journal of the Royal Statistical Society, Series A*, **60,** 812–854.

[122] Zelen, M. and Severo, N. C. (1960). Graphs for bivariate normal probabilities, *Annals of Mathematical Statistics*, **31,** 619–624.

[123] Zelen, M. and Severo, N. C. (1964). Probability function. Applied Mathemathematics Series **55**, National Bureau of Standards, Washington, D.C. [Also pp. 936–940, *Handbook of Mathematical Functions*, M. Abramowitz and Irene A. Stegun, Eds.]

37

Multivariate t-Distributions

1. Introduction

The univariate central and noncentral t distributions are the topics of Chapters 27 and 31 respectively. It will be recalled that noncentral t with ν degrees of freedom and noncentrality parameter δ was defined as

$$t'_\nu(\delta) = (U + \delta)(\chi_\nu/\sqrt{\nu})^{-1},$$

where U, χ_ν are independent random variables distributed as unit normal and as chi with ν degrees of freedom, respectively. If $\delta = 0$ we have t_ν, that is, t with ν degrees of freedom.

Generalization of these distributions to multivariate situations can take a number of forms, so that there is not a unique "multivariate (central or noncentral) t distribution." The forms that we describe here are not exhaustive, but they include those that have arisen naturally in useful applications. We devote most attention (see Section 3) to one particular form which at present is the most generally useful.

2. Definitions

The joint density function of a number (m) of independent (central or noncentral) t variables is simply the product of the individual t density functions, and calls for no special discussion. The m variates can be expressed as $Y_j = (U_j + \delta_j)\{S_j/\sqrt{\nu_j}\}^{-1}$ $(j = 1,\ldots,m)$ where the U's and S's are all mutually independent; each U_j has a unit normal distribution, and S_j has a χ distribution with ν_j degrees of freedom.

There are two simple ways in which dependence can be introduced into the joint distribution:

(I) Replacing each S_j by the *same* S, and ν_j by ν, with S distributed as χ with ν degrees of freedom, so that

$$Y_j = (U_j + \delta_j)\{S/\sqrt{\nu}\}^{-1} \qquad (j = 1,2,\ldots,m).$$

(II) Retaining different and independent S_j's, but supposing $(U_1,\ldots,U_m)$ to have a joint standardized multinormal distribution with some correlations nonzero.

Cases (I) and (II) can be combined. They do not exhaust all the possibilities. For example (III) $S_1^2,\ldots,S_m^2$ might be supposed to have a joint multivariate gamma distribution of some kind (see Chapter 40). We have, in fact, a combination of (III) and (I) for the joint distribution of

$$Y_1 = \frac{\sqrt{n}(\bar{X}_1 + \theta_1)}{S_1/\sqrt{n-1}}; \qquad Y_2 = \frac{\sqrt{n}(\bar{X}_2 + \theta_2)}{S_2/\sqrt{n-1}}$$

with

$$\bar{X}_t \mp n^{-1}\sum_{j=1}^{n} X_{tj}; \qquad S_t^2 = n^{-1}\sum_{j=1}^{n}(X_{tj} - \bar{X}_t)^2 \qquad (t = 1,2),$$

when (X_{1j},X_{2j}) $(j = 1,\ldots,n)$ are n independent pairs of random variables, each having a bivariate normal distribution with parameters $\xi_1,\xi_2;\sigma_1,\sigma_2;\rho$ (Chapter 35). Then (a) $(\bar{X}_1,\bar{X}_2)$ and (S_1,S_2) are mutually independent; (b) $\bar{X}_1,\bar{X}_2$ have a joint bivariate normal distribution with parameters ξ_1,ξ_2; $\sigma_1/\sqrt{n},\sigma_2/\sqrt{n}$; (c) S_1^2,S_2^2 have a joint bivariate gamma distribution as described in Section 3 of Chapter 40.

The statistics Y_1, Y_2 can be expressed as

$$\frac{U_t + \sqrt{n}(\xi_t + \theta_t)\sigma_t^{-1}}{\sqrt{V_t/(n-1)}} \qquad (t = 1,2),$$

where V_1,V_2 have a joint *standard* bivariate gamma distribution [see (12), Chapter 40].

In each case, the quantities added to the U's in the numerators are called noncentrality parameters. If every one of the noncentrality parameters is zero the distribution is called a *central* multivariate t distribution; otherwise it is called a *noncentral* multivariate t distribution. For the most part, we shall consider central distributions.

3. Multivariate t with Common Denominator

These distributions are formed in the way defined in (I) of Section 2. If (II) is also present—that is, if the numerators are correlated—we have the *general multivariate t distribution* (as it is often called). The central distribution is the joint distribution of $Y_j = X_j(S/\sqrt{\nu})^{-1}$ ($j = 1,\ldots,m$) where $X_1,X_2,\ldots,X_m$ have a joint standardized multinormal distribution with variance-covariance matrix $\mathbf{R}$ (this is also the correlation matrix since the X's are standardized) and S, independent of $(X_1,\ldots,X_m)$ is distributed as χ_ν. The joint probability density function is

$$p_{\mathbf{Y}}(\mathbf{y}) = p_{Y_1,\ldots,Y_m}(y_1,\ldots,y_m) = \frac{\Gamma(\frac{1}{2}(\nu+m))}{(\pi\nu)^{(1/2)m}\Gamma(\frac{1}{2}\nu)\,|\mathbf{R}|^{1/2}}(1+\nu^{-1}\mathbf{y}'\mathbf{R}^{-1}\mathbf{y})^{-\frac{1}{2}(\nu+m)}. \tag{1}$$

(Cornish [12], Dunnett and Sobel [24], and Laurent [54]). A more general form of distribution can be obtained as the joint distribution of $Z_j = \eta_j + \sigma_j Y_j$ ($j = 1,\ldots,m$) with $\sigma_j > 0$.

In the special case when only (I) is present—that is, the X's are mutually independent—we have

$$p_{\mathbf{Y}}(\mathbf{y}) = \frac{\Gamma(\frac{1}{2}(\nu+m))}{(\pi\nu)^{(1/2)m}\Gamma(\frac{1}{2}\nu)}\left(1+\nu^{-1}\sum_{j=1}^{m} y_j^2\right)^{-\frac{1}{2}(\nu+m)}. \tag{2}$$

It follows that $Y_1^2, Y_2^2,\ldots,Y_m^2$ have a joint multivariate F distribution (see Chapter 40), with parameters $1,1,\ldots,1,\nu+m$. The special case of (2) with $\nu = 1$ is termed a *multivariate Cauchy* distribution (see also Chapter 42, Section 6).

Since the joint distribution of any subset of the Y's is of form (2) (with appropriate changes in values of the parameters), it is easy to find the conditional probability density functions. In particular, in the case when the X's are mutually independent (and so $\mathbf{R} = \mathbf{I}$) we have, for any $s \le m$,

$$p_{Y_1,\ldots,Y_s}(y_1,\ldots,y_s) = \frac{\Gamma(\frac{1}{2}(\nu+s))}{(\pi\nu)^{(1/2)s}\Gamma(\frac{1}{2}\nu)}\left(1+\nu^{-1}\sum_{j=1}^{s} y_j^2\right)^{-\frac{1}{2}(\nu+s)}.$$

Hence

$$(3)\quad p(y_{s+1},\ldots,y_m \mid y_1,\ldots,y_s)$$

$$= \frac{\Gamma(\frac{1}{2}(\nu+m))}{(\pi\nu)^{\frac{1}{2}(m-s)}\Gamma(\frac{1}{2}(\nu+s))} \frac{\left(1+\nu^{-1}\sum_{j=1}^{s} y_j^2\right)^{\frac{1}{2}(\nu+s)}}{\left(1+\nu^{-1}\sum_{j=1}^{m} y_j^2\right)^{\frac{1}{2}(\nu+m)}}$$

$$= \frac{\Gamma(\frac{1}{2}(\nu+m))[A_s(\nu+s)/\nu]^{\frac{1}{2}(m-s)}}{[\pi(\nu+s)]^{\frac{1}{2}(m-s)}\Gamma(\frac{1}{2}(\nu+s))}\left[1+\frac{1}{\nu+s}\frac{\nu+s}{\nu A_s}\sum_{j=s+1}^{m} y_j^2\right]^{-\frac{1}{2}(\nu+m)}$$

with

$$A_s = 1+\nu^{-1}\sum_{j=1}^{s} y_j^2.$$

It follows that the joint conditional distribution of $y_t' = y_t(\nu+s)^{1/2}(A_s\nu)^{-1/2}$ $(t = s+1,\ldots,m)$ is that of multivariate t with $\mathbf{R} = \mathbf{I}$ and $(\nu+s)$ degrees of freedom.

Conditional distributions, even in the general case with $\mathbf{R} \neq \mathbf{I}$, can be derived in a straightforward manner without using the joint distribution. For example, since for any fixed value of S the distribution of X_i, given X_j, is normal with expected value $\rho_{ij}X_j$ and variance $(1-\rho_{ij}^2)$, it follows that $E[Y_i \mid Y_j,S] = \rho_{ij}Y_j$ and so $E[Y_i \mid Y_j] = \rho_{ij}Y_j$—that is, the regression is linear. The conditional distribution of Y_i, given Y_j and S, is normal with expected value $\rho_{ij}Y_j$ and variance $(1-\rho_{ij}^2)\{S/\sqrt{\nu}\}^{-2}$. Hence averaging over the distribution of S, the conditional distribution of Y_i, given Y_j, is that of $\sqrt{1-\rho_{ij}^2}\,t_\nu + \rho_{ij}Y_j$ (t_ν denotes 't with ν degrees of freedom').

As ν tends to infinity, the joint distribution of $Y_1,Y_2,\ldots,Y_m$ tends to a multinormal distribution with zero expected value vector and variance-covariance matrix $\mathbf{R}$.

The product moments of $Y_1,\ldots,Y_m$ are easily found by exploiting the independence of $(X_1,\ldots,X_m)$ and S. We have

$$(4)\quad \mu'_{r_1,r_2,\ldots,r_m} = E\left[\prod_{j=1}^{m} Y_j^{r_j}\right] = \nu^{(1/2)\Sigma r_j}E\left[\left(\prod_{j=1}^{m} X_j^{r_j}\right)S^{-\Sigma r_j}\right]$$

$$= \nu^{(1/2)\Sigma r_j}E\left[\prod_{j=1}^{m} X_j^{r_j}\right]E[\chi_\nu^{-\Sigma r_j}]$$

$\left(\text{provided that } \sum_{j=1}^{m} r_j < \frac{1}{2}\nu\right)$. In the special case when $X_1,X_2,\ldots,X_m$ are mutually independent we have

$$(5.1)\quad \mu'_{r_1,r_2,\ldots,r_m} = \nu^{(1/2)\Sigma r_j}E[\chi_\nu^{-\Sigma r_j}]\prod_{j=1}^{m} E[X_j^{r_j}].$$

If any of the r_j's are odd, the moment is zero. If all are even, then

$$\mu'_{r_1,r_2,\ldots,r_m} = \frac{\nu^{(1/2)\Sigma r_j}\prod_{j=1}^{m}\{1\cdot 3\cdot 5\cdots(2r_j-1)\}}{(\nu-2)(\nu-4)\cdots(\nu-\Sigma r_j)}. \tag{5.2}$$

(These are also *central* product moments, since $E[Y_j] = 0$ for all j.)

The moments of noncentral distributions can be obtained in a similar way, with X_j replaced by $X_j + \delta_j$ ($j = 1,2,\ldots,m$) in (4).

Hengartner [40] has shown how moments may be derived by direct integration using the density function (1).

For the case $\mathbf{R} = \mathbf{I}$ [corresponding to (2)], Ihm [41] has suggested a method of computing the probability integral by first taking the denominator (5) fixed, evaluating the resulting multinormal integral, and then evaluating the average with respect to S by a process of numerical or graphical quadrature.

In general, the m-dimensional multivariate t distribution depends on the degrees of freedom, ν, and on $\frac{1}{2}m(m-1)$ different correlations in $\mathbf{R}$.

For calculation of the probability integral, John [42] (see also [43] and [44]) proposed a method similar to that used by Kendall (Chapter 35, Section 4) for evaluating multinormal probability integrals. He first obtained the joint characteristic function of $Y_1,\ldots,Y_m$ in the form

$$E[e^{i\mathbf{t}'\mathbf{Y}}] = [\Gamma(\tfrac{1}{2}\nu)]^{-1}\int_0^\infty x^{(1/2)\nu-1}\exp[-x - \tfrac{1}{4}\nu x^{-1}(\mathbf{t}'\mathbf{R}\mathbf{t})]\,dx$$

and then expressed the integrand as a power series in the correlations.

For the case $m = 2$, the formula used is

$$\exp[-\tfrac{1}{4}\nu x^{-1}\mathbf{t}'\mathbf{R}\mathbf{t}] = \exp[-\tfrac{1}{4}\nu x^{-1}\mathbf{t}'\mathbf{t}]\sum_{j=0}^{\infty}(j!)^{-1}(-\tfrac{1}{2}\nu x^{-1}\rho)^j(t_1t_2)^j.$$

Finally inversion formulas were applied to give the density function and probability integral.' The resulting series is, unfortunately, complicated to use. Provision of adequate tables is difficult. Tables that have been produced are mostly intended for special applications. This has led to specialization of limits to

$$\text{(i)}\ \Pr\left[\bigcap_{j=1}^{m}(Y_j \le t)\right] \quad \text{and} \quad \text{(ii)}\ \Pr\left[\bigcap_{j=1}^{m}(|Y_j| \le t)\right]$$

(i.e., distributions of $\max_j Y_j = (\max_j X_j)[S/\sqrt{\nu}]^{-1}$, and of $\max_j |Y_j| = (\max_j |X_j|)[S/\sqrt{\nu}]^{-1}$), and usually of $\mathbf{R}$ to cases where $\rho_{ij} = \rho$ for all i,j—in particular to $\rho = 0$ (independent X's) and $\rho = -(m-1)^{-1}$ (corresponding to $X_j = U_j - m^{-1}(U_1 + \cdots + U_m)$ with $U_1,\ldots,U_m$ independent unit normal random variables).

In 1954, Dunnett and Sobel [24] obtained the following formulas:

1. *For ν odd*

$$(6.1)\quad \Pr[(Y_1 \le h_1) \cap (Y_2 \le h_2)]$$

$$= \frac{1}{2\pi}\tan^{-1}\left[-\sqrt{\nu}\,\frac{(h_1+h_2)(h_1h_2+\rho\nu)-(h_1h_2-\nu)g}{(h_1h_2-\nu)(h_1h_2+\rho\nu)-\nu(h_1+h_2)g}\right]$$

$$+ \frac{1}{4\sqrt{\pi\nu}}\sum_{j=1}^{\frac{1}{2}(\nu-1)}\frac{\Gamma(j)}{\Gamma(j+\frac{1}{2})}\{h_1(1+h_1^2/\nu)^{-j}[1+\operatorname{sgn}(h_2-\rho h_1)I_{f(h_2,h_1)}(\tfrac{1}{2},j)]$$

$$+ h_2(1+h_2^2/\nu)^{-j}[1+\operatorname{sgn}(h_1-\rho h_2)I_{f(h_1,h_2)}(\tfrac{1}{2},j)]\},$$

where

$$g = \{h_1^2 - 2\rho h_1h_2 + h_2^2 + \nu(1-\rho^2)\}^{1/2},$$

$$f(h_1,h_2) = \frac{(h_1-\rho h_2)^2}{(h_1-\rho h_2)^2 + (1-\rho^2)(\nu+h_2^2)},$$

$$\operatorname{sgn}(\theta) = \begin{cases}1 & (\theta \ge 0)\\ 0 & (\theta < 0)\end{cases},$$

and $I_p(a,b)$ is the incomplete beta function ratio (Chapter 1, Section 3).

2. *For ν even*

$$(6.2)\quad \Pr[(Y_1 \le h_1) \cap (Y_2 \le h_2)]$$

$$= \frac{1}{2\pi}\tan^{-1}\left(\frac{-\sqrt{1-\rho^2}}{\rho}\right) + \frac{1}{4\sqrt{\pi\nu}}\sum_{j=1}^{\frac{1}{2}\nu}\frac{\Gamma(j-\frac{1}{2})}{\Gamma(j)}\{h_1(1+h_1^2/\nu)^{-j+(1/2)}$$

$$\times [1+\operatorname{sgn}(h_2-\rho h_1)I_{f(h_2,h_1)}(\tfrac{1}{2},j-\tfrac{1}{2})]$$

$$+ h_2(1+h_2^2/\nu)^{-j+(1/2)}[1+\operatorname{sgn}(h_1-\rho h_2)I_{f(h_1,h_2)}(\tfrac{1}{2},j-\tfrac{1}{2})]\}.$$

Dunnett and Sobel also obtained asymptotic expansions for these quantities, and for the percentage points $t_{\nu(2),\alpha}$ satisfying

$$(7)\quad \Pr[\max(Y_1,Y_2) \le t_{\nu(2),\alpha}] = \alpha.$$

Dunnett and Sobel [24] give tables of $\Pr[\max(Y_1,Y_2) \le t]$ to five decimal places for $\rho = -0.5, 0.5$; $\nu = 1(1)30(3)60(15)120, 150, 300, 600, \infty$; $t = 0.00(0.25)2.50(0.5)3.5$; for $\nu = 1(1)6$, some higher values of t are included. In [25] there are also tables of $t_{\nu(2),\alpha}$, as defined in (7), to three decimal places for the same values of ν, and $\alpha = 0.5, 0.75, 0.9, 0.95$, and 0.99.

Dunn et al. [21] have given *approximate* tables of $\Pr[\max_{j=1,\ldots,m} |Y_j| \leq t]$ to four decimal points for

$$\rho(\text{common value of } \rho_{ij}) = -(m-1)^{-1}, 0(0.1)0.9,$$
$$\nu = 4(2)12(4)24,30,\infty,$$
$$m = 2(2)20,$$
$$t = 0.2(0.2)6.0.$$

The values for $\nu = \infty$ were obtained from a Monte Carlo (sampling) experiment. Values for finite ν were obtained from the $\nu = \infty$ values by quadrature. It is stated that the tabulated values are correct to two and sometimes three decimal places; for $t > 3.0$, there is usually a three-place accuracy.

Dunnett [23] gives tables of $t_{\nu(m),\alpha}$ such that

$$(7)' \qquad \Pr[\max(Y_1, Y_2, \ldots, Y_m) \leq t_{\nu(m),\alpha}] = \alpha$$

to two decimal places for $\rho_{ij} = \rho = \frac{1}{2}$(all i and j); $m = 1(1)9$; $\alpha = 0.95,0.99$; $\nu = 5(1)20,24,30,40,60,120$. Gupta and Sobel [35] give tables of $t_{\nu(m),\alpha}\sqrt{2}$ to two decimal places for the same $\rho\ (=\frac{1}{2})$; $\alpha = 0.75,0.9,0.95,0.975,0.99$; $\nu = 15(1)20,24,30,36,40,48,60,80,100,120,360,\infty$; $m = 1,4,9(1)15,17,19(5)39,49$. (The $\sqrt{2}$ multiplier was chosen for convenience in certain applications.) For the case $\rho = 0$, Pillai and Ramachandran [61] give $t_{\nu(m),\alpha}$ to two decimal places for $\alpha = 0.95$; $m = 1(1)8$; $\nu = 3(1)10(2)14(1)16(2)20,24,30,40,60,120,\infty$.

Krishnaiah and Armitage [48] give a table of $t_{\nu(m),\alpha}$ to two decimal places for $\nu = 5(1)35$; $m = 1(1)10$; $\rho = 0.0(0.1)0.9$; $\alpha = 0.9,0.95,0.975,0.99$. The values for $\alpha = 0.9,0.95$ are also given in [49]. Hahn [36] gives three decimal places for $\nu = 3(1)12,15(5)30,40,60$; $m = 1(1)6(2)12,15,20$; $\rho = 0.0,0.2,0.4$; $\alpha = 0.9,0.95,0.99$.

Freeman et al. [28] have given a table of $t_{\nu(m),\alpha}$ for $\alpha = 0.95$; $\rho = \frac{1}{2}$; $m = 2,3,4$; and $\nu/(m+1) = 9(10)99,199,499$. For $m = 2$ there are three decimal places; elsewhere two decimal places are given. (Note that if there are $m + 1$ populations with equal variances and samples of size N are chosen from each, then the number of degrees of freedom for the within-populations estimate of variance is $(m+1)(N-1)$.) Freeman and Kuzmack [28a] recently extended these tables for $m = 6, 8, 10, 15, 25, 30$.

Halperin et al. [39] have given, for the limiting case $\rho_{ij} = -(m-1)^{-1}$ (all i and j), values of $t_{|\nu(m)|,\alpha}\sqrt{m(m-1)}$, where

$$(8) \qquad \Pr\left[\bigcap_{j=1}^{m}(|Y_j| \leq t_{|\nu(m)|,\alpha})\right] = \alpha$$

to two decimal places for $\nu = 3(1)10,15,20,30,40,60,120,\infty$; $m = 3(1)10,15,20,30,40,60$; and $\alpha = 0.01,0.05,0.95,0.99$.

This is, in fact a table of the upper and lower 1 and 5% points of the distribution of $\max_j |U_j - \bar{U}| [S/\sqrt{\nu}]^{-1}$ with $U_1, \ldots, U_m$ independent unit normal variates (independent of S) and $\bar{U} = m^{-1} \sum_{j=1}^{m} U_j$.

It is pointed out in [39] that (for $\alpha > \frac{1}{2}$) there are approximate limits

$$t_{\nu,\alpha_1} \leq t_{|\nu(m)|,\alpha} \leq t_{\nu,\alpha_2}, \tag{9}$$

where

$$\alpha_1 = 1 - \tfrac{1}{2}(m-1)^{-1}[1 - \{1 - z(1 - m^{-1})(1-\alpha)\}^{\frac{1}{2}}],$$

$$\alpha_2 = \tfrac{1}{2}(1 + \alpha^{1/m}).$$

For the case $\rho = 0$ Pillai and Ramachandran [61] give $t_{|\nu(m)|,\alpha}$ to two decimal places for $\alpha = 0.05, 0.95$; $m = 1(1)8$; $\nu = 5(5)20,24,30,40,60,120,\infty$; additional values are given for $\alpha = 0.05$; $m = 9,10$; $\nu = 1(1)4$.

Zanella [75] gives tables of $t_{|\nu(m)|,\alpha}$ to three decimal places for $m = 2(1)8$; $\nu = 2(1)30,\infty$; $\alpha = 0.95, 0.90$.

Krishnaiah and Armitage [50] have given values of $t^2_{|\nu(m)|,\alpha}$ to two decimal places for $m = 1(1)10$; $\nu = 5(1)35$; $\rho = 0.05(0.05)0.90$; $\alpha = 0.90,0.95,0.975,0.99$. Hahn and Hendrickson [37] have given values of $t_{|\nu(m)|,\alpha}$, mostly to three decimal places, for $m = 1(1)6(2)12,15,20$; $\nu = 3(1)12,15(5)30,40,60$; $\rho = 0.0(0.2)0.4,0.5$; $\alpha = 0.90,0.95,0.99$.

For the case $m = 2$, there have been extensive further tabulations. Krishnaiah et al. [51] have given tables of $\Pr[\max(|Y_1|,|Y_2|) \leq a]$ to six decimal places for $a = 1.0(0.1)5.5$; $|\rho| = 0.0(0.1)0.9$; $\nu = 5(1)35$.

Carolis and Gori [11] have given similar tables, to five decimal places, for $a = 0.2(0.2)6.0(1)50(5)100(10)200(25)300(50)500(100)900$; $\nu = 1(1)40(5)50(10)100,\infty$, $|\rho| = 0(0.25)0.75$. (The upper limit for a decreases as ν increases.) In [9] there are also values of the upper 95, 99 and 99.9% points of the distribution of $\max(|Y_1|,|Y_2|)$ to five decimal places for $\nu = 1(1)40(5)50(10)100,\infty$; $|\rho| = 0(0.25)0.75$.

Steffens [65, 67] has given values of percentage points of various kinds for the special case $m = 2$, $\rho = 0$. In [65] there are tables of a, to four decimal places where

(i) $\Pr[\max(|Y_1|,|Y_2|) \leq a] = \alpha$,

(ii) $\Pr[\max(Y_1,Y_2) \leq a] = \alpha$

for $\nu = 1(1)100(2)200(10)300(50)650,\infty$; $\alpha = 0.50(0.10)0.90,0.95,0.99$. In [67] there are shorter tables of a, to four decimal places where, in addition to cases (i) and (ii) above, there are also

$$\text{(iii)}\quad \Pr[(Y_1 \le a) \cap (|Y_2| \le a)] = \alpha,$$
$$\text{(iv)}\quad \Pr[\min(|Y_1|,|Y_2|) \ge a] = 1 - \alpha,$$
$$\text{(v)}\quad \Pr[\min(Y_1, Y_2) \ge a] = 1 - \alpha$$

for $\nu = 1(1)20(2)30,48,60,120,240,600,\infty$; $\alpha = 0.90,0.95,0.99$.

In [65] there are also tables of

$$\text{(vi)}\quad \tfrac{1}{4} - \Pr[(0 \le Y_1 \le a) \cap (0 \le Y_2 \le a)]$$

and

$$\text{(vii)}\quad \Pr[(Y_1 \ge a) \cap (Y_2 \ge a)]$$

to four decimal places for $\nu = 1(1)100(2)150(5)200(100)400,\infty$; $a = 0(0.1)3$ [for (vi)], $a = 0(0.1)2$ [for (vii)].

Patil and Kovner [57] have produced tables of the probability integral of a trivariate t distribution with $\rho_{12} = \rho\ (\neq 0)$; $\rho_{13} = \rho_{23} = 0$. Values of $\Pr\left[\bigcap_{j=1}^{3}(Y_j \le t)\right]$ are given to five decimal places for $\rho = -0.5,0.5$; $\nu = 3(2)27,\infty$; $-t = 0.25(0.25)3.00,3.5$.

There are, we believe, no other tables of the probability integral or percentage points of this multivariate t with ρ_{ij}'s not all equal. We may note that Carolis [10] has pointed out that with $m = 3$, the value of

$$\Pr\left[\bigcap_{j=1}^{3} (|Y_j| < a)\right]$$

depends only on $(\rho_{23}^2 + \rho_{13}^2 + \rho_{12}^2)$ and $\rho_{23}\rho_{13}\rho_{12}$, so that tabulation with three separate ρ arguments is not necessary. Dunnett and Sobel [25] have suggested approximate methods of calculation for the case $\rho_{ij} = \varepsilon_i\varepsilon_j$ (for all i,j). We have

$$\Pr\left[\bigcap_{j=1}^{m}(Y_j \le a_j)\right] = \int_0^\infty p_S(s)\Pr\left[\bigcap_{j=1}^{m}(X_j \le a_j s/\sqrt{\nu}) \mid S = s\right] ds. \tag{10}$$

Since $X_1,X_2,\ldots,X_m$ are independent of S,

$$\Pr\left[\bigcap_{j=1}^{m}(X_j \le a_j s/\sqrt{\nu}) \mid S = s\right] = \Pr\left[\bigcap_{j=1}^{m}(X_j \le a_j s/\sqrt{\nu})\right].$$

This is a multinormal probability integral and, utilizing the fact that $X_1,\ldots,X_m$ can be represented by $X_j = \sqrt{1 - \varepsilon_j^2}\, U_j + \varepsilon_j U_0$ with $U_0,U_1,\ldots,U_m$ independent unit normal variables (see Chapter 35, Section 4.3), it can be represented as

$$\int_{-\infty}^{\infty} Z(u_0) \prod_{j=1}^{m} \Phi\left(\frac{a_j s \nu^{-1/2} + \varepsilon_j u_0}{(1 - \varepsilon_j^2)^{1/2}}\right) du_0.$$

This can be regarded as the expected value of

$$\prod_{j=1}^{m} \Phi\left(\frac{a_j s \nu^{-1/2} + \varepsilon_j U_0}{(1-\varepsilon_j^2)^{1/2}}\right)$$

when U_0 has a unit normal distribution. Dunnett and Sobel [24] point out that if all ε's are positive this cannot be less than the product of expected values of

$$\Phi\left(\frac{a_j s \nu^{-1/2} + \varepsilon_j U_0}{(1-\varepsilon_j^2)^{1/2}}\right)$$

(since $\Phi(\cdot)$ are all increasing functions of U_0). Because these expected values are simply

$$\Pr[U_j\sqrt{(1-\varepsilon_j^2)} - \varepsilon_j U_0 \le a_j s \nu^{-1/2}] = \Pr[X_j \le a_j s \nu^{-1/2}]$$

it follows, on using this result in (10), that

$$\Pr\left[\bigcap_{j=1}^{m} (Y_j \le a_j)\right] \ge \prod_{j=1}^{m} \Pr[Y_j \le a_j]. \tag{11.1}$$

An alternative lower bound, based directly on Bonferroni's inequalities, is

$$1 - \sum_{j=1}^{m} \Pr[Y_j > a_j]. \tag{11.2}$$

The accuracy of these lower bounds is compared in Table 1, taken from [14].

TABLE 1

Comparison of Exact Values of $t_{\nu(m),\alpha}$ Points with Approximations for Selected Values of ν, m, and α when $\rho_{ij} = \frac{1}{2}$ for All i and j

		$m = 3$			$m = 9$		
α	ν	Approximations (11.2)	Approximations (11.1)	Exact values	Approximations		Exact value
0.99	5	4.46	4.46	4.21	5.75	5.75	5.03
	∞	2.71	2.71	2.68	3.06	3.06	3.00
0.95	5	2.91	2.90	2.68	3.93	3.90	3.30
	∞	2.13	2.12	2.06	2.54	2.53	2.42
0.75	5	1.62	1.55	1.32	2.48	2.38	1.81
	∞	1.38	1.33	1.19	1.19	1.86	1.60
0.50	5	1.07	0.89	0.62	1.93	1.71	1.10
	∞	0.97	0.82	0.59	1.59	1.45	1.04

The approximate values are obtained by regarding the corresponding inequalities as equalities. It can be seen that (11.1) is rather more accurate, though neither is very good.

Dunnett and Sobel [25] give further lower bounds based on bivariate t probabilities. These are more accurate than (11.1–2) but considerable inaccuracy still remains.

We also note that for the case when $\rho_{ij} = \rho\ (> 0)$ for all i,j, Tong [74] has shown that for all $m \geq k \geq 2$

$$\Pr\left[\bigcap_{j=1}^{m}(Y_j \leq t)\right] \geq \left\{\Pr\left[\bigcap_{j=1}^{k}(Y_j \leq t)\right]\right\}^{m/k}$$

$$\geq \left\{\Pr\left[\bigcap_{j=1}^{2}(Y_j \leq t)\right] - \left(\Pr[Y_1 \leq t]\right)^2\right\}^{1/2}$$

[cf. equation (11.3) of Chapter 35].

The same inequalities hold (for $t > 0$) if Y_j is replaced by $|Y_j|$ ($j = 1,2,\ldots,m$).

Halperin [38] has extended (11) to the case when

$$Y_j = U_{j0}\left[\sum_{i=1}^{\nu+n_j} U_{ji}^2/(\nu + n_j)\right]^{-1/2}, \quad j = 1,2$$

where (U_{1i},U_{2i}) are mutually independent (for different i), with the same joint standardized bivariate normal distribution for $i = 0,1,\ldots,\nu$ and with $U_{1i},U_{2i'}$ independent if either i or i' exceeds ν.

Dunn [20] has shown that while $\Pr[|Y_1| < t]$ is an increasing functions of ν, this is not true of $\Pr\left[\bigcap_{j=1}^{m}(|Y_j| < t)\right]$ for all m. She shows, in fact, that if $\rho_{ij} = 0$ for all i,j then for any given t and any $\nu_1 > \nu_2$ there is a number $m(t,\nu_1,\nu_2)$ such that, for all $m > m(t,\nu_1,\nu_2)$, $\Pr\left[\bigcap_{j=1}^{m}(|Y_j| < t)\right]$ is less for $\nu = \nu_1$ than for $\nu = \nu_2$. Considerations of continuity indicate that this is also true when the ρ_{ij}'s are not all zero. This is borne out by numerical investigation, though the lower limit $m(t,\nu_1,\nu_2)$ for m tends to increase as the ρ_{ij}'s depart from zero. (If all ρ's are 1 then we are effectively in the univariate t_ν case, and $m(t,\nu_1,\nu_2)$ becomes infinite.)

Krishnaiah and Armitage [49] point out that the method can be extended directly to the noncentral case when the expected value ξ_j, of X_j is not zero for each j. The only change necessary in (10) is replacement of $a_j s\nu^{-1/2}$ by $(a_j s\nu^{-1/2} - \xi_j)$.

Noncentral multivariate t distributions, being the joint distribution of

$$Y_j = (U_j + \delta_j)(S/\sqrt{\nu})^{-1} \qquad (j = 1,\ldots,m)$$

[as described in (I) of Section 2], have been studied by Zanella [75] [76]. He has given the following expression for the joint density function, assuming the standardized multinormal variables **U** to have correlation matrix **R**:

$$(12)\quad p_{\mathbf{Y}}(\mathbf{y}) = \exp[-\tfrac{1}{2}\boldsymbol{\delta}'\mathbf{R}^{-1}\boldsymbol{\delta}](\nu\pi)^{-(1/2)m}|\mathbf{R}|^{-1/2}\{\Gamma(\tfrac{1}{2}\nu)\}^{-1} \times (1 + \nu^{-1}\mathbf{y}'\mathbf{R}^{-1}\mathbf{y})^{-1/2(\nu+m)} \times \sum_{j=0}^{\infty}\frac{\Gamma(\frac{1}{2}(\nu+m+j))}{j!}\left[\frac{2(\boldsymbol{\delta}'\mathbf{R}^{-1}\mathbf{y})^2}{\nu(1+\nu^{-1}\mathbf{y}'\mathbf{R}^{-1}\mathbf{y})}\right]^{(1/2)j}.$$

Independently, Miller [55] has expressed (12) in terms of the parabolic cylinder function

$$D_S(z) = \frac{2^{S/2}\Gamma(\frac{1}{2})}{\Gamma(-S/2+\frac{1}{2})}e^{-z^2/4}M\left(-\frac{S}{2},\frac{1}{2};\frac{z^2}{2}\right) + \frac{2^{\frac{1}{2}(S-1)}\Gamma(-\frac{1}{2})}{\Gamma(-S/2)}ze^{-z^2/4}M\left(-\frac{S}{2}+\frac{1}{2},\frac{3}{2};\frac{z^2}{2}\right),$$

where $M(\cdot)$ is the confluent hypergeometric function defined in Chapter 1, Section 3, obtaining

$$(12)'\quad p_{\mathbf{Y}}(\mathbf{y}) = \frac{\Gamma(\frac{1}{2}(\nu+m))}{\Gamma(\frac{1}{2}\nu)}\frac{1}{(\nu\pi)^{(1/2)m}|\mathbf{R}|^{1/2}}(1+\nu^{-1}\mathbf{y}'\mathbf{R}^{-1}\mathbf{y})^{-\frac{1}{2}(\nu+m)} \times \exp[-\tfrac{1}{2}\boldsymbol{\delta}'\mathbf{R}^{-1}\boldsymbol{\delta}] \times \exp[\tfrac{1}{4}(\mathbf{y}'\mathbf{R}^{-1}\boldsymbol{\delta})^2(\nu+\mathbf{y}'\mathbf{R}^{-1}\mathbf{y})^{-1}]D_{-(\nu+m)}(-\mathbf{y}'\mathbf{R}^{-1}\boldsymbol{\delta}(\nu+\mathbf{y}'\mathbf{R}^{-1}\mathbf{y})^{-\frac{1}{2}})$$

Miller [55] has also obtained the joint distribution of Y_j when $\delta_1 = \delta_2 = \cdots \delta_m = 0$, but S has a noncentral $\chi'_\nu(\lambda)$ distribution. The density then is

$$(13)\quad p_{\mathbf{Y}}(\mathbf{y}) = \frac{\Gamma(\frac{1}{2}(\nu+m))}{\Gamma(\frac{1}{2}\nu)}\frac{1}{(\nu\pi)^{(1/2)m}|\mathbf{R}|^{1/2}}(1+\nu^{-1}\mathbf{y}'\mathbf{R}^{-1}\mathbf{y})^{-\frac{1}{2}(\nu+m)} \times e^{-(1/2)\lambda}M(\tfrac{1}{2}(\nu+m),\tfrac{1}{2}\nu;\tfrac{1}{2}\lambda(1+\nu^{-1}\mathbf{y}'\mathbf{R}^{-1}\mathbf{y})^{-1}).$$

Steffens [68] has considered the joint distribution of

$$Y_1 = U_1[\chi_\nu/\sqrt{\nu}]^{-1}$$

and

$$Y_2 = U_2[\{\chi_\nu^2 + (U_3+\delta)^2\}/(\nu+1)]^{-1/2}$$

(U_1,U_2,U_3,χ_ν all mutually independent), which might be regarded as a noncentral form of the distribution studied by Halperin [38]. In [68] there are given upper 5% points of $\max(Y_1,Y_2)$ for $\nu = 1,2,5,10,20,50,\infty$ and noncentrality parameters $\delta = 0(1)5$.

Patil and Kovner [58] have discussed a doubly noncentral bivariate t distribution where

$$(14)\qquad Y_1 = (U_1 + \delta_1)(X/\nu)^{-1/2}; \qquad Y_2 = (U_2 + \delta_2)(X/\nu)^{-1/2}$$

and X has a noncentral $\chi_\nu'^2$ distribution.

Krishnan [52] has discussed a form of doubly "noncentral" bivariate t distribution obtained by replacing the common denominator X in (14) by variables X_1,X_2 having a joint noncentral bivariate chi-square distribution with ν degrees of freedom (see Chapter 40, Section 4).

4. Genesis and Applications

Ando and Kaufman [3] have shown that the multivariate t distribution of Section 3 can be obtained as the distribution of the sample mean vector for random samples from a mixture of multinormal populations in which the expected value vector has a joint multinormal distribution and the variance-covariance matrix an independent joint Wishart distribution (see Chapter 38).

In other words, an equivalent representation to $\mathbf{t} = (\chi_\nu^2/\nu)^{-1/2}\mathbf{U}$ (where $\mathbf{U}$ has a standardized multinormal distribution with correlation matrix $\mathbf{R}$), is

$$(15)\qquad \mathbf{t} = \sqrt{\nu}\,\mathbf{J}^{-1}\mathbf{X},$$

where $\mathbf{JJ}'$ has a Wishart distribution with variance-covariance matrix $\mathbf{R}^{-1}$ and degrees of freedom $(\nu + m - 1)$ (see Chapter 38) and the m variables in $\mathbf{X}$ are mutually independent, each having a unit normal distribution. Earlier, Cornish [13] had obtained the distribution by a fiducial argument. Geisser and Cornfield [29] used a Bayesian argument with (as pointed out by Stone [70]) an improper prior distribution.

They supposed that the parameters $\boldsymbol{\xi},\mathbf{V}$ have a joint prior distribution with density proportional to $|\mathbf{V}|^{-(1/2)\nu}$. (This implies that the "density" of $\boldsymbol{\xi}$ is uniform and so not proper, but this is just a formal "derivation.") Geisser and Cornfield [29] show that the posterior joint distribution of $\boldsymbol{\xi}$, given a random sample of size n with sample mean vector $\bar{\mathbf{X}}$ and sample covariance matrix $(n - 1)^{-1}\mathbf{S}$ is the multivariate t distribution:

$$(16)\qquad p(\boldsymbol{\xi} \mid \mathbf{X},\mathbf{S}) = \frac{\Gamma(\frac{1}{2}(n + m - \nu + 1))}{\pi^{(1/2)m}\Gamma(\frac{1}{2}(n - \nu + 1))} \times |\mathbf{S}|^{-(1/2)m}[1 + n(\bar{\mathbf{X}} - \boldsymbol{\xi})'\mathbf{S}^{-1}(\bar{\mathbf{X}} - \boldsymbol{\xi})]^{-\frac{1}{2}(n+m-\nu+1)}.$$

The distribution obtained by putting $m = 2$ in (16) is that given by Cornish

[13] (see also Fisher [26]) as a "fiducial" distribution for $\boldsymbol{\xi}$. (For another approach, based on a "structural" model, see Fraser and Haq [27].)

Tiao and Zellner [73] obtained a general multivariate t distribution as the posterior distribution of estimated linear regression coefficients in a multinormal population with uniform prior distribution, assuming that the prior density of the variance-covariance matrix $\mathbf{V}$ is proportional to $|\mathbf{V}_0|^{-\frac{1}{2}(m+1)}$ with $m > 0$.

The multivariate t distribution can be used for fitting observed data (Bennett [6]). When used in this way, a further set of m parameters ($\boldsymbol{\eta}$) is introduced in (1), giving the joint density function

$$(17)\quad p_Y(\mathbf{y}) = \frac{\Gamma(\frac{1}{2}(\nu + m))}{(\pi\nu)^{m/2}\Gamma(\nu/2)\,|\mathbf{R}|^{1/2}}\,[1 + \nu^{-1}(\mathbf{y} - \boldsymbol{\eta})'\mathbf{R}^{-1}(\mathbf{y} - \boldsymbol{\eta})]^{-\frac{1}{2}(\nu+m)}$$

[cf. (16)]. There are $1 + \frac{1}{2}m(m + 1)$ parameters (ν, $\mathbf{R}$, and $\boldsymbol{\eta}$) that can be fitted. The parameter ν can, of course, be assigned a fractional value. Even if the value of ν be supposed known, the maximum likelihood equations for the remaining parameters are "quite involved" (Bennett [6]).

Multivariate t distributions of the kind described of Section 3 can also be used in constructing simultaneous confidence intervals for expected values of a number of normal populations (John [42]). Suppose that a variable X has expected value ξ_i and standard deviation σ in the ith population. Given random samples of sizes $n_1,n_2,\ldots,n_k$ with sample means $\bar{X}_1,\bar{X}_2,\ldots,\bar{X}_k$ and a combined unbiased within-population mean square estimator of σ^2, V_0, distributed as $\chi^2_{\nu_0}\sigma^2/\nu_0$ with $\nu_0 = \sum_{j=1}^{k} n_j - k$ degrees of freedom, then the statistics

$$\sqrt{n_j}(\bar{X}_j - \xi_j)/\sqrt{V_0} \qquad (j = 1,2,\ldots,k)$$

have a k-dimensional multivariate t distribution with ν_0 degrees of freedom, and all ρ_{ij}'s equal to zero. If $t_{|\nu_0(k)|,\alpha}$ be defined as in (8), with all ρ's equal to zero, then the set of simultaneous confidence intervals

$$\bar{X}_j - t_{|\nu_0(k)|,\alpha}\sqrt{V_0/n_j} < \xi_j < \bar{X}_j + t_{|\nu_0(k)|,\alpha}\sqrt{V_0/n_j} \qquad (j = 1,2,\ldots,k)$$

has joint confidence coefficient $100\alpha\%$.

Applications to certain problems of ranking and selecting normal populations according to their expected values have been described by Bechhofer et al. [4], Dunnett [23], Dunnett and Sobel [24], Gupta and Panchapakesan [34], Gupta and Sobel [35], and Krishnaiah [47]. (Details of many other ranking and selection procedures are given in the book by Bechhofer et al. [5].) Applications to construction of confidence bands for a normal cumulative distribution have been described by Kanofsky [45].

If (i) $\bar{X}_1,\bar{X}_2,\ldots,\bar{X}_k$ are not independent, but have a joint multinormal distribution with correlation coefficients ρ_{ij} and (ii) the variances of

$\bar{X}_1,\bar{X}_2,\ldots,\bar{X}_k$ are not necessarily proportional to $n_1^{-1},n_2^{-1},\ldots,n_k^{-1}$ but are estimated by independent statistics $V_1/n_1,V_2/n_2,\ldots,V_k/n_k$ with V_j/n_j distributed as $\chi^2_{\nu_j}$ var$(\bar{X}_j)$ then the statistics $Y'_j = \sqrt{n_j}(X_j - \xi_j)/\sqrt{V_j}$ $(j = 1,\ldots,k)$ have a joint multivariate t distribution purely of type (II) (Section 2) which is different from that discussed in Section 3. In the next section we give a general review of these and other types of multivariate t distributions.

5. Other Kinds of Multivariate t Distributions

Dunn and Massey [22] have described a multivariate t distribution of type (II) of Section 1. They point out that to use this distribution in the construction of sets of simultaneous confidence intervals it is desirable to have tables of percentage points of the distribution of $\max_j |Y'_j|$, where Y'_j is as defined near the end of Section 4. Such tables are not available. There is, however, an inequality due to Halperin of the same form as (9), which is also valid for this kind of multivariate t distribution. This makes it possible to give bounds for the percentage points, though these may not always be very close.

Several kinds of multivariate t distributions have been discussed by Miller [55]. These are included under the general form

$$Y_j = X_j\{R_j/\nu_j\}^{-1/2} \qquad (j = 1,\ldots,m),$$

where $X_1,X_2,\ldots,X_m$ have a joint multinormal distribution with var$(X_j) = 1$ for all j and $R_j = \sum_{l=1}^{\nu_j} X_{jl}^2$ where $(X_{j1},\ldots,X_{j\nu_j})$ have a joint standardized multinormal distribution $(j = 1,\ldots,m)$. (The vectors $(X_{j1},\ldots,X_{j\nu_j})$ may not be independent.) If the expected values of $X_1,\ldots,X_m$ are all zero, the distributions are central; otherwise they are noncentral. [See also (14) and (15) above.]

This class includes the bivariate t distribution obtained by Siddiqui [64], which is the joint distribution of central t statistics constructed separately for the two variables of a bivariate normal distribution from a random sample of size n. Clearly the joint distribution of the two t statistics (T_1,T_2, say) depends only on ρ, the correlation between the variables. Siddiqui [64] shows that the joint density function of T_1,T_2 and R (the sample correlation) is

$$(18)\quad p_{T_1,T_2,R}(t_1,t_2,r) = \frac{(1-\rho^2)^{(\frac{1}{2})n}(n-2)\Gamma(n)}{(2\pi)^{3/2}\Gamma(n+\frac{1}{2})}\left[\left(1+\frac{t_1^2}{n-1}\right)\left(1+\frac{t_2^2}{n-1}\right)\right]^{-(\frac{1}{2})n} \times (1-r^2)^{\frac{1}{2}(n-4)}(1-b-cr)^{-n+\frac{1}{2}}F(\tfrac{1}{2},\tfrac{1}{2};n+\tfrac{1}{2};\tfrac{1}{2}(1+b+cr)),$$

where $F(\cdot)$ is the hypergeometric function defined in Chapter 1, Section 3,

$$b = \frac{\rho t_1 t_2}{n-1}\left[\left(1+\frac{t_1^2}{n-1}\right)\left(1+\frac{t_2^2}{n-1}\right)\right]^{-1/2},$$

$$c = \rho\left[\left(1+\frac{t_1^2}{n-1}\right)\left(1+\frac{t_2^2}{n-1}\right)\right]^{-1/2},$$

Note that if $\rho = 0$, then $b = c = 0$ and T_1, T_2, and R are mutually independent.

Approximating the value of

$$\int_{-1}^{1}(1-r^2)^{\frac{1}{2}(n-4)}(1-b-cr)^{-\frac{1}{2}(n+\frac{1}{2})}F(\tfrac{1}{2},\tfrac{1}{2};n+\tfrac{1}{2};\tfrac{1}{2}(1+b+cr))\,dr$$

by a saddle-point method, Siddiqui [64] obtains the approximation

(19)

$$p_{T_1\,T_2}(t_1,t_2) = \frac{(1-\rho^2)^{(1/2)n}(n-2)\Gamma(n)}{2\pi\sqrt{n}\,\Gamma(n+\frac{1}{2})\rho^n}\,c^n(1-b)^{3/2}[(1-b)^2-c^2]^{-(1/2)n+1}$$
$$\times F\left(\tfrac{1}{2},\tfrac{1}{2};n+\tfrac{1}{2};\frac{1-b^2+c^2}{1-b}\right).$$

For large n, the distribution is approximated by a standardized bivariate normal distribution with correlation ρ.

Steffens [66] has defined a *stepwise multivariate t distribution* which can be applied in stepwise linear multiple regression analysis. We take the following independent random variables: (a) X_1, distributed as $\chi_\nu^2\sigma^2$ and (b) $Z_1, Z_2, \ldots, Z_n$, with Z_j distributed normally with expected value ζ_j and standard deviation σ. Then we consider the joint distribution of

$$Y_j = Z_j[(\nu+j-1)/X_j]^{1/2} \qquad (j = 1,\ldots,m)$$

with

$$X_j = X_1 + \sum_{i=2}^{j-1} Z_i^2 \qquad (j = 2,\ldots,m).$$

Since X_j $(j \geq 2)$ is distributed as σ^2 times a noncentral χ^2, in fact as $\sigma^2\chi'^2_{\nu+i-1}\left(\sigma^{-2}\sum_{i=2}^{j-1}\zeta_i^2\right)$ it follows that for $j \geq 2$, Y_j is distributed as a doubly noncentral t (Chapter 31, Section 8.2) with $(\nu+j-1)$ degrees of freedom and noncentrality parameters ζ_j/σ (numerator), $\sigma^{-2}\sum_{i=1}^{j-1}\zeta_i^2$ (denominator). Of course, Y_1 is distributed as noncentral t with ν degrees of freedom and noncentrality parameter ζ_1/σ.

In the central case ($\zeta_1 = \zeta_2 = \cdots = \zeta_m = 0$) the Y_j's are mutually independent (see also Section 5, Chapter 40). This is not so in the noncentral case.

Yet another kind of "multivariate t" distribution (though with marginals that are not t distributions) is obtained as the joint distribution of

$$Y_i = \sqrt{n}\bar{X}_i[S/\{m(n-1)\}]^{-1/2} \qquad (i = 1,\ldots,m), \tag{20}$$

where $\{X_{ij},\ldots,X_{mj})$ $(j = 1,\ldots,n)$ are n independent vectors, each having the same standardized multinormal distribution, and

$$\bar{X}_i = n^{-1}\sum_{j=1}^{n} X_{ij}; \qquad S = \sum_{i=1}^{m} S_i; \qquad S_i = \sum_{j=1}^{n}(X_{ij} - \bar{X}_i)^2.$$

In the bivariate case we can use the results of Section 3 of Chapter 40 to obtain the joint distribution of Y_1 and Y_2. From (12) of that section it can be deduced that $(S_1 + S_2)$ is distributed as a mixture of $(1-\rho^2)\chi^2_{2(n-1+2j)}$ $(j = 0,1,\ldots)$ with weights c_j = coefficient of u^j in the negative binomial expansion of

$$\left(\frac{1}{1-\rho^2} - \frac{\rho^2 u}{1-\rho^2}\right)^{-\frac{1}{2}(n-1)},$$

which is

$$\binom{\frac{1}{2}(n-3)+j}{j}\rho^{2j}(1-\rho^2)^{\frac{1}{2}(n-1)}.$$

Hence the joint distribution of Y_1 and Y_2 is a mixture of the joint distributions of

$$Y_{i,\nu} = \sqrt{n}\;\bar{X}_i[\chi^2_\nu/\{2(n-1)\}]^{-1/2}(1-\rho^2)^{-1/2} \qquad (i = 1,2)$$

with $\nu = 2(n-1+2j)$ $(j = 0,1,\ldots)$ having weight c_j. Now the joint distribution of

$$Y_{i,\nu}(1-\rho^2)^{1/2}[\nu/\{2(n-1)\}]^{1/2} \qquad (i = 1,2)$$

is a standard bivariate t with ν degrees of freedom. Hence, using (1),

(21) $p_{Y_1,Y_2}(y_1,y_2)$

$$= \frac{1}{2\pi\sqrt{(1-\rho^2)}}\sum_{j=0}^{\infty} c_j\,\frac{(1-\rho^2)(n-1+2j)}{n-1}\left[1 + \frac{y_1^2 - 2\rho y_1 y_2 + y_2^2}{2(n-1)}\right]^{-n-2j}$$

$$= \frac{(1-\rho^2)^{(1/2)n}}{2\pi}\sum_{j=0}^{\infty}\binom{\frac{1}{2}(n-1)+j}{j}\rho^{2j}\left[1 + \frac{y_1^2 - 2\rho y_1 y_2 + y_2^2}{2(n-1)}\right]^{-n-2j}.$$

Another form is

$$(21)' \quad p_{Y_1,Y_2}(y_1,y_2) = \frac{(1-\rho^2)^{(1/2)n}}{2\pi}\left[1+\frac{y_1^2-2\rho y_1y_2+y_2^2}{2(n-1)}\right]^{-n}$$
$$\times\left[1-\rho^2\left(1+\frac{y_1^2-2\rho y_1y_2+y_2^2}{2(n-1)}\right)^{-2}\right]^{-\frac{1}{2}(n+1)}.$$

Further forms for the density function are given by Patil and Liao [59].

Dickey [17] has constructed a *multivariate Behrens-Fisher distribution* as the joint distribution of the elements of the vector $\sum_{j=1}^{k}\mathbf{B}_j\mathbf{Y}_j$ where $\mathbf{Y}_1,\ldots,\mathbf{Y}_k$ are independent vectors, each of m elements having a joint multivariate t distribution of the kind described in Section 3, with degrees of freedom $\nu_1,\ldots,\nu_k$ respectively, with $\mathbf{R}=\mathbf{I}$ (i.e., with joint density function of form (2)); and $\mathbf{B}_1,\ldots,\mathbf{B}_k$ are each square nonsingular matrices. This kind of distribution had been encountered by Cornish [15] as a result of applying fiducial methods to comparison of means of two multinormal populations. In an obvious notation, we have

$$\boldsymbol{\xi}_j = \overline{\mathbf{X}}_j + \sqrt{V_j}\,\mathbf{t}_j \qquad (j=1,2),$$

and to test $\boldsymbol{\xi}_1=\boldsymbol{\xi}_2$ it is natural to consider using the critical region

$$|\sqrt{V_1}\,\mathbf{t}_1-\sqrt{V_2}\,\mathbf{t}_2-(\overline{\mathbf{X}}_1-\overline{\mathbf{X}}_2)|>\kappa.$$

The quantities $\sqrt{V_1},\sqrt{V_2},\overline{\mathbf{X}}_1,\overline{\mathbf{X}}_2$ are regarded as fixed; $\mathbf{t}_1$ and $\mathbf{t}_2$ have independent multivariate t distributions.

We finally note a univariate distribution—that of the ratio of two variables having a joint density of type (17).

The ratio of the two (central) t_ν variates $Y_1=U_1[\chi_\nu/\sqrt{\nu}]^{-1}$; $Y_2=U_2[\chi_\nu/\sqrt{\nu}]^{-1}$ is equal to U_1/U_2. It is therefore distributed as the ratio of two unit normal (possibly correlated) variables.

The distribution of the ratio

$$(22) \qquad T_{12}=(Y_1+\eta_1)/(Y_2+\eta_2)$$

has been studied by Press [62]. He showed that it is possible to obtain the distribution of T_{12} from a knowledge of the distribution when U_1 and U_2 are uncorrelated. If the correlation between U_1 and U_2 is ρ (>0, as can always be arranged), then U_1 can be represented as $\sqrt{1-\rho}\,U+\sqrt{\rho}\,U_2$, where U is a unit normal variable independent of U_2. Then since we can write $U_1 + \eta_1\chi_\nu/\sqrt{\nu}$ in the form

$$\sqrt{1-\rho}\,(U_2 + \eta_2\chi_\nu/\sqrt{\nu}) + \sqrt{\rho}\left\{U + \left(\frac{\eta_1}{\sqrt{\rho}} - \eta_2\sqrt{\frac{1-\rho}{\rho}}\right)\chi_\nu/\sqrt{\nu}\right\}$$

it follows that

$$\frac{Y_1+\eta_1}{Y_2+\eta_2} = \frac{U_1 + \eta_1\chi_\nu/\sqrt{\nu}}{U_2 + \eta_2\chi_\nu/\sqrt{\nu}} = \sqrt{1-\rho} + \frac{Y + \rho^{-1/2}\{\eta_1 - \eta_2\sqrt{1-\rho}\}}{Y_2+\eta_2}\sqrt{\rho}$$

with $Y = U[\chi_\nu/\sqrt{\nu}]^{-1}$ and U independent of U_2.

Press [62] showed that if U_1 and U_2 are independent, then the density function of T_{12} is

$$(23)\quad p_{T_{12}}(t) = [\pi^{-1}(1+t^2)^{-1}]\{1 + \nu^{-1}(\eta_1^2+\eta_2^2)\}^{-(1/2)\nu}$$
$$\times\left[1 - \frac{\sqrt{\nu}\{1+\nu^{-1}(\eta_1^2+\eta_2^2)\}^{(1/2)\nu}}{B(\frac{1}{2},(\nu+1)/2)}\right.$$
$$\left.\times\frac{(\eta_1 t + \eta_2)(1+t^2)^{(1/2)\nu}}{\{1+t^2+\nu^{-1}(\eta_1-\eta_2 t)^2\}^{\frac{1}{2}(\nu-1)}}\{2\Pr[t_{\nu+1} < g] - 1\}\right],$$

where $g = (\eta_1 t + \eta_2)(1+\nu^{-1}) \times \{1 + t^2 + \nu^{-1}(\eta_1 - \eta_2 t)^2\}^{-1/2}$. Press gives values of upper and lower 1, 5, and 10% points of the distribution of (22), to three decimal places for $\nu = 1,2,5,10,30$; $\eta_1,\eta_2 = 0(1)3$.

When η_2 is large (say greater than $t_{\nu,0.995}$) a useful approximation can be made by neglecting the probability that the denominator of T_{12} is not positive. Then

$$\Pr[T_{12} \le t] \doteqdot \Pr[Y_1 + \eta_1 \le t(Y_2 + \eta_2)].$$

This last probability is

$$\Pr[U_1 + \eta_1\chi_\nu/\sqrt{\nu} \le t(U_2 + \eta_2\chi_\nu/\sqrt{\nu})] = \Pr\left[\frac{U_1 - tU_2}{\chi_\nu/\sqrt{\nu}} \le t\eta_2 - \eta_1\right].$$

If U_1,U_2 have a standard bivariate normal distribution with correlation coefficient ρ then $U_1 - tU_2$ is distributed as $(1 - 2\rho t + t^2)^{1/2}$ times a unit normal variable, independently of χ_ν. Hence

$$(24)\qquad \Pr[T_{12} \le t] = \Pr\left[t_\nu \le \frac{t\eta_2 - \eta_1}{(1 - 2t\rho + t^2)^{1/2}}\right].$$

As an example, take $\eta_2 = 3$, $\eta_1 = 2$, $\rho = 0$. Then approximate percentage points for T_{12} are obtained by solving the equation

$$t_{\nu,\alpha} = \frac{3t - 2}{\sqrt{1 + t^2}}. \tag{25}$$

Taking $\nu = 10$ and $\alpha = 0.90$ we find from Press's tables the value 1.468. Inserting this value for t in (24) gives 1.353 as compared with the exact value for $t_{10,0.90}$ (to three decimal places) which is 1.372. For $\nu = 30$ and $\alpha = 0.90$, Press's tables give the value 1.415, leading to 1.296 from (24) as compared with $t_{30,0.90} = 1.310$.

For ν large the distribution of T_{12} tends to that of the ratio of two normal variables.

Kappenman [46] has extended this work, studying the joint distribution of $Z_j = Y_j/Y_1$ $(j = 2,\ldots,m)$ when $Y_1,\ldots,Y_m$ have the joint density (17).

. Matrix t Distributions

A natural generalization of (15) is obtained by considering the joint distribution of elements of the matrix $\mathbf{T} = \mathbf{J}^{-1}\mathbf{X}$ where $\mathbf{X}$ is now an $m \times q$ matrix of random variables, each row having a multinormal distribution with expected value vector $\mathbf{O}$ and variance-covariance matrix $\mathbf{Q}$; different rows are mutually independent. $\mathbf{JJ}'$ has a Wishart $W_m(\nu + m - 1, \mathbf{P})$ distribution (see Chapter 38); $\mathbf{P}$ and $\mathbf{Q}$ are positive definite.

The joint density function of the elements of $\mathbf{T}$ is

$$\pi^{-(1/2)mq}\Gamma_q(\tfrac{1}{2}(\nu + m + q - 1))\{\Gamma_q(\tfrac{1}{2}(\nu + q - 1))\}^{-1} \times |\mathbf{Q}|^{\frac{1}{2}(\nu+q-1)}|\mathbf{P}|^{(1/2)q}|\mathbf{Q} + \mathbf{T}'\mathbf{PT}|^{-\frac{1}{2}(\nu+mq+-1)}. \tag{26.1}$$

An alternative expression is

$$\pi^{-(1/2)mq}\Gamma_q(\tfrac{1}{2}(\nu + m + q - 1))\{\Gamma_m(\tfrac{1}{2}(\nu + m - 1))\}^{-1} \times |\mathbf{P}|^{-(1/2)(\nu+m-1)}|\mathbf{Q}|^{-(1/2)m}|\mathbf{P}^{-1} + \mathbf{TQ}^{-1}\mathbf{T}'|^{-(1/2)(\nu+m+q-1)}, \tag{26.2}$$

[$\Gamma_m(\cdot)$ is defined in Chapter 38, equation (12).]

These results were obtained by Dickey [18]. It is natural to call the distribution the *matric-t distribution.*

A special case of this distribution, obtained by Tan [72], was called by him the *restricted matric-t distribution.* This is the joint distribution of $\mathbf{T} = \mathbf{ZS}^{-1/2}$ where $\mathbf{S}$ has a Wishart distribution of dimension m, degrees of freedom ν, and variance-covariance matrix $\mathbf{V}$, $\mathbf{S}^{-1/2}$ is the symmetric square root of $\mathbf{S}^{-1}$, and the p variables $\mathbf{Z}$, independent of $\mathbf{S}$ have a singular multinormal distribution with expected value $\mathbf{O}$ and variance-covariance matrix

$\mathbf{V}_0 \otimes \mathbf{V}$ (where $\otimes$ denotes Kronecker product), subject to the conditions (of rank r) $\mathbf{BZ} = \mathbf{0}$. The joint density is

(27)

$$p_{\mathbf{T}}(\mathbf{t}) = \frac{\Gamma_m(\frac{1}{2}(\nu + p - r))}{\pi^{\frac{1}{2}m(p-r)}\Gamma_m(\frac{1}{2}\nu)} |\mathbf{V}_0|^{-(1/2)m} |\mathbf{BV}_0\mathbf{B}'|^{(1/2)m} |\mathbf{I}_m + \mathbf{t}'\mathbf{V}_0^{-1}\mathbf{t}|^{-\frac{1}{2}(\nu+p-r)} .$$

Tan [71] has also discussed in detail a complex analog of this distribution.

REFERENCES

[1] Amos, D. E. (1970). *A Note on a Multivariate t-Distribution*, Technical Memorandum SC-TM-70-467, Sandia Laboratories, Albuquerque, New Mexico.

[2] Amos, D. E. and Bulgren, W. E. (1969). On the computation of a bivariate t-distribution, *Mathematics of Computation*, **23**, 319–333.

[3] Ando, A. and Kaufman, G. M. (1965). Bayesian analysis of the independent multinormal process—neither mean nor precision known, *Journal of the American Statistical Association*, **60**, 347–358.

[4] Bechhofer, R. E., Dunnett, C. W., and Sobel, M. (1954). A two-sample multiple decision procedure for ranking means of normal populations with a common unknown variance, *Biometrika*, **41**, 170–176.

[5] Bechhofer, R. E., Kiefer, J., and Sobel, M. (1969). *Sequential Identification and Ranking Procedures*, Chicago and London: University of Chicago Press.

[6] Bennett, B. M. (1961). On a certain multivariate nonnormal distribution, *Proceedings of the Cambridge Philosophical Society*, **57**, 434–436.

[7] Bowden, D. C. and Graybill, F. A. (1966). Confidence bounds of uniform and proportional width for linear models, *Journal of the American Statistical Association*, **61**, 182–198.

[8] Bulgren, W. G. (1969). Representations of the multivariate t and multivariate F distribution, In *Empirical Bayes Estimation and Computing in Statistics*. T. A. Atchison and N. F. Mortz, Eds., pp. 199–211. *Math Series No. 6*, Texas Tech University, Lubbock, Texas.

[9] Carolis, Linda V. de (1965). Osservazioni sopra l'analisi delle medie nel case di più confronti, *Pubblicazione dell'Istituto di Calcolo delle Probabilità dell'Università di Roma*, *Serie 2*, **52**.

[10] Carolis, Linda V. de (1967). Osservazioni sopra la struttura dell tavola dell t multipla, *Statistica* (*Bologna*), **27**, 789–803.

[11] Carolis, Linda V. de and Gori, F. (1967). Tavole numeriche della t doppia, *Pubblicazione dell'Istituto de Calcolo delle Probabilità dell'Università di Roma*, *Serie 2*, **64**.

[12] Cornish, E. A. (1954). The multivariate t-distribution associated with a set of normal sample deviates, *Australian Journal of Physics*, **7**, 531–542.

[13] Cornish, E. A. (1961). *Simultaneous Fiducial Distribution of Location Parameters*, Technical Paper No. 8, Commonwealth Scientific and Industrial Research Organization, Australia.

[14] Cornish, E. A. (1962). *The Multivariate t-Distribution Associated with the General Multivariate Normal Distribution*, Technical Paper No. 13, Division of Mathematical Statistics, Commonwealth Scientific and Industrial Research Organization, Australia.

[15] Cornish, E. A. (1966). A multiple Behrens-Fisher distribution, in *Multivariate Analysis*, P. R. Krishnaiah, Ed., New York: Academic Press, pp. 203–207.

[16] Davis, A. W. (1967). A counter-example relating to certain multivariate generalizations of t and F, *Annals of Mathematical Statistics*, **38,** 613–615.

[17] Dickey, J. M. (1966). On a multivariate generalization of the Behrens-Fisher distribution (abstract), *Annals of Mathematical Statistics*, **37,** 763.

[18] Dickey, J. M. (1967). Matricvariate generalizations of the multivariate t-distribution, *Annals of Mathematical Statistics*, **38,** 511–518.

[19] Dickey, J. M. (1968). Three dimensional integral identities with Bayesian applications, *Annals of Mathematical Statistics*, **39,** 1615–1627.

[20] Dunn, Olive J. (1965). A property of the multivariate t-distribution, *Annals of Mathematical Statistics*, **36,** 712–714.

[21] Dunn, Olive J., Kronmal, R. A., and Yee, W. J. (1968). *Tables of the Multivariate t-Distribution*, School of Public Health, University of California at Los Angeles.

[22] Dunn, Olive J. and Massey, F. J. (1965). Estimation of multiple contrasts using t-distributions, *Journal of the American Statistical Association*, **60,** 573–583.

[23] Dunnett, C. W. (1955). A multiple comparison procedure for comparing several treatments with a control, *Journal of the American Statistical Association*, **50,** 1096–1121.

[24] Dunnett, C. W. and Sobel, M. (1954). A bivariate generalization of Student's t-distribution, with tables for certain special cases, *Biometrika*, **41,** 153–169.

[25] Dunnett, C. W. and Sobel, M. (1955). Approximations to the probability integral and certain percentage points of a multivariate analogue of Student's t-distribution, *Biometrika*, **42,** 258–260.

[26] Fisher, R. A. (1954). Contribution to discussion; Symposium on interval estimation, *Journal of the Royal Statistical Society, Series B*, **16,** 212–213.

[27] Fraser, D. A. S. and Haq, S. (1969). Structural probability and prediction for the multivariate model, *Journal of the Royal Statistical Society, Series B*, **31,** 317–331.

[28] Freeman, H., Kuzmack, A., and Maurice, Rita J. (1967). Multivariate t and the ranking problem, *Biometrika*, **54,** 305–308.

[28a] Freeman, H. and Kuzmack, A. M. (1972). Tables of multivariate in six and more dimensions, *Biometrika*, **59,** 217–219.

[29] Geisser, S. and Cornfield, J. (1963). Posterior distributions for multivariate normal parameters, *Journal of the Royal Statistical Society, Series B*, **25,** 368–376.

[30] Graybill, F. A. and Bowden, D. C. (1967). Linear segment confidence bands for simple linear models, *Journal of the American Statistical Association*, **62,** 403–408.

[31] Gupta, R. P. (1964). Some extensions of the Wishart and multivariate t-distributions in the complex case, *Journal of the Indian Statistical Association*, **2**, 131–136.

[32] Gupta, S. S. (1963). Probability integrals of multivariate normal and multivariate t, *Annals of Mathematical Statistics*, **34**, 792–828.

[33] Gupta, S. S. (1963). Bibliography on the multivariate normal integrals and related topics, *Annals of Mathematical Statistics*, **34**, 829–838.

[34] Gupta, S. S. and Panchapakesan, S. (1969). Some selection and ranking procedures for multivariate normal populations, In *Multivariate Analysis II*, P. R. Krishnaiah, Ed., New York: Academic Press, pp. 475–505.

[35] Gupta, S. S. and Sobel, M. (1957). On a statistic which arises in selection and ranking problems, *Annals of Mathematical Statistics*, **28**, 957–967.

[36] Hahn, G. J. (1970). A new tabulation of percentage points for the multivariate Student $|t|$ distribution and its use in constructing prediction intervals, *Presented at American Statistical Association Meeting, Detroit.*

[37] Hahn, G. J. and Hendrickson, R. W. (1971). A table of percentage points of the distribution of the largest absolute value of k Student t variates and its application, *Biometrika*, **58**, 323–332.

[38] Halperin, M. (1967). An inequality on a bivariate Student's "t" distribution, *Journal of the American Statistical Association*, **62**, 603–606.

[39] Halperin, M., Greenhouse, S. W., Cornfield, J., and Zalokar, Julia (1955). Tables of percentage points for the studentized maximum absolute deviate in normal samples, *Journal of the American Statistical Association*, **50**, 185–195.

[40] Hengartner, O. (1965). Ausgewählte zwei und dreidimensionale Prüfverteilungen, Part 2, *Metrika*, **9**, 105–148.

[41] Ihm, P. (1957). Berechnung von Integralen der n-dimensionalen Student-Verteilung mittels Stieltjesintegralpapier, *Mitteilingsblatt für Mathematische Statistik*, **9**, 143–146.

[42] John, S. (1964). On the evaluation of the probability integral of the multivariate t-distribution, *Biometrika*, **48**, 409–417.

[43] John, S. (1964). Methods for the evaluation of probabilities of polygonal and angular regions when the distribution is bivariate t, *Sankhyā*, *Series A* **26**, 47–54.

[44] John, S. (1966). On the evaluation of probabilities of convex polyhedra under multivariate normal and t-distributions, *Journal of the Royal Statistical Society*, *Series B*, **28**, 366–369.

[45] Kanofsky, P. B. (1965). Parametric confidence bands on cumulative distributions, *Institute of Statistics*, *University of North Carolina Mimeo Series No. 444* [also (1968) *Sankhyā*, *Series A*, **30**, 369–378].

[46] Kappenman, R. F. (1971). A note on the multivariate t-ratio distribution, *Annals of Mathematical Statistics*, **42**, 349–351.

[47] Krishnaiah, P. R. (1965). Multi-comparison tests in multi-response experiments, *Sankhyā*, *Series A*, **27**, 65–72.

[48] Krishnaiah, P. R. and Armitage, P. V. (1965). *Percentage points of the multivariate t-distribution, Report ARL-65-199*, Aerospace Research Laboratories, Wright-Patterson Air Force Base, Ohio.

[49] Krishnaiah, P. R. and Armitage, P. V. (1966). Tables for multivariate t-distribution, *Sankhyā, Series B*, **28,** 31–56.

[50] Krishnaiah, P. R. and Armitage, P. V. (1970). On a multivariate t distribution, in *Essays in Probability and Statistics* (*S.N. Roy Memorial Volume*), Chapel Hill: University of North Carolina Press, pp. 439–468.

[51] Krishnaiah, P. R., Armitage, P. V., and Breiter, M. C. (1969). *Tables for the bivariate* $|t|$ *distribution*, ARL-69-0210, Aerospace Research Laboratories, Wright-Patterson Air Force Base, Ohio.

[52] Krishnan, M. (1970). The bivariate doubly noncentral t distribution (abstract), *Annals of Mathematical Statistics*, **41,** 1135.

[53] Kshirsagar, A. M. (1960). Some extensions of multivariate t distribution and the multivariate generalization of the distribution of the regression coefficient, *Proceedings of the Cambridge Philosophical Society*, **57,** 80–86.

[54] Laurent, A. G. (1955). Distribution d'échantillon et de caractéristiques d'échantillons quand la population de référence est Laplace-Gaussienne de paramètres inconnus, *Journal de la Société de Statistique de Paris*, **96,** 262–296.

[54a] Li Pi-Erh (1970). A characterization of a multivariate t distribution, *Annals of Mathematical Statistics,* **40,** 2188 (abstract).

[55] Miller, K. S. (1968). Some multivariate t-distributions, *Annals of Mathematical Statistics*, **39,** 1605–1609.

[56] Owen, D. B. (1965). A special case of a bivariate non-central t-distribution, *Biometrika*, **52,** 437–446.

[57] Patil, S. A. and Kovner, J. L. (1968). On the probability of trivariate "t" distributions (abstract), *Annals of Mathematical Statistics*, **39,** 1784.

[58] Patil, S. A. and Kovner, J. L. (1969). On the bivariate doubly noncentral t distributions (abstract), *Annals of Mathematical Statistics*, **40,** 1868.

[59] Patil, S. A. and Liao, S. H. (1970). The distribution of the ratios of means to the square root of the sum of variances of a bivariate normal sample, *Annals of Mathematical Statistics*, **41,** 723–728.

[60] Paulson, E. (1952). On the comparison of several experimental categories with a control, *Annals of Mathematical Statistics*, **23,** 239–246.

[61] Pillai, K. C. S. and Ramachandran, K. V. (1954). On the distribution of the ratio of the ith observation in an ordered sample from a normal population to an independent estimate of the standard deviation, *Annals of Mathematical Statistics*, **25,** 565–572.

[62] Press, S. J. (1969). The t-ratio distribution, *Journal of the American Statistical Association*, **64,** 242–252.

[63] Sidak, Z. (1971). On probabilities of rectangles in multivariate Student distributions; their dependence on correlations, *Annals of Mathematical Statistics*, **42,** 169–175.

[64] Siddiqui, M. (1967). A bivariate t-distribution, *Annals of Mathematical Statistics*, **38,** 162–166 (Correction: **38,** 1594).

[65] Steffens, F. E. (1968). *Probability Integrals and Critical Values of a Bivariate Student t-Distribution*, Report WISK 44, Council for Scientific and Industrial Research, Pretoria, South Africa.

[66] Steffens, F. E. (1969). A stepwise multivariate t-distribution, *South African Statistical Journal*, **3,** 17–26.

[67] Steffens, F. E. (1969). Critical values for bivariate Student t-tests, *Journal of the American Statistical Association*, **64,** 637–646.

[68] Steffens, F. E. (1969). *Noncentral Bivariate t-Tables*, Report WISK 61, Council for Scientific and Industrial Research, Pretoria, South Africa.

[69] Steffens, F. E. (1970). Power of bivariate Studentized maximum and minimum modulus tests, *Journal of the American Statistical Association*, **65,** 1639–1644.

[70] Stone, M. (1964). Comments on a posterior distribution of Geisser and Cornfield, *Journal of the Royal Statistical Society, Series B*, **26,** 274–276.

[71] Tan, W. Y. (1968). Some distribution theory associated with complex Gaussian distributions, *Tamkang Journal*, **7,** 263–302.

[72] Tan, W. Y. (1969). *The Restricted Matric-t Distribution and Its Applications in Deriving Posterior Distributions of Parameters in Multivariate Regression Analysis*, Technical Report No. 205, Department of Statistics, University of Wisconsin, Madison.

[73] Tiao, G. C. and Zellner, A. (1964). On the Bayesian estimation of multivariate regression, *Journal of the Royal Statistical Society, Series B*, **26,** 277–285.

[74] Tong, Y. L. (1970). Some probability inequalities of multivariate normal and multivariate t, *Journal of the American Statistical Association*, **65,** 1243–1247.

[75] Zanella, A. (1967). Sulla distribuzione della variabile t non centrale a più dimensioni in relazione ad un problema di decisione multipla, *Pubblicazioni dell'Università Cattolica del S. Cuore, Milan, Serie 3, Scienze Statistiche*, **1.**

[76] Zanella, A. (1971). *Sulla funzione di Potenza del Test t Multiplo per il Confronto di piu Trattamenti con uno di Controllo*, Milan: Vita e Pensiero.

38

Wishart Distribution

1. Introduction

We saw in Chapter 35 that the observations in a random sample of size n from an m-variate multinormal population may be represented by n independent vectors

$$\mathbf{X}' = (X_{i1},X_{i2},\ldots,X_{im})$$

with

$$p_{\mathbf{X}_i'}(\mathbf{x}_i) = (2\pi)^{-(1/2)m}|\mathbf{V}|^{-1/2}\exp[-\tfrac{1}{2}(\mathbf{X}_i - \boldsymbol{\xi})'\mathbf{V}^{-1}(\mathbf{X}_i - \boldsymbol{\xi})].$$

The maximum likelihood estimators of the elements of $\mathbf{V}$ are the corresponding elements of $n^{-1}\mathbf{S}$, where

$$S_{jk} = \sum_{i=1}^{n}(X_{ij} - \bar{X}_{\cdot j})(X_{ik} - \bar{X}_{\cdot k})$$

with

$$\bar{X}_{\cdot j} = n^{-1}\sum_{i-1}^{n} X_{ij} \qquad (j,k = 1,2,\ldots,m).$$

We are now going to consider the joint distribution of the elements of $\mathbf{S}$. For the univariate case ($m = 1$) there is just the single variate

$$S_{11} = \sum_{i=1}^{n}(X_{i1} - \bar{X}_{\cdot 1})^2,$$

which has a $v_{11}\chi^2$ distribution with $(n - 1)$ degrees of freedom, so that the joint distributions can be regarded as generalizations of univariate χ^2 or, more generally, gamma distributions. They are not, however, multivariate gamma distributions of the kind to be described in Chapter 40. In these, *all* marginal distributions are of the gamma type, while, for $j \neq k$, S_{jk} does not have a distribution of this kind.

The joint distribution of the elements of **S** was obtained by Wishart [52] in 1928 and it is called a Wishart distribution. There have been a number of other derivations (Wishart and Bartlett [54], Madow [35], Aitken [1], Mahalanobis et al. [36], Hsu [22], Fisher [11], Fog [12], Elfving [9], Simonsen [44], Sverdrup [46], Jambunathan [23], and Fraser [13]). In Section 2 we give a derivation based on that of Hsu [22].

2. Derivation of Wishart Distribution

By applying Helmert transformations (Chapter 13, Section 3), to each set of variables $X_{1j},X_{2j},\ldots,X_{nj}$ $(j = 1,2,\ldots,m)$, S_{jk} can be expressed in the form

$$S_{jk} = \sum_{i=2}^{n} Y_{ij}Y_{ik},$$

where $\mathbf{Y}_i' = (Y_{i1},\ldots,Y_{im})$ $(i = 2,3,\ldots,n)$ are independent vectors, and $\mathbf{Y}_i'$ has a multinormal distribution with expected value vector **O** and variance-covariance matrix **V**. The required distribution is therefore a solution (with $\nu = n - 1$) of the following problem.

Given ν independent vectors $\mathbf{Z}_i' = (Z_{ii},\ldots,Z_{im})$ $(i = 1,\ldots,\nu)$ with

$$p_{\mathbf{Z}_i'}(\mathbf{z}_i) = (2\pi)^{-(1/2)m}|\mathbf{V}|^{-1/2}\exp(-\tfrac{1}{2}\mathbf{z}_i'\mathbf{V}^{-1}\mathbf{z}_i),$$

what is the joint distribution of the $\frac{1}{2}m(m+1)$ statistics,

$$S_{jk} = \sum_{i=1}^{\nu} Z_{ij}Z_{ik} \qquad (j \leq k;j,k = 1,2,\ldots,m)? \tag{1}$$

The parameters of the distribution are m (the number of variates), ν (number of degrees of freedom), and **V** (variance-covariance matrix). In order that **S** should not be singular, it is necessary that $\nu \geq m$, and we shall suppose that this is so. The distribution will be denoted symbolically by $W_m(\nu;\mathbf{V})$. We now proceed to derive it.

The joint density of all νm Z's is

$$(2\pi)^{-(1/2)\nu m}|\mathbf{V}|^{-(1/2)\nu}\exp\left(-\frac{1}{2}\sum_{i=1}^{\nu}\mathbf{z}_i'\mathbf{V}^{-1}\mathbf{z}_i\right) \tag{2}$$
$$= (2\pi)^{-(1/2)\nu m}|\mathbf{V}|^{-(1/2)\nu}\exp(-\tfrac{1}{2}\operatorname{tr}\mathbf{V}^{-1}\mathbf{s})$$
$$= (2\pi)^{-(1/2)\nu m}|\mathbf{V}|^{-(1/2)\nu}\operatorname{etr}(-\tfrac{1}{2}\mathbf{V}^{-1}\mathbf{s}),$$

where

$$\mathbf{s} = (s_{jk}); \qquad s_{jk} = \sum_{i=1}^{n} z_{ij} z_{ik}.$$

The new symbol etr(.) has been introduced as an abbreviation for exp(tr(.)). We shall make use of this notation several times in this and the following chapters.

The density function depends on the z's only through the functions $s_{11}, s_{12}, \ldots, s_{mm}$. Our derivation will, in fact, apply to any situation when the joint density function of the Z's can be expressed in the form $f(s_{11}, \ldots, s_{mm})$. (From Chapter 35, Section 6, this condition characterizes the multinormal distribution of the vectors Z_i when they are mutually independent; but may not do so if they are not independent.) We first make transformations from $(Z_{1j}, \ldots, Z_{\nu j})$ to $(Z_{1j(2)}, \ldots, Z_{\nu j(2)})$ for $j \geq 2$, with coefficients depending on $(Z_{11}, \ldots, Z_{\nu 1})$, and such that

$$(3) \qquad Z_{1j(2)} = S_{1j} S_{11}^{-1/2} = \sum_{i=1}^{\nu} [Z_{i1} S_{11}^{-1/2}] Z_{ij},$$

the other coefficients being chosen so as to make each transformation orthogonal. This ensures that

$$(4) \qquad S_{jk} = \sum_{i=1}^{\nu} Z_{ij(2)} Z_{ik(2)} = S_{1j} S_{1k} S_{11}^{-1} + \sum_{i=2}^{\nu} Z_{ij(2)} Z_{ik(2)} \qquad (j,k \geq 2).$$

The joint distribution of $Z_{11}, \ldots, Z_{\nu 1}; Z_{12(2)}, \ldots, Z_{\nu m(2)}$ is then simply $f(s_{11}, \ldots, s_{mm})$ with the s's expressed in terms of $z_{jk(2)}$ according to transformations corresponding to (3) and (4).

(The Jacobian of the combined transformations is 1, since each component transformation is orthogonal.)

Introducing the new variables $T_{1j} = S_{1j} S_{11}^{-1/2} = Z_{1j(2)}$ $(j \geq 2)$, we see that the joint density of $Z_{11}, \ldots, Z_{\nu 1}; T_{12}, \ldots, T_{1m}; Z_{22(2)}, \ldots, Z_{\nu m(2)}$ depends on $z_{11}, \ldots, z_{\nu 1}$ only through $s_{11} = \sum_{i=1}^{\nu} z_{i1}^2$. Making a polar transformation to

$$t_{11} = s_{11}^{1/2}$$

and $(\nu - 1)$ angles, and integrating the latter, we obtain the joint density function of $T_{11} (= S_{11}^{1/2}), T_{12}, \ldots, T_{1m}; Z_{22(2)}, \ldots, Z_{\nu m(2)}$ is the form

$$(5) \quad 2\pi^{(1/2)\nu} [\Gamma(\tfrac{1}{2}\nu)]^{-1} t_{11}^{\nu-1} f(t_{11}^2, t_{11} t_{12}, \ldots, t_{11} t_{1m}; t_{12}^2 + s_{22(2)}, \ldots, t_{1m}^2 + s_{mm(2)}),$$

where

$$s_{jk(2)} = \sum_{i=2}^{\nu} Z_{ij(2)} Z_{ik(2)} \qquad (j,k \geq 2).$$

We now operate on $Z_{22(2)},\ldots,Z_{\nu m(2)}$ in exactly the same way as we did on $Z_{11},\ldots,Z_{\nu m}$ (keeping in mind that ν is now replaced by $(\nu - 1)$ and m by $(m - 1)$). In this way we obtain the joint density function of variables

$$T_{11},T_{12},\ldots,T_{1m};T_{22},\ldots,T_{2m};Z_{33(3)},\ldots,Z_{\nu m(3)},$$

where

$$S_{2k} = T_{12}T_{1k} + T_{22}T_{2k} \qquad (k = 2,\ldots,m),$$

$$S_{jk} = T_{1j}T_{1k} + T_{2j}T_{2k} + \sum_{i=3}^{\nu} Z_{ij(3)}Z_{ik(3)},$$

in the form

$$(6)\quad (2\pi)^{\frac{1}{2}(\nu-1)}\left[\Gamma\left(\frac{\nu-1}{2}\right)\right]^{-1} t_{22}^{\nu-2} 2\pi^{(1/2)\nu}\left[\Gamma\left(\frac{\nu}{2}\right)\right]^{-1} t_{11}^{\nu-1}$$
$$\times f(t_{11}^2,\ldots,t_{11}t_{1m};t_{12}^2 + t_{22}^2,\ldots,t_{12}t_{1m} + t_{22}t_{2m};$$
$$t_{13}^2 + t_{23}^2 + s_{33(3)},\ldots,t_{1m}^2 + t_{2m}^2 + s_{mm(3)}),$$

with

$$s_{jk(3)} = \sum_{i=3}^{\nu} z_{ij(3)}z_{ik(3)} \qquad (j,k \geq 3).$$

Applying this operation m times in all we finally obtain the joint density function of the T_{jk}'s ($j < k;j,k = 1,\ldots,m$) in the form

$$(7)\qquad \prod_{j=1}^{m} [2\pi^{\frac{1}{2}(\nu-j+1)}\{\Gamma(\tfrac{1}{2}(\nu - j + 1))\}^{-1}t_{jj}^{\nu-j}]f(s_{11}(\mathbf{t}),\ldots,s_{mm}(\mathbf{t})),$$

where $s_{jk}(\mathbf{t})$ means s_{jk} expressed in terms of elements of the lower triangular matrix

$$\mathbf{t} = \begin{pmatrix} t_{11} & 0 & \cdots & 0 \\ t_{12} & t_{22} & \cdots & 0 \\ \cdot & \cdot & \cdots & \cdot \\ \cdot & \cdot & \cdots & \cdot \\ \cdot & \cdot & \cdots & \cdot \\ t_{1m} & t_{2m} & \cdots & t_{mm} \end{pmatrix}.$$

Clearly $\mathbf{s} = \mathbf{tt}'$ (and $\mathbf{S} = \mathbf{TT}'$).

The final stage of the derivation consists of transforming from the variables in $\mathbf{T}$ to those in $\mathbf{S}$. Since (for $j < k$)

$$s_{jk} = t_{1j}t_{1k} + t_{2j}t_{2k} + \cdots + t_{jj}t_{jk},$$

it is a straightforward matter to obtain

$$(8)\qquad \frac{\partial(\mathbf{s})}{\partial(\mathbf{t})} = (2t_{11}^m)(2t_{22}^{m-1})\cdots(2t_{mm}) = 2^m \prod_{j-1}^{m} t_{jj}^{m-j+1}.$$

Hence, from (7) and (8), noting that $|\mathbf{s}| = |\mathbf{t}|^2 = \left[\prod_{j=1}^{m} t_{jj}\right]^2$, we find

$$(9) \qquad p_{\mathbf{S}}(\mathbf{s}) = \frac{\pi^{(1/2)\nu m-(1/4)m(m-1)}}{\prod_{j=1}^{m} \Gamma[(\nu - j + 1)/2]} |\mathbf{s}|^{\frac{1}{2}(\nu-m-1)} f(s_{11},\ldots,s_{mm}).$$

In the multinormal case

$$f(s_{11},\ldots,s_{mm}) = (2\pi)^{-(1/2)\nu m} |\mathbf{V}|^{-(1/2)\nu} \operatorname{etr}(-\tfrac{1}{2}\mathbf{V}^{-1}\mathbf{s}).$$

Hence

$$(10) \qquad p_{\mathbf{S}}(\mathbf{s}) = K(\nu;\mathbf{V}^{-1}) |\mathbf{s}|^{\frac{1}{2}(\nu-m-1)} \operatorname{etr}(-\tfrac{1}{2}\mathbf{V}^{-1}\mathbf{s}),$$

where

$$(11) \qquad K(\nu;\mathbf{C}) = |\mathbf{C}|^{(1/2)\nu} \left[2^{(1/2)\nu m} \pi^{(1/4)m(m-1)} \prod_{j=1}^{m} \Gamma\left(\frac{\nu - j + 1}{2}\right)\right]^{-1}.$$

The notation

$$(12) \qquad \Gamma_m(\tfrac{1}{2}\nu) = \pi^{(1/4)m(m-1)} \prod_{j=1}^{m} \Gamma\left(\frac{\nu - j + 1}{2}\right),$$

so that $K(\nu;\mathbf{C}) = |\mathbf{C}|^{(1/2)\nu}[2^{(1/2)\nu m}\Gamma_m(\frac{1}{2}\nu)]^{-1}$, is often used. The function $\Gamma_m(\frac{1}{2}\nu)$ is called "multivariate gamma function."

The range of variation of the elements of **s** is over all values such that **s** is positive definite (i.e., "$\mathbf{s} > 0$").

The method of proof used above has been applied to the solution of a number of other distributional problems by Kshirsagar [31, 32] and Wijsman [51].

The joint distribution of the $\frac{1}{2}m(m + 1)$ elements of $\mathbf{S}^{-1} = \mathbf{T}$ is called the "inverse Wishart" distribution. The joint density function is

$$(13) \qquad p_{\mathbf{T}}(\mathbf{t}) = K(\nu; \mathbf{V}^{-1}) |\mathbf{t}|^{-\frac{1}{2}(\nu+m+1)} \operatorname{etr}(-\tfrac{1}{2}\mathbf{V}^{-1}\mathbf{t}^{-1}) \qquad (\mathbf{t} > 0).$$

This distributional form is also obtained as the posterior distribution of **V**, if it be supposed that the prior distribution is proportional to $|\mathbf{V}|^{\beta}$.

Bagai [6] has obtained the distribution of the ratio of $|\mathbf{S}|$ to any of its principal minors (including as a special case, reciprocals of the diagonal elements of $\mathbf{S}^{-1}$). The distribution of $|\mathbf{S}|$ will be discussed in Section 7 of Chapter 39.

The result (9) has been extended by Goodman [15] and Srivastava [45] to complex random variables. If the density function of the $m \times \nu$ complex random matrix **Y** can be expressed in the form

$$(14) \qquad p_{\mathbf{Y}}(\mathbf{y}) = f(\mathbf{y}\tilde{\mathbf{y}}'),$$

the density function of $\mathbf{S} = \mathbf{Y}\tilde{\mathbf{Y}}'$ is

$$p_{\mathbf{S}}(\mathbf{s}) = \frac{\pi^{m(\nu-\frac{1}{2}(m-1))}|\mathbf{s}|^{\nu-m}}{\left[\prod_{j=1}^{m}\Gamma(\nu-j+1)\right]} f(\mathbf{s}) \tag{15}$$

or

$$p_{\mathbf{S}}(\mathbf{s}) = \frac{\pi^{m(\nu-\frac{1}{2}(m-1))}}{\tilde{\Gamma}_m(\nu)} |\mathbf{s}|^{\nu-m} f(\mathbf{s}) \qquad (\nu > m; \mathbf{s} > 0), \tag{15$'$}$$

where $\tilde{\Gamma}_m(\nu) = \pi^{(1/2)m(m-1)} \prod_{j=1}^{m} \Gamma(\nu - j + 1)$. Using this result, one can derive (as a special case) the *complex Wishart distribution*, which is the joint distribution of $\mathbf{S} = \mathbf{Z}\tilde{\mathbf{Z}}'$ when the $\mathbf{Z}$ has the complex multinormal distribution [equation (73), Chapter 35] with $\boldsymbol{\zeta} = \mathbf{0}$. The density function is

$$p_{\mathbf{S}}(\mathbf{s}) = \frac{|\mathbf{s}|^{\nu-m}\operatorname{etr}(-\mathbf{V}^{-1}\mathbf{s})}{\pi^{(1/2)m(m-1)}\left[\prod_{j=1}^{m}\Gamma(\nu-j+1)\right]|\mathbf{V}|} \qquad (\nu > m; \mathbf{s} > 0). \tag{16}$$

Introducing the complex multivariate gamma function

$$\tilde{\Gamma}_m(\nu) = \pi^{(1/2)m(m-1)} \prod_{j=1}^{m} \Gamma(\nu - j + 1),$$

(16) can be written

$$p_{\mathbf{S}}(\mathbf{s}) = \frac{1}{|\mathbf{V}|\,\tilde{\Gamma}_m(\nu)} |\mathbf{s}|^{\nu-m} \operatorname{etr}(-\mathbf{V}^{-1}\mathbf{s}). \tag{16$'$}$$

(See also Gupta [16].)

3. Properties

Since (10) is a joint density function, it follows that

$$\int\cdots\int |\mathbf{s}|^{\frac{1}{2}(\nu-m-1)} \operatorname{etr}(-\tfrac{1}{2}\mathbf{V}^{-1}\mathbf{s})\, d\mathbf{s} = [K(\nu;\mathbf{V}^{-1})]^{-1}, \tag{17}$$

the region of integration being defined by $\mathbf{s}$ positive definite ($\mathbf{s} > 0$).

The moment generating function is

$$E[\operatorname{etr}(\boldsymbol{\theta}\mathbf{S})] = \frac{K(\nu;\mathbf{V}^{-1})}{K(\nu;\mathbf{V}^{-1}+\boldsymbol{\theta})} = \left[\frac{|\mathbf{V}^{-1}|}{|\mathbf{V}^{-1}+\boldsymbol{\theta}|}\right]^{(1/2)\nu}, \tag{18.1}$$

where

$$\mathbf{\theta} = \begin{pmatrix} -2\theta_{11} & -\theta_{12} & \cdots & -\theta_{1m} \\ -\theta_{12} & -2\theta_{22} & \cdots & -\theta_{2m} \\ \cdot & \cdot & & \cdot \\ \cdot & \cdot & & \cdot \\ \cdot & \cdot & & \cdot \\ -\theta_{1m} & -\theta_{2m} & \cdots & -2\theta_{mm} \end{pmatrix}.$$

The characteristic function is

$$E[\text{etr}(i\mathbf{\theta S})] = \left[\frac{|\mathbf{V}^{-1}|}{|\mathbf{V}^{-1} + i\mathbf{\theta}|}\right]^{(1/2)\nu}. \tag{18.2}$$

It is easy to see that $E[\mathbf{S}] = \nu\mathbf{V}$. It can also be shown that

$$E[\mathbf{S}^{-1}] = (\nu - m - 1)^{-1}\mathbf{V}^{-1}. \tag{19}$$

It follows that if $\mathbf{S}_1,\mathbf{S}_2,\ldots,\mathbf{S}_M$ are independently distributed, with $\mathbf{S}_j$ distributed as $W_m(\nu_j;\mathbf{V})$ $(j = 1,2,\ldots,M)$, then $(\mathbf{S}_1 + \mathbf{S}_2 + \cdots + \mathbf{S}_M)$ is distributed as $W_m\left(\sum_{j=1}^{M} \nu_j;\mathbf{V}\right)$. This is obvious, for integer ν_j, from the definition given early in Section 2. It is also true for fractional $\nu_j(>m - 1)$, and for some or all integers less than m, provided that $\sum_{j=1}^{M} \nu_j > m$, the corresponding $W_m(\nu_j;\mathbf{V})$ being understood to be singular Wishart distributions.

Lévy [34] has shown that the Wishart distribution is not infinitely divisible. The form of the characteristic function (18.2) might lead one to expect that the distribution would be infinitely divisible, but it has to be remembered that for the distribution to be nonsingular it is necessary that ν exceed m.

Wishart [52] has given a table of central moments, up to the fourth order, of the statistics $n^{-1}S_{jk}$. Our Table 1 is based on a part of this table. It gives formulas for the case $\sigma_1 = \sigma_2 = \cdots = \sigma_m = 1$. To obtain general formulas, multiply the expressions in the last column by $\prod_{i=1}^{r} \sigma_i^{b_i}$ with b_i = sum of a_j's over all $j_l = i$ and all $k_l = i$. For example, if $a_1 = 2$, $a_2 = 1$, $(j_1,k_1) = (1,1)$ and $(j_2,k_2) = (1,2)$, then $b_1 = 2 + 2 + 1 = 5$; $b_2 = 1$.

If $\mathbf{V} = \mathbf{I}$, then the Z_{il}'s of Section 2 are independent unit normal variables. It follows, in particular, that S_{jk} for $j,k \geq 2$, are independent of S_{11}. Furthermore, $S_{1j}S_{11}^{-1/2}$ and $S_{jk}^* = S_{jk} - S_{1j}S_{1k}S_{11}^{-1}$ (for all $j,k = 2,\ldots,m$) are mutually independent of each other, and of S_{11}. (Note that S_{jk}^* is the "sum of products" for deviations of Z_j,Z_k from linear regression on Z_1.) Also the $(m-1) \times (m-1)$ matrix $\mathbf{S}^*_{(11)} = (S^*_{jk})$ has a Wishart distribution $W_{m-1}(\nu - 1, \mathbf{I})$. (See, for example, Kshirsagar [33].)

Among interesting properties of the Wishart distribution given by Olkin and Ruben [40] are the following:

(a) Suppose that $\mathbf{S}_1, \mathbf{S}_2, \ldots, \mathbf{S}_k$ are mutually independent, with $\mathbf{S}_j$ distributed as $W_m(\nu_j; \mathbf{V})$. Then if $\mathbf{Z} = \sum_{j=1}^{k} \mathbf{S}_j$ and $g(\mathbf{S}_1, \ldots, \mathbf{S}_k)$ are mutually independent, the random variable $g(\mathbf{A}\mathbf{S}_1\mathbf{A}', \ldots, \mathbf{A}\mathbf{S}_k\mathbf{A}')$ has the same distribution as $g(\mathbf{S}_1, \ldots, \mathbf{S}_k)$ for any nonsingular $m \times m$ matrix $\mathbf{A}$.

(b) If for every positive definite $m \times m$ matrix $\mathbf{B}$ there is $\mathbf{M}$ such that $\mathbf{M}\mathbf{M}' = \mathbf{B}$, and $g(\mathbf{M}\mathbf{S}_1\mathbf{M}', \ldots, \mathbf{M}\mathbf{S}_k\mathbf{M}')$ has the same distribution as $g(\mathbf{S}_1, \ldots, \mathbf{S}_k)$, then $\mathbf{Z}$ and $g(\mathbf{S}_1, \ldots, \mathbf{S}_k)$ are mutually independent.

(c) The statistics

$$\mathbf{W}_j = (\mathbf{S}_1 + \cdots + \mathbf{S}_j)^{-1/2} \mathbf{S}_{j+1} (\mathbf{S}_1 + \cdots + \mathbf{S}_j)^{1/2}$$

$(j = 1, \ldots, k-1)$ are mutually independent. (The square roots are defined by requiring them to be triangular.)

(d) The statistics

$$\mathbf{W}_j = (\mathbf{S}_1 + \cdots + \mathbf{S}_{j+1})^{-1/2} \mathbf{S}_{j+1} (\mathbf{S}_1 + \cdots + \mathbf{S}_{j+1})^{-1/2} \quad (j = 1, \ldots, k-1)$$

are mutually independent.

(e) However, the statistics $\mathbf{S}_1 + \mathbf{S}_2$ and $\mathbf{S}_1^{-1/2}\mathbf{S}_2\mathbf{S}_1^{-1/2}$ are *not* mutually independent.

It can easily be shown (Anderson [4], p. 162) that if $\mathbf{C}$ is a nonsingular $m \times m$ matrix and $\mathbf{S}$ has a $W_m(\nu, \mathbf{V})$ distribution, then $\mathbf{C}^{-1}\mathbf{S}\mathbf{C}'^{-1}$ has a $W_m(\nu; \mathbf{C}\mathbf{V}\mathbf{C}')$ distribution. If $\mathbf{C}$ be chosen so that $\mathbf{C}'\mathbf{C} = \mathbf{V}^{-1}$ then $\mathbf{C}^{-1}\mathbf{S}\mathbf{C}'^{-1}$ has a $W_m(\nu; \mathbf{I})$ distribution, because $\mathbf{C}\mathbf{V}\mathbf{C}' = \mathbf{C}(\mathbf{C}'\mathbf{C})^{-1}\mathbf{C}' = \mathbf{I}$. (Tan and Guttman [47] give a special case of this, with $\mathbf{C}$ lower triangular.)

Tan and Guttman [47] show that if $\mathbf{S} = \mathbf{T}\mathbf{T}'$ and $\mathbf{T}$ is lower triangular (as in Section 2) then the joint density function of $\mathbf{R} = \mathbf{T}'\mathbf{V}^{-1}\mathbf{T}$ is

$$p_{\mathbf{R}}(\mathbf{r}) = 2^{-(1/2)m\nu} \pi^{-(1/4)m(m-1)} \left[\prod_{j=1}^{m} \Gamma\left(\frac{\nu - j + 1}{2} \right) \right]^{-1}$$
$$\times \left\{ |\mathbf{r}|^{\frac{1}{2}(\nu - m - 1)} \operatorname{etr}(-\tfrac{1}{2}\mathbf{r}) \right\} \prod_{j=1}^{m} (r_{jj(1)}^{m-2j+1})$$

where

$$r_{jj(1)} = (|\mathbf{r}_{(j)}| / |\mathbf{r}_{(j+1)}|)^{1/2} \qquad (j = 1, 2, \ldots, m-1),$$

$$r_{jj(m)} = r_{jj}^{1/2},$$

TABLE 1

Formulas for $\mu_{a_1 \cdots a_r}(S_{j_1 k_1}, \ldots, S_{j_r k_r}) = E\left[\prod_{l=1}^{r} (S_{j_l k_l} - E[S_{j_l k_l}])^{a_l}\right]$

a_1	a_2	a_3	j_1,k_1	j_2,k_2	j_3,k_3	$(n-1)^{-1}\mu_{a_1 \cdots a_r}$
1	—	—	1,1	—	—	1
1	—	—	1,2	—	—	ρ_{12}
2	—	—	1,1	—	—	2
2	—	—	1,2	—	—	$1 + \rho_{12}^2$
1	1	—	1,1	2,2	—	$2\rho_{12}^2$
1	1	—	1,1	1,2	—	$2\rho_{12}$
1	1	—	1,1	2,3	—	$2\rho_{12}\rho_{13}$
1	1	—	1,3	2,3	—	$\rho_{12} + \rho_{13}\rho_{23}$
1	1	—	1,2	3,4	—	$\rho_{13}\rho_{24} + \rho_{14}\rho_{23}$
3	—	—	1,1	—	—	8
3	—	—	1,2	—	—	$2\rho_{12}(1 + \rho_{12}^2)$
2	1	—	1,1	2,2	—	$8\rho_{12}^2$
2	1	—	1,1	1,2	—	$8\rho_{12}$
2	1	—	1,2	1,1	—	$2(1 + 3\rho_{12}^2)$
2	1	—	1,1	2,3	—	$8\rho_{12}\rho_{13}$

2	1	—	2,3	1,1	—	$2(\rho_{12}^2 + \rho_{13}^2 + 2\rho_{12}\rho_{13}\rho_{23})$
2	1	—	2,3	1,3	—	$2(\rho_{13} + 2\rho_{12}\rho_{23} + \rho_{12}\rho_{23}^2)$
2	1	—	1,2	3,4	—	$2[\rho_{13}\rho_{24} + \rho_{14}\rho_{23} + \rho_{12}(\rho_{13}\rho_{24} + \rho_{14}\rho_{13})]$
1	1	1	1,1	2,2	3,3	$8\rho_{12}\rho_{23}\rho_{13}$
1	1	1	1,1	1,2	1,3	$2(\rho_{23} + 3\rho_{12}\rho_{13})$
1	1	1	1,2	1,3	2,3	$1 + \rho_{12}^2 + \rho_{13}^2 + \rho_{23}^2 + \rho_{12}\rho_{13}\rho_{23}$
1	1	1	1,1	2,2	2,3	$4\rho_{12}(\rho_{13} + \rho_{12}\rho_{23})$
1	1	1	1,1	1,3	2,3	$2(\rho_{12} + \rho_{13}\rho_{23} + 2\rho_{12}\rho_{13}^2)$
1	1	1	1,1	2,2	3,4	$4\rho_{12}(\rho_{13}\rho_{24} + \rho_{14}\rho_{23})$
1	1	1	1,1	2,3	3,4	$2[\rho_{12}\rho_{14} + \rho_{13}(\rho_{12}\rho_{34} + \rho_{13}\rho_{24} + \rho_{14}\rho_{23})]$
1	1	1	1,2	1,3	1,4	$2(\rho_{12}\rho_{34} + \rho_{13}\rho_{24} + \rho_{14}\rho_{23} + \rho_{12}\rho_{13}\rho_{14})$
1	1	1	1,1	1,2	3,4	$2(\rho_{13}\rho_{24} + \rho_{14}\rho_{23} + 2\rho_{12}\rho_{13}\rho_{14})$
1	1	1	1,2	1,3	2,4	$\rho_{34} + \rho_{13}\rho_{14} + \rho_{23}\rho_{24} + \rho_{12}(\rho_{12}\rho_{34} + \rho_{13}\rho_{24} + 3\rho_{14}\rho_{23})$
1	1	1	1,1	2,3	4,5	$2[\rho_{12}(\rho_{14}\rho_{35} + \rho_{15}\rho_{34}) + \rho_{13}(\rho_{14}\rho_{25} + \rho_{15}\rho_{24})]$
1	1	1	1,2	2,3	4,5	$\rho_{14}\rho_{35} + \rho_{15}\rho_{34} + 2\rho_{13}\rho_{24}\rho_{35} + \rho_{12}(\rho_{24}\rho_{35} + \rho_{25}\rho_{34}) + \rho_{23}(\rho_{14}\rho_{25} + \rho_{15}\rho_{24})$
1	1	1	1,2	3,4	5,6	$\rho_{13}(\rho_{25}\rho_{46} + \rho_{26}\rho_{45}) + \rho_{14}(\rho_{25}\rho_{36} + \rho_{26}\rho_{35}) + \rho_{15}(\rho_{23}\rho_{46} + \rho_{24}\rho_{36}) + \rho_{16}(\rho_{23}\rho_{45} + \rho_{24}\rho_{35})$

with

$$\mathbf{r}_{(j)} = \begin{pmatrix} r_{jj} & r_{j,j+1} & \cdots & r_{j,m} \\ r_{j,j+1} & r_{j+1,j+1} & \cdots & r_{j+1,m} \\ \cdot & \cdot & & \cdot \\ \cdot & \cdot & & \cdot \\ \cdot & \cdot & & \cdot \\ r_{j,m} & r_{j+1,m} & \cdots & r_{m,m} \end{pmatrix}.$$

Note that $p_{\mathbf{R}}(\mathbf{r})$ is obtained by multiplying a Wishart density (as in (10)) by $\prod_{j=1}^{m} (r_{jj(1)}^{m-2j+1})$.

Hayakawa [17] has pointed out that any matrix

$$\mathbf{Y} = \mathbf{XAX}'$$

of quadratic forms in the independent, identically multinormal distribution vectors $\mathbf{X}_i' = (X_{i1},\ldots,X_{in})$ $(i = 1,\ldots,m)$, each expected value vector being $\mathbf{O}$, can be expressed as a linear function of independent matrices each having a Wishart or singular Wishart distribution. The converse is also true—any such linear function can be represented in the form $\mathbf{Y} = \mathbf{XAX}'$. (The distribution of $\mathbf{Y}$ will be discussed in Chapter 39.)

We further note that for any fixed $m \times 1$ vector $\boldsymbol{\alpha}$, provided that $\boldsymbol{\alpha}'\mathbf{V}\boldsymbol{\alpha} \neq 0$, the ratio $\boldsymbol{\alpha}'\mathbf{S}\boldsymbol{\alpha}/\boldsymbol{\alpha}'\mathbf{V}\boldsymbol{\alpha}$ is distributed as χ_ν^2. (If $\boldsymbol{\alpha}'\mathbf{V}\boldsymbol{\alpha} = 0$ then $\boldsymbol{\alpha}'\mathbf{S}\boldsymbol{\alpha} = 0$ with probability 1.)

Mitra [38] has shown that these properties do not characterize the Wishart distribution, by noting that they are also possessed by the variable $W\mathbf{S}$, where W is independent of $\mathbf{S}$ and has a (univariate) beta distribution.

However, if $\boldsymbol{\alpha}'\mathbf{V}\boldsymbol{\alpha} = 0$ implies $\boldsymbol{\alpha}'\mathbf{S}\boldsymbol{\alpha} = 0$ with probability 1, and for *every* matrix $\mathbf{A}$ (not necessarily square) with the property $\mathbf{AVA}' = \mathbf{I}$ the diagonal elements of $\mathbf{ASA}'$ are distributed as independent χ_ν^2 variables, then $\mathbf{S}$ must have a Wishart distribution (Mitra [38]).

Ghurye and Olkin [14] have studied the problem of estimating the density function of a Wishart distribution. It is interesting to note that an unbiased estimator of (10) can be obtained from an observed set of random variables $\mathbf{S}^*$ having a similar distribution only if the degrees of freedom of the latter ν^*, say, *exceed* $(\nu + m - 1)$. If such a set is available, then the minimum variance unbiased estimator of (10) is

$$(20) \quad \begin{cases} \dfrac{\Gamma_m(\frac{1}{2}\nu^*)}{\Gamma_m(\frac{1}{2}\nu)\Gamma_m(\frac{1}{2}(\nu^* - \nu))} |\mathbf{s}|^{\frac{1}{2}(\nu-m-1)} |\mathbf{S}^*|^{-\frac{1}{2}(\nu^*-m-1)} |\mathbf{S}^* - \mathbf{s}|^{\frac{1}{2}(\nu^*-\nu-m-1)} \\ \qquad\qquad (\mathbf{S}^*, \mathbf{S}^* - \mathbf{s} \text{ each positive definite}), \\ 0 \quad \text{otherwise.} \end{cases}$$

If it is known that $\mathbf{V} = \mathbf{V}_0\sigma^2$ with $\mathbf{V}_0$ known, but σ^2 unknown, the minimum variance unbiased estimator of (10) is

$$(21)\quad \begin{cases} \dfrac{\Gamma(\frac{1}{2}\nu^* m)\,|\mathbf{V}_0|^{-(1/2)\nu}\,|\mathbf{s}|^{\frac{1}{2}(\nu-m-1)}}{\Gamma(\frac{1}{2}(\nu^*-\nu)m)\Gamma_m(\frac{1}{2}\nu)}(\operatorname{tr}\mathbf{V}_0^{-1}\mathbf{S}^*)^{-(1/2)m\nu^*+1} \\ \qquad\qquad \times (\operatorname{tr}\mathbf{V}_0^{-1}(\mathbf{S}^*-\mathbf{s}))^{(1/2)m(\nu^*-\nu)-1} \\ \qquad\qquad (\text{provided that } \mathbf{S}^* - \mathbf{s} \text{ positive definite}), \\ 0 \quad \text{otherwise.} \end{cases}$$

The distribution of $\mathbf{S}$ when the population distribution is not multinormal but can be expressed in a generalized Gram-Charlier expansion [see equation (12) of Chapter 34 for the case $m = 3$] has been studied by Quensel [41].

4. Noncentral Wishart Distribution

4.1. *Introduction*

The Wishart distribution was introduced in earlier sections of this chapter as the joint distribution of statistics

$$S_{jk} = \sum_{i=1}^{n}(X_{ij} - \bar{X}_{.j})(X_{ik} - \bar{X}_{.k}) \qquad (j,k = 1,\ldots,m),$$

where the vectors $\mathbf{X}_i' = (X_{i1},\ldots,X_{im})$ have a common joint multinormal distribution for $i = 1,2,\ldots,n$. If the expected value vectors $\boldsymbol{\xi}_i' = E[X_i']$ are not all equal (but each $\mathbf{X}_i'$ still has a multinormal distribution with common variance-covariance matrix $\mathbf{V}$), the corresponding joint distribution of the elements of $\mathbf{S} \equiv (S_{jk})$ is called a *noncentral Wishart distribution*. The form of this distribution depends on the rank of the matrix

$$(22)\qquad \boldsymbol{\Xi} = (\boldsymbol{\xi}_1,\boldsymbol{\xi}_2,\ldots,\boldsymbol{\xi}_n).$$

Complexity of formal expression increases rapidly with rank of $\boldsymbol{\Xi}$. Anderson and Girshick [5] and Anderson [3] obtained explicit formulas for the case of $\operatorname{rank}(\boldsymbol{\Xi}) = 1,2$ (and Weibull [50] tackled the case of rank equal to 3) but even these were very complicated. Reasonably convenient formal handling of these distributions became possible only with the introduction of *zonal polynomials* (James [25, 26]). We devote the next subsection to a brief account of these functions and to some related functions that will be very useful in the remainder of this chapter and in Chapter 39.

4.2. *Zonal Polynomials and Related Functions*

We shall need to use the notation $\varkappa(j)$ for a *partition* of the number j. A *partition of weight* r is a set of r positive integers $(j_1,j_2,\ldots,j_r)$ such that $\sum_{i=1}^{r} j_i = j$. Conventionally we take $j_1 \geq j_2 \cdots \geq j_r > 0$. If a particular number is repeated, this can be denoted by an exponent. Thus the partition (2,1,1) of 4 can be written (21^2). (In suitable circumstances, the parentheses can be omitted.)

The *zonal polynomial* $C_{\varkappa(j)}(\mathbf{Z})$ corresponding to the partition $\varkappa(j)(j_1,\ldots,j_r)$ of j is a symmetrical homogeneous polynomial function of the latent roots of $\mathbf{Z}$, of degree j. If $\mathbf{Z}$ is a $m \times m$ matrix, then (James [26])

$$(\text{tr}\,\mathbf{Z})^j = \sum_{\varkappa(j)} C_\varkappa(\mathbf{Z}) \tag{23.1}$$

and so

$$\text{etr}(\mathbf{Z}) = \sum_{j=0}^{\infty} \sum_{\varkappa(j)} [C_\varkappa(\mathbf{Z})/j!], \tag{23.2}$$

where the summation with respect to $\varkappa(j)$ is restricted to partitions of weight not exceeding m, and $C_\varkappa$ means $C_{\varkappa(j)}$. (We shall use these conventions consistently.)

Although no explicit general expression for $C_\varkappa(\mathbf{Z})$ is available, tables are available for values of j up to 9 (James [25], Kitchen [30]). The polynomials are conveniently expressed in terms of the quantities

$$s_g = \text{sum of } g\text{th powers of latent roots of } \mathbf{Z}.$$

In Table 2 we give some values for $j \leq 4$, based on James [25]. Note that formulas for $C_\varkappa(\mathbf{I}_m)$ can be obtained from those for $C_\varkappa(\mathbf{Z})$ by putting $s_g = m$ for all g.

Tumura [49] has given the following explicit formula for the zonal polynomial $C_{\varkappa(j)}(\mathbf{L})$ where $\mathbf{L} = \text{diag}(l_1,l_2)$ and $\varkappa(j) = (j_1,j_2)$ is of weight 2:

$$C_{(j_1,j_2)}(\mathbf{L}) = \frac{2^{2j_1}[2(j_1-j_2)+1]}{2j_1+1}\left(\prod_{i=1}^{j_1}\frac{j_2+1}{j_1+i}\right) \tag{24}$$
$$\times \sum_{\alpha_1+2\alpha_2=j_1-j_2} (-1)^{\alpha_2}\left[\prod_{i=1}^{\alpha_1}(1-\tfrac{1}{2}i^{-1})\prod_{i=1}^{\alpha_2}(1+(\alpha_1-\tfrac{1}{2})i^{-1})\right]$$
$$\times (l_1+l_2)^{\alpha_1}(l_1l_2)^{\alpha_2+j_2}.$$

The following formulas (taken from James [25] and Constantine [8]) have been used in deriving expressions for certain multivariate distributions in terms of zonal polynomials.

TABLE 2

Zonal Polynomials

j	$\varkappa(j)$	$C_\varkappa(\mathbf{Z})$	$C_\varkappa(I_m)$
1	1	s_1	m
2	1^2	$\frac{2}{3}(s_1^2 - s_2)$	$\frac{2}{3}m(m-1)$
	2	$\frac{1}{3}(s_1^2 + 2s_2)$	$\frac{1}{3}m(m+2)$
3	1^3	$\frac{1}{3}(s_1^3 - 3s_1s_2 + 2s_3)$	$\frac{1}{3}m(m-1)(m-2)$
	21	$\frac{3}{5}(s_1^3 + s_1s_2 - 2s_3)$	$\frac{3}{5}m(m+2)(m-1)$
	3	$\frac{1}{15}(s_1^3 + 6s_1s_2 + 8s_3)$	$\frac{3}{15}m(m+2)(m+4)$
4	1^4	$\frac{2}{15}(s_1^4 - 6s_1^2s_2 + 3s_2^2 + 8s_1s_3 - 6s_4)$	$\frac{2}{15}m(m-1)(m-2)(m-3)$
	21^2	$\frac{8}{15}(s_1^4 - s_1^2s_2 - 2s_2^2 - 2s_1s_3 + 4s_4)$	$\frac{8}{15}m(m+2)(m-1)(m-2)$
	31	$\frac{4}{1}(s_1^4 + 5s_1^2s_2 - 2s_2^2 + 4s_1s_3 - 8s_4)$	$\frac{4}{21}m(m+2)(m+4)(m-1)$
	2^2	$\frac{2}{15}(s_1^4 + 2s_1^2s_2 + 7s_2^2 - 8s_1s_3 - 2s_4)$	$\frac{2}{15}m(m+2)(m-1)(m+1)$
	4	$\frac{1}{105}(s_1^4 + 12s_1^2s_2 + 12s_2^2 + 32s_1s_3 + 48s_4)$	$\frac{1}{105}m(m+2)(m+4)(m+6)$

If $\mathbf{A}$ is a real symmetric $m \times m$ matrix and $\mathbf{B}$ an arbitrary real $m \times m$ matrix, then

(25) $$\int_{\mathbf{S}>0} \operatorname{etr}(-\mathbf{A}\mathbf{S})\, |\mathbf{S}|^{t-(1/2)(m+1)}\, C_\varkappa(\mathbf{S}\mathbf{B})\, d\mathbf{S} = \Gamma_m(t;\varkappa)\, |\mathbf{A}|^{-t}\, C_\varkappa(\mathbf{A}^{-1}\mathbf{B}),$$

where $\mathbf{S} > \mathbf{0}$ means "$\mathbf{S}$ is positive definite," and

(26.1) $$\Gamma_m(t;\varkappa) = \Gamma_m(t) \prod_{j=1}^{m} (t - \tfrac{1}{2}(j-1))^{[k_j]}.$$

[The $\Gamma_m(t)$ is defined in (12) and $\varkappa^{[k]}$ in Chapter 1, equation (22).]

The symbol

$$t^{\{\varkappa\}} = \prod_{j=1}^{m} (t - \tfrac{1}{2}(j-1))^{[k_j]}$$

is often used, so that we can write (26.1) as

(26.2) $$\Gamma_m(t;\varkappa) = \Gamma_m(t) t^{\{\varkappa\}}.$$

For $\varkappa(j) = (j_1, \ldots, j_r)$,

(27) $$C_\varkappa(\mathbf{I}_m) = \left[2^{2j} j! \left\{\prod_{i<l}^{r} (g_i - g_l)\right\} (\tfrac{1}{2}m)^{\{\varkappa\}}\right] \Big/ \left[\prod_{i=1}^{r} g_i!\right],$$

where $g_i = 2j_i + r - i$.

If $\mathbf{T} > 0$, then

$$(28)\quad \int_0^{\mathbf{A}} |\mathbf{S}|^{t-(1/2)(m+1)}\, C_\varkappa(\mathbf{TS})\, d\mathbf{S} = \frac{\Gamma_m(t;\varkappa)\Gamma_m(\frac{1}{2}(m+1))}{\Gamma_m(t+\frac{1}{2}(m+1);\varkappa)}\, |\mathbf{A}|^t\, C_\varkappa(\mathbf{AT})$$

($\int_0^{\mathbf{A}}$ means integration over all $\mathbf{S}$ for which both $\mathbf{S} > \mathbf{0}$ and $\mathbf{A} - \mathbf{S} > 0$.) A similar result is

$$(29)\quad \int_0^{\mathbf{I}} |\mathbf{S}|^{t-(1/2)(m+1)}\, |\mathbf{I} - \mathbf{S}|^{u-(1/2)(m+1)}\, C_\varkappa(\mathbf{R}\,\mathbf{S})\, d\,\mathbf{S} = \frac{\Gamma_m(t;\varkappa)\Gamma_m(u)}{\Gamma_m(t+u;\varkappa)}\, C_\varkappa(R).$$

A further useful result is stated in general form

$$(30)\quad \int_{O(N)} \operatorname{etr}(\mathbf{SHTH}')\, d(\mathbf{H}) = \sum_{j=0}^{\infty} \sum_{\varkappa} \frac{C_\varkappa(\mathbf{S})C_\varkappa(\mathbf{T})}{j!\,C_\varkappa(\mathbf{I}_N)},$$

where $d(\mathbf{H})$ denotes "an invariant measure over the orthogonal group $O(N)$, normalized to total 1." (In many applications $d(H)$ is ordinary Euclidean measure and $O(N)$ finite Euclidean space.)

James [25] and Constantine [8] used zonal polynomials in defining *generalized hypergeometric functions with matrix arguments*

$$(31.1)\quad {}_pF_q(a_1,\ldots,a_p;b_1,\ldots,b_q;\mathbf{S}) = \sum_{j=0}^{\infty} \sum_{\varkappa(j)} \left[\prod_{l=1}^{p} a_l^{\{\varkappa\}} \Big/ \prod_{l=1}^{q} b_l^{\{\varkappa\}}\right] [C_\varkappa(\mathbf{S})/j!]$$

and

$$(31.2)\quad {}_pF_q(a_1,\ldots,a_p;b_1,\ldots,b_q;\mathbf{S},\mathbf{T})$$
$$= \sum_{j=0}^{\infty} \sum_{\varkappa(j)} \left[\prod_{l=1}^{p} a_l^{\{\varkappa\}} \Big/ \prod_{l=1}^{q} b_l^{\{\varkappa\}}\right] [C_\varkappa(\mathbf{S})C_\varkappa(\mathbf{T})\{j!\; C_\varkappa(\mathbf{I}_N)\}^{-1}].$$

It is assumed that $p \le q + 1$, and $2(b_j - (m - 1))$ is not a negative integer. (Sometimes the dimensions of the matrices are indicated as a superscript $^{(m)}$ after F_j; we shall not use this notation.) Note that we can write (23.2) as

$$\operatorname{etr}(\mathbf{Z}) = {}_0F_0(\mathbf{Z}).$$

[When $p = 0$ or $q = 0$, there are no a's or b's, respectively, among the arguments of ${}_pF_q(\cdot)$.]

In the derivation of the noncentral Wishart distribution (see Section 4.3) the following formula is used:

$$(32)\quad {}_pF_{q+1}(a_1,\ldots a_p;b_1,\ldots,b_q,c;-\mathbf{U})\, |\mathbf{U}|^{c-(m+1)}$$
$$= \Gamma_m(c)\frac{2^{m(m-1)}}{(2i)^{m(m+1)}} \int_{R(\mathbf{Z})>0} \operatorname{etr}(\mathbf{UZ})$$
$$\times\, {}_pF_q(a_1,\ldots,a_p;b_1,\ldots,b_q;-\mathbf{U}^{-1})\, |\mathbf{Z}|^{-c}\, d\mathbf{Z},$$

where $\mathbf{Z} = \mathbf{X} + i\mathbf{Y}$ is a $m \times m$ symmetric (complex) matrix and $\mathbf{U}$ is a real symmetric positive definite matrix.

The *Bessel function of order* γ *with* $(m \times m)$ *matrix argument*, $\mathbf{G}$, is

$$(33)\quad A_\gamma(\mathbf{G}) = [\Gamma_m(\gamma + \tfrac{1}{2}(m+1))]^{-1}\,{}_0F_1(\gamma + \tfrac{1}{2}(m+1); -\mathbf{G})$$

$$= [\Gamma_m(\gamma + \tfrac{1}{2}(m+1))]^{-1}\sum_{k=0}^{\infty}(k!)^{-1}\sum_{\varkappa(k)}[C_\varkappa(-\mathbf{G})/(\gamma + \tfrac{1}{2}(m+1))^{\{\varkappa\}}]$$

(Herz [20]). The *generalized Laguerre polynomial of order* γ *with* $(m \times m)$ *matrix argument*, $\mathbf{G}$, *corresponding to the partition* $\boldsymbol{\varkappa}(k)$ is

$$(34)\qquad L_\varkappa^\gamma(\mathbf{G}) = \{\mathrm{etr}(\mathbf{G})\}\int_{\mathbf{R}>0} A_\gamma(\mathbf{RG})\,|\mathbf{R}|^\gamma\, C_\varkappa(\mathbf{R})\mathrm{etr}(-\mathbf{R})\,d\mathbf{R}.$$

This definition is due to Constantine [8] who showed, *inter alia*, that

$$(35.1)\qquad L_\varkappa^\gamma(\mathbf{0}) = (\gamma + \tfrac{1}{2}(m+1))^{\{\varkappa\}}\, C_\varkappa(\mathbf{J}_m)$$

and for $\boldsymbol{\varkappa} \not\equiv \boldsymbol{\tau}$

$$(35.2)\qquad \int_{\mathbf{S}>0}\{\mathrm{etr}(-\mathbf{S})\}\,|\mathbf{S}|^\gamma\, L_\varkappa^\gamma(\mathbf{S})L_\tau^\gamma(\mathbf{S})\,d\mathbf{S} = 0,$$

that is, $L_\varkappa^\gamma(\mathbf{S})$ and $L_\tau^\gamma(\mathbf{S})$ are orthogonal over $\mathbf{S}$ positive definite, with weight function $|\mathbf{S}|^\gamma\,\mathrm{etr}(-\mathbf{S})$. Hayakawa [17] has introduced another class of polynomials. *The generalized Hermite polynomial with* $(m \times n, m < n)$ *matrix argument* $\mathbf{G}$, *corresponding to the partition* $\boldsymbol{\varkappa}(k)$, is

$$(36)\qquad H_\varkappa(\mathbf{G}) = \pi^{-(1/2)mn}\,\mathrm{etr}(\mathbf{GG}')\int_{\mathbf{U}}\mathrm{etr}(-2i\mathbf{TU}' - \mathbf{UU}')C_\varkappa(\mathbf{UU}')\,d\mathbf{U}$$

(where $i = \sqrt{-1}$ and $\mathbf{U}$ is a $m \times n$ matrix; $\int_{\mathbf{u}}$ denotes integration with respect to each element of $\mathbf{U}$, from $-\infty$ to ∞). Hayakawa [17] showed that

$$(37.1)\qquad H_\varkappa(\mathbf{G}) = (-1)^k L_\varkappa^{(n-m-1)/2}(\mathbf{GG}'),$$

$$(37.2)\qquad \sum_{\varkappa(k)} H_\varkappa(\mathbf{G}) = (-1)^k\,\mathrm{etr}(\mathbf{GG}')\cdot\frac{\Gamma(\tfrac{1}{2}mn + k)}{\Gamma(\tfrac{1}{2}mn)} \times {}_1F_1(\tfrac{1}{2}mn + k, \tfrac{1}{2}mn; -\mathrm{tr}\,\mathbf{GG}'),$$

and [from (37.1) and (35.1)]

$$(37.3)\qquad H_\varkappa(\mathbf{O}) = (-1)^k(\tfrac{1}{2}n)^{\{\varkappa\}}C_\varkappa(\mathbf{I}_m).$$

As particular consequences of (37.2) we have

$$\sum_{k=0}^{\infty}(k!)^{-1}\sum_{\varkappa(k)} H_{\varkappa}(\mathbf{G}) = 2^{-(1/2)mn}\,\mathrm{etr}(\mathbf{GG}'), \tag{38.1}$$

$$\sum_{k=0}^{\infty}(k!)^{-1}\sum_{\varkappa(k)}[(\tfrac{1}{2}n)^{\{\varkappa\}}]^{-1}H_{\varkappa}(\mathbf{G}) = e^{-m}{}_0F_1(\tfrac{1}{2}n;\mathbf{GG}') \tag{38.2}$$

$$\sum_{\varkappa(k)}(\tfrac{1}{2}n)^{\{\varkappa\}}C_{\varkappa}(\mathbf{I}_m) = (\tfrac{1}{2}mn)^{(k)}. \tag{38.3}$$

For complex variables (in particular for complex multinormally distributed variables of the form described in Section 10 of Chapter 35) the following definitions have been found useful:

$$\tilde{\Gamma}_m(t) = \pi^{(1/2)m(m-1)}\prod_{j=1}^{m}\Gamma(t-j+1) \tag{39.1}$$

("multivariate complex gamma function");

$$\tilde{\Gamma}_m(t;\varkappa) = \pi^{(1/2)m(m-1)}\prod_{j=1}^{m}\Gamma(t+k_j-j+1), \tag{39.2}$$

where $\varkappa \equiv \varkappa(k)$ denotes a partition of k into not more than m parts $k_1 \le k_2 \cdots \le k_m$ with $\sum_{j=1}^{m} k_j = k$; and

$$a^{\{\varkappa\}} = \prod_{j=1}^{m}(a-j+1)^{(k_j)} = \tilde{\Gamma}_m(a;\varkappa)/\tilde{\Gamma}_m(a). \tag{39.3}$$

The complex generalized hypergeometric functions with Hermitian matrix arguments **A**,**B** are

$$(40)\quad {}_p\tilde{F}_q(a_1,\ldots,a_p;b_1,\ldots,b_q;\mathbf{A},\mathbf{B}) = \sum_{j=0}^{\infty}(j!)^{-1}\sum_{\varkappa(j)}\left[\frac{\prod_l a_l^{\{\varkappa\}}}{\prod_l b_l^{\{\varkappa\}}}\right]\frac{\tilde{C}_{\varkappa}(\mathbf{A})\tilde{C}_{\varkappa}(\mathbf{B})}{\tilde{C}_{\varkappa}(\mathbf{I}_m)}.$$

Complex forms of the other functions defined earlier are (Hayakawa [18]):

1. *Generalized Bessel function*

$$\tilde{A}_{\gamma}(\mathbf{G}) = {}_0\tilde{F}_1(\gamma+m;-\mathbf{G})/\tilde{\Gamma}_m(\gamma+m). \tag{41}$$

2. *Generalized Laguerre polynomial*

$$\tilde{L}_{\varkappa}^{\gamma}(\mathbf{G}) = \mathrm{etr}(\mathbf{G})\int_{\mathbf{R}'=\mathbf{R}>0}\tilde{A}_{\gamma}(\mathbf{RG})\,|\mathbf{R}|^{\gamma}\tilde{C}_{\varkappa}(\mathbf{R})\mathrm{etr}(-\mathbf{R})\,d\mathbf{R}, \tag{42}$$

$$(43)\quad \tilde{H}_{\varkappa}(\mathbf{G}) = (-1)^k\,\mathrm{etr}(\mathbf{GG}')\pi^{-mn} \times\int_{\mathbf{U}}\mathrm{etr}(-i(\mathbf{G}\tilde{\mathbf{U}}'+\mathbf{U}\tilde{\mathbf{G}}')-\mathbf{U}\tilde{\mathbf{U}}')\tilde{C}_{\varkappa}(\mathbf{U}\,\tilde{\mathbf{U}})\,d\mathbf{U}.$$

Corresponding to (37.1) and (37.3), we have

$$\tilde{H}_\varkappa(\mathbf{G}) = (-1)^k \tilde{L}_\varkappa^{n-m}(\mathbf{G}\tilde{\mathbf{G}}'), \tag{44.1}$$

$$\tilde{H}_\varkappa(\mathbf{O}) = (-1)^k n^{\{\varkappa\}} \tilde{C}_\varkappa(\mathbf{I}_m). \tag{44.3}$$

But note that

$$\begin{aligned}\sum_{\varkappa(k)} \tilde{H}_\varkappa(\mathbf{G}) &= (-1)^k \sum_{\varkappa(k)} \tilde{L}_\varkappa^{n-m}(\mathbf{G}\tilde{\mathbf{G}}') \\ &= (-1)^k L_k^{mn-1}(\operatorname{tr} \mathbf{G}\tilde{\mathbf{G}}'),\end{aligned} \tag{44.2}$$

which is much simpler than (37.2).

We have used in (44.2) a special case of the general formula

$$\sum_{\varkappa(k)} \tilde{L}_\varkappa^\gamma(\mathbf{T}) = L_k^{m(\gamma+m)-1}(\operatorname{tr} \mathbf{T}) \tag{45}$$

for any γ and any positive definite Hermitian matrix $\mathbf{T}$.

4.3. *General Noncentral Wishart Distributions*

We give here a derivation based on the work of Constantine [8]. For earlier derivations see James [24–26].

Under the conditions stated in Section 4.1, the columns of the $m \times n$ matrix

$$\mathbf{X} = (\mathbf{X}_1, \mathbf{X}_2, \ldots, \mathbf{X}_n)$$

are independent, and $\mathbf{X}_i$ has a multinormal distribution with expected value vector $\boldsymbol{\xi}_i$ and variance covariance matrix $\mathbf{V}$. The density function of $\mathbf{X}$ is therefore, in obvious notation,

$$(2\pi)^{-(1/2)mn} |\mathbf{V}|^{-(1/2)n} \operatorname{etr}(-\tfrac{1}{2}\mathbf{V}^{-1}(\mathbf{x} - \Xi)(\mathbf{x} - \Xi)') \tag{46}$$

[Ξ is defined in (22).]

It will be convenient to consider the joint distribution of the elements of

$$\mathbf{S} = \mathbf{X}\mathbf{X}'.$$

A moment generating function for $\mathbf{S}$ is

$$\begin{aligned} E[\operatorname{etr}(-\mathbf{T}\mathbf{S})] = \frac{\operatorname{etr}(-\frac{1}{2}\mathbf{V}^{-1}\Xi\Xi')}{2^{(1/2)mn}\,|\mathbf{V}|^{(1/2)n}} &|\mathbf{T} + \tfrac{1}{2}\mathbf{V}^{-1}|^{(-1/2)n} \\ &\times \operatorname{etr}[\tfrac{1}{4}\mathbf{V}^{-1}\Xi\Xi'\mathbf{V}^{-1}(\mathbf{T} + \tfrac{1}{2}\mathbf{V}^{-1})^{-1}]. \end{aligned} \tag{47}$$

Putting $\mathbf{T} + \frac{1}{2}\mathbf{V}^{-1} = \mathbf{W}$ in (47), and applying an inversion formula, we obtain the density function of the $\frac{1}{2}m(m+1)$ distinct elements of $\mathbf{S}$ in the form

$$(48)\quad p_{\mathbf{S}}(\mathbf{s}) = \frac{\operatorname{etr}(-\mathbf{\Omega})}{2^{(1/2)mn}\,|\mathbf{V}|^{(1/2)n}} \operatorname{etr}(-\tfrac{1}{2}\mathbf{V}^{-1}\mathbf{s})\tfrac{1}{2}(\pi i)^{-(1/2)m(m+1)}$$

$$\times \int_{\mathbf{W}>0} \operatorname{etr}(\mathbf{W}\mathbf{s})\operatorname{etr}(\tfrac{1}{2}\mathbf{V}^{-1}\mathbf{\Omega}\mathbf{W}^{-1})\,|\mathbf{W}|^{(-1/2)n}\,d\mathbf{W},$$

where

$$\mathbf{\Omega} = \tfrac{1}{2}\mathbf{V}^{-1}\mathbf{\Xi}\mathbf{\Xi}'.$$

Using (32) and (31.1), the integral can be evaluated in terms of zonal polynomials, giving

$$(49.1)\quad p_{\mathbf{S}}(\mathbf{s}) = \frac{\operatorname{etr}(-\mathbf{\Omega})}{2^{(1/2)mn}\Gamma_m(\frac{1}{2}n)\,|\mathbf{V}|^{(1/2)n}} \operatorname{etr}(-\tfrac{1}{2}\mathbf{V}^{-1}\mathbf{s})\sum_{j=0}^{\infty}\sum_{\varkappa} \frac{C_\varkappa(\frac{1}{2}\mathbf{V}^{-1}\mathbf{\Omega}\,\mathbf{s})}{j!(\frac{1}{2}n)^{\{\varkappa\}}}$$

This is a noncentral Wishart distribution. The $\mathbf{\Omega}$ is the *noncentrality matrix.* An equivalent formula is

$$(49.2)\quad p_{\mathbf{S}}(\mathbf{s}) = \frac{\operatorname{etr}(-\mathbf{\Omega})}{2^{(1/2)mn}\Gamma_m(\frac{1}{2}n)\,|\mathbf{V}|^{(1/2)n}}\,|\mathbf{s}|^{(1/2)(n-m-1)}$$

$$\times \operatorname{etr}(-\tfrac{1}{2}\mathbf{V}^{-1}\mathbf{s})\,{}_0F_1(\tfrac{1}{2}n;\tfrac{1}{2}\mathbf{V}^{-1}\mathbf{\Omega}\,\mathbf{s}).$$

From this second formula it is easy to see that the distribution becomes a central Wishart distribution (with n degrees of freedom and variance-covariance matrix $\mathbf{V}$) when $\mathbf{\Omega} = 0$. For $m = 1$, one obtains noncentral (or central) χ^2 distributions (Chapters 28, 17).

For the *linear case*, when $|\mathbf{\Omega} - \Theta\mathbf{I}| = 0$ has only one nonzero root, Θ_m, we have

$$(50)\quad p_{\mathbf{S}}(\mathbf{s}) = \left[2^{\frac{1}{2}(nm-n+2)}\pi^{\frac{1}{4}nm(m-1)}\prod_{j=1}^{m-1}\Gamma(\tfrac{1}{2}(n-j))\right]^{-1}\operatorname{etr}(-\tfrac{1}{2}\mathbf{V}^{-1}(\mathbf{\Omega}+\mathbf{s}))$$

$$\times\,|\mathbf{V}|^{-(\frac{1}{2})n}|\mathbf{s}|^{\frac{1}{2}(n-m-1)}(\operatorname{tr}\mathbf{\Omega}\mathbf{s})^{-\frac{1}{4}(n-s)}I_{\frac{1}{2}(n-s)}(\sqrt{\operatorname{tr}\mathbf{\Omega}\mathbf{s}}),$$

where $I_x(\cdot)$ is a modified Bessel function (Chapter 1, Section 3) (Anderson [3], Anderson and Girshick [5], and also, using a different approach, Fraser [13]).

Noncentral complex Wishart distributions have been studied by Khatri [29] and Kabe [28].

4.4. *Properties and Applications*

From the genesis of the noncentral Wishart distribution, the validity of the following result (obtained by Anderson [3]) is apparent.

If $\mathbf{S}_1,\mathbf{S}_2$ are independent noncentral $m \times m$ Wishart matrices with common variance-covariance matrix $\mathbf{V}$, but different degrees of freedom ν_1,ν_2 and noncentrality matrices $\mathbf{\Omega}_1,\mathbf{\Omega}_2$, then $\mathbf{S}_1 + \mathbf{S}_2$ has a noncentral Wishart distribution with $(\nu_1 + \nu_2)$ degrees of freedom, variance-covariance matrix $\mathbf{V}$, and noncentrality matrix $\mathbf{\Omega}_1 + \mathbf{\Omega}_2$.

The following result has been obtained by Rao [42]. If $\mathbf{S}$ has a noncentral Wishart distribution with degrees of freedom ν, variance-covariance matrix $\mathbf{V}$, and noncentrality matrix $\mathbf{\Omega}$, and $\mathbf{L}$ is a $(m \times 1)$ column vector, then the scalar $\mathbf{L}'\mathbf{S}\mathbf{L}$ is distributed as

$$(\mathbf{L}'\mathbf{V}\mathbf{L})\chi_{\nu}'^2(\lambda)$$

with

$$\lambda = 2\mathbf{L}'\mathbf{V}\mathbf{\Omega}\mathbf{L}/(\mathbf{L}'\mathbf{V}\mathbf{L}).$$

The noncentral Wishart distribution is applicable wherever it is desired to assess the effect of changing mean values on the distribution of statistics computed from second order sample moments and product moments. In particular we note possibilities for application in connection with tests of collinearity (Fisher [10]), comparison of scales of measurement (Cochran [7]), and multiple regression in time series analysis (Tintner [48]). It should be remembered, however, that numerical evaluation of probabilities connected with noncentral Wishart distributions is still not easy, despite the existence of formal expressions of relatively simple structure, such as (49.1) and (49.2).

REFERENCES

[1] Aitken, A. C. (1949). On the Wishart distribution in statistics, *Biometrika*, **36,** 59–62.

[2] Anderson, G. A. (1970). An asymptotic expansion for the non-central Wishart distribution, *Annals of Mathematical Statistics*, **41,** 1700–1707.

[3] Anderson, T. W. (1946). The non-central Wishart distribution and certain problems of multivariate statistics, *Annals of Mathematical Statistics*, **17,** 409–431.

[4] Anderson, T. W. (1958). *An Introduction to Multivariate Statistical Analysis*, New York: John Wiley and Sons.

[5] Anderson, T. W. and Girshick, M. A. (1944). Some extensions of the Wishart distribution, *Annals of Mathematical Statistics*, **15,** 345–357.

[6] Bagai, O. P. (1964). Distribution of the ratio of the generalized variance to any of its principal minors, *Journal of the Indian Statistical Association*, **2,** 80–96.

[7] Cochran, W. G. (1943). The comparison of different scales of measurement for experimental results, *Annals of Mathematical Statistics*, **14,** 205–216.

[8] Constantine, A. G. (1963). Some non-central distribution problems in multivariate analysis, *Annals of Mathematical Statistics*, **34,** 1270–1284.

[9] Elfving, G. (1947). A simple method of deducing certain distributions connected with multivariate sampling, *Skandinavisk Aktuarietidskrift*, **30,** 56–74.

[10] Fisher, R. A. (1938). The statistical utilization of multiple measurements, *Annals of Eugenics, London*, **8,** 376–386.

[11] Fisher, R. A. (1939). The sampling distribution of some statistics obtained from non-linear equations, *Annals of Eugenics, London*, **9,** 238–249.

[12] Fog, D. (1948). The geometrical method in the theory of sampling, *Biometrika*, **35,** 46–54.

[13] Fraser, D. A. S. (1968). The conditional Wishart: normal and non-normal, *Annals of Mathematical Statistics*, **39,** 593–605.

[14] Ghurye, S. G. and Olkin, I. (1969). Unbiased estimation of some multivariate probability densities, *Annals of Mathematical Statistics*, **40,** 1261–1271.

[15] Goodman, N. R. (1963). Statistical analysis based on a certain multivariate complex Gaussian distribution, *Annals of Mathematical Statistics*, **34,** 152–177.

[16] Gupta, R. P. (1964). Some extensions of the Wishart and multivariate *t*-distributions in the complex case, *Journal of the Indian Statistical Association*, **2,** 131–136.

[17] Hayakawa, T. (1969). On the distribution of the latent roots of a positive definite random symmetric matrix, I, *Annals of the Institute of Statistical Mathematics, Tokyo*, **21,** 1–21.

[18] Hayakawa, T. (1970). *On the Distribution of the Latent Roots of a Complex Wishart Matrix* (*Non-Central Case*), Mimeo Series No. 667, Institute of Statistics, University of North Carolina at Chapel Hill.

[19] Hengartner, O. (1965). Ausgewählte zwei- und dreidimensionale Prüfverteilungen, *Metrika*, **9,** 127–148.

[20] Herz, C. S. (1955). Bessel functions of matrix argument, *Annals of Mathematics*, **61,** 474–523.

[21] Hocking, R. R. and Smith, Wm. B. (1967). Generation of random samples from a Wishart distribution, *Texas A&M Institute of Statistics*, Technical Report No. 6, 1–6.

[22] Hsu, P. L. (1939). A new proof of the joint product moment distribution, *Proceedings of the Cambridge Philosophical Society*, **35,** 336–338.

[23] Jambunathan, M. V. (1965). A quick method of deriving Wishart's distribution, *Current Science*, **34,** 78.

[24] James, A. T. (1953). The non-central Wishart distribution, *Annals of Mathematical Statistics*, **24,** 491 (Abstract).

[25] James, A. T. (1954). Normal multivariate analysis and the orthogonal group, *Annals of Mathematical Statistics*, **25,** 40–75.

[26] James, A. T. (1955). The non-central Wishart distribution, *Proceedings of the Royal Society of London, Series A*, **229,** 364–366.

[27] James, A. T. (1964). Distributions of matrix variates and latent roots derived from normal samples, *Annals of Mathematical Statistics*, **35,** 475–501.

[28] Kabe, D. G. (1966). Complex analogues of some classical non-central multivariate distributions, *Australian Journal of Statistics*, **8,** 99–103.

[29] Khatri, C. G. (1965). Classical statistical analysis based on a certain multivariate complex Gaussian distribution, *Annals of Mathematical Statistics*, **36,** 98–114.

[30] Kitchen, J. O. (1968). *Extended Tables of Zonal Polynomials*, Institute of Statistics, University of North Carolina at Chapel Hill, Mimeo Series No. 565.

[31] Kshirsagar, A. M. (1959). Bartlett decomposition and Wishart distribution, *Annals of Mathematical Statistics*, **30,** 239–241.

[32] Kshirsagar, A. M. (1960). Some extensions of multivariate t distributions and multivariate generalization of the distribution of regression coefficient, *Proceedings of the Cambridge Philosophical Society*, **57,** 80–85.

[33] Kshirsagar, A. M. (1970). An alternative derivation of the direction and collinearity statistics in discriminant analysis, *Bulletin of the Calcutta Statistical Association*, **19,** 123–124.

[34] Lévy, P. (1948). The arithmetical character of the Wishart distribution, *Proceedings of the Cambridge Philosophical Society*, **44,** 295–297.

[35] Madow, W. A. (1938). Contributions to the theory of multi-variate statistical analysis, *Transactions of the American Mathematical Society*, **44,** 454–495.

[36] Mahalanobis, P. C., Bose, R. C., and Roy, S. N. (1937). Normalization of statistical variates and the use of rectangular co-ordinates in the theory of sampling distributions, *Sankhyā*, **3,** 1–40.

[37] Mauldon, J. G. (1955). Pivotal quantities for Wishart's and related

distributions, and a paradox in fiducial theory, *Journal of the Royal Statistical Society, Series B*, **17**, 79–85.

[38] Mitra, S. K. (1969). Some characteristic and non-characteristic properties of the Wishart distributions, *Sankhyā, Series A*, **31**, 19–22.

[39] Olkin, I. and Roy, S. N. (1954). On multivariate distribution theory, *Annals of Mathematical Statistics*, **25**, 329–339.

[40] Olkin, I. and Rubin, H. (1962). A characterization of the Wishart distribution, *Annals of Mathematical Statistics*, **33**, 1272–1273.

[41] Quensel, C.-E. (1953). The distribution of the second order moments in random samples from non-normal multivariate universes, *Lunds Universitets Årsskrift., N.F Åvd. 2*, **48**, No. 4.

[42] Rao, C. R. (1965). *Linear Statistical Inference and Its Applications.* New York: John Wiley & Sons, Inc.

[43] Rasch, G. (1948). A functional equation for Wishart's distribution, *Annals of Mathematical Statistics*, **19**, 262–266.

[44] Simonsen, W. (1944–1945). On distributions of functions of samples from a normally distributed infinite population, *Skandinavisk Aktuarietidskrift*, **27**, 235–261; **28**, 20–43.

[45] Srivastava, M. S. (1965). On the complex Wishart distribution, *Annals of Mathematical Statistics*, **36**, 313–315.

[46] Sverdrup, E. (1947). Derivation of the Wishart distribution of the second order sample moments by straightforward integration of a multiple integral, *Skandinavisk Aktuarietidskrift*, **30**, 151–166.

[47] Tan, W. Y. and Guttman, I. (1971). A disguised Wishart variable and a related theorem, *Journal of the Royal Statistical Society, Series B*, **33**, 147–152.

[48] Tintner, G. (1944). An application of the variate difference method to multiple regression, *Econometrica*, **12**, 97–113.

[49] Tumura, Y. (1965). The distribution of latent roots and vectors, *Tokyo Rika University, TRU Mathematics*, **1**, 1–16.

[50] Weibull, M. (1953). The distribution of t- and F-statistics and of correlation and regression coefficients in stratified samples from normal populations with different means, *Skandinavisk Aktuarietidskrift*, **36**, *Suppl.* 1–106.

[51] Wijsman, R. A. (1957). Random orthogonal transformations and their use in some classical distribution problems in multivariate analysis, *Annals of Mathematical Statistics*, **28**, 415–423.

[52] Wishart, J. (1928). The generalized product moment distribution in samples from a normal multivariate population, *Biometrika*, **20A**, 32–52. (Note: 424).

[53] Wishart, J. (1948). Proofs of the distribution law of the second order moment statistics, *Biometrika*, **35**, 55–57. (Note: 422).

[54] Wishart, J. and Bartlett, M. S. (1933). The generalised product moment distribution in a normal system, *Proceedings of the Cambridge Philosophical Society*, **29**, 260–270.

39

Some Other Distributions Associated with the Multinormal Distributions

1. Introduction

Most of the statistics used in multivariate analysis based on multinormal models can be expressed as functions of the nonzero roots $L_1 \leq L_2 \leq \cdots \leq L_p$ of determinantal equations of the form

$$|\mathbf{S}_1 - L\mathbf{S}_2| = 0, \tag{1}$$

where $\mathbf{S}_1,\mathbf{S}_2$ are independent symmetric $m \times m$ matrices, the elements of each of which have a joint Wishart distribution with degrees of freedom ν_1, ν_2 respectively. The distribution of $\mathbf{S}_1$ may be singular, but we shall suppose that the distribution of $\mathbf{S}_2$ is nonsingular. Then, with probability 1, $|\mathbf{S}_2| \neq 0$, and the L's are roots of

$$|\mathbf{S}_1\mathbf{S}_2^{-1} - L\mathbf{I}| = 0, \tag{2}$$

that is, they are latent roots (eigenvalues) of $\mathbf{S}_1\mathbf{S}_2^{-1}$. Also $p = \min(m,\nu_1)$.

In many cases the distributions of $\mathbf{S}_1$ and $\mathbf{S}_2$ have the same parameters, except for the degrees of freedom ν_1,ν_2 ($> m$) respectively, that is, $\mathbf{S}_j$ is distributed as $W_m(\nu_j;\mathbf{V})$, with $\mathbf{V}$ not depending on j. In such cases the joint distribution of the L's is the same as it would be if $\mathbf{V} = \mathbf{I}$. To see why this is so, we first recall (Chapter 38) that $\mathbf{S}_j$ can be represented as $\mathbf{Z}_j\mathbf{Z}_j'$, where $\mathbf{Z}_j$ is a $m \times \nu$ matrix of ν independent columns, each column having a joint m-variate multinormal distribution with expected value vector $\mathbf{0}$ and variance-covariance matrix $\mathbf{V}$. Furthermore, a nonsingular $m \times m$ matrix $\mathbf{A}$ can be found such that $\mathbf{AVA} = \mathbf{I}$, so that $\mathbf{AZ}_j\mathbf{Z}_j'\mathbf{A}' = \mathbf{AS}_j\mathbf{A}'$ has a Wishart distribution $W_m(\nu_j;\mathbf{I})$.

Since the roots of (1) are also those of

$$|\mathbf{A}(\mathbf{S}_1 - L\mathbf{S}_2)\mathbf{A}'| = |\mathbf{AS}_1\mathbf{A}' - L\mathbf{AS}_2\mathbf{A}'| = 0,$$

we may take $\mathbf{V} = \mathbf{I}$ without affecting the joint distribution of the L's.

In most cases we shall suppose $\nu_1 \geq m$, as well as $\nu_2 \geq m$. If $\nu_1 < m$, appropriate formulas can be derived by replacing m by ν_1, ν_1 by m, and ν_2 by $(\nu_1 + \nu_2 - m)$.

A number of the results used in this chapter are included in a survey paper by Asoo [5], who points out the analogy between the Wishart distribution and the univariate gamma distribution. (See also Olkin and Rubin [66].)

2. "Generalized Beta" Distributions

Equation (1) can be rewritten in the form

$$|(1 + L)\mathbf{S}_1 - L(\mathbf{S}_1 + \mathbf{S}_2)| = 0$$

or

$$|\mathbf{S}_1 - G(\mathbf{S}_1 + \mathbf{S}_2)| = 0, \tag{3}$$

with $G = L/(1 + L)$. The roots of (3), $G_j = L_j/(1 + L_j)$ satisfy the inequalities $0 \leq G_1 \leq G_2 \leq \cdots \leq G_m \leq 1$. They are with probability 1, the eigenvalues of the matrix $\mathbf{S}_1(\mathbf{S}_1 + \mathbf{S}_2)^{-1}$. The joint distribution of the G's takes different forms, according as ν_1 is greater or less than m.

For the case $\nu_1 \geq m$, there are, with probability 1, m nonzero G's, with joint density function

$$\text{(4.1)}\quad p_{G_1,G_2,\ldots,G_m}(g_1,\ldots,g_m) = C\prod_{j=1}^{m}\prod_{k=j+1}^{m}(g_k - g_j)\left[\prod_{j=1}^{m} g_j\right]^{\frac{1}{2}(\nu_1-m-1)}\left[\prod_{j=1}^{m}(1 - g_j)\right]^{\frac{1}{2}(\nu_2-m-1)}$$
$$(0 \leq g_1 \leq g_2 \leq \cdots \leq g_m \leq 1),$$

where

$$C = \pi^{(1/2)m}\prod_{j=1}^{m}[\{\Gamma(\tfrac{1}{2}(\nu_1 + \nu_2 - j + 1))\}\{\Gamma(\tfrac{1}{2}(\nu_1 - j + 1)) \times \Gamma(\tfrac{1}{2}(\nu_2 - j + 1))\Gamma(\tfrac{1}{2}(m - j + 1))\}^{-1}]$$
$$= \pi^{(1/2)m^2}\Gamma_m(\tfrac{1}{2}(\nu_1 + \nu_2))[\Gamma_m(\tfrac{1}{2}\nu_1)\Gamma_m(\tfrac{1}{2}\nu_2)\Gamma_m(\tfrac{1}{2}m)]^{-1}.$$

If $\nu_1 < m$ there are, with probability 1, only ν_1 nonzero G's. They have joint density function

$$(4.2)\quad p_{G_1,\ldots,G_{\nu_1}}(g_1,\ldots,g_{\nu_1})$$
$$= C\prod_{j=1}^{\nu_1}\prod_{k=j+1}^{\nu_1}(g_k-g_j)\left[\prod_{j=1}^{\nu_1}g_j\right]^{\frac{1}{2}(m-\nu_1+1)}\left[\prod_{j=1}^{\nu_1}(1-g_j)\right]^{\frac{1}{2}(\nu_2-m-1)}$$
$$(0\le g_1\le g_2\le\cdots\le g_{\nu_1}\le 1)$$

with

$$C=\pi^{(1/2)\nu_1}\prod_{j=1}^{\nu_1}[\{\Gamma(\tfrac{1}{2}(\nu_1+\nu_2-j+1))\}\{\Gamma(\tfrac{1}{2}(\nu_1-j+1))$$
$$\times\Gamma(\tfrac{1}{2}(\nu_1+\nu_2-m-j+1))\Gamma(\tfrac{1}{2}(m-j+1))\}^{-1}]$$
$$=\pi^{(1/2)\nu_1^2}\Gamma_{\nu_1}(\tfrac{1}{2}(\nu_1+\nu_2))[\Gamma_{\nu_1}(\tfrac{1}{2}\nu_1)\Gamma_{\nu_1}(\tfrac{1}{2}(\nu_1+\nu_2-m))\Gamma_{\nu_1}(\tfrac{1}{2}m)]^{-1}.$$

Note that (4.2) can be obtained from (4.1) by changing m to ν_1, ν_1 to m, and ν_2 to $(\nu_1+\nu_2-m)$. (We recall that ν_2 is assumed to be not less than m.)

These results were obtained by a number of different authors (Fisher **[18]**, Girshick **[23]**, Hsu **[37]**, and Roy **[88]**) about the same time (1939).

The joint distributions (4.1) and (4.2) have been called *generalized beta distributions* (e.g., Foster and Rees **[20]**, Foster **[19]**). They are to be distinguished from the multivariate beta distributions discussed in Chapter 40 by the fact that, in general, not all the marginal distributions are beta distributions. For example, with $m=3$, $\nu_1=4$, $\nu_2=6$ we have

$$(5)\quad p_{G_1,G_2,G_3}(g_1,g_2,g_3)$$
$$=2520(g_2-g_1)(g_3-g_1)(g_3-g_2)(1-g_1)(1-g_2)(1-g_3)$$
$$(0\le g_1\le g_2\le g_3\le 1),$$

from which we obtain

$$(6.1)\quad p_{G_1}(g_1)=9(1-g_1)^8 \qquad (0\le g_1\le 1),$$
$$(6.2)\quad p_{G_2}(g_2)=105g_2^2(1-g_2)^4 \qquad (0\le g_2\le 1),$$
$$(6.3)\quad p_{G_3}(g_3)=3g_3^5(1-g_3)(3g_3^2-21g_3+28) \qquad (0\le g_3\le 1).$$

Although G_1 and G_2 have beta distributions, G_3 does not.

Equation (6.1) is a special case of the general result that if $\nu_1=m+1$ and $\nu_2\ge m$,

$$(7)\quad p_{G_1}(g_1)=2[3(\nu_2-m)+7]^{-1}(1-g_1)^{\frac{1}{2}[3(\nu_2-m)+7]} \qquad (0\le g_1\le 1).$$

Similarly, if $\nu_2=m+1$, then

$$(8)\quad p_{G_3}(g_3)=2[3(\nu_1-m)+7]^{-1}g^{\frac{1}{2}[3(\nu_1-m)+7]} \qquad (0\le g_3\le 1).$$

Also, if the values of ν_1 and ν_2 are interchanged (with $\min(\nu_1,\nu_2)\ge m$), then the joint distribution of $1-G_m, 1-G_{m-1},\ldots,1-G_1$ is the same as that of $G_1,G_2,\ldots,G_m$ for the original distribution. In particular, the distribution of G_a with $\nu_1 = \nu_1^*$, $\nu_2 = \nu_2^*$ is the same as that of $(1 - G_{m+1-a})$ with $\nu_1 = \nu_2^*$, $\nu_2 = \nu_1^*$.

The joint distribution in both (4.1) and (4.2) is of the form

$$(9) \quad p_{\mathbf{G}}(\mathbf{g}) = C(m,\alpha,\beta) \prod_{j=1}^{p} [g_j^{\alpha}(1 - g_j)^{\beta}] \prod_{i>j} (g_i - g_j)$$

$$(0 < g_1 \leq g_2 \cdots \leq g_p < 1), \quad (p = \min(\nu_1,m))$$

with

$$C(p,\alpha,\beta) = \pi^{\frac{1}{2}p} \prod_{j=1}^{p} \left[\frac{\Gamma(\alpha + \beta + 1 + \frac{1}{2}(p + j))}{\Gamma(\alpha + \frac{1}{2}(j + 1))\Gamma(\beta + \frac{1}{2}(j + 1))\Gamma(\frac{1}{2}j)}\right]$$
$$= \pi^{(1/2)p^2}\Gamma_p(\alpha + \beta + 1 + p)$$
$$\times \{\Gamma_p(\alpha + \tfrac{1}{2}(p + 1))\Gamma_p(\beta + \tfrac{1}{2}(p + 1))\Gamma_p(\tfrac{1}{2}p)\}^{-1}.$$

Although (for α,β integers) formula (9) is simply a polynomial in $\mathbf{g}$, the restrictions on the range of variation of $\mathbf{g}$ often render analysis difficult, even for fairly small values of p.

Particular attention has been paid to the distribution of G_p (the greatest of the G's), since this statistic is sometimes used as a test criterion. Roy [88] has obtained the elegant determinantal expression

$$(10) \quad \Pr[G_p \leq g] = C(m,\alpha,\beta) \begin{vmatrix} \int_0^g t_p^{\alpha+p-1}(1 - t_p)^{\beta}\, dt_p & \cdots & \int_0^g t_p^{\alpha}(1 - t_p)^{\beta}\, dt_p \\ \vdots & & \vdots \\ \int_0^{t_2} t_1^{\alpha+p-1}(1 - t_1)^{\beta}\, dt_1 & \cdots & \int_0^{t_2} t_1^{\alpha}(1 - t_1)^{\beta}\, dt_1 \end{vmatrix}$$

in which the determinant on the right-hand side (the element in the $i(\geq 2)$th row and jth column of which is

$$\int_0^{t_{p-i+2}} t_{p-i+1}^{\alpha+p-j}(1 - t_{p-i+1})^{\beta}\, dt_{p-i+1}),$$

is to be expanded in the usual way and each term to be evaluated as a multiple integral. Alternative formulas to (10) have been given by Sugiyama and Fukutomi [102] in the form of a sum of incomplete beta functions, see also Krishnaiah and Chang [54a] and by Sugiyama [98]. The latter gave

$$(10)' \quad \Pr[G_p \leq g] = \frac{\Gamma_m(\frac{1}{2}(p + 1))\Gamma_p(\frac{1}{2}(\nu_1 + \nu_2))}{\Gamma_p(\frac{1}{2}\nu_2)\Gamma_p(\frac{1}{2}(\nu_1 + m + 1))}$$
$$\times {}_2F_1(-\tfrac{1}{2}(\nu_2 + p + 1),\tfrac{1}{2}\nu_1;\tfrac{1}{2}(\nu_1 + p + 1);g\mathbf{I}_p)g^{(1/2)\nu_1 p}.$$

We may note that

$$ {}_2F_1(-\tfrac{1}{2}(\nu_2 + p + 1), \tfrac{1}{2}\nu_1; \tfrac{1}{2}(\nu_1 + p + 1); g\mathbf{I}_p) $$

$$ = \sum_{j=0}^{\infty} \sum_{\varkappa(j)} \frac{(\frac{1}{2}(\nu_2 + p + 1))^{\{\varkappa\}}(\frac{1}{2}\nu_1)^{\{\varkappa\}}}{(\frac{1}{2}(\nu_1 + p + 1))^{\{\varkappa\}}} \frac{C_\varkappa(\mathbf{I}_p)}{j!} g^j. $$

Note that $C_\varkappa(\mathbf{I}_p)$ can be evaluated from (27) of Chapter 38.

Pillai and his co-workers (see references **68, 70–76, 79, 80**) have used formula (10) to construct tables of the distribution of G_p. Upper 5 and 1% points for $p = 2(1)6$, $\alpha = 0(1)4$, and $\beta = 5(5)30,40(20)100(30)160,200,300,500,1000$ to five significant figures are collected together in **[72]**. Further values, for $\alpha = 5,7,10,15$ (and the same m and β) were given by Jacildo **[40]**. These tables have been extended by Pillai to $p = 7$ in **[73]**, to $p = 8,9,10$ in **[74]**, and (to four significant figures) to $p = 14(2)20$ in **[75]**. In all cases the same sets of α and β values were used (including $\alpha = 5,7,10,15$). (Approximations were used in the course of the calculations. The errors arising therefrom appear to have been carefully checked.) There is a gap between $p = 10$ and $p = 14$; Pillai **[75]** refers to unpublished tables giving values for $p = 11(1)20$.

Note that tables of the distribution of G_p can also be used for the distribution of the smallest root G_1. (See the remarks following equation (8).)

When $m = 2$ some simplifications are possible. We have

$$ C(2,\alpha,\beta) = \sqrt{\pi}\,\frac{\Gamma(\alpha + \beta + \frac{5}{2})\Gamma(\alpha + \beta + 3)}{\Gamma(\alpha + 1)\Gamma(\alpha + \frac{3}{2})\Gamma(\beta + 1)\Gamma(\beta + \frac{3}{2})} $$

$$ = \frac{\Gamma(2(\alpha + \beta + 2))}{4\Gamma(2(\alpha + 1))\Gamma(2(\beta + 1))}, $$

and (if α and β are integers)

(11) $\Pr[G_2 \le t]$

$$ = C(2,\alpha,\beta) $$

$$ \times \int_0^t \int_0^{t_2} [t_1^\alpha t_2^{\alpha+1}(1 - t_1)^\beta (1 - t_2)^\beta - t_1^{\alpha+1} t_2^\alpha (1 - t_1)^\beta (1 - t_2)^\beta]\, dt_1\, dt_2 $$

$$ = C(2,\alpha,\beta) \int_0^t t_2^{2(\alpha+1)}(1 - t_2)^{2\beta} \left[\frac{1}{(\alpha + 1)^{[2]}} + \frac{2\beta}{(\alpha + 1)^{[3]}} \frac{t_2}{1 - t_2} \right. $$

$$ \left. + \frac{3\beta^{(2)}}{(\alpha + 1)^{[4]}} \frac{t_2^2}{(1 - t_2)^2} + \cdots + \frac{(\beta + 1)!}{(\alpha + 1)^{[\beta+2]}} \frac{t_2^\beta}{(1 - t_2)^\beta} \right] dt_2 $$

$$ = C(2,\alpha,\beta) \sum_{j=1}^{\beta+1} \frac{j\beta^{(j-1)}}{(\alpha + 1)^{[j+1]}} B_t(2\alpha + j + 3, 2\beta - j + 1), $$

where $B_t(\cdot)$ denotes the incomplete beta function (Chapter 1, equation 40)), $\beta^{(j)} = \beta(\beta - 1)\cdots(\beta - j + 1)$ and $(\alpha + 1)^{[j]} = (\alpha + 1)(\alpha + 2)\cdots(\alpha + j)$. For $p = 2$, Foster and Rees [20] have given upper percentage points (20, 15, 10, 5, and 1%) of G_p (i.e., G_2) to decimal places for $\alpha = -0.5,0(1)9$; $\beta = 1(1)19(5)49,59,79$. Foster [19] has extended these tables to the cases $p = 3$ and $p = 4$.

Charts from which upper 5, 2.5, and 1% points can be read for $p = 2(1)5$; $\alpha = -\frac{1}{2},0(1)10$; $\beta \geq 5$ have been given by Heck [33].

Krishnaiah and Waikar [56–57] have derived expressions for various subsets of the ordered roots. Although necessarily rather complicated, they are in a convenient form to use as a basis for computer programs.

A *multivariate beta* distribution is obtained as the joint distribution of $\mathbf{H} = \mathbf{C}^{-1}\mathbf{S}_2(\mathbf{C}^{-1})'$ where $\mathbf{C}$ is the lower triangular "square root of $(\mathbf{S}_1 + \mathbf{S}_2)$, satisfying

$$\mathbf{S}_1 + \mathbf{S}_2 = \mathbf{C}\mathbf{C}'.$$

If $\mathbf{S}_1$ and $\mathbf{S}_2$ are independent, with $\mathbf{S}_j$ distributed as $W_m(\nu_j;\mathbf{V})$ $(j = 1,2)$ then

(12)

$$p_{\mathbf{H}}(\mathbf{h}) = \Gamma_m(\tfrac{1}{2}(\nu_1 + \nu_2))[\Gamma_m(\tfrac{1}{2}\nu_1)\Gamma_m(\tfrac{1}{2}\nu_2)]^{-1}\,|\mathbf{h}|^{\frac{1}{2}(\nu_2-m-1)}\,|\mathbf{I} - \mathbf{h}|^{\frac{1}{2}(\nu_1-m-1)}$$

$$(\mathbf{h} > 0;\mathbf{I} - \mathbf{h} > 0).$$

A generalization of this distribution is given in Chapter 40, Eq. 36.

Writing $\mathbf{H}$ in the form $(\mathbf{S}_1 + \mathbf{S}_2)^{-1/2}\mathbf{S}_2\{(\mathbf{S}_1 + \mathbf{S}_2)^{-1/2}\}'$ we see that $\mathbf{H}$ is a generalization of the univariate "correlation ratio."

3. Noncentral "Generalized Beta" Distributions

Suppose now that $\mathbf{S}_1$ has a *noncentral* Wishart distribution (as defined in Section 4 of Chapter 38). Constantine [9] and James [42] have shown that the joint distribution of $G_1,\ldots,G_p$ has density function

$$(13)\quad p_{\mathbf{G}}(\mathbf{g}) = C(p,\alpha,\beta)\text{etr}(-\tfrac{1}{2}\mathbf{\Omega})\prod_{j=1}^{p}[g_j^{\alpha}(1 - g_j)^{\beta}]\prod_{i>j}(g_i - g_j)$$

$$\times\ {}_1F_1(\tfrac{1}{2}\nu;\tfrac{1}{2}\nu_2;\tfrac{1}{2}\mathbf{\Omega},\mathbf{T})\qquad (0 \leq g_1 \leq \cdots \leq g_p \leq 1),$$

where $\nu = \nu_1 + \nu_2$ and $\mathbf{T} = \text{diag}(g_1,g_2,\ldots,g_p)$; $\alpha = \frac{1}{2}(\nu_2 - p - 1)$; $\beta = \frac{1}{2}(\nu_1 - p - 1)$; [${}_1F_1(\cdot)$ is given by (31.2) of Chapter 38.]

Pillai and Jayachandran [82] have applied this formula to evaluate power functions of certain multivariate tests, in the special cases $p = 2$, 3, and 4.

The noncentral density corresponding to (12) is of form

$$|\mathbf{h}|^{\frac{1}{2}(\nu_2-m-1)}\,|\mathbf{I}-\mathbf{h}|^{\frac{1}{2}(\nu_1-m-1)} \times \text{(function of the } s \times s \text{ principal minor of } \mathbf{h})$$

where s is the rank of $\mathbf{\Omega}$. (Radcliffe [87]. See also Gupta and Kabe [26].)

Another form of noncentral distribution arises when the two Wishart matrices have different variance-covariance matrices $\mathbf{V}_1,\mathbf{V}_2$. The distribution then depends on the values of the characteristic roots $\lambda_1 \le \lambda_2 \le \cdots \le \lambda_m$ of $\mathbf{V}_1\mathbf{V}_2^{-1}$. Khatri [48] has obtained a formula for the joint density function of the roots $l_1 \le l_2 \le \cdots \le l_m$ of (2) in this case, which can be expressed (e.g., Chang [8]) in the form (for $m > \nu_1,\nu_2$)

$$(14)\quad p_{\mathbf{L}}(\mathbf{l}) = K\prod_{i=1}^{m} - \lambda_i^{(1/2)\nu_1} l_i^{\frac{1}{2}(\nu_1-m-1)}(1-l_i)^{\frac{1}{2}(\nu_2-m-1)}\left[\prod_{i<j}(l_j-l_i)\right]$$
$$\times \sum_{k=0}^{\infty}(k!)^{-1}\sum_{\kappa}\frac{C_\kappa(-\mathbf{\Lambda}^{-1})C_\kappa(\mathbf{L})(\nu_1+\nu_2)^{\{\kappa\}}}{C_\kappa(\mathbf{I}_m)},$$

where $\mathbf{L} = \operatorname{diag}(l_1,\ldots,l_m)$; $\mathbf{\Lambda} = \operatorname{diag}(\lambda_1,\ldots,\lambda_m)$ and

$$K = \pi^{\frac{1}{2}m(m-1)}\Gamma_m(\tfrac{1}{2}(\nu_1+\nu_2))\{\Gamma_m(\tfrac{1}{2}m)\Gamma_m(\tfrac{1}{2}\nu_1)\Gamma_m(\tfrac{1}{2}\nu_2)\}^{-1}.$$

[The $(\nu_1+\nu_2)^{\{\kappa\}}$ and C_κ are defined in Chapter 38, Section 4.2.]

Chang [8] has shown, using an argument similar to that of Anderson [4], that when $(\nu_1+\nu_2)$ is large the joint density function of $l_1,\ldots,l_m$ is approximately

$$(15)\quad p_{\mathbf{L}}(\mathbf{l}) = K\prod_{i>j}^{m}(\lambda_j^{-1}-\lambda_i^{-1})^{-1/2}$$
$$\times \prod_{i=1}^{m}[l_i^{\frac{1}{2}(\nu_1-m-1)}\lambda_i^{-(1/2)\nu_1}(1+\lambda_i^{-1}l_i)^{-\frac{1}{2}(\nu_1+\nu_2-m+1)}]$$
$$(l_1 \le l_2 \le \cdots \le l_m),$$

where

$$K = [2\pi^2(\nu_1+\nu_2)^{-1}]^{(1/4)m(m-1)}\left[\prod_{j=1}^{m}\Gamma(\tfrac{1}{2}j)\right]\Gamma_m(\tfrac{1}{2}(\nu_1+\nu_2))$$
$$\times\{\Gamma_m(\tfrac{1}{2}m)\Gamma_m(\tfrac{1}{2}\nu_1)\Gamma_m(\tfrac{1}{2}\nu_2)\}^{-1}$$

and $\lambda_1 \ge \lambda_2 \ge \cdots \ge \lambda_m$ are the roots of $|\mathbf{V}_1 - \lambda\mathbf{V}_2| = 0$.

Pillai and Al-Ani [77] have obtained formulas for the cumulative distribution functions of individual L_j's in terms of linear functions of incomplete beta functions. For $m = 2$ they give tables of the probabilities of L_1,L_2 exceeding their upper 5% points (calculated on the distribution with $\lambda_1 = \lambda_2 = 1$ corresponding to $\mathbf{V}_1 = \mathbf{V}_2$), to 3–5 significance figures for various combinations of values of λ_1 and λ_2, and for

$$\tfrac{1}{2}(|\nu_1 - 2| - 1) = 0,1,2,5,$$
$$\tfrac{1}{2}(\nu_2 - 3) = 5,15,40.$$

For $m = 2$, there is a similar set of tables (for L_1, L_2, and L_3) with:

$$\tfrac{1}{2}(|\nu_1 - 3| - 1) = 0,1,2,5,$$
$$\tfrac{1}{2}(\nu_2 - 4) = 5,15,40.$$

4. Distribution of Latent Roots of a (Central or Noncentral) Wishart Matrix

If $\mathbf{S}$ has the Wishart distribution $W_m(\nu;\mathbf{I}_m\sigma^2)$, then the joint density function of the ordered latent roots $T_m \geq T_{m-1} \geq \cdots \geq T_1 \geq 0$ of $\mathbf{S}$ is

$$(16)\quad p_{\mathbf{T}}(\mathbf{t}) = (2\sigma^2)^{-(1/2)\nu m}\pi^{(1/2)m}\prod_{j=1}^{m}[\Gamma(\tfrac{1}{2}j)\Gamma(\tfrac{1}{2}(\nu - j + 1))]^{-1}$$
$$\times \exp\left(-\tfrac{1}{2}\sigma^{-2}\sum_{j=1}^{m} t_j\right)\left[\prod_{j=1}^{m} t_j\right]^{\frac{1}{2}(\nu-m-1)}\prod_{i>j}(t_i - t_j)$$
$$(0 \leq t_1 \leq t_2 \leq \cdots \leq t_m)$$

(Fisher [18], Hsu [37], and Roy [88].)

The distribution (16) can be obtained from distribution (4.2) by setting $T_j = \nu_2 G_j$ $(j = 1,\ldots,m)$ and letting $\nu_2 \to \infty$ (Nanda [65]).

From (16) it is a simple matter to obtain the moment generating function of $\sum_{j=1}^{m} T_j$. It is

$$(17)\qquad E\left[\exp\left(u\sum_{j=1}^{m} T_j\right)\right] = (1 - 2u\sigma^2)^{-(1/2)\nu m},$$

from which we see that

$$\sum_{j=1}^{m} T_j \qquad (= tr\mathbf{S})$$

has a $\chi^2\sigma^2$ distribution with νm degrees of freedom.

In the remainder of this section we shall suppose that $\sigma = 1$.

For the special case $m = 2$, John [44] has shown that

$$(18)\quad \Pr[T_1 \leq t] = \Pr[\chi^2_{2\nu} \leq 2t] + \frac{\sqrt{\pi}}{\Gamma(\frac{1}{2}\nu)}(\tfrac{1}{2}t)^{\frac{1}{2}(\nu-1)}e^{-(1/2)t}\Pr[\chi^2_{\nu+1} > t].$$

Using this formula, Kleinbaum and John [52] have given tables of the upper and lower 1, 5, and 10% points of the distribution of T_1, to five decimal places, for $\nu = 2(1)30(10)100$. For values of ν greater than 30, interpolation for $t/\chi^2_{\nu-1,1-\sqrt{1-\beta}}$ (where $\beta = \Pr[T_1 \leq t]$), rather than for t itself, is recommended.

In [52], an approximation due to John is noted, according to which, for large ν, T_1 is approximately distributed as the minimum of two independent variables each having a $\chi^2_{\nu-1}$ distribution.

Pillai and Chang [80] obtained the following approximations:

1. *m even*

$$\Pr[\nu^{-1}T_m \leq t] \doteqdot 1 + \sum_{j=1}^{m-1}(-1)^j a_j t^{\frac{1}{2}(\nu+m-1)-j}e^{-t}. \tag{19.1}$$

2. *m odd*

$$\Pr[\nu^{-1}T_m \leq t] \doteqdot \{\Gamma(\tfrac{1}{2}(\nu - m + 1))\}^{-1}\int_0^t x^{\frac{1}{2}(\nu-m-1)}e^{-x}\,dx + \sum_{j=1}^{m-1}(-1)^j a_j t^{\frac{1}{2}(\nu+m-1)-j}e^{-t} \tag{19.2}$$

where

$$a_1 = \sqrt{\pi}[\Gamma(\tfrac{1}{2}m)\Gamma(\tfrac{1}{2}(\nu - m + 1))]^{-1}$$

and

$$a_j = a_1\left[\binom{m-1}{j-1}2^{-j+1}(\nu - 1)^{(j-1)} - \{\tfrac{1}{2}(\nu + m + 1) - j\}a_{j-1}\right].$$

Using these approximations, they have calculated approximate upper percentage points of the distribution of T_m for $m = 2(1)20$. Values for $m = 11(1)20$ are published in [80]. Upper 10 and 5% points are given to four decimal places for $\nu = 2(1)20(2)30(5)50(10)100(20)160,200$. Comparison with exact values in a few cases (see Table 2) for $m = 3$ gives some confidence in the tabulated values. Note that accuracy increases as the upper tail area decreases.

Sugiyama [100] has published a table of upper 5 and 1% points of the distribution of T_m/ν (T_m is the largest latent root of $\mathbf{S}$) for $\nu = 2(2)50$, $m = 2,3$; six decimal places are given. For $m = 4$, four places at 5% and two at 1% are given, for $\nu = 2(2)10(10)30$. Our Table 1 is based on this.

Sugiyama used the formula [see (21.2)]

$$\Pr[T_m \leq t] = \frac{\Gamma_m(\frac{1}{2}(m + 1))}{2^{(1/2)m\nu}\Gamma_m(\frac{1}{2}(\nu + m + 1))}t^{(1/2)m\nu} \times e^{-(1/2)m\nu t}\,{}_1F_1(\tfrac{1}{2}(m + 1);\tfrac{1}{2}(m + \nu + 1);\tfrac{1}{2}\nu t\mathbf{I}).$$

Convergence of the series for ${}_1F_1(\cdot)$ is so slow that more than 100 terms were needed to give the values tabled.

TABLE 1

Upper Percentage Points of Greatest Root of $|\nu^{-1}\mathbf{S} - T\mathbf{I}| = 0$

	Upper 5% points			Upper 1% points		
ν	$m = 2$	$m = 3$	$m = 4$	$m = 2$	$m = 3$	$m = 4$
2	4.30	5.37	6.34	6.08	7.28	8.36
4	3.17	3.81	4.38	4.18	4.88	5.49
6	2.70	3.18	3.60	3.44	3.95	4.40
8	2.44	2.83	3.17	3.03	3.44	3.80
10	2.26	2.60	2.89	2.76	3.11	3.42
20	1.85	2.06	2.24	2.15	2.37	2.56
30	1.67	1.84	1.98	1.91	2.07	2.22
40	1.58	1.71	—	1.77	1.90	—
50	1.51	1.63	—	1.68	1.79	—

Thompson [103] has published tables (to five significant figures) of upper percentage points ($T_{m,1-\alpha}$) of T_m, lower percentage points ($T_{1,\alpha}$) of T_1, and values $T'_{m,1-\alpha}$ such that $\Pr[T_{1,\alpha} \leq T_1 \leq T_m \leq T'_{m,1-\alpha}] = 1 - 2\alpha$ for $m = 2$, $\alpha = 0.005, 0.01, 0.025, 0.05$, $\nu = 2(1)20(2)30(5)50(10)100$. ($T'_{m,1-\alpha}$, only for $\alpha = 0.005, 0.025$.)

Hanumara and Thompson [27] have given *approximate* values (to four significant figures) of $T_{1,\alpha}$ and $T_{m,1-\alpha}$ for $m = 2(1)10$; $\nu = m(1)10(5)30(10)300$; $\alpha = 0.005, 0.01, 0.025, 0.05$. (For practical purposes $T'_{m,1-\alpha}$ can be taken equal to $T_{m,1-\alpha}$.)

In Pearson and Hartley [67] some interesting, and useful, *approximate* relations among the percentage points of the distribution of T_m are noted. These relations, which hold for all values of ν and m, are

$$T_{m,0.90} \doteqdot \tfrac{3}{2}T_{m,0.95} - \tfrac{1}{2}T_{m,0.99},$$

$$T_{m,0.975} \doteqdot 0.55T_{m,0.95} + 0.45T_{m,0.99},$$

$$T_{m,0.995} \doteqdot 1.39T_{m,0.99} - 0.39T_{m,0.95}.$$

Thus approximate upper 10, $2\frac{1}{2}$, and $\frac{1}{2}$% points can be obtained from tables of the upper 5 and 1% points.

For the distribution of the smallest root, T_1, we have approximate formulas for the lower $2\frac{1}{2}$ and $\frac{1}{2}$% points:

$$T_{1,0.025} \doteqdot T_{1,0.01} + \beta(\nu)(T_{1,0.05} - T_{1,0.01}),$$

$$T_{1,0.005} \doteqdot T_{1,0.01} - \gamma(\nu)(T_{1,0.05} - T_{1,0.01}),$$

TABLE 2

Comparison of Exact and Approximate Upper α Points of the Distribution of the Largest Root When $m = 3$

α	.10		.05		.025		.01	
ν	Exact	Approximate	Exact	Approximate	Exact	Approximate	Exact	Approximate
2		4.5008	5.37017	5.36964		6.20804	7.28405	7.28400
4	3.3154	3.3151	3.81017	3.80973	4.27995	4.28000	4.87535	4.87531
6	2.8206	2.8205	3.18146	3.18110	3.52116	3.52124	3.94846	3.94843
8	2.5377	2.5378	2.82800	2.82770	3.09975	3.09974	3.43979	3.43976
10	2.3504	2.3506	2.59661	2.59635	2.82607	2.82607	3.11206	3.11203
14	2.1125	2.1120	2.30574	2.30553	2.48470	2.48473	2.70649	2.70646
20	1.9085	1.9080	2.05909	2.05892	2.19777	2.19781	2.36865	2.36863
30	1.7240	1.7236	1.83858	1.83845	1.94342	1.94338	2.07182	2.07181
40	1.6176	1.6173	1.71252	1.71241	1.79901	1.79897	1.90454	1.90453
50	1.5466	1.5463	1.62884	1.62874	1.70360	1.70357	1.79455	1.79454

where $\beta(\nu)$ and $\gamma(\nu)$ do not depend on m but vary slightly with ν. For $\nu \geq 20$,

$$\beta(\nu) \doteqdot 0.54 - 0.60\nu^{-1},$$
$$\gamma(\nu) \doteqdot 0.37 - \nu^{-1}.$$

James [41] has obtained the joint density function of the T's when $\mathbf{S}$ has the distribution $W_m(\nu;\mathbf{V})$ for general positive definite $\mathbf{V}$. It is

$$(20)\quad p_{\mathbf{T}}(\mathbf{t}) = (2\pi)^{-(1/2)\nu m}\left[\prod_{j=1}^{m}(\sigma_j^2\nu^{-1})\right]^{-(1/2)\nu}\prod_{j=1}^{m}[\Gamma(\tfrac{1}{2}j)\Gamma(\tfrac{1}{2}(\nu-j+1))]^{-1}$$
$$\times \exp\left(-\frac{\nu}{2\sigma_0^2}\sum_{j=1}^{m}t_j\right)\left(\prod_{j=1}^{m}t_j\right)^{\frac{1}{2}(\nu-m-1)}\prod_{i>j}(t_i-t_j)$$
$$\times\sum_{j=0}^{\infty}\sum_{\kappa,j)}\frac{C_\kappa(\boldsymbol{\beta})C_\kappa(\mathbf{t})}{j!C_\kappa(\mathbf{I}_m)},$$

where $\boldsymbol{\beta} = \operatorname{diag}(\beta_1,\beta_2,\ldots,\beta_m)$ with $\beta_i = \frac{1}{2}(\sigma_0^{-2}-\sigma_i^{-2})$; $\mathbf{t} = \operatorname{diag}(t_1,t_2,\ldots,t_m)$, and $\sigma_1^2,\ldots,\sigma_m^2$ are the latent roots of $\mathbf{V}$. Note that σ_0^2 can be chosen arbitrarily. It will usually be desirable to choose σ_0^2 to improve the rate of convergence of the series in (20). It is likely that a convenient choice for σ_0^2 will be some form of average of the σ_j^2's; if $\sigma_1^2 = \cdots = \sigma_m^2 = \sigma^2$, so that $\mathbf{V} = \mathbf{I}_m\sigma^2$, then $\sigma_0^2 = \sigma^2$ is the natural choice.

Sugiyama [98] and Sugiyama and Fukutomi [102] have obtained the density function of the greatest root, T_m. It is

$$(21.1)\quad p_{T_m}(t) = \frac{\Gamma_m(\frac{1}{2}(m+1))}{2^{(1/2)\nu m}|\mathbf{V}|^{(1/2)\nu}\Gamma_m(\frac{1}{2}(\nu+m+1))}$$
$$\times\sum_{j=0}^{\infty}\sum_{\kappa,j)}(\tfrac{1}{2}\nu m+j)\frac{(\frac{1}{2}\nu)^{\{\kappa\}}}{(\frac{1}{2}(\nu+m+1))^{\{\kappa\}}}\frac{C_\kappa(-\frac{1}{2}\mathbf{V}^{-1})}{j!}t^{\frac{1}{2}(\nu m+j-1)}$$
$$(0 < t).$$

The cumulative distribution function is

$$(21.2)\quad \Pr[T_m \leq t] = \frac{\Gamma_m(\frac{1}{2}(m+1))t^{(1/2)\nu m}}{2^{(1/2)\nu m}|\mathbf{V}|^{(1/2)\nu}\Gamma_m(\frac{1}{2}(\nu+m+1))}$$
$$\times\operatorname{etr}(-\tfrac{1}{2}t\mathbf{V}^{-1})\,{}_1F_1(\tfrac{1}{2}(m+1);\tfrac{1}{2}(\nu+m+1);\tfrac{1}{2}t\mathbf{V}^{-1}),$$

where ${}_1F_1(\cdot)$ is a confluent hypergeometric function with matrix argument. Krishnaiah and Chang [54a] have obtained an expression in terms of double integrals.

Muirhead [64] has obtained an asymptotic expansion of the form

$$(21.2)'\quad \Pr[T_m \leq t]$$
$$= \frac{\Gamma_m(\frac{1}{2}(m+1))t^{(1/2)\nu m}\operatorname{etr}(-\frac{1}{2}t\mathbf{V}^{-1})}{2^{(1/2)\nu m}|\mathbf{V}|^{(1/2)\nu}\Gamma_m(\frac{1}{2}(\nu+m+1))}|\mathbf{I}-\nu^{-1}t\mathbf{V}^{-1}|^{-\frac{1}{2}(m+1)}G(t),$$

where

$$G(t) = 1 + \tfrac{1}{4}\nu^{-1}(m+1)\{-\omega_1^2 - (m+2)\omega_2 + 2(m+1)\omega_1\} + O(\nu^{-2})$$

and ω_r is the sum of rth powers of the latent roots of $\mathbf{I} - (\mathbf{I} - \nu^{-1}t\mathbf{V}^{-1})^{-1}$. (An explicit term in ν^{-2} is also given in [64].)

Anderson [4] has constructed confidence bounds for the latent roots of $\mathbf{V}$. These are b_1T_1 and b_mT_m, where b_1 and b_m are such that

$$\Pr[\chi_\nu^2 \geq b_m^{-1}]\Pr[\chi_{\nu-m+1}^2 \leq b_1^{-1}] = 1 - \alpha. \tag{22}$$

Then for any $\mathbf{V} > 0$,

$$\Pr[b_1T_1 \leq \sigma_1^2 \leq \cdots \leq \sigma_m^2 \leq b_mT_m] \geq 1 - \alpha.$$

Note that there is an infinity of pairs of values (b_1,b_m) satisfying (22). It appears reasonable to choose values such that the two probabilities in (22) are equal, though these will not actually minimize the expected length of the confidence interval.

In [4], also, are given similar confidence limits c_1L_1,c_mL_m for the latent roots of $\mathbf{V}_1\mathbf{V}_2^{-1}$ (see Section 1). If c_1,c_m satisfy the equation

$$\Pr[F_{\nu_1,\nu_2-m+1} \geq c_1^{-1}]\Pr[F_{\nu_1-m+1,\nu_2} \leq c_m^{-1}] = 1 - \alpha, \tag{23}$$

then the interval (c_1L_1,c_mL_m) includes all the latent roots with probability at least $1 - \alpha$.

If $\mathbf{S}$ has a noncentral Wishart distribution (Chapter 38, Section 4.3) with noncentrality parameter $\mathbf{\Omega}$ and variance-covariance matrix $\mathbf{I}$ then the joint distribution of $T_1,T_2,\ldots,T_m$ has density function

$$p_{\mathbf{T}}(\mathbf{t}) = \frac{\pi^{(1/2)m^2}\operatorname{etr}(-\frac{1}{2}\mathbf{\Omega})}{2^{(1/2)m\nu}\Gamma_m(\frac{1}{2}\nu)\Gamma_m(\frac{1}{2}m)}\left[\prod_{j=1}^m t_j\right]^{\frac{1}{2}(\nu-m-1)}\prod_{i>j}^m (t_i - t_j) \times \exp\left(-\tfrac{1}{2}\sum_{j=1}^m t_j\right){}_0F_1(\tfrac{1}{2}\nu;\tfrac{1}{4}\mathbf{\Omega},\boldsymbol{\tau}) \tag{24}$$

$$(0 \leq t_1 \leq t_2 \leq \cdots \leq t_m; \nu \geq m)$$

where $\boldsymbol{\tau} = \operatorname{diag}(t_1,\ldots,t_m)$ (James [42]).

Hayakawa [30] gives an alternative form obtained by using the identity

$${}_0F_1(\tfrac{1}{2}\nu;\tfrac{1}{4}\mathbf{\Omega},\boldsymbol{\tau}) = \sum_{\kappa=0}^\infty (k!)^{-1}\sum_{\varkappa'k)} \frac{H_\varkappa[(1/\sqrt{2})\mathbf{\Omega}^{1/2}]C_\varkappa(\frac{1}{2}\boldsymbol{\tau})}{(\frac{1}{2}\nu)^{\{\varkappa\}}C_\varkappa(\mathbf{I}_m)} \tag{25}$$

(where $H_\varkappa(\cdot)$ is the generalized Hermite polynomial defined in Chapter 38, Section 4.2). Hayakawa also gives the cumulative density function of the greatest root T_m, in the form

$$(24)' \quad \Pr[T_m \leq t] = \frac{\Gamma_m(\frac{1}{2}(m+1))}{2^{(1/2)m\nu}\Gamma_m(\frac{1}{2}(m+\nu+1))} \operatorname{etr}(-\tfrac{1}{2}\boldsymbol{\Omega})t^{(1/2)m\nu} \times \sum_{k=0}^{\infty} \frac{(\frac{1}{2}t)^k}{k!} \sum_{\kappa(k)} \frac{H_\kappa[(1/\sqrt{2})\boldsymbol{\Omega}^{1/2}]}{(\frac{1}{2}\nu + m + 1)^{\{\kappa\}}}$$

Waal [109] has shown that

$$E[\operatorname{tr}_m \mathbf{S}] = |\mathbf{V}|\nu^{(m)}{}_1F_1(\tfrac{1}{2}\nu + 1; \tfrac{1}{2}\nu; \tfrac{1}{2}\boldsymbol{\Omega})\operatorname{etr}(-\tfrac{1}{2}\boldsymbol{\Omega})$$

where $\operatorname{tr}_m(\mathrm{S})$ denotes the sum of all possible products of latent roots of S, taken m at a time. He also conjectures that if $\mathbf{V} = \sigma^2\mathbf{I}_m$ then for $j \leq p$,

$$E[\operatorname{tr}_j \mathbf{S}] = \sigma^{2j} \sum_{i=0}^{j} (\nu - i)^{(m-i)} \operatorname{tr}_i \boldsymbol{\Omega}$$

(with $\operatorname{tr}_0(\cdot) = 1 = (\cdot)^{(0)}$).

For a complex noncentral Wishart matrix, with variance covariance matrix $\mathbf{I}_{2m}$, the joint density function of the latent roots $T_1 \leq T_2 \leq \cdots \leq T_m$ is given by Hayakawa [32] as

$$(26) \quad \frac{\pi^{m(m-1)}}{\tilde{\Gamma}_m(\nu)\tilde{\Gamma}_m(m)} \operatorname{etr}(-\boldsymbol{\Omega}) \left(\prod_{j=1}^{m} t_j\right)^{\nu-m} \prod_{i>j}^{m} (t_i - t_j)^2 \times \sum_{k=0}^{\infty} (k!)^{-1} \sum_{\kappa(k)} \frac{\tilde{H}_\kappa(\boldsymbol{\Omega}^{1/2})C_\kappa(\boldsymbol{\tau})}{\nu^{\{\kappa\}}\tilde{C}_\kappa(\mathbf{I}_m)}.$$

The cumulative distribution function of the greatest root (T_m) is

$$(27) \quad \Pr[T_m \leq t] = \frac{\tilde{\Gamma}_m(\nu)}{\tilde{\Gamma}_m(\nu+m)} \operatorname{etr}(-\boldsymbol{\Omega})t^{m\nu} \sum_{\kappa=0}^{\infty} \frac{t^k}{k!} \sum_{\kappa(k)} \frac{\tilde{H}_\kappa(\boldsymbol{\Omega}^{1/2})}{(\nu+m)^{\{\kappa\}}}.$$

Comparison with (24) and (24′) is interesting.

Hayakawa [32] shows that the sum of the roots $(T_1 + T_2 + \cdots + T_m) = \operatorname{tr} \tilde{\mathbf{S}}$ is distributed as

$$2\chi'^2_{2m\nu}(\operatorname{tr} \boldsymbol{\Omega}).$$

5. Multinormal Quadratic Forms

Khatri [47] has used zonal polynomials and generalized hypergeometric functions with matrix arguments, as defined in Section 5.2 of Chapter 38, to obtain formulas for distributions related to the set of quadratic forms

$$\mathbf{Y} = \mathbf{XAX}',$$

where $\mathbf{A}$ is a $n \times n$ real symmetric nonsingular matrix and the columns of the $m \times n$ random matrix $\mathbf{X}$ are independent ($m < n$), each column having the same multinormal distribution with expected value vector $\mathbf{O}$ and variance-covariance matrix $\mathbf{V}$. The joint density of the $\frac{1}{2}m(m+1)$ distinct quadratic forms $\mathbf{Y}$ is

$$(28) \quad p_{\mathbf{Y}}(\mathbf{y}) = [\Gamma_m(\tfrac{1}{2}n)2^{(1/2)nm}\,|\mathbf{V}|^{(1/2)n}\,|\mathbf{A}|^{(1/2)m}]^{-1}\,|\mathbf{y}|^{\frac{1}{2}(n-m-1)} \times {}_0F_0(\mathbf{I}_n - \mathbf{A}^{-1},\tfrac{1}{2}q^{-1}\mathbf{V}^{-1}\mathbf{y})\text{etr}(-\tfrac{1}{2}q^{-1}\mathbf{V}^{-1}\mathbf{y}).$$

The quantity q must be positive, but otherwise can be chosen arbitrarily. Hayakawa [28] obtained the different (but equivalent) form

$$p_{\mathbf{Y}}(\mathbf{y}) = [\Gamma_m(\tfrac{1}{2}n)2^{(1/2)nm}\,|\mathbf{V}|^{(1/2)n}\,|\mathbf{A}|^{(1/2)m}]^{-1}\,|\mathbf{y}|^{\frac{1}{2}(n-m-1)}{}_0F_0(\mathbf{A}^{-1},-\tfrac{1}{2}\mathbf{V}^{-1}\mathbf{y}). \quad (28)'$$

In either (28) or (28)′ the series expansion

$${}_0F_0(\mathbf{S},\mathbf{T}) = \sum_{j=0}^{\infty}(j!)^{-1}\sum_{\varkappa(j)}\frac{C_\varkappa(\mathbf{S})C_\varkappa(\mathbf{T})}{C_\varkappa(\mathbf{I}_n)}$$

may be used. The resulting series are, however, only slowly convergent. For computational purposes, it is likely that the following expansion in terms of generalized multivariate Laguerre polynomials ($L_\varkappa^\nu$) (see Chapter 38, Section 4.2), due to Shah [91], may be preferable:

$$(28)'' \quad p_{\mathbf{Y}}(\mathbf{y}) = \sum_{j=0}^{\infty}(j!)^{-1}\sum_{\varkappa(j)}C_\varkappa(\mathbf{I}_n - q^{-1}\mathbf{A}^{-1})\{C_\varkappa(\mathbf{I}_n)\}^{-1}L_\varkappa^{1/2(\nu-m-1)}(\tfrac{1}{2}q\mathbf{V}^{-1}\mathbf{y})]$$

$\times$ (Wishart density [(10) of Chapter 38] with n degrees of freedom and variance-covariance matrix $q\mathbf{V}$).

This formula may be regarded as a generalization of the univariate formula (51) in Chapter 29.

Khatri [50] has also generalized formulas (35) and (65) of Chapter 29, giving, respectively, the distribution function of $\mathbf{Y}$ as a mixture of Wishart distributions and a zonal polynomial "power-series."

Hayakawa [28] has shown the probability that the matrix $\mathbf{G} - \mathbf{Y}$ is positive definite is

$$(29) \quad \Pr[\mathbf{XAX}' \le \mathbf{G}] = \frac{\Gamma_m(\frac{1}{2}(m+1))}{\Gamma_m(\frac{1}{2}(n+m+1))}\frac{|\mathbf{G}|^{(1/2)n}}{2^{(1/2)nm}\,|\mathbf{V}|^{(1/2)n}\,|\mathbf{A}|^{(1/2)m}} \times {}_1F_1(\tfrac{1}{2}n;\tfrac{1}{2}(n+m+1);\mathbf{A}^{-1},-\tfrac{1}{2}\mathbf{V}^{-1}\mathbf{G}).$$

Hayakawa further shows that the joint density function of the latent roots $L_1 \le L_2 \le \cdots \le L_m$ of

$$|\mathbf{XAX}' - L\mathbf{I}_n| = 0$$

is

$$(30)\quad p_{\mathbf{L}}(\mathbf{l}) = \frac{\pi^{(1/2)m^2} \prod_{j=1}^{m} l_j^{\frac{1}{2}(n-m-1)} \prod_{i>j} (l_i - l_j)}{2^{(1/2)nm} |\mathbf{A}|^{(1/2)m} |\mathbf{V}|^{(1/2)n} \Gamma_m(\frac{1}{2}n)\Gamma_m(\frac{1}{2}m)} \sum_{j=0}^{\infty} (j!)^{-1} \times \sum_{\varkappa(j)} \frac{C_\varkappa(\mathbf{V}^{-1})C_\varkappa(\mathbf{A}^{-1})C_\varkappa(-\frac{1}{2}\mathbf{D})}{C_\varkappa(\mathbf{I}_n)C_\varkappa(\mathbf{I}_m)},$$

where $\mathbf{D} = \text{diag}(l_1,\ldots,l_m)$ $(0 \le l_1 \le \cdots \le l_m)$. Putting $\mathbf{A} = \mathbf{I}$ gives (16).

A moment generating function of $\mathbf{XAX}'$ is (Shah [91])

$$(31)\quad E[\exp(-\text{tr}\boldsymbol{\theta}\mathbf{XAX}')] = |\mathbf{G}|^{-(1/2)\nu} \sum_{k=0}^{\infty} \frac{1}{k!} \sum_{\varkappa(k)} (\tfrac{1}{2}\nu)^{\{\varkappa\}} \frac{C_\varkappa(\mathbf{I} - q^{-1}\mathbf{A})C_\varkappa(\mathbf{I} - \mathbf{G}^{-1})}{C_\varkappa(\mathbf{I}_\nu)},$$

where $\mathbf{G} = \mathbf{I}_\nu + 2q\boldsymbol{\theta}\mathbf{V}$. [The q is arbitrary, as in (28) and (28)″; $\boldsymbol{\theta}$ is a symmetric $m \times m$ matrix.]

For distributions associated with noncentral quadratic forms (i.e., when $\mathbf{XX}'$ has a noncentral Wishart distribution) Hayakawa [30] found it convenient to introduce a further class of polynomials, defined by

$$(32)\quad P_\varkappa(\mathbf{G},\mathbf{A}) = (-1)^k \text{etr}(\mathbf{GG}')\pi^{-(1/2)\nu} \int_{\mathbf{U}} \text{etr}(-2i\mathbf{GV}' - \mathbf{UU}')C_\varkappa(\mathbf{UAU}')\, d\mathbf{U}$$

(where $\mathbf{G}$ and $\mathbf{U}$ are $m \times \nu$ matrices and $\boldsymbol{\varkappa}$ is a partition of k.)

We note the properties

$$(33.1)\quad P_\varkappa(\mathbf{G},\mathbf{I}_\nu) = H_\varkappa(\mathbf{G}),$$

$$(33.2)\quad P_\varkappa(\mathbf{O},\mathbf{A}) = (-1)^k C_\varkappa(\mathbf{A})C_\varkappa(\mathbf{I}_m)/C_\varkappa(\mathbf{I}_\nu).$$

The joint density function of the latent roots $L_1 \le L_2 \le \cdots \le L_m$ of $\mathbf{XAX}'$ is then

$$(34)\quad P_{\mathbf{L}}(\mathbf{l}) = \frac{\text{etr}(-\frac{1}{2}\boldsymbol{\Omega})}{2^{(1/2)m\nu}\Gamma_m(\frac{1}{2}\nu)\Gamma_m(\frac{1}{2}m) |\mathbf{A}|^{(1/2)m}} \prod_{j=1}^{m} l_j^{\frac{1}{2}(\nu-m-1)} \prod_{i>j}^{m} (l_i - l_j) \times \sum_{k=0}^{\infty} (k!)^{-1} \sum_{\varkappa(k)} \frac{P_\varkappa[(1/\sqrt{2})\boldsymbol{\Omega}^{1/2},\mathbf{A}^{-1}]C_\varkappa(\frac{1}{2}\mathbf{D})}{(\frac{1}{2}\nu)^{\{\varkappa\}} C_\varkappa(\mathbf{I}_\nu)} \quad (0 \le l_1 \le \cdots \le l_m),$$

where $\mathbf{D} = \text{diag}(l_1,\ldots,l_m)$.

The cumulative distribution function of the greatest root is

$$(35)\quad \Pr[L_m \le u] = \frac{\Gamma_m(\frac{1}{2}(m+1))\text{etr}(-\frac{1}{2}\boldsymbol{\Omega})}{2^{(1/2)m\nu}\Gamma_m(\frac{1}{2}(\nu+m+1) |\mathbf{A}|^{(1/2)m}} u^{(1/2)m\nu} \times \sum_{k=0}^{\infty} \frac{(\frac{1}{2}u)^k}{k!} \sum_{\varkappa(u)} \frac{P_\varkappa[(1/\sqrt{2})\boldsymbol{\Omega}^{1/2},\mathbf{A}^{-1}]}{(\frac{1}{2}(\nu+m+1))^{\{\varkappa\}}}.$$

Distributions of quadratic forms in complex multinormal variables were considered by Turin [105] and later by Khatri [47]. Turin showed that if $\mathbf{Z}' = (Z_1,Z_2,\ldots,Z_m)$ have a joint complex multinormal distribution with expected value vector $\boldsymbol{\xi}' = (\xi_1,\ldots,\xi_m)$ and variance covariance matrix

$$\mathbf{V} = E[(\mathbf{Z} - \boldsymbol{\xi})(\tilde{\mathbf{Z}} - \tilde{\boldsymbol{\xi}})'],$$

then the characteristic function of $\tilde{\mathbf{Z}}'\mathbf{A}\mathbf{Z}$, where $\mathbf{A}$ is a nonsingular Hermitian matrix, is

$$E[\exp(it\tilde{\mathbf{Z}}'\mathbf{A}\mathbf{Z})] = |\mathbf{I} - it\mathbf{V}\mathbf{A}|^{-1} \exp[-\tilde{\boldsymbol{\xi}}'\mathbf{V}^{-1}\{\mathbf{I} - (\mathbf{I} - it\mathbf{V}\mathbf{A})^{-1}\}\boldsymbol{\xi}]. \tag{36}$$

6. Some Univariate Distributions

In this section we summarize work done on certain univariate distributions that are of importance in statistical analysis associated with multinormal population distributions. These distributions have been studied, for the most part, because of their connection with tests of hypotheses about parameter values in multinormal populations. We are not here interested in the tests as such, but only in the distributions.

6.1. *Distribution of Generalized Variance*

The determinant $|\mathbf{V}|$ of the variance-covariance matrix is called the *generalized variance*. The corresponding determinant $|\nu^{-1}\mathbf{S}|$ calculated from sample values is often called the generalized variance also. If we are considering random samples from a multinormal population, then $\mathbf{S}$ has the Wishart distribution with density function (10) of Chapter 38. We assume $\nu > m$.

Since $|\nu^{-1}\mathbf{S}| = \nu^{-m}\,|\mathbf{S}|$, we study the distribution of $|\mathbf{S}|$. From (13) of Chapter 38,

$$\begin{aligned} \mu_h'(|\mathbf{S}|) &= K(\nu;\mathbf{V}^{-1})/K(\nu + 2h;\mathbf{V}^{-1}) \\ &= |\mathbf{V}|^h\, 2^{hm} \frac{\Gamma_m(\tfrac{1}{2}\nu + h)}{\Gamma_m(\tfrac{1}{2}\nu)} \\ &= |\mathbf{V}|^h \prod_{j=1}^{m} \left\{\frac{2^h\Gamma[(\nu - j + 1)/2 + h]}{\Gamma[(\nu - j + 1)/2]}\right\}. \end{aligned} \tag{37}$$

It follows that

$$\mu_h'(|\mathbf{S}|/|\mathbf{V}|) = \prod_{j=1}^{m} \mu_h'(\chi^2_{\nu-j+1}), \tag{38}$$

and it can be shown that, in fact, $|\mathbf{S}|/|\mathbf{V}|$ is distributed as the product of m independent variables, distributed as χ^2 with $\nu,\nu-1,\ldots,\nu-m+1$ degrees of freedom respectively. Hence we can write

$$\log(|\mathbf{S}|/|\mathbf{V}|) = \sum_{j=1}^{m} \log X_j,$$

with $X_1,\ldots,X_m$ mutually independent and X_j distributed as $\chi^2_{\nu-j+1}$. Approximating the distribution of $\log X_j$ as normal with expected value $[\psi(\frac{1}{2}(\nu-j+1)) + \log 2]$ and variance $\psi'(\frac{1}{2}(\nu-j+1))$ (see Chapter 17, Section 8.3), we have:

$\log(|\mathbf{S}|/|\mathbf{V}|)$ is approximately normally distributed with expected value

$$m \log 2 + \sum_{j=1}^{m} \psi(\tfrac{1}{2}(\nu-j+1))$$

and variance

$$\sum_{j=1}^{m} \psi'(\tfrac{1}{2}(\nu-j+1)).$$

[The $\psi(\cdot)$ and $\psi'(\cdot)$ are the digamma and trigamma functions, defined in Section 3 of Chapter 1.]

It is of interest that this approximation improves not only with increasing ν (which might be expected), but also with increasing m.

Hoel [34] suggested the approximation:

$|\mathbf{S}|$ is approximately distributed as $c\chi^2_f$,

where

$$c = m^{-1}[1 - \tfrac{1}{2}(\nu-1)^{-1}(m-1)(m-2)]^{-1/m}$$

$$f = m(\nu - m + 1).$$

The approximation is exact for $m = 1$ and $m = 2$. Gnanadesikan and Wilk [24] checked this approximation empirically and found that while the approximation is still good for $m = 3$, the accuracy decreases as m increases. It seems that while Hoel's approximation can be used for $m \leq 3$, it is likely to be better to use the normal approximation for larger m. In [24] it is suggested that the distribution of $\log |\mathbf{S}|$ might be approximated by a Gram-Charlier series (Chapter 12, Section 4.2).

Steyn [95] has described a method of deriving the distribution of $|\mathbf{S}|$ by forming a differential equation satisfied by the moment generating function. Details are given for the cases $m = 2$ and $m = 3$. Generally

$$\frac{d^k\phi}{dt^k} = |\mathbf{V}| \prod_{j=1}^{k} \left(\nu - k + j + 2k^{-1}t \frac{d}{dt}\right) \phi(t) \tag{39}$$

where $\phi(t) = E[\exp[t\,|\mathbf{S}|]]$. Further results on the distribution of $|\mathbf{S}|$ can be found in Bagai [6].

The noncentral distribution of generalized variance (i.e., when $\mathbf{S}$ has a noncentral Wishart distribution) has been expressed in the form of an asymptotic (as $m\nu \to \infty$ with $\mathbf{\Omega} = O(1)$, $O(\sqrt{\nu})$) expansion by Fujikoshi [21, 21a], using the result (due to Constantine [9]):

$$\mu_h'(|\mathbf{S}|) = |\mathbf{V}|^h |2^{hm}| \frac{\Gamma_m(\frac{1}{2}\nu + h)}{\Gamma_m(\frac{1}{2}\nu)} {}_1F_1(-h;\tfrac{1}{2}\nu;-\tfrac{1}{2}\mathbf{\Omega}). \tag{40}$$

The case $\mathbf{\Omega} = O(\nu)$ has been solved by Sugiura and Nagao [97a].

When the noncentrality is of rank 1 (i.e., there is only one nonzero root of $|\mathbf{V} - \theta\mathbf{I}| = 0$) it is possible to obtain exact formulas for the distribution. Bagai [6] gives such formulas for $m = 2(1)10$.

For $m = 2$, the density function of $\sqrt{|\mathbf{S}|} = W$, when $m = 2$, is

$$p_W(w) = w^{\nu-2} e^{-w-(1/2)\theta} [\Gamma(\nu - 2)]^{-1} \sum_{j=0}^{\infty} (T_j/j!)\theta^{2j} [\nu(\nu + 2)\cdots(\nu + 2j)]^{-1},$$

where

$$T_j = (\tfrac{1}{2}w)^j \sum_{i=0}^{\infty} (w\sqrt{2})^{-i} [(j + i)^{(2i)}]^{-1}.$$

The distribution of $|\mathbf{S}|$ when $\mathbf{S}$ has a complex Wishart distribution, has been discussed by Goodman [25]. An asymptotic expansion for this case has been obtained by Hayakawa [31].

6.2. *Hotelling's Generalized* T_0^2

The statistic

$$T_0^2 = \nu_2 \operatorname{tr}(\mathbf{S}_1\mathbf{S}_2^{-1}) \qquad (\nu_2 \geq m)$$

was introduced by Hotelling [35] in 1951. It is equal to $\nu_2 \sum_{j=1}^{p} L_j$ in the notation of Section 2 (equation (9)).

For the case $p = 2$, Hotelling [35] showed that

$$\Pr[T_0^2 \leq \tau] = I_w(\nu_1 - 1, \nu_2) - \sqrt{\pi}\, \frac{\Gamma(\frac{1}{2}(\nu_1 + \nu_2) - 1)}{\Gamma(\frac{1}{2}\nu_1)\Gamma(\frac{1}{2}\nu_2)}, \tag{41}$$

where

$$w = (1 + \tfrac{1}{2}\nu_2^{-1}\tau)\nu_2^{-1}\tau.$$

The distribution is of much more complicated form when $p > 2$. Constantine [10] showed that the density function of $T = T_0^2/\nu_2 = \operatorname{tr}(\mathbf{S}_1\mathbf{S}_2^{-1})$

is, for $|T| < 1$, $(p = m)$

$$(42)\quad p_T(t) = \frac{\Gamma_m(\frac{1}{2}(\nu_1+\nu_2))}{\Gamma(\frac{1}{2}m\nu_1)\Gamma_m(\frac{1}{2}\nu_2)} t^{(1/2)m\nu_1 - 1} \sum_{j=0}^{\infty} [(-t)^j / \{j!(\tfrac{1}{2}m\nu_1)^{[j]}\}] \times \sum_{\varkappa(j)} (\tfrac{1}{2}\nu_1)^{\{\varkappa\}} (\tfrac{1}{2}(\nu_1+\nu_2))^{\{\varkappa\}} C_\varkappa(\mathbf{I}).$$

Davis [15] showed that the density function satisfies a linear homogeneous differential equation, of order m, with regular singularities at $t = 0, -1, \ldots, m$ and infinity; and that (42) is the solution of this equation in the unit circle $|t| < 1$. In 1956, Ito [38] gave an approximate formula, the first two terms of which are

$$(43.1)\quad \Pr[T_0^2 \le \tau] = \Pr[\chi^2_{\nu_1 p} \le \tau] - 2\nu_2^{-1}\left[\frac{(p+\nu_1+1)\tau^2}{p\nu_1+2} + (p-\nu_1+1)\tau\right]\frac{d\Pr[\chi^2_{\nu_1 p} \le \tau]}{d\tau}.$$

(The next term is a multiple of ν_2^{-2}.)

About the same time, Siotani [92] obtained another expansion, of which the first two terms were

$$(43.2)\quad \Pr[T_0^2 \le \tau] = \Pr[\chi^2_{\nu_1} \le \tau] + \tfrac{1}{4}\nu_1 p \nu_2^{-1}[(\nu_1 - p - 1)\Pr[\chi^2_{\nu_1} \le \tau] - 2\nu_1 \Pr[\chi^2_{\nu_1 p+2} \le \tau] + (\nu_1 + p + 1)\Pr[\chi^2_{\nu_1 p+4}].$$

Note that

$$(44)\quad \lim_{\nu_2 \to \infty} \Pr[T_0^2 \le \tau] = \Pr[\chi^2_{\nu_1 p} \le \tau].$$

Siotani [92] also obtained an expansion for the $100\alpha\%$ point of the distribution of T_0^2, the first two terms of which are

$$(45)\quad T^2_{0,\alpha} = \chi^2_{\nu_1 p,\alpha} + \tfrac{1}{2}\nu_1 p \nu_2^{-1}[(p+1)(\phi_4+\phi_2) + \nu_1(\phi_4 - \phi_2)],$$

where

$$\phi_j = \{\chi^2_{\nu_1 p,\alpha}\}^j \left[\prod_{i=1}^{j} (\nu_1 p + 2i - 2)\right]^{-1}.$$

Using the fact that S_1 and S_2 are independent, we have (with $p = m$)

$$E[T_0^2] = \nu_2 \operatorname{tr}\{E[S_1]E[S_2^{-1}]\} = m\nu_1\nu_2(\nu_2 - m - 1)^{-1}$$

[using (19) of Chapter 38]. Also,

$$\operatorname{var}(T_0^2) = 2m\nu_1\nu_2(\nu_2 - 1)(\nu_1 + \nu_2 - m - 1)^{-2}(\nu_2 - m)^{-1}(\nu_2 - m - 3)^{-1}$$

(Constantine [10]). Expressions for the third and fourth central moments of T_0^2 have been given by Pillai and Samson [84] and Davis [15] respectively.

Pillai and Samson [84] used the first four moments of T_0^2 and fitted a Pearson curve to obtain approximate values for $\nu_2^{-1}T_{0,\alpha}^2$ to three decimal places for

$$\alpha = 0.95,0.99; \qquad p = 3,4;$$
$$n_1 = \tfrac{1}{2}(\nu_1 - p - 1) = 0.0(0.5)5.0(5)30,50;$$
$$n_2 = \tfrac{1}{2}(\nu_2 - p - 1) = 15(5)50,60(20)100.$$

Exact values for $p = 2$, calculated from (39), are also given.

Recently, Davis [15], by analytic continuation of (40.1) to $|t| \geq 1$, has given tables of *exact* values, to five significant figures, of the upper 1 and 5% points of $\nu_1^{-1}T_0^2 = (\nu_2/\nu_1)\mathrm{tr}(\mathbf{S}_1\mathbf{S}_2^{-1})$ for

$$m = 3,4; \qquad \nu_1 = m(1)6(2)12,15(5)25,40,60;$$
$$\nu_2 = m(1)10(2)20(5)40(10)100,200,\infty.$$

(If $\nu_1 < m$, then enter ν_1 as "m," m as "ν_1," and $\nu_1 + \nu_2 - m$ as "ν_2.")

Davis [15a] has also published similar tables for $m = 5$. In [14], also, properties of the limiting distribution of ν_1^{-1} tr $\mathbf{S}_1\mathbf{S}_2^{-1}$ as $\nu \to \infty$ are studied.

If $\mathbf{S}_1$ has a noncentral Wishart distribution, then the limiting distribution, as $\nu_2 \to \infty$, is noncentral χ^2 with ν_1 degrees of freedom and noncentrality parameter to $\mathbf{\Omega}$. The noncentral distribution of T_0^2 has been studied by Constantine [10], Siotani [92, 93] and Ito [39]. Constantine gives the density function (for $|T| < 1$):

$$(46) \quad p_T(t) = \frac{\Gamma_m(\frac{1}{2}(\nu_1 + \nu_2))}{\Gamma(\frac{1}{2}m\nu_1)\Gamma_m(\frac{1}{2}\nu_2)}\, t^{(1/2)m\nu_1 - 1}\, \mathrm{etr}(-\mathbf{\Omega}) \sum_{j=0}^{\infty}\left[\frac{(-t)^j}{j!(\frac{1}{2}m\nu_1)^{[j]}}\right] \times \sum_{\varkappa(j)} (\tfrac{1}{2}(\nu_1 + \nu_2))^{\{\varkappa\}} L_{\varkappa}^{\frac{1}{2}(\nu_1 - m - 1)}(\mathbf{\Omega}).$$

Siotani and Ito each give asymptotic expansions for the cumulative distribution function.

The joint distribution of T_0^2 statistics based on nested subsets of variables [i.e., on $(X_1,X_{p_1})(X_1,\ldots,X_{p+_1p_2})$] for random samples from a multinormal distribution has been given by Giri [22]; and for random samples from a complex multinormal distribution by Giri [22a].

6.3. *Distribution of Likelihood Ratio Criterion* $|\mathbf{S}_1|/|\mathbf{S}_1 + \mathbf{S}_2|$

The distribution of the ratio $|\mathbf{S}_1|/|\mathbf{S}_1 + \mathbf{S}_2|$, where $\mathbf{S}_1,\mathbf{S}_2$ are independent Wishart matrices with common variance-covariance matrices, is the null hypothesis distribution appropriate to the likelihood ratio test of the general linear hypothesis in multivariate analysis (Wilks [112]), and, as such, has received a considerable amount of attention. (Kshirsagar [58] gives an interesting general discussion.) In terms of the roots $G_1, \ldots, G_m$ of (3),

$$|\mathbf{S}_1|/|\mathbf{S}_1 + \mathbf{S}_2| = \prod_{j=1}^{m} G_j.$$

(Note that we do not require $\nu_2 \geq m$ here, but are assuming $\nu_1 \geq m$.) The hth moment of the distribution is

$$\mu_h' = \frac{K(\nu_1;\mathbf{V}^{-1})K(\nu_1 + \nu_2 + 2h;\mathbf{V}^{-1})}{K(\nu_1 + 2h;\mathbf{V}^{-1})K(\nu_1 + \nu_2;\mathbf{V}^{-1})} \tag{47}$$

$$= \prod_{j=1}^{m} \frac{\Gamma(\frac{1}{2}(\nu_1 - j + 1) + h)\Gamma(\frac{1}{2}(\nu_1 + \nu_2 - j + 1))}{\Gamma(\frac{1}{2}(\nu_1 - j + 1))\Gamma(\frac{1}{2}(\nu_1 + \nu_2 - j + 1) + h)}.$$

The right-hand side can be expressed as

$$\prod_{j=1}^{m} \mu_h'(Z_j),$$

where Z_j has a standard beta distribution (Chapter 24) with parameters $\frac{1}{2}(\nu_1 - j + 1), \frac{1}{2}\nu_2$. It follows (since the range of variation of each variable if finite) that $|\mathbf{S}_1|/|\mathbf{S}_1 + \mathbf{S}_2|$ is distributed as the product $Z_1Z_2 \cdots Z_m$, the Z's being mutually independent. (Wilks [112].)

For certain special values of ν_1, ν_2, and m the distribution of

$$L = |\mathbf{S}_1|/|\mathbf{S}_1 + \mathbf{S}_2|$$

takes fairly simple explicit forms. In particular:

(i) When $m = 2$,

$$\frac{1 - \sqrt{L}}{\sqrt{L}} \frac{\nu_1 - 1}{\nu_2}$$

is distributed as $F_{2\nu_2, 2(\nu_1 - 1)}$.

(ii) When $\nu_2 = 2$,

$$\frac{1 - \sqrt{L}}{\sqrt{L}} \frac{\nu_1 - m + 1}{m}$$

is distributed as $F_{2m, 2(\nu_1 - m + 1)}$.

Explicit expressions can be obtained for the probability integral of L in several other cases (e.g., Wald and Brookner [110], Consul [11–13], Schatzoff [90], Mathai and Rathie [59]) but we do not give details here.

A general method of Box [7] gives the following approximate formula:

$$(48)\quad \Pr[-\{\nu_1 - \tfrac{1}{2}(m - \nu_2 + 1)\}\log L \leq M_0]$$
$$\doteqdot \Pr[\chi^2_{\nu_1\nu_2} \leq M_0] + \{\nu_1 - \tfrac{1}{2}(m - \nu_2 + 1)\}^{-2}\frac{m\nu_2(m^2 + \nu_2^2 - 5)}{48}$$
$$\times \{\Pr[\chi_{\nu_1\nu_2+4} \leq M_0] - \Pr[\chi^2_{\nu_1\nu_2} \leq M_0]\}.$$

(The next term is a multiple of $\{\nu_1 - \frac{1}{2}(m - \nu_2 + 1)\}^{-4}$ (see Anderson [3], p. 208).)

Davis [16] has given a similar type of series, analogous to a Cornish-Fisher expansion(Chapter12,Section5) for the percentage points of the distribution.

Wall [111] has given lower 1 and 5% points of the distribution of L, to six decimal places, for $m = 1(1)8$:

$$\nu_1 = 1(1)30,40(20)140(30)200,240,320,440,600(200)1000,\infty.$$

These were calculated from the exact distribution for $m = 1,2$ and using an extended version of the expansion (48) for $m \geq 3$.

The noncentral distribution (when $\mathbf{S}_2$ has a noncentral Wishart distribution) has been studied by Khatri and Pillai [51] and by Sugiura and Fujikoshi [97]. The noncentral distribution for complex variables has been studied by Hayakawa [32]. The latter obtains the asymptotic expansion

$$(49)\quad \Pr[-(2\nu_1 + \nu_2 - m)\log\{|\mathbf{S}_1|/|\mathbf{S}_1 + \mathbf{S}_2|\} \leq u]$$
$$= \Pr[\chi'^2_{2\nu_2 m}(\operatorname{tr}\boldsymbol{\Omega}) \leq u]$$
$$+ \tfrac{1}{2}(2\nu_1 + \nu_2 - m)^{-1}\{\operatorname{tr}\boldsymbol{\Omega}^2 \Pr[\chi_{2\nu_2 m+6}(\operatorname{tr}\boldsymbol{\Omega}) \leq u]$$
$$+ [(\nu_2 + m)\operatorname{tr}\boldsymbol{\Omega} - \operatorname{tr}\boldsymbol{\Omega}^2]\Pr[\chi'^2_{2\nu_2 m+4}(\operatorname{tr}\boldsymbol{\Omega}) \leq u]\}$$
$$- (\nu_2 + m)\operatorname{tr}\boldsymbol{\Omega}\Pr[\chi'^2_{2\nu_2 m+2}(\operatorname{tr}\boldsymbol{\Omega}) \leq u]\}$$
$$+ \text{terms of order } (2\nu_1 + \nu_2 - m)^{-2}.$$

Many other likelihood ratio criteria for tests connected with multinormal distributions have moments of a form similar to (47), when the null hypothesis is valid. That is, they can be expressed in the form

$$(50)\qquad E[L^h] = \mu'_h = K\phi^h \prod_{j=1}^{p}\Gamma(\nu + b_j + ah)\Big/\prod_{j=1}^{k}\Gamma(\nu + c_j + ah),$$

where K, ϕ, b_j, c_j, and a are constants and ν is of the order of sample size. Consul [11] has shown that there is a general solution for the density function of L such that it should have moments given by (50). This is (Consul [12])

$$p_L(l) = K(al)^{-1}(l/\phi)^{(m+v)/a}G^{p,0}_{k,p}\left((l/\phi)^{1/a} \,\Big|\, {c-m,\ldots,c_k-m \atop b-m,\ldots,b_p-m}\right), \tag{51}$$

where m can be chosen arbitrarily, and $G(\cdot)$ is a Meijer G-function. The latter is defined in terms of a contour integral by the equation ($m < q, n < p$):

$$G^{m,n}_{p,q}\left(x \,\Big|\, {a_1,\ldots,a_p \atop b_1,\ldots,b_q}\right) = (2\pi i)^{-1}\int_C \frac{\prod_{j=1}^{m}\Gamma(b_j - s)\prod_{j=1}^{n}\Gamma(s+1-a_j)}{\prod_{j=m+1}^{q}\Gamma(s+1-b_j)\prod_{j=n+1}^{p}\Gamma(a_j - s)}\, x^s\, ds, \tag{52}$$

where C is a curve separating the singularities of $\prod_{j=1}^{m}\Gamma(b_j - s)$ from those of $\prod_{l=1}^{n}\Gamma(s+1-a_j)$.

Usually (52) will be too complicated to be of practical use. However in a number of cases the G-function can be expressed in terms of simple functions (e.g., Erdelyi et al. [17], also appendix to [11]). Consul [11, 13] has thoroughly exploited this approach and has obtained many useful and interesting results. See also Khatri and Srivastava [51a].

6.4. *Distribution of Canonical Correlations*

If a set of variables $\mathbf{X}' = (X_1,\ldots,X_m)$ is split into two subsets $\mathbf{X}'_{(1)} = (X_1,\ldots,X_{m_1})$ and $\mathbf{X}'_{(2)} = (X_{m_1+1},\ldots,X_m)$, then the roots of the equation

$$|\mathbf{V}_{11} - \rho^2\mathbf{V}_{12}\mathbf{V}_{22}^{-1}\mathbf{V}_{21}| = 0 \tag{53}$$

(where

$$\mathbf{V} = \begin{vmatrix} \mathbf{V}_{11} & \mathbf{V}_{12} \\ \mathbf{V}_{21} & \mathbf{V}_{22} \end{vmatrix},$$

with $\mathbf{V},\mathbf{V}_{11},\mathbf{V}_{22}$ the variance-covariance matrices of $\mathbf{X}',\mathbf{X}'_{(1)},\mathbf{X}_{(2)}$, respectively) are called the *canonical correlations* between $\mathbf{X}'_{(1)}$ and $\mathbf{X}'_{(2)}$. It can always be arranged that $m_1 \leq m - m_1 = m_2$, so that there will in general be m_1 positive values $\rho_1^2 \leq \rho_2^2 \leq \cdots \leq \rho_{m_1}^2$ of ρ^2, satisfying (53). The values $R_1^2 \leq R_2^2 \leq \cdots \leq R_{m_1}^2$ satisfying the corresponding equation in sample statistics,

$$|\mathbf{S}_{11} - r^2\mathbf{S}_{12}\mathbf{S}_{22}^{-1}\mathbf{S}_{21}| = 0, \tag{54}$$

where

$$\mathbf{S} = \begin{pmatrix} \mathbf{S}_{11} & \mathbf{S}_{12} \\ \mathbf{S}_{21} & \mathbf{S}_{22} \end{pmatrix}$$

has a Wishart distribution with ν degrees of freedom and a variance-covariance matrix $\mathbf{V}$, have the joint distribution (Constantine [9]),

$$(55)\quad p_{\mathbf{R}^2}(\mathbf{r}^2) = \frac{\pi^{(1/2)m_1^2}\Gamma_{m_1}(\frac{1}{2}\nu)}{\Gamma_{m_1}(\frac{1}{2}m_1)\Gamma_{m_1}(\frac{1}{2}m_2)\Gamma_{m_1}(\frac{1}{2}(\nu - m_2))} \times \prod_{j=1}^{m_1} [(1-\rho_j^2)^{(1/2)\nu}(r_j^2)^{\frac{1}{2}(m_2-m_1-1)}(1-r_j^2)^{\frac{1}{2}(\nu-m-1)}] \times \left[\prod_{i>j}^{m_1}(r_i^2 - r_j^2)\right] {}_2F_1(\tfrac{1}{2}\nu;\tfrac{1}{2}\nu;\tfrac{1}{2}m_2;\mathbf{P}^2,\mathbf{D}^2)$$

$$(0 \le r_1^2 \le \cdots \le r_{m_1}^2 \le 1),$$

where $\mathbf{P}^2 = \text{diag}(\rho_1^2,\ldots,\rho_{m_1}^2)$; $D^2 = \text{diag}(r_1^2,\ldots,r_{m_1}^2)$.

In the case $\mathbf{P} = \mathbf{O}$ (complete independence if multinormal) (55) simplifies to

$$(56)\quad p_{\mathbf{R}^2}(\mathbf{r}^2) = \frac{\pi^{\frac{1}{2}m_1^2}\Gamma_{m_1}(\frac{1}{2}\nu)}{\Gamma_{m_1}(\frac{1}{2}m_1)\Gamma_{m_1}(\frac{1}{2}m_2)\Gamma_{m_1}(\frac{1}{2}(\nu - m_2))} \times \prod_{j=1}^{m_1} [(r_j^2)^{\frac{1}{2}(m_2-m_1-1)}(1-r_j^2)^{\frac{1}{2}(\nu-m-1)}] \prod_{i>j}^{m_1}(r_i^2 - r_j^2),$$

$$(0 \le r_1^2 \le \cdots \le r_{m_1}^2 \le 1).$$

6.5. *Distributions of Various Functions of Roots of Determinantal Equations*

The statistics discussed in Sections 7.1 to 7.4 have all been functions of roots of certain determinantal equations. Here we take note of distributions of some additional functions of this type.

Distributions of *ratios* of latent roots of various determinants have been rather thoroughly discussed by Krishnaiah and Waikar [55–57]. In many cases the formulas are rather complicated and we shall give only a few examples. For the roots $T_1 \le \cdots \le T_m$ of the Wishart matrix $\mathbf{S}$, the joint distribution of the ratios

$$B_j = T_j/T_1 \qquad (j = 2,\ldots,m)$$

has the density function

$$(57)\quad p_{\mathbf{B}}(\mathbf{b}) = \frac{\pi^{(1/2)m^2}\Gamma(\frac{1}{2}m\nu)}{|\mathbf{V}|^{(1/2)\nu}\Gamma_m(\frac{1}{2}\nu)\Gamma_m(\frac{1}{2}m)}\left(\prod_{j=2}^{m}[(b_j-1)b_j^{\frac{1}{2}(m-\nu-1)}]\right) \times \left(\prod_{\substack{i>j\\=2}}^{m}(b_i-b_j)\right)\left(1+\sum_{j=2}^{m}b_j\right)^{-(1/2)m\nu}\sum_{k=0}^{\infty}\left\{\left(1+\sum_{j=2}^{m}b_j\right)^k k!\right\}^{-1} \times \sum_{\kappa(k)}\frac{C_\kappa(\mathbf{I}_m - \mathbf{V}^{-1})C_\kappa(\mathbf{B}_1)}{C_\kappa(\mathbf{I}_m)},$$

where $\mathbf{B}_1 = \text{diag}(B_2,\ldots,B_m,1)$.

For the case $m = 2$ the rates (L_2/L_1) of the greater to the smaller latent root has been used as a test for "ellipticity" (i.e., inequality of variance). In 1941, Girshick [23] showed that the density function of

$$D = 2(L_1L_2)^{1/2}(L_1 + L_2)^{-1}$$

(which is a function of L_2/L_1) is

$$(58)\quad p_D(d) = \frac{\delta^{\nu-1}}{(\nu-1)!}\, d^{\nu-1} \sum_{j=0}^{\infty} \frac{(\nu+2j)!}{(j!)^2} [\tfrac{1}{4}(1-\delta^2)(1+d^2)]^j \qquad (0 \le d \le 1),$$

where $\delta = 2(\lambda_1\lambda_2)^{1/2}(\lambda_1 + \lambda_2)^{-1}$.

If $\lambda_1 = \lambda_2$ (and so $\delta = 1$) we have the null hypothesis distribution of D, which has the simple power function density

$$p_D(d) = \nu d^{\nu-1} \qquad (0 \le d \le 1).$$

This result has been obtained by Hsu ([36], equation (28)) and Mauchly [60].

Pillai [68, 69] has studied the distribution of tr $\mathbf{S}_1(\mathbf{S}_1 + \mathbf{S}_2)^{-1} = \sum_{j=1}^{p} G_j$ (in the notation of Section 2). Nanda [65] obtained the distribution for the cases $|\nu_1 - m| = 3,5,7$ with $p = 3$, and $|\nu_1 - m| = 1,2$ with $p = 4$. He gives tables of exact upper 1 and 5% points of the distribution for these cases with $\tfrac{1}{2}(\nu_2 - m - 1) = 5(5)25(5)515$ for $p = 4$, $|\nu_1 - m| = 2$.

Pillai [69] gave tables of approximate upper points of the distribution, obtained by fitting standard beta distributions to the first moments.

A. W. Davis (personal communication) has calculated tables of the upper 5 and 1% points of the distribution, to four decimal places for $m = 2(1)5$; $\nu_1,\nu_2 = 2(1)8(2)20(5)40(10)80,100,200$; with some gaps for $m > 2$. Comparison with these tables showed that Pillai's values are usually in error by only 0.001 to 0.003.

The exact distribution has been given by Pillai and Jayachandran [82].

The cumulative distribution function of the trace of the multivariate quadratic form $\mathbf{Y} = \mathbf{XAX}'$ is

$$(59)\quad \Pr[\text{tr}\,\mathbf{XAX}' < u] = \frac{u^{(1/2)m\nu}}{\Gamma(\tfrac{1}{2}m\nu)2^{(1/2)m\nu}\,|\mathbf{V}|^{(1/2)\nu}\,|\mathbf{A}|^{(1/2)m}} \times \sum_{k=0}^{\infty} \frac{1}{k!} \sum_{\kappa(k)} \frac{\Gamma(\tfrac{1}{2}m\nu;\kappa)}{\Gamma(\tfrac{1}{2}m\nu + 1;\kappa)} \frac{C_\kappa(-\tfrac{1}{2}\mathbf{V}^{-1} \otimes \mathbf{A}^{-1})C_\kappa(u)}{C_\kappa(\mathbf{I}_{m\nu})},$$

where $\otimes$ denotes the Kronecker product.

Siotani [92, 93] has discussed the distribution of the ratio

$$[\text{tr}\,\mathbf{S}_1\mathbf{S}_2^{-1}][\text{tr}\,\mathbf{S}_3\mathbf{S}_2^{-1}]^{-1},$$

where $\mathbf{S}_1$, $\mathbf{S}_2$, and $\mathbf{S}_3$ are independent Wishart matrices with a common variance-covariance matrix. The limiting distribution as $\nu_2 \to \infty$ (ν_1 and ν_3 remaining fixed) is that of $(\nu_1/\nu_3)F_{\nu_1 m, \nu_3 m}$.

The distribution of the largest, and other individually ordered, latent roots of a Wishart matrix has been referred to in Section 4. Pillai and Sugiyama [85] and de Waal [106] have given expressions (which are quite complicated) for the cumulative distribution function of the largest squared canonical correlation ($R^2_{m_1}$, in the notation of Section 6.4).

De Waal [106] gives the formula in the form

$$\Pr[R^2_{m_1} \le \tau^2] = \frac{\Gamma_{m_1}(\frac{1}{2}\nu)\Gamma_{m_1}(\frac{1}{2}(m_1+1))}{\Gamma_{m_1}(\frac{1}{2}(\nu - m))\Gamma_{m_1}(\frac{1}{2}(m_1+m+1))}\left(\prod_{j=1}^{m_1}(1-\rho_j^2)\right)^{(1/2)\nu}$$
$$\times \sum_k \sum_K \sum_j \sum_J \sum_\delta (\tau^2)^{(1/2)mm_1+k+j} A^{\delta}_{K,J}(\rho_1^2, \ldots, \rho_{m_1}^2),$$

where J,K are partitions of j and k, and δ of $j+k$, into one more than m_1 components; j and k are summed from 0 to ∞. The A's are constants, each of which requires a complicated formula for its evaluation.

Distributions of roots of complex noncentral Wishart matrices have been obtained by Hayakawa [32]. Tables of the distribution of the largest root in modulus (obtained by Khatri [46]) have been given by Pillai and Young [86]. They give the upper $100\alpha\%$ points for $m = 2(1)11$; $\nu - m = 0(1)20(2)30$ $(5)50(10)100$; $\alpha = 0.90, 0.95, 0.975, 0.99, 0.995$ to five significant figures.

The statistic

$$L = (e/\nu)^{(1/2)m\nu}\,|\mathbf{S}\mathbf{V}_0^{-1}|^{(1/2)\nu}\operatorname{etr}(-\tfrac{1}{2}\mathbf{S}\mathbf{V}_0^{-1})$$

is used in testing the hypothesis $\mathbf{V} = \mathbf{V}_0$. The hth moment of about zero of L, when $\mathbf{S}$ has a Wishart distribution with variance-covariance matrix $\mathbf{V}$, is

$$(e/\nu)^{(1/2)m\nu h}\frac{\Gamma_m(\frac{1}{2}\nu(1+h))}{\Gamma_m(\frac{1}{2}\nu)}\left[\frac{|\mathbf{V}\mathbf{V}_0^{-1}|^h}{|\mathbf{I} + h\mathbf{V}\mathbf{V}_0^{-1}|^{1+h}}\right]^{(1/2)\nu}. \tag{60}$$

Sugiura [96] has shown that if

$$\mathbf{V}_0^{-1/2}\mathbf{V}\mathbf{V}_0^{-1/2} = \mathbf{I} + \nu^{-\delta}\boldsymbol{\theta} \qquad (j > 0),$$

where $\mathbf{V}_0^{1/2}$ is the symmetric positive definite square root of $\mathbf{V}_0$ and $\boldsymbol{\theta}$ is positive definite then for large ν, then:

(i) For $j < \frac{1}{2}$, the limiting distribution of

$$\nu^{\delta - 1/2}[-2\log[-\nu\{\operatorname{tr}(\mathbf{V}\mathbf{V}_0^{-1} - \mathbf{I}) - \log|\mathbf{V}\mathbf{V}_0^{-1}|\}]$$

as $\nu \to \infty$ is normal with expected value zero and variance $2\operatorname{tr}\boldsymbol{\theta}^2$.

(ii) For $j > \frac{1}{2}$, the limiting distribution of $-2\log L$ is χ^2 with $\frac{1}{2}m(m+1)$ degrees of freedom.

(iii) For $\delta = \frac{1}{2}$, the limiting distribution of $-2 \log L$ is noncentral χ^2 with $\frac{1}{2}m(m+1)$ degrees of freedom and noncentrality parameter $\frac{1}{2} \operatorname{tr} \boldsymbol{\theta}^2$.

For $j = 1$, Sugiura [96] gave an asymptotic expansion for the cumulative distribution function of $-2 \log L$ of which the first two terms are

$$(61) \quad \Pr[-2 \log L \leq \lambda] \doteqdot \Pr[\chi_f^2 < \lambda] + \tfrac{1}{4}\nu^{-1}\{\Pr[\chi_{f+2}^2 < \lambda] - \Pr[\chi_f^2 < \lambda]\} \times [\tfrac{1}{6}m(2m^2 + 3m - 1) + \operatorname{tr} \boldsymbol{\theta}^2].$$

REFERENCES

[1] Al-Ani, S. (1970). On the noncentral distributions of the second largest roots of three matrices in multivariate analysis, *Canadian Mathematical Bulletin*, **13,** 299–304.

[2] Anderson, G. A. (1965). The asymptotic expansion for the distribution of the latent roots for the estimated covariance matrix, *Annals of Mathematical Statistics*, **36,** 1153–1166.

[3] Anderson, T. W. (1958). *An Introduction to Multivariate Statistical Analysis*, New York: John Wiley and Sons, Inc.

[4] Anderson, T. W. (1965). Some optimum confidence bounds for roots of determinantal equations, *Annals of Mathematical Statistics*, **36,** 468–488.

[5] Asoo, Y. (1969). On the Γ-distribution of matrix argument and its related distributions, *Memoirs of the Faculty of Literature and Science, Shimane University, Natural Sciences*, **2,** 1–13.

[6] Bagai, O. P. (1965). The distribution of the generalized variance, *Annals of Mathematical Statistics*, **36,** 120–129.

[7] Box, G. E. P. (1949). A general distribution theory for a class of likelihood criteria, *Biometrika*, **36,** 317–346.

[8] Chang, T. C. (1970). On an asymptotic representation of the distribution of the characteristic roots of $S_1S_2^{-1}$, *Annals of Mathematical Statistics*, **41,** 440–445.

[9] Constantine, A. G. (1963). Some non-central distribution problems in multivariate analysis, *Annals of Mathematical Statistics*, **34,** 1270–1284.

[10] Constantine, A. G. (1966). The distribution of Hotelling's generalized measure of multivariate dispersion, *Annals of Mathematical Statistics*, **37,** 215–225.

[11] Consul, P. C. (1965). The exact distribution of certain likelihood criteria useful in multivariate analysis, *Bulletin de l'Académie Royale de Belgique* (*Classe des Sciences*), **51,** 683–691.

[12] Consul, P. C. (1967). On the exact distributions of likelihood ratio criteria for testing independence of sets of variates under the null hypothesis, *Annals of Mathematical Statistics*, **38,** 1160–1169.

[13] Consul, P. C. (1969). The exact distributions of likelihood criteria for different hypotheses, in *Multivariate Analysis*, Vol. 2, P. R. Krishnaiah, Ed., New York: Academic Press.

[14] Davis, A. W. (1968). A system of linear differential equations for the distribution of Hotelling's generalized T_0^2, *Annals of Mathematical Statistics*, **39,** 815–832.

[15] Davis, A. W. (1970). Exact distributions of Hotelling's generalized T_0^2, *Biometrika*, **57,** 187–191.

[15a] Davis, A. W. (1970). Further applications of a differential equation for Hotelling's generalized T_0^2, *Annals of the Institute of Statistical Mathematics, Tokyo*, **22,** 77–87.

[16] Davis, A. W. (1971). Percentile approximations for a class of likelihood criteria, *Biometrika*, **58,** 349–356.

[17] Erdélyi, A., Magnus, W., Oberhettinger, F., and Tricomi, F. G. (1953). *Higher Transcendental Functions*, **3,** New York: McGraw-Hill.

[18] Fisher, R. A. (1939). The sampling distribution of some statistics obtained from non-linear equations, *Annals of Eugenics*, **9,** 238–249.

[19] Foster, F. G. (1957, 1958). Upper percentage points of the generalized Beta distribution. II, III, *Biometrika*, **44,** 441–453; **45,** 492–502.

[20] Foster, F. G. and Rees, D. H. (1957). Upper percentage points of the generalized Beta distribution, *Biometrika*, **44,** 237–247.

[21] Fujikoshi, Y. (1968). Asymptotic expansion of the distribution of the generalized variance in the non-central case, *Journal of Science of the Hiroshima University, Series A-I*, **32,** 293–299.

[21a] Fujikoshi, Y. (1970). Asymptotic expansions of the distributions of test statistics in multivariate analysis, *Journal of Science of the Hiroshima University, Series A-I*, **34,** 73–144.

[22] Giri, N. (1971). On the distribution of a multivariate statistic, *Sankhyā, Series A*, **33,** 207–210.

[22a] Giri, N. (1971). On the distribution of a complex multivariate statistic, *Archiv der Mathematik*, **22,** 431–435.

[23] Girshick, M. A. (1941). The distribution of the ellipticity statistic L_e when the hypothesis is false, *Terrestrial Magnetism and Atmospheric Electricity*, **46,** 455–457 (also *Statistica*, Ferrara, **2,** 157–162).

[24] Gnanadesikan, M. and Wilk, M. B. (1970). Selection procedures for multivariate normal populations in terms of the generalized variances, *Technometrics*, **12,** 103–117.

[25] Goodman, N. R. (1963). The distribution of the determinant of a complex Wishart distributed matrix, *Annals of Mathematical Statistics*, **34,** 178–180.

[26] Gupta, R. P. and Kabe, D. G. (1971). Distribution of certain factors useful in discriminant analysis, *Annals of the Institute of Statistical Mathematics, Tokyo*, **23,** 97–103.

[27] Hanumara, R. C. and Thompson, W. A. (1968). Percentage points of the extreme roots of a Wishart matrix, *Biometrika*, **55,** 505–512.

[28] Hayakawa, T. (1966). On the distribution of a quadratic form in a multivariate normal sample, *Annals of the Institute of Statistical Mathematics, Tokyo*, **18,** 191–200.

[29] Hayakawa, T. (1967). On the distribution of the maximum latent roots of a positive definite symmetric random matrix, *Annals of the Institute of Statistical Mathematics, Tokyo*, **19,** 1–17. (Errata, *ibid.*, **21,** 221.)

[30] Hayakawa, T. (1969). On the distribution of the latent roots of a positive definite random symmetric matrix, I, *Annals of the Institute of Statistical Mathematics, Tokyo*, **21,** 1–21.

[31] Hayakawa, T. (1969). *The asymptotic distributions of the statistics based on the complex Gaussian distribution*, Mimeo Series No. 654, Institute of Statistics, University of North Carolina, Chapel Hill.

[32] Hayakawa, T. (1970). *On the distribution of the latent roots of a complex Wishart matrix (non-central case)*, Mimeo Series No. 667, Institute of Statistics, University of North Carolina, Chapel Hill. (Abstract in *Annals of Mathematical Statistics*, **41,** 1150.)

[33] Heck, D. L. (1960). Charts on some upper percentage points of the distribution of the largest characteristic root, *Annals of Mathematical Statistics*, **31,** 625–641.

[34] Hoel, P. G. (1937). A significance test for component analysis, *Annals of Mathematical Statistics*, **8,** 149–158.

[35] Hotelling, H. (1951). A generalized T-test and measure of multivariate dispersion, *Proceedings of the 2nd Berkeley Symposium on Mathematical Statistics and Probability*, 23–41.

[36] Hsu, C. T. (1940). On samples from a normal bivariate population, *Annals of Mathematical Statistics*, **11,** 410–426.

[37] Hsu, P. L. (1939). On the distribution of roots of certain determinantal equations, *Annals of Eugenics*, **9,** 250–258.

[38] Ito, K. (1956). Asymptotic formulae for the distribution of Hotelling's generalized T_0^2 statistic, *Annals of Mathematical Statistics*, **27,** 1091–1105.

[39] Ito, K. (1960). Asymptotic formulae for the distribution of Hotelling's generalized T_0^2 statistic, II, *Annals of Mathematical Statistics*, **31,** 1148–1153.

[40] Jacildo, L. (1959). *Further Studies on the Distributions of the Largest of Two and Three Roots*, Statistical Center, University of the Philippines.

[41] James, A. T. (1960). The distribution of the latent roots of the covariance matrix, *Annals of Mathematical Statistics*, **31,** 151–158.

[42] James, A. T. (1964). Distributions of matrix variates and latent roots derived from normal samples, *Annals of Mathematical Statistics*, **35,** 475–501.

[43] James, A. T. (1966). Inference on latent roots by calculation of hypergeometric functions of matrix argument, in *Multivariate Analysis*, P. R. Krishnaiah, Ed., New York: Academic Press, pp. 209–235.

[44] John, S. (1963). A tolerance region for multivariate normal distribution, *Sankhyà, Series A*, **25,** 363–368.

[45] Kabe, D. G. (1963). Some results on the distribution of two random matrices used in classification procedures, *Annals of Mathematical Statistics*, **34,** 181–185.

[46] Khatri, C. G. (1964). Distribution of the largest or the smallest characteristic root under the null hypothesis concerning complex multivariate normal populations, *Annals of Mathematical Statistics*, **35,** 1807–1810.

[47] Khatri, C. G. (1966). On certain distribution problems based on positive definite quadratic functions in normal vectors, *Annals of Mathematical Statistics*, **37,** 468–479.

[48] Khatri, C. G. (1967). Some distribution problems connected with the characteristic roots of $\mathbf{S}_1\mathbf{S}_2^{-1}$, *Annals of Mathematical Statistics*, **38**, 944–948.

[49] Khatri, C. G. (1969). Non-central distributions of the *i*th characteristic roots of three matrices concerning complex multivariate normal populations, *Annals of the Institute of Statistical Mathematics, Tokyo*, **21**, 23–32.

[50] Khatri, C. G. (1971). Series representations of distributions of quadratic form in the normal vectors and generalized variance, *Journal of Multivariate Analysis*, **1**, 199–214.

[51] Khatri, C. G. and Pillai, K. C. S. (1965). Some results on the non-central multivariate beta distribution and moments of traces of two matrices, *Annals of Mathematical Statistics*, **36**, 1511–1520.

[51a] Khatri, C. G. and Srivastava, M. S. (1971). On exact non-null distributions of likelihood ratio criteria for sphericity test and equality of two covariance matrices, *Sankhyā, Series A*, **33**, 201–206.

[52] Kleinbaum, D. G. and John, S. (1969). A table of percentage points of the smallest latent root of a 2 × 2 Wishart matrix, *Mimeo Series No. 619, Institute of Statistics*, University of North Carolina, Chapel Hill.

[53] Korin, B. P. (1968). On the distribution of a statistic used for testing a covariance matrix, *Biometrika*, **55**, 171–178.

[54] Krishnaiah, P. R. and Chang, T. C. (1970). *On the Exact Distributions of the Traces of* $S_1(S_1 + S_2)^{-1}$ *and* $S_1S_2^{-1}$, ARL 70-0241, Aerospace Research Laboratories, Wright-Patterson Air Force Base, Ohio.

[54a] Krishnaiah, P. R. and Chang, T. C. (1971). On the exact distributions of the extreme roots of the Wishart and MANOVA matrices, *Journal of Multivariate Analysis*, **1**, 108–117.

[55] Krishnaiah, P. R. and Waikar, V. B. (1969). *Simultaneous Tests for Equality of Latent Roots against Certain Alternatives, I, II*, ARL-6S-0119, 0178 Aerospace Research Laboratories, Wright-Patterson Air Force Base, Ohio.

[56] Krishnaiah, P. R. and Waikar, V. B. (1970). Exact joint distributions of few roots of a class of random matrices, ARL 70-0345, *ibid.*

[57] Krishnaiah, P. R. and Waikar, V. B. (1970). Exact distributions of the intermediate roots of a class of random matrices, ARL 70-0280, *ibid.*

[58] Kshirsagar, A. M. (1964). Wilks' Λ criterion, *Journal of the Indian Statistical Association*, **2**, 1–20.

[59] Mathai, A. M. and Rathie, P. N. (1969). *The Exact Distribution of Wilks' Criterion*, Preprint No. 1969-28, Department of Mathematics, Queen's University, Kingston, Ontario (abstract in *Annals of Mathematical Statistics*, **41**, 1156).

[60] Mauchly, J. W. (1940). A significance test for ellipticity in the harmonic dial, *Terrestrial Magnetism and Electricity*, **45**, 145–148.

[61] Mehta, M. L. and Gaudin, M. (1960). On the density of eigenvalues of a random matrix, *Nuclear Physics*, **18**, 420–427.

[62] Mijares, T. A. (1964). On elementary symmetric functions of the roots of a multivariate matrix: distributions, *Annals of Mathematical Statistics*, **35**, 1186–1198.

[63] Mood, A. M. (1951). On the distribution of the characteristic roots of normal second-moment matrices, *Annals of Mathematical Statistics*, **22**, 266–273.

[64] Muirhead, R. J. (1970). Asymptotic distributions of some multivariate tests, *Annals of Mathematical Statistics*, **41**, 1002–1010.

[65] Nanda, D. N. (1948). Limiting distribution of a root of a determinantal equation, *Annals of Mathematical Statistics*, **19**, 340–350.

[66] Olkin, I. and Rubin, H. (1964). Multivariate beta distributions and independence properties of the Wishart distributions, *Annals of Mathematical Statistics*, **35**, 261–269.

[67] Pearson, E. S. and Hartley, H. O. (1971). *Biometrika Tables for Statisticians*, **2**, Cambridge University Press.

[68] Pillai, K. C. S. (1954). *On Some Distribution Problems in Multivariate Analysis*, Mimeo Series No. 88, Institute of Statistics, University of North Carolina, Chapel Hill.

[69] Pillai, K. C. S. (1955). Some new test criteria in multivariate analysis, *Annals of Mathematical Statistics*, **26**, 117–121.

[70] Pillai, K. C. S. (1956). On the distribution of the largest or the smallest root of a matrix in multivariate analysis, *Biometrika*, **43**, 122–127.

[71] Pillai, K. C. S. (1956). Some results useful in multivariate analysis, *Annals of Mathematical Statistics*, **27**, 1106–1113.

[72] Pillai, K. C. S. (1960). *Statistical Tables for Tests of Multivariate Hypotheses*. Statistical Center, University of the Philippines.

[73] Pillai, K. C. S. (1964). On the distribution of the largest of seven roots of a matrix in multivariate analysis, *Biometrika*, **51**, 270–275.

[74] Pillai, K. C. S. (1965). On the distribution of the largest characteristic root of a matrix in multivariate analysis, *Biometrika*, **52**, 405–414.

[75] Pillai, K. C. S. (1967). Upper percentage points of the largest root of a matrix in multivariate analysis, *Biometrika*, **54**, 189–194.

[76] Pillai, K. C. S. (1967). On the distribution of the largest root of a matrix in multivariate analysis, *Annals of Mathematical Statistics*, **38**, 616–617.

[77] Pillai, K. C. S. and Al-Ani, S. (1970). Power comparisons of equality of two covariance matrices based on individual characteristic roots, *Journal of the American Statistical Association*, **65**, 438–446.

[78] Pillai, K. C. S., Al-Ani, S., and Jouris, G. M. (1969). On the distribution of the ratios of the roots of a covariance matrix and Wilks' criterion for tests of three hypotheses, *Annals of Mathematical Statistics*, **40**, 2033–2040.

[79] Pillai, K. C. S. and Bantegui, C. G. (1959). On the distributions of the largest of six roots of a matrix in multivariate analysis, *Biometrika*, **46**, 237–240.

[80] Pillai, K. C. S. and Chang, T. C. (1969). An approximation to the c.d.f. of the

largest root of a covariance matrix, *Annals of the Institute of Statistical Mathematics, Tokyo*, **6** (Supplement), 115–124.

[81] Pillai, K. C. S. and Gupta, A. K. (1969). On the exact distribution of Wilks' criterion, *Biometrika*, **56,** 109–118.

[82] Pillai, K. C. S. and Jayachandran, Kante (1970). On the exact distribution of Pillai's $V^{(s)}$ criterion, *Journal of the American Statistical Association*, **65,** 447–454.

[83] Pillai, K. C. S. and Jouris, G. M. (1969). On the moments of elementary symmetric functions of two matrices, *Annals of the Institute of Statistical Mathematics, Tokyo*, **21,** 309–320.

[84] Pillai, K. C. S. and Samson, P. (1959). On Hotelling's generalization of T^2, *Biometrika*, **46,** 160–168.

[85] Pillai, K. C. S. and Sugiyama, T. (1969). Non-central distribution of the largest roots of three matrices in multivariate analysis, *Annals of the Institute of Statistical Mathematics, Tokyo*, **21,** 321–333.

[86] Pillai, K. C. S. and Young, D. L. (1971). An approximation of the distribution of the largest root of a complex Wishart matrix, *Annals of the Institute of Statistical Mathematics, Tokyo*, **23,** 89–96.

[87] Radcliffe, J. (1968). The distribution of certain factors occurring in discriminant analysis, *Proceedings of the Cambridge Philosophical Society*, **64,** 731–740.

[88] Roy, S. N. (1939). *p*-statistics, or some generalizations in analysis of variance appropriate to multivariate problems, *Sankhyà*, **4,** 381–396.

[89] Roy, S. N. (1945). The individual sampling distribution of the maximum, the minimum and any intermediate of the *p* statistics on the null hypothesis, *Sankhyà*, **8,** 133–158.

[90] Schatzoff, M. (1966). Exact distributions of Wilks' likelihood ratio criterion, *Biometrika*, **53,** 347–358 (correction, *ibid.*, **54,** 688).

[91] Shah, B. K. (1970). Distribution theory of positive definite quadratic forms with matrix argument, *Annals of Mathematical Statistics*, **41,** 692–697.

[92] Siotani, M. (1956). On the distributions of the Hotelling's T^2-statistics, *Annals of the Institute of Statistical Mathematics*, **8,** 1–14.

[93] Siotani, M. (1968). Some methods for asymptotic distributions in the multivariate analysis, *Mimeo Series No. 595, Institute of Statistics*, University of North Carolina, Chapel Hill.

[94] Srivastava, M. S. (1968). On the distribution of a multiple correlation matrix: Noncentral multivariate beta distributions, *Annals of Mathematical Statistics*, **39,** 227–232.

[95] Steyn, H. S. (1967). On the distribution of the determinant for sums of squares and products, *Tydskrif vir Natuurwetenskappe*, **7,** 498–505.

[96] Sugiura, N. (1969). *Asymptotic Non-Null Distributions of the Likelihood Criterion for Covariance Matrix under Local Alternatives*, Mimeo Series No. 609, Institute of Statistics, University of North Carolina, Chapel Hill.

[97] Sugiura, N. and Fujikoshi, Y. (1969). Asymptotic expansions of the non-null distributions of the likelihood ratio criteria for multivariate linear hypothesis and independence, *Annals of Mathematical Statistics*, **40**, 942–952.

[97a] Sugiura, N. and Nagao, H. (1971). Asymptotic expansion of the distribution of the generalized variance for noncentral Wishart matrix, when $\Omega = O(n)$, *Annals of the Institute of Statistical Mathematics, Tokyo*, **23**, 469–475.

[98] Sugiyama, T. (1967). On the distribution of the largest latent root of the covariance matrix, *Annals of Mathematical Statistics*, **38**, 1148–1151.

[99] Sugiyama, T. (1967). Distribution of the largest latent root and the smallest latent root of the generalized B statistic and F statistic in multivariate analysis, *Annals of Mathematical Statistics*, **38**, 1152–1159.

[100] Sugiyama, T. (1968). *Percentile points of the largest latent root of a matrix and power calculations for testing the hypothesis* $\mathbf{\Sigma} = \mathbf{I}$, Mimeo Series No. 590, Institute of Statistics, University of North Carolina, Chapel Hill.

[101] Sugiyama, T. (1970). Joint distribution of the extreme roots of a covariance matrix, *Annals of Mathematical Statistics*, **41**, 655–657.

[102] Sugiyama, T. and Fukutomi, K. (1967). On the distribution of the extreme characteristic roots of the matrices in multivariate analysis, *JUSE Reports of Statistical Application in Research*, **14**, 156–160.

[103] Thompson, W. A. (1962). Estimation of dispersion parameters, *Journal of Research of the National Bureau of Standards, Series B*, **60**, 161–164.

[104] Tumura, Y. (1965). The distribution of latent roots and vectors, *Tokyo Rika University, TRU Mathematics*, **1**, 1–16.

[105] Turin, G. L. (1960). The characteristic function of Hermitian quadratic forms, *Biometrika*, **47**, 199–201.

[106] Waal, D. J. de (1969). On the non-central distribution of the largest canonical correlation coefficient, *South African Statistical Journal*, **3**, 91–93.

[107] Waal, D. J. de (1969). The non-central multivariate beta type 2 distribution, *South African Statistical Journal*, **3**, 101–108.

[108] Waal, D. J. de (1970). Distributions connected with a multivariate beta statistic, *Annals of Mathematical Statistics*, **41**, 1091–1095.

[109] Waal, D. J. de (1972). On the expected values of the elementary symmetric functions of a noncentral Wishart matrix, *Annals of Mathematical Statistics*, **43**, 344–347.

[110] Wald, A. and Brookner, R. J. (1941). On the distribution of Wilks' statistic for testing the independence of several groups of variates, *Annals of Mathematical Statistics*, **12**, 137–152.

[111] Wall, F. J. (1967). *The Generalized Variance Ratio or U-Statistic*, Dikewood Corporation, Albuquerque, New Mexico.

[112] Wilks, S. S. (1932). Certain generalizations in the analysis of variance, *Biometrika*, **24**, 471–494.

40

Multivariate Beta and Gamma Distributions

1. Introduction

The distributions discussed in this chapter can be regarded as generalizations of the univariate beta (Chapter 24) and gamma (Chapter 17) distributions. As is often the case, generalization can take a number of different forms. We describe a number, but these are not exhaustive. We omit many possible forms that are not in use at present and are not likely to have useful applications. This does not mean, however, that these excluded forms may not become of greater importance at a later date.

Among bivariate gamma distributions that are studied only incidentally is a system introduced by I. O. Sarmanov [62] which has some points of similarity with (but differs from) a system described by Eagleson [13] and the system investigated by D'jachenko [10–12].

Occasionally, Wishart distributions have been referred to as "multivariate gamma" distributions (e.g., Tan [66]). We restrict this term to those distributions for which *all* marginal distributions are of gamma form.

2. Multivariate Gamma Distributions—I

A multivariate generalization of the gamma distribution may be constructed by methods similar to those leading to bivariate Poisson and Neyman Type A distributions (Chapter 11, Sections 4 and 7).

Let $X_0,X_1,\ldots,X_m$ be independent random variables, X_j having a standard gamma distribution with density function

$$(1)\qquad p_{X_j}(x_j) = \{\Gamma(\theta_j)\}^{-1}x_j^{\theta_j-1}e^{-x_j} \qquad (x_j > 0;\theta_j > 0;j = 0,1,\ldots,m).$$

Now consider the joint distribution of

$$Y_j = X_0 + X_j \qquad (j = 1,\ldots,m).$$

The joint density of $X_0,X_1,\ldots,X_m$ is

$$\left\{\prod_{j=0}^{m}\Gamma(\theta_j)\right\}^{-1}\left\{\prod_{j=0}^{m}x_j^{\theta_j-1}\right\}\exp\left(-\sum_{j=0}^{m}x_j\right) \qquad (x_j > 0).$$

The joint density of $X_0, Y_1,\ldots, Y_m$ is

$$\left\{\prod_{j=0}^{m}\Gamma(\theta_j)\right\}^{-1}x_0^{\theta_0-1}\left\{\prod_{j=0}^{m}(y_j - x_0)^{\theta_j-1}\right\}\exp\left\{(m-1)x_0 - \sum_{j=1}^{m}y_j\right\}$$
$$(y_j \geq x_0 \geq 0;j = 1,\ldots,m).$$

In order to "integrate out" the variable X_0, it is necessary to evaluate

$$(2)\qquad \int_0^{\tilde{y}} x_0^{\theta_0-1}\left\{\prod_{j=1}^{m}(y_j - x_0)^{\theta_j-1}\right\}e^{(m-1)x_0}\,dx_0,$$

where $\tilde{y} = \min(y_1,y_2,\ldots,y_m)$. In the general case (2) leads to very complicated expressions. Some special cases are, however, reasonably simple. If $\theta_1 = \theta_2 = \cdots = \theta_m = 1$ (i.e., $X_1,\ldots,X_m$ each have an exponential distribution), then

$$(3)\qquad p_{Y_1,\ldots,Y_m}(y_1,\ldots,y_m) = \{\Gamma(\theta_0)\}^{-1}\left\{\exp\left(-\sum_{j=1}^{m}y_j\right)\right\}g(\tilde{y};\theta_0) \qquad (y_j > 0),$$

where $g(\tilde{y};\theta_0) = \int_0^{\tilde{y}} x_0^{\theta_0-1}e^{(m-1)x_0}\,dx_0$. It can be seen that $\tilde{y} = \min(y_1,\ldots,y_m)$ is a sufficient statistic for θ_0. The maximum likelihood estimator, $\hat{\theta}_0$, of θ_0 satisfies the equation

$$\frac{\partial}{\partial\hat{\theta}_0}\log g(\tilde{y};\hat{\theta}_0) = \psi(\hat{\theta}_0).$$

where $\psi(\cdot)$ is the digamma function (Chapter 1, Section 3). When $m = 2$, we have a bivariate gamma distribution, with density function

$$(4)\qquad \frac{e^{-(y_1+y_2)}}{\Gamma(\theta_0)\Gamma(\theta_1)\Gamma(\theta_2)}\int_0^{\min(y_1,y_2)} x_0^{\theta_0-1}(y_1 - x_0)^{\theta_1-1}(y_2 - x_0)^{\theta_2-1}e^{x_0}\,dx_0.$$

If also $\theta_1 = \theta_2 = 1$ and θ_0 is an integer, then

$$(5)\quad p_{Y_1,Y_2}(y_1,y_2) = \{\Gamma(\theta_0)\}^{-1}e^{-(y_1+y_2)}\int_0^{\min(y_1,y_2)} x_0^{\theta_0-1}e^{x_0}\,dx_0$$

$$= \{\Gamma(\theta_0)\}^{-1}e^{-(y_1+y_2)}[e^{\tilde{y}}\{\tilde{y}^{\theta_0-1} - (\theta_0-1)\tilde{y}^{\theta_0-2}$$

$$+ (\theta_0-1)(\theta_0-2)\tilde{y}^{\theta_0-3} + \cdots$$

$$+ (-1)^{\theta_0-1}(\theta_0-1)!\} + (-1)^{\theta_0}(\theta_0-1)!]$$

$$= e^{-(y_1+y_2)}(-1)^{\theta_0}$$

$$\times\left[1 - e^{\tilde{y}}\left\{1 - \frac{\tilde{y}}{1!} + \frac{\tilde{y}^2}{2!} - \cdots + (-1)^{\theta_0-1}\frac{\tilde{y}^{\theta_0-1}}{(\theta_0-1)!}\right\}\right],$$

where $\tilde{y} = \min(y_1,y_2)$.

In the general case, the marginal distribution of Y_j is a standard gamma distribution with parameter $\theta_0 + \theta_j$. The covariance between Y_j and $Y_{j'}$ is

$$\operatorname{var}(X_0) = \theta_0$$

and so

$$(6)\qquad \operatorname{corr}(Y_j,Y_{j'}) = \theta_0[(\theta_0+\theta_j)(\theta_0+\theta_{j'})]^{-1/2}.$$

The conditional distribution of X_0, given that $Y_j = X_0 + X_j = y_j$, may be derived from the fact that the random variables X_0/Y_j and Y_j are independent. It follows, therefore, that the conditional distribution of X_0, given Y_j is that of $Y_j \times$ (beta variable with parameters θ_0,θ_j). In particular,

$$E[X_0 \mid Y_j] = Y_j\theta_0(\theta_0+\theta_j)^{-1},$$

$$\operatorname{var}(X_0 \mid Y_j) = Y_j^2\theta_0\theta_j(\theta_0+\theta_j)^{-2}(\theta_0+\theta_j+1)^{-1}.$$

Hence

$$(7.1)\qquad E[Y_{j'} \mid Y_j] = E[X_0 \mid Y_j] + E[X_{j'}] = Y_j\theta_0(\theta_0+\theta_j)^{-1} + \theta_{j'}$$

(noting that X_j and X_0 are independent) and

$$(7.2)\qquad \operatorname{var}(Y_{j'} \mid Y_j) = \operatorname{var}(X_0 \mid Y_j) + \operatorname{var}(X_{j'})$$

$$= Y_j^2\theta_0\theta_j(\theta_0+\theta_j)^{-2}(\theta_0+\theta_j+1)^{-1} + \theta_{j'}.$$

Thus the regression of $Y_{j'}$ on Y_j is linear, but variation about the regression is not homoscedastic. We further note that the conditional distribution of $Y_{j'}$, given Y_j, is that of the sum of two independent random variables, one distributed as $Y_j \times$ (standard beta variable, parameters θ_0 and θ_j) and the other as a standard gamma variable with parameter $\theta_{j'}$.

The joint moment generating function of $Y_1, Y_2, \ldots, Y_m$ is

$$E\left[\exp\left(\sum_{j=1}^{m} t_j Y_j\right)\right] = E\left[\exp\left(X_0 \sum_{j=1}^{m} t_j\right) \prod_{j=1}^{m} \exp(t_j X_j)\right] \tag{8}$$

$$= E\left[\exp\left(X_0 \sum_{j=1}^{m} t_j\right)\right] \prod_{j=1}^{m} E[\exp(t_j X_j)]$$

$$= \left(1 - \sum_{j=1}^{m} t_j\right)^{-\theta_0} \prod_{j=1}^{m} (1 - t_j)^{-\theta_j}.$$

(Cheriyan [6], Ramabhadran [59].)

More parameters may be introduced by considering the joint distribution of

$$\lambda_j(X_0 + X_j) \qquad (j = 1,2,\ldots,m).$$

Ghirtis [18] calls the case $m = 2$ the *double-gamma* distribution. He gives a method of fitting the parameters $\theta_1,\theta_2,\theta_0,\lambda_1,\lambda_2$ by using sample moments and product moments.

Jensen [24] has shown that if X_1 and X_2 have a bivariate gamma distribution of this type, then

$$\Pr\left[\bigcap_{j=1}^{2} (c_1 \le X_j \le c_2)\right] \ge \prod_{j=1}^{2} \Pr[c_1 \le X_j \le c_2] \tag{9}$$

for any $c_2 > c_1 \ge 0$. Another way of expressing (9) is

$$\Pr[c_1 \le X_2 \le c_2 \,|\, c_1 \le X_1 \le c_2] \ge \Pr[c_1 \le X_2 \le c_2],$$

that is, if X_1 is between c_1 and c_2, it increases the probability that X_2 is between c_1 and c_2 [cf. (10), Chapter 35].

Moran [52] has pointed out that a bivariate distribution with characteristic function (originally introduced by Kibble [34])

$$\{(1 - it_1)(1 - it_2) + \omega^2 t_1 t_2\}^{-\alpha} \tag{10.1}$$

has marginal distributions that are each gamma distributions with parameter α. The correlation ρ between the variables is ω^2. An explicit expression for the joint density function is

$$p_{X_1,X_2}(x_1,x_2) = \sum_{j=0}^{\infty} \omega^{2j}(\alpha^{[j]}/j!)\left[\prod_{k=1}^{2}\left\{\sum_{g=0}^{j}(-1)^j\binom{j}{g}(g!)^{-1}x_k^g e^{-x_k}\right\}\right]. \tag{10.2}$$

[Cf. Section 3.5, Chapter 41 and (18) in the next section.]

Moran [53, 54] has also discussed the use of a bivariate gamma distribution such that normalizing transformations on each variate produce a joint bivariate normal distribution in the analysis of data from rainmaking experiments.

The characteristic function of the standard gamma distribution with parameter α (Chapter 17, equation (2)) is $(1 - it)^{-\alpha}$. It follows that the compound gamma distribution

$$\text{gamma } (\alpha + \theta,1,0) \bigwedge_{\theta} \text{negative binomial } (\alpha,\beta)$$

has characteristic function

$$(1 - it)^{-\alpha}\{\beta + 1 - \beta(1 - it)^{-1}\}^{-\alpha} = \{(\beta + 1)(1 - it) - \beta\}^{-\alpha}$$

and so has a gamma distribution with parameters $\alpha,\beta + 1$ (and 0).

This fact has been exploited by Gaver [17] to construct a bivariate gamma distribution by compounding, in the same way, the joint distribution of independent variables (X_1,X_2) each having the same standard gamma distribution with parameter $\alpha + \theta$. The resulting joint characteristic function is

$$(1 - it_1)^{-\alpha}(1 - it_2)^{-\alpha}\{\beta + 1 - \beta(1 - it_1)^{-1}(1 - it_2)^{-1}\}^{-\alpha}$$
$$= \{(\beta + 1)(1 - it_1)(1 - it_2) - \beta\}^{-\alpha}$$

[cf. equation (10.1)]. Since α can take any positive value, the distribution is infinitely divisible, as was pointed out by Vere-Jones [71].

A straightforward extension of the argument leads to a general multivariate gamma distribution, with characteristic function

$$\left\{(\beta + 1)\prod_{j=1}^{m}(1 - it_j) - \beta\right\}^{-\alpha} \qquad (\alpha,\beta > 0).$$

This distribution is symmetrical in all m variates. The covariance between any two is

$$E_\theta[(\alpha + \theta)^2] - [\alpha(\beta + 1)]^2 = \alpha\beta(\beta + 1)$$

and the correlation is $\beta/(\beta + 1)$.

3. Multivariate Gamma Distributions—II

A distribution with marginal χ^2 distributions arises naturally in the following way. Consider a random sample of size n represented by n independent vectors $(X_{i1},\ldots,X_{im})$ $(i = 1,2,\ldots,n)$, each vector having the same multinormal distribution with variance-covariance matrix $\mathbf{V}$ and having each diagonal element equal to 1 ($\mathbf{V}$ is, of course, also the correlation matrix). Then the statistics $S_j = \sum_{i=1}^{n}(X_{ij} - \bar{X}_{.j})^2$ $(j = 1,2,\ldots,m)$ each have a χ^2_{n-1} distribution. Their joint distribution may, following Krishnaiah et al. [38], be called a *multivariate chi-square* distribution. It is also called *generalized Rayleigh distribution* (e.g., Miller [47]). Derivation of an explicit form for the density function is straightforward in the bivariate case ($m = 2$).

The conditional distribution of $(X_{11},\ldots,X_{n1})$ given $(X_{12},\ldots,X_{n2})$ is that of n independent normal variables with expected values $(X_{12},\ldots,X_{n2})$ and common variance $(1-\rho^2)$ where $\rho = \operatorname{corr}(X_{i1},X_{i2})$. It follows that X_{i1} can be represented as $\rho X_{i2} + \sqrt{1-\rho^2}U_i$ where $U_1,U_2,\ldots,U_n$ are independent unit normal variables. Hence given $(X_{12},\ldots,X_{n2})$, S_1 is distributed as

$$\sum_{j=1}^{n}\{\rho(X_{i2}-\bar{X}_2)+\sqrt{1-\rho^2}\,(U_i-\bar{U})\}^2 \tag{11}$$

that is, as $(1-\rho^2)\times$ (noncentral χ^2 with $(n-1)$ degrees of freedom and noncentrality parameter $\rho^2S_2(1-\rho^2)^{-1}$). Since this depends on $\{X_{i2}\}$ only in S_2, this is also the conditional distribution of S_1 given S_2, so that (see Chapter 28, Section 3)

$$\Pr[S_1 \le s \mid S_2] = \exp\left[-\frac{1}{2}\frac{\rho^2S_2}{1-\rho^2}\right]\sum_{j=0}^{\infty}\frac{1}{j!}\left[\frac{1}{2}\frac{\rho^2S_2}{1-\rho^2}\right]^j \times \Pr[\chi^2_{n-1+2j} \le (1-\rho^2)^{-1}s].$$

Noting that S_2 has a χ^2_{n-1} distribution, we calculate

$$\begin{aligned}\Pr[(S_1<s_1)\cap(S_2<s_2)] &= \int_0^{s_2}\Pr[S_1\le s_1 \mid s_2]p_{S_2}(s_2)\,ds_2\\ &= \sum_{j=0}^{\infty}c_j\Pr[\chi^2_{n-1+2j}\le(1-\rho^2)^{-1}s_1]\\ &\quad\times\Pr[\chi^2_{n-1+2j}\le(1-\rho^2)^{-1}s_2],\end{aligned}\tag{12}$$

with

$$c_j = \frac{\Gamma(\frac{1}{2}(n-1)+j)(1-\rho^2)^{\frac{1}{2}(n-1)}\rho^{2j}}{j!}$$

(Bose [4], Finney [14], Johnson [32], Vere-Jones [71], Moran and Vere-Jones [55]).

This is a *standard* bivariate gamma distribution. Additional parameters can be introduced by considering the variables $S'_j = S_j\sigma_j^2$ giving a *general* bivariate gamma distribution. Note that $c_0,c_1,c_2,\ldots$ are terms in the expression of the negative binomial

$$\left(\frac{1}{1-\rho^2}-\frac{\rho^2}{1-\rho^2}\right)^{-\frac{1}{2}(n-1)},$$

so that $\sum_{j=0}^{\infty}c_j = 1$. The joint distribution of S_1 and S_2 can thus be regarded as a mixture of joint distributions, with weights c_j, in which S_1 and S_2 each have independent χ^2_{n-1+2j} distributions.

It follows that S_1/S_2 is distributed as a mixture, in the same proportions as c_j, of $F_{n-1+2j,n-1+2j}$ distributions (see Chapter 30).

The density function of $G = S_1/S_2$ can also be written

$$(13) \qquad p_G(g) = \frac{(1-\rho^2)^{\frac{1}{2}\nu}}{B(\frac{1}{2},\frac{1}{2}\nu)} \frac{g^{(1/2)\nu-1}}{(1+g)^{\nu}}\left(1 - \frac{4\rho^2 g}{(1+g)^2}\right)^{-\frac{1}{2}(\nu+1)} \qquad (g > 0)$$

(Bose [4], Finney [14]). The sum $(S_1 + S_2)$ is distributed as a mixture of $\chi^2_{2(n-1)+4j}$ distributions with weights c_j.

Furthermore, the expected value of $S_1^{\alpha_1}S_2^{\alpha_2}$ is

$$(14) \quad \mu'_{\alpha_1,\alpha_2} = \sum_{j=0}^{\infty} c_j \mu'_{\alpha_1}(\chi^2_{n-1+2j})\mu'_{\alpha_2}(\chi^2_{n-1+2j})$$

$$= \sum_{j=0}^{\infty} c_j \frac{2^{\alpha_1+\alpha_2}\Gamma[\frac{1}{2}(n-1)+j+\alpha_1]\Gamma[\frac{1}{2}(n-1)+j+\alpha_2]}{\{\Gamma[\frac{1}{2}(n-1)+j]\}^2}.$$

This formula applies for any values of α_1 and α_2, provided only that $\min(\alpha_1,\alpha_2) > -\frac{1}{2}(n-1)$.

From (11) it is clear that

$$(15.1) \qquad E[S_1 \mid S_2] = (1-\rho^2)E\left[\chi'^2_{n-1}\left(\frac{\rho^2 S_2}{1-\rho^2}\right)\right]$$
$$= (n-1)(1-\rho^2) + \rho^2 S_2$$

[using (13) of Chapter 28].

Also

$$(15.2) \qquad \text{var}(S_1 \mid S_2) = (1-\rho^2)^2[2(n-1) + 4\rho^2 S_2/(1-\rho^2)]$$
$$= 2(n-1)(1-\rho^2)^2 + 4\rho^2(1-\rho^2)S_2.$$

The regression of S_1 on S_2 is linear, but the array distributions are not homoscedastic.

The joint distribution of $\sqrt{S_1}$ and $\sqrt{S_2}$ (the *bivariate chi* distribution) has been studied by Krishnaiah et al. [38].

Probabilities associated with the distribution of S_1/S_2 can be evaluated from tables of the incomplete beta function ratio using the relation (Finney [14]).

$$(16) \qquad \Pr[\max(S_1/S_2,S_2/S_1) > y^2] = I_\eta(\tfrac{1}{2}(n-1),\tfrac{1}{2}(n-1)),$$

where $\eta = \frac{1}{2}[1 - (y - y^{-1})\{(y + y^{-1})^2 - 4\rho^2\}^{-1/2}]$, with $y > 1$. Johnson [32] showed that a useful approximation to (16) is

$$2\Pr[F_{\nu',\nu'} > y^2]$$

with $\nu' = (\nu - 2\rho^2)/(1-\rho^2)$.

Note that we can define a *general standard bivariate gamma* distribution by replacing $(n-1)$ in (12) by ν, which should be positive, but need not be an integer. This distribution depends on the two parameters ν,ρ. All the properties of (12) are also valid for the general case. Thus, for example, S_1/S_2 is distributed as a mixture of $F_{\nu+2j,\nu+2j}$ distributions with weights that are terms in the expansion of the negative binomial

$$\left(\frac{1}{1-\rho^2} - \frac{\rho^2}{1-\rho^2}\right)^{-\nu/2}.$$

For $m > 2$, derivation of the joint distribution of $S_1,S_2,\ldots,S_m$ is more difficult. Using the methods employed in this section for $m = 2$ one can show, for example, that the conditional distribution of S_1 given

$$(X_{12},\ldots,X_{n2})(X_{13},\ldots,X_{n3})\cdots(X_{1m},\ldots,X_{nm})$$

is that of $(1 - R^2_{1\cdot 23\ldots m}) \times$ (noncentral χ^2 with $(n-1)$ degrees of freedom and noncentrality parameter

$$(1 - R^2_{1\cdot 2\,3\ldots m})^{-1}\cdot\left\{\sum_{j=2}^m a_j^2 S_j + \sum_{j\le k}^m \sum_{k=2}^m a_j a_k P_{jk}\right\},$$

where

$$a_j = \rho_{1j\cdot 2\ldots(j-1),(j+1)\ldots m},$$

$$P_{jk} = \sum_{i=1}^n (X_{ij} - \bar{X}_j)(X_{ik} - \bar{X}_k).$$

and $R^2_{1\cdot 23\ldots m}$ is the multiple correlation of X_1 on $X_2,\ldots,X_m$. The joint distribution of $S_2,\ldots,S_n,P_{23},\ldots,P_{m-1,m}$ is a Wishart distribution $W_{m-1}(n-1;\mathbf{V}_{11})$, where $\mathbf{V}_{11}$ is the cofactor of the first diagonal element of $\mathbf{V}$. It is thus simple to obtain the joint distribution of $S_1,S_2,\ldots,S_m$, $P_{23},\ldots,P_{m-1}$, but elimination of the P's poses difficulties.

For the special case when

$$\mathbf{V} = \begin{pmatrix} 1 & \rho & \cdots & \rho \\ \rho & 1 & \cdots & \rho \\ \cdot & \cdot & & \cdot \\ \cdot & \cdot & & \cdot \\ \cdot & \cdot & & \cdot \\ \rho & \rho & \cdots & 1 \end{pmatrix},$$

Johnson [32] has suggested the approximate formula

$$\Pr\left[\bigcap_{j=1}^m (S_j \le s_j)\right] \doteqdot \sum_{j=0}^\infty c_j \prod_{k=1}^m \Pr[\chi^2_{n-1+2j} < s_k] \tag{17}$$

with c_j's as in (12). This gives the correct values for $\Pr[S_j \leq s_j]$ and $\Pr[S_j \leq s_j) \cap (S_{j'} \leq s_{j'})]$ for any j,j' (i.e., all marginal univariate and bivariate distributions are correct). It would seem likely that (17) should give usefully accurate values for $m = 3$ or 4, but that the accuracy would decrease with increasing m.

Krishnamoorthy and Parthasarathy [40] and Lukacs and Laha [44] have shown that the joint characteristic function of $S_1,\ldots,S_m$ is

$$E\left[\exp\left(i\sum_{j=1}^{m} t_j S_j\right)\right] = |\mathbf{I} - 2i\mathbf{V}\mathbf{D}_t|^{-\nu/2}$$

where $\mathbf{D}_t = \operatorname{diag}(t_1,\ldots,t_m)$.

This joint distribution could be used to construct simultaneous confidence intervals of the variances $\sigma_1^2,\ldots,\sigma_m^2$ (diagonal elements of $\mathbf{V}$). This would require a knowledge of the correlation coefficients (elements of $\mathbf{R}$). Jensen and Jones [30] have shown, however, that very good approximations can be obtained without the need to use this distribution. *Bonferroni intervals* (Bens and Jensen [2]) are formed by using ordinary univariate intervals (see Chapter 17) for each σ_j^2 with confidence coefficients $1 - \gamma_j = 1 - \alpha m^{-1}$ ($1 - \alpha$ being the required joint confidence coefficient). These give good results with $m = 2$ for $\alpha = 0.01, 0.10$, over a wide range of values of ν and ρ (the correlation coefficient).

Moran and Vere-Jones [55] show that if $\rho_{ij} = \rho$ for all i,j, the joint distribution of $S_1,\ldots,S_m$ is infinitely divisible (i.e., for any α (>0), $|\mathbf{I} - 2i\mathbf{V}\mathbf{D}_t|^{-\alpha}$ is a characteristic function). They also show that this is true for $m = 3$ with

$$\mathbf{V} = \begin{pmatrix} 1 & \rho & \rho^2 \\ \rho & 1 & \rho \\ \rho^2 & \rho & 1 \end{pmatrix}.$$

The distribution of the maximum of $S_1,\ldots,S_m$ has been considered by Fomin [16]. He also gives an approximate formula for the cumulative distribution.

If $\mathbf{X}' = (\mathbf{X}'_{(1)},\mathbf{X}'_{(2)})$ has a multinormal distribution with zero expected value vector and variance covariance matrix

$$\mathbf{V} = \begin{pmatrix} \mathbf{V}_{11} & \mathbf{V}_{12} \\ \mathbf{V}_{21} & \mathbf{V}_{22} \end{pmatrix},$$

where the $\nu_j \times \nu_j$ matrix $\mathbf{V}_{jj}$ is the variance-covariance matrix of $\mathbf{X}'_{(j)}$, ($j = 1,2$), then the quadratic forms

$$\mathbf{Y}_j = \mathbf{X}'_{(j)}\mathbf{V}_{jj}^{-1}\mathbf{X}_{(j)}$$

have χ^2 distributions with ν_j degrees of freedom ($j = 1,2$). The joint distribution of $\mathbf{Y}_1$ and $\mathbf{Y}_2$ is thus a form of bivariate χ^2 distribution. It has been studied by Jensen [27], who points out that the distribution is the same as that of

$$Y_1 = \sum_{j=1}^{\nu_1} Z_{1j}^2; \qquad Y_2 = \sum_{j=1}^{\nu_2} Z_{2j}^2, \qquad (\nu_1 \leq \nu_2)$$

where (Z_{1j}, Z_{2j}) ($j = 1, \ldots, \nu_1$) are independent and have standardized bivariate normal distributions with correlations $\rho_1, \rho_2, \ldots, \rho_{\nu_1}$ (the canonical correlations between $\mathbf{X}_{(1)}$ and $\mathbf{X}_{(2)}$) and $Z_{2,\nu_1+1} \cdots Z_{2,\nu_2}$ are independent unit normal variables which are also independent of all other Z's.

Jensen [28] has also considered the joint distribution of

$$Y_j = \sum_{k=1}^{\nu} Z_{kj}^2 \qquad (j = 1,2,\ldots,m),$$

where $\mathbf{Z}_k = (Z_{k1}, \ldots, Z_{km})$ are mutually independent ($k = 1,2,\ldots,\nu$) and $\mathbf{Z}_k$ has a standardized multinormal distribution with variance-covariance matrix $\mathbf{V}_k$ (not necessarily the same for all k).

For the case $m = 2$, the joint characteristic function of Y_1 and Y_2 is

$$(18.1) \quad [(1 - 2it_1)(1 - 2it_2)]^{(-1/2)\nu} \times \sum_{j=0}^{\infty} C_j(\rho_1, \rho_2, \ldots, \rho_\nu) \left\{ - \frac{4t_1 t_2}{(1 - 2it_1)(1 - 2it_2)} \right\}^j,$$

where

$$C_j(\rho_1, \rho_2, \ldots, \rho_\nu) = \sum_{j_1 + \cdots + j_\nu = j} \cdots \sum a_{j_1}(\rho_1) \cdots a_{j_\nu}(\rho_\nu)$$

with

$$a_j(\rho_l) = \rho_l^{2j} \Gamma(j + \tfrac{1}{2})[\sqrt{\pi}\,\Gamma(j + 1)]^{-1}$$

and

$$\rho_l = \operatorname{corr}(Z_{l1}, Z_{l2}).$$

The joint density function of Y_1 and Y_2 is

$$(18.2) \quad p_{(Y_1,Y_2)} = \left[\frac{y_1^{(1/2)\nu - 1} e^{(-1/2)y_1}}{2^{(1/2)\nu} \Gamma(\frac{1}{2}\nu)} \right] \left[\frac{y_2^{(1/2)\nu - 1} e^{(-1/2)y_2}}{2^{(1/2)\nu} \Gamma(\frac{1}{2}\nu)} \right] \times \sum_{j=0}^{\infty} \left\{ \frac{j!\,\Gamma(\frac{1}{2}\nu)}{\Gamma(\frac{1}{2}\nu + j)} \right\}^2 C_j(\rho_1, \ldots, \rho_\nu) L_j^{(1/2)\nu}(\tfrac{1}{2}y_1) L_j^{(1/2)\nu}(\tfrac{1}{2}y_2),$$

where $L_j^{\alpha-1}(x)$ is the Laguerre polynomial (see Chapter 1, Section 3)

$$L_j^{\alpha-1}(x) = \left[\frac{\Gamma(\alpha)\Gamma(\alpha + j)}{j!} \right]^{1/2} \sum_{h=0}^{j} \frac{(-1)^h \binom{j}{h} x^h}{\Gamma(\alpha + h)}.$$

The correlation between Y_1 and Y_2 is clearly

$$(2\nu)^{-1}\operatorname{cov}(Y_1,Y_2) = (2\nu)^{-1}\sum_{k=1}^{\nu}\operatorname{cov}(Z_{k1}^2,Z_{k2}^2)$$
$$= \nu^{-1}\sum_{k=1}^{\nu}\rho_k^2.$$

Jensen [28] also obtains the general joint distribution of Y_1, Y_2, and Y_3; and of $Y_1, Y_2, \ldots, Y_m$ for general m, when the variance-covariance matrices $\mathbf{V}_k$ are each of Jacobi form, that is, with all elements zero except those on the principal and its two adjacent diagonals.

A bivariate expansion of the density function (10.2) in terms of Laguerre polynomials

$$(18.3)\quad p_{X_1,X_2}(x_1,x_2) = \left\{\prod_{j=1}^{2}\left[\frac{x_j^{\alpha-1}e^{-x_j}}{\Gamma(\alpha)}\right]\right\}\left[1+\sum_{j=1}^{\infty}\rho^j L_j^{\alpha-1}(x_1)L_j^{\alpha-1}(x_2)\right]$$
$$(\alpha > 0; 0 \le \rho < 1; x_1,x_2 > 0)$$

was constructed by Kibble [34]. It is interesting to compare (18.3) and (18.2).

Hamdan and Martinson [21a] have obtained, for this distribution, a formula analogous to (73.1) of Chapter 36 for the bivariate normal distribution, with the left-hand-side multiplied by $\alpha(\tilde{h}_1\tilde{h}_2)^{-1}$ and Laguerre polynomials replacing Hermite polynomials on the right-hand-side.

The density (18.3) [or (10.2)] was extensively studied by D'jachenko ([10–12]) who also gives tables and "prisomograms" of (18) for $\rho = 0.9$ and $\alpha = 2(1)5$. It is termed by Sarmanov [61] a *symmetric gamma distribution.* The same author [62–63] has also constructed *asymmetrical bivariate gamma distributions* with probability density function

$$(18.4)\quad p_{X_1,X_2}(x_1,x_2) = \prod_{j=1}^{2}[\{\Gamma(\alpha_j)\}^{-1}x_j^{\alpha_j-1}e^{-x_j}][1+\sum_{j=1}^{2}a_jL_j^{\alpha_1-1}(x_1)L_j^{\alpha_2-1}(x_2)]$$
$$(x_1,x_2 > 0),$$

where $\alpha_1 > \alpha_2$ and (for some $\lambda > 0$ and <1)

$$a_j = \lambda^j\sqrt{\frac{\Gamma(\alpha_1)\Gamma(\alpha_2+j)}{\Gamma(\alpha_2)\Gamma(\alpha_1+j)}}.$$

The correlation between X_1 and X_2 is

$$a_1 = \lambda\sqrt{\alpha_2/\alpha_1}\,.$$

For distribution (18.3), the correlation between $\log X_1$ and $\log X_2$ is $R_\alpha = \sum_{j=1}^{\infty} C_j\rho^j$ where

$$C_j = \left[j^2\binom{\alpha-1+j}{j}\sum_{i=0}^{\infty}(i+\alpha)^{-2}\right]^{-1}.$$

For (18.4), the correlation is

$$R_{\alpha 1}\left[\sum_{i=0}^{\infty}(\alpha_1+i)^{-2}\right]^{1/2}\left[\sum_{i=0}^{\infty}(\alpha_2+i)^{-2}\right]^{-1/2}.$$

A generalized symmetric gamma distribution is obtained by replacing $\rho,\rho^2,\rho^3,\ldots$ in (18.3) by a sequence of nonnegative numbers $c_1,c_2,c_3,\ldots$ such that $\sum_{j=1}^{\infty} c_j^2$ converges. The function so obtained is (cf. (18.4))

$$(19)\quad f_{X_1,X_2}(x_1,x_2)=\prod_{j=1}^{2}[(1/\Gamma(\alpha))x_j^{\alpha-1}e^{-x_j}]\left[1+\sum_{j=1}^{\infty}c_jL_j^{\alpha-1}(x_1)L_j^{\alpha-1}(x_2)\right] \qquad (x_1,x_2>0).$$

Since

$$(20)\qquad \int_0^\infty x^{\alpha-1}e^{-x}L_j^{(\alpha-1)}(x)\,dx=0 \qquad (j\geq 1),$$

the function (19) satisfies the condition

$$\iint f(x_1,x_2)\,dx_1\,dx_2=1$$

for it to be a density function. For the other condition ($f(x_1,x_2)\geq 0$) to be satisfied, Sarmanov [61] showed that it is necessary and sufficient for $c_1,c_2,\ldots$ to be the moments of a random variable Y, for which

$$\Pr[0\leq Y<1]=1.$$

(See also Griffiths [19].)

It should be noted that first putting $\alpha=\frac{1}{2}$ and then replacing X_j by X_j^2 ($j=1,2$) so that Z_j has a unit normal distribution, we obtain an expansion in Hermite polynomials.

Krishnamoorthy and Parthasarathy [40], Miller et al. [48], and Zaharov et al. [75] have extended distributions of type (18) to the multivariate case ($m>2$). In [75] the authors consider the joint distribution of series of $\frac{1}{2}\chi_\nu^2$ statistics obtained sequentially by increasing the sample size, taking groups of observations at a time. They show that the limiting joint distribution of the first r variables $X_1,\ldots,X_r$, as $n_1,\ldots,n_r$ (the corresponding numbers of observations) tend to infinity in fixed ratios ($n_i/n_j=\rho_{ij}$) is

$$(21)\quad p_{\mathbf{X}}(\mathbf{x})=\frac{(x_1x_m/\lambda_1\lambda_m)^{(1/2)\nu-1}\exp\left[-\sum_{j=1}^{m}x_j/\lambda_j\right]}{K^{(1/2)\nu}\left(\prod_{i=1}^{m-1}b_j\right)^{(1/2)\nu}\Gamma(\frac{1}{2}\nu)\prod_{i=1}^{m}\lambda_j}\prod_{i=1}^{m-1}I_{(1/2)\nu-1}\left(2\sqrt{\frac{b_ix_ix_{i+1}}{\lambda_i\lambda_{i+1}}}\right),$$

where

$$K = \prod_{i=1}^{m-1} \left[\frac{1 - \rho_j^2 \rho_{j-1}^2}{1 - \rho_j^2} \right] \qquad (\rho_j = \rho_{j,j+1}; \rho_0 = 0),$$

$$b_j = \frac{\rho_j^2(1 - \rho_{j-1}^2)(1 - \rho_{j+1}^2)}{(1 - \rho_{j-1}^2\rho_j^2)(1 - \rho_j^2\rho_{j+1}^2)},$$

$$\lambda_j = \frac{(1 - \rho_{j-1}^2)(1 - \rho_j^2)}{1 - \rho_{j-1}^2\rho_j^2},$$

and $I(\cdot)$ is a modified Bessel function of the first kind, as defined in Chapter 1, Section 4.

This distribution has been generalized by Jensen [26] in a way now to be described. In Chapter 35 we have seen that if $\mathbf{X}' = (X_1, \ldots, X_p)$ has a multinormal distribution function with zero expected value vector and variance-covariance matrix $\mathbf{V}$, then each of the disjoint subsets $\mathbf{X}'_{(1)} = (X_1, \ldots, X_{p_1})$ $\mathbf{X}'_{(2)} = (X_{p_1+1}, \ldots, X_{p_1+p_2}), \ldots, \mathbf{X}'_{(m)} = (X_{p-p_m+1}, \ldots, X_p)$ has a multinormal distribution with zero expected value vector and variance-covariance matrices $\mathbf{V}_{11}, \mathbf{V}_{22}, \ldots, \mathbf{V}_{mm}$ respectively, where

$$\mathbf{V} = \begin{pmatrix} \mathbf{V}_{11} & \mathbf{V}_{12} & \cdots & \mathbf{V}_{1m} \\ \mathbf{V}_{21} & \mathbf{V}_{22} & \cdots & \mathbf{V}_{2m} \\ \cdot & \cdot & & \cdot \\ \cdot & \cdot & & \cdot \\ \cdot & \cdot & & \cdot \\ \mathbf{V}_{m1} & \mathbf{V}_{m2} & \cdots & \mathbf{V}_{mm} \end{pmatrix}$$

is partitioned into sets of $p_1, p_2, \ldots, p_m$ rows and columns. Given ν independent sets of $\mathbf{X}$'s, $\mathbf{X}_j = (X_{1j}, \ldots, X_{pj})$ $(j = 1, \ldots, m)$, the Wishart matrix

$$\mathbf{S} = \sum_{j=1}^{\nu} \mathbf{X}_j \mathbf{X}'_j$$

can be partitioned similarly, with elements $(\mathbf{S}_{kl})$. From Chapter 35 (Section 2), also, we know that the variables $Y_j = \text{tr}\mathbf{S}_{jj}\mathbf{V}_{jj}^{-1}$ $(j = 1, 2, \ldots, m)$ each have a χ^2 distribution—the number of degrees of freedom for Y_j is νp_j. The joint distribution of $Y_1, \ldots, Y_m$ can be regarded as a multivariate chi-squared or, more generally (allowing ν and the p_j's to take fractional values), a multivariate gamma distribution. As might be expected [from (21)] the mathematical expression of this distribution is rather complicated. Jensen [26], however, has shown that the *structure* of the density function is easily comprehended. The joint density function is

$$p_{\mathbf{Y}}(\mathbf{y}) = 2^m \sum_{h=0}^{\infty} \frac{\Gamma(\frac{1}{2}\nu + h)}{h!\Gamma(\frac{1}{2}\nu)} \sum_{j_1=0}^{h} \sum_{j_2=0}^{h} \cdots \sum_{j_m=0}^{h} A_{\mathbf{j}'} f_{\mathbf{j}'}(\tfrac{1}{2}\mathbf{y}; \tfrac{1}{2}\nu\mathbf{p}), \tag{22}$$

where

(i)
$$\mathbf{j}' = (j_1,\ldots,j_m);\ \mathbf{p}' = (p_1,\ldots,p_m);$$

(ii)
$$f_{\mathbf{j}'}(\mathbf{s};\boldsymbol{\theta}) = \prod_{h=1}^{m} \{\Gamma(\theta_h + j_h)\}^{-1}\left(-\frac{d}{ds_h}\right)^{j_h}[s_h^{\theta_h+j_h-1}e^{-s_h}];$$

and (iii) A_j is defined by the identities

$$[B(z)]^h \equiv \sum_{j_1=0}^{h}\sum_{j_2=0}^{h}\cdots\sum_{j_m=0}^{h}\left\{A_j \prod_{h=1}^{m} z_h^{j_h}\right\},$$

where
$$B(z) = 1 - \begin{vmatrix} \mathbf{I}_{p_1} & -z_1\mathbf{R}_{12} & -z_1\mathbf{R}_{13} & \cdots & -z_1\mathbf{R}_{1m} \\ -z_2\mathbf{R}_{21} & \mathbf{I}_{p_2} & -z_2\mathbf{R}_{23} & \cdots & -z_2\mathbf{R}_{2m} \\ -z_3\mathbf{R}_{31} & -z_3\mathbf{R}_{32} & \mathbf{I}_{p_3} & \cdots & -z_3\mathbf{R}_{3m} \\ \vdots & \vdots & \vdots & & \vdots \\ -z_m\mathbf{R}_{m1} & -z_m\mathbf{R}_{m2} & -z_m\mathbf{R}_{m3} & \cdots & \mathbf{I}_{p_m} \end{vmatrix}$$

and $\mathbf{R}_{gh} = \mathbf{V}_{gg}^{-1/2}\mathbf{V}_{gh}\mathbf{V}_{hh}^{-1/2}$ (symmetric positive definite square roots). (Note that $f_j(\mathbf{s};\boldsymbol{\theta})$ can be expressed as a multiple of a product of Laguerre polynomials.)

The characteristic function of distribution (22) is

(23)
$$E[\exp(i\mathbf{t}'\mathbf{Y})] = |\mathbf{I}_p - 2i\mathbf{D}(\mathbf{t})\mathbf{V}|^{-(1/2)\nu}$$

where

$$\mathbf{D}(\mathbf{t}) = \text{diag}(t_1\mathbf{V}_{11}^{-1},\ldots,t_m\mathbf{V}_{mm}^{-1})$$

is a "block-diagonal" matrix.

An alternative form to (23) is

(23)′
$$|\mathbf{I}_p - 2i\mathbf{D}(\mathbf{t})\mathbf{R}|^{-(1/2)\nu},$$

where

$$\mathbf{R} = \begin{pmatrix} \mathbf{I}_{p_1} & \mathbf{R}_{12} & \cdots & \mathbf{R}_{1m} \\ \mathbf{R}_{21} & \mathbf{I}_{p_2} & \cdots & \mathbf{R}_{2m} \\ \vdots & & & \\ \mathbf{R}_{m1} & \mathbf{R}_{m2} & \cdots & \mathbf{I}_{p_m} \end{pmatrix}.$$

The cumulant generating function is

$$\tfrac{1}{2}\nu\sum_{j=0}^{\infty} j^{-1}(2i)^j\text{tr}[\mathbf{D}(\mathbf{t})\mathbf{R}]^j.$$

From this we can find, for example,

$$\operatorname{cov}(Y_j, Y_h) = 2\nu \operatorname{tr}(\mathbf{R}_{jh}\mathbf{R}_{hj}). \tag{24}$$

Jensen [24] has also shown that

$$\Pr\left[\bigcap_{j=1}^{m}(Y_j \le c_j)\right] \le \prod_{j=1}^{m} \Pr[Y_j \le c_j]. \quad \text{(cf. equation (9))}. \tag{25}$$

4. Noncentral Multivariate Gamma Distributions

Each of the types of multivariate gamma distributions discussed in Sections 2 and 3 can be extended to noncentral cases in a natural fashion. Distributions of type I (Section 2) can be generalized by supposing each X_k $(k = 0,1,\ldots,m)$ to have a noncentral gamma distribution (as defined in Chapter 17). Since this means that the distribution of X_k is a mixture of (central) gamma distributions with Poisson weights, the joint distribution of $Y_j = X_0 + X_j$ $(j = 1,\ldots,m)$ will be a mixture of joint distributions of the kind described in Section 2, with weights that are products of Poisson weights.

For distribution of type II (see Section 3) we may suppose that the expected value vector of $\mathbf{X}_i' = (X_{i1},\ldots,X_{im})$ depends on i, though the other conditions (multinormality, homoscedasticity, independence of $\mathbf{X}_i'$ and $\mathbf{X}_j'$) remain satisfied. The resulting distribution is sometimes called a *biased generalized Rayleigh distribution*. The marginal distributions of $S_1,\ldots,S_m$ are then noncentral χ^2 distributions each with $(n - 1)$ degrees of freedom and noncentralities

$$\sum_{i=1}^{n}(\xi_{i1} - \bar{\xi}_1)^2,\ldots,\sum_{i=1}^{n}(\xi_{im} - \bar{\xi}_m)^2$$

respectively, where

$$E[X_{ij}] = \xi_{ij}; \qquad \bar{\xi}_j = n^{-1}\sum_{i=1}^{n}\xi_{ij}.$$

Derivation of explicit expressions for the joint distribution is difficult, even for $m = 2$. A particular case for general m with all elements ν^{ij} of $\mathbf{V}^{-1}$ zero except for $|i - j| \le 1$, has been worked at by Blumenson and Miller [3]. (Miller and Sackrowitz [49, eq. (2.3)] have obtained a fairly simple form for the *ratio* of a noncentral distribution with m dimensions to the central distribution with $(m + 1)$ dimensions.) The conditional distribution of X_{i1}, given $(X_{12},\ldots,X_{n2})$ is normal with expected value $\rho X_{i2} + \xi_{i1} - \rho\xi_{i2}$ and variance $(1 - \rho^2)$, where $\rho = \operatorname{corr}(X_{i1},X_{i2})$. Hence the conditional distribution of S_1, given $(X_{12},\ldots,X_{n2})$ is that of

$$\sum_{i=1}^{n}[\rho(X_{i2} - \bar{X}_{\cdot 2}) + (\xi_{i1} - \bar{\xi}_1) - \rho(\xi_{i2} - \bar{\xi}_2) + (U_i - \bar{U})\sqrt{1 - \rho^2}]^2,$$

where $U_1,\ldots,U_n$ are independent unit variables. This distribution is that of

$$(26)\quad (1-\rho^2)\times\Big(\text{noncentral }\chi^2\text{ with }(n-1)\text{ degrees of freedom and noncentrality parameter } (1-\rho^2)^{-1}\sum_{i=1}^{n}[\rho(X_{i2}-\bar{X}_{\cdot 2})+(\xi_{i1}-\bar{\xi}_1)-\rho(\xi_{i2}-\bar{\xi}_2)]^2\Big).$$

Unfortunately, the noncentrality is now not a function of S_2 only, as it was in the central case.

Jensen **[25]** has shown that the limiting joint distribution, as the noncentrality parameters tend to infinity, is multinormal. Zaharov et al. **[75]** have obtained a noncentral form of (21) (corresponding to a departure from specified values of multinomial cell probabilities $p_1,\ldots,p_{\nu+1}$). The ratio of the noncentral to the central density function is

$$\Gamma(\tfrac{1}{2}\nu)\exp(-\tfrac{1}{2}\theta)[g(x_m)]^{-(1/2)\nu+1}I_{(1/2)\nu-1}(2g(x_m)),$$

where $g(x_m)=[\tfrac{1}{2}\theta(1-\rho_{m-1}^2)x_m/\lambda_m]^{1/2}$, and θ is the noncentrality parameter.

5. Dirichlet Distributions and Generalizations

Suppose that $X_0,X_1,\ldots,X_m$ are independent random variables, with X_j distributed as χ^2 with ν_j degrees of freedom, for $j=0,1,\ldots,m$ (ν_j need not be an integer, though it must be greater than zero.) We seek the joint distribution of $Y_1,Y_2,\ldots,Y_m$ where

$$Y_j=X_j\left[\sum_{i=0}^{m}X_i\right]^{-1}\qquad(j=1,2,\ldots,m).$$

The joint probability density function of $X_0,X_1,\ldots,X_m$ is

$$(27)\quad p_{X_0,\ldots,X_m}(x_0,\ldots,x_m)=\left[\prod_{j=0}^{m}\Gamma(\tfrac{1}{2}\nu_j)\right]^{-1}2^{-(1/2)\sum_0^m\nu_j}\left[\prod_{j=0}^{m}x_j^{(1/2)\nu_j-1}\right]\times\exp\left[-\tfrac{1}{2}\sum_{j=0}^{m}x_j\right]\qquad(0\le x_j;j=1,\ldots,m).$$

Making the transformation to new variables $Y_0=\sum_{i=1}^{m}X_i,Y_1,Y_2,\ldots,Y_m$, we find

$$(28)\quad p_{Y_0,\ldots,Y_m}(y_0,\ldots,y_m)=\left[\prod_{j=0}^{m}\Gamma(\tfrac{1}{2}\nu_j)\right]^{-1}2^{-(1/2)\sum_0^m\nu_j}\times\left[\left\{y_0\left(1-\sum_{j=1}^{m}y_j\right)\right\}^{(1/2)\nu_0-1}\prod_{j=1}^{m}(y_0y_j)^{(1/2)\nu_j-1}\right]\exp[-\tfrac{1}{2}y_0].J$$

$$\left(0\le y_j,j=0,1,\ldots,m;\ \sum_{j=1}^{m}y_j\le 1\right),$$

where J is the Jacobian:

$$J = \frac{\partial(x_0,x_1,\ldots,x_m)}{\partial(y_0,y_1,\ldots,y_m)} = \begin{vmatrix} 1-\sum_{j=1}^m y_j & -y_0 & -y_0 & \cdots & -y_0 \\ y_1 & y_0 & 0 & \cdots & 0 \\ y_2 & 0 & y_0 & \cdots & 0 \\ \cdot & \cdot & \cdot & \cdots & \cdot \\ \cdot & \cdot & \cdot & \cdots & \cdot \\ \cdot & \cdot & \cdot & \cdots & \cdot \\ y_m & 0 & 0 & \cdots & y_0 \end{vmatrix} = y_0^{m-1}.$$

Formula (28) can be rearranged in the form

$$(28)' \quad p_{Y_0,Y_1,\ldots,Y_m}(y_0,y_1,\ldots,y_m) = \left[2^{(1/2)\sum_0^m \nu_j} \prod_{j=0}^m \Gamma(\tfrac{1}{2}\nu_j)\right]^{-1} \left[\prod_{j=1}^m y_j^{(1/2)\nu_j-1}\right]$$

$$\times\, y_0^{(1/2)\sum_0^m \nu_j - 1}\left(1-\sum_{j=1}^m y_j\right)^{(1/2)\nu_0-1} e^{-(1/2)y_0}$$

$$\left(y_j \geq 0; j = 0,1,\ldots,m; \sum_{j=1}^m y_j \leq 1\right).$$

Integrating out the variable y_0 we obtain the joint density of $Y_1, Y_2,\ldots,Y_m$:

$$(29) \quad p_{Y_1,\ldots,Y_m}(y_1,\ldots,y_m) = \frac{\Gamma\left(\tfrac{1}{2}\sum_{j=0}^m \nu_j\right)}{\prod_{j=0}^m \Gamma(\tfrac{1}{2}\nu_j)} \left[\prod_{j=i}^m y_j^{(1/2)\nu_j-1}\right]\left(1-\sum_{j=1}^m y_j\right)^{(1/2)\nu_0-1}$$

$$\left(y_j \geq 0; j = 1,\ldots,m; \sum_{j=1}^m y_j \leq 1\right).$$

Since (29) is a density function,

$$(30) \quad \iint\cdots\int\left[\prod_{j=1}^m y_j^{(1/2)\nu_j-1}\right]\left(1-\sum_{j=1}^m y_j\right)^{(1/2)\nu_0-1} dy_1\cdots dy_m = \frac{\prod_{j=0}^m \Gamma(\tfrac{1}{2}\nu_j)}{\Gamma\left(\tfrac{1}{2}\sum_{j=0}^m \nu_j\right)}$$

[integration being over the region $\omega(\mathbf{y})$ defined in (29)]. Formula (30) is a particular case of a multiple integral evaluated by Dirichlet. The name *Dirichlet distribution* has been given to the class of distributions (29). It is usual to replace $\frac{1}{2}\nu_j$ by θ_j $(j = 0,1,\ldots,m)$; the *standard Dirichlet* distribution with parameters $\theta_1, \ldots, \theta_m$, θ_0 has density function

$$(31) \quad p_{Y_1,\ldots,Y_m}(y_1,\ldots,y_m) = \frac{\Gamma\left(\sum_{j=0}^{m}\theta_j\right)}{\prod_{j=0}^{m}\Gamma(\theta_j)}\left(1-\sum_{j=1}^{m}y_j\right)^{\theta_0-1}\prod_{j=1}^{m}y_j^{\theta_j-1}$$

$$\left(0 \le y_j; j=1,\ldots,m; \sum_{j=1}^{m}y_j \le 1\right).$$

Tiao and Afonja [68] have given approximations to the probability integral

$$\Pr\left[\bigcap_{j=1}^{m}(Y_j \le a_j)\right] = \int_0^{a_m}\cdots\int_0^{a_1} p_{Y_1,\ldots,Y_m}(y_1,\ldots,y_m)\,dy_1\cdots dy_m$$

with $p_{Y_1,\ldots,Y_m}(y_1,\ldots,y_m)$ given by (29). It is clear, from our derivation of the Dirichlet distribution, that Y_j has a standard beta distribution with parameters $\theta_j, \sum_{i=0}^{m}\theta_i - \theta_j$. It is thus reasonable to regard the distribution as a *multivariate generalization* of the beta distribution. The mixed moments can be easily evaluated using (30). We have

$$(32) \quad \mu_{r_1,\ldots,r_m} = E\left[\prod_{j=1}^{m}y_j^{r_j}\right]$$

$$= \frac{\Gamma\left(\sum_0^m\theta_j\right)}{\sum_{j=0}^{m}\Gamma(\theta_j)}\iint_{\omega(\mathbf{y})}\cdots\int\left(1-\sum_{j=1}^{m}y_j\right)^{\theta_0-1}\prod_{j=1}^{m}y_j^{\theta_j+r_j-1}\,d\mathbf{y}$$

$$= \frac{\Gamma\left(\sum_{j=0}^{m}\theta_j\right)}{\prod_{j=0}^{m}\Gamma(\theta_j)}\frac{\prod_{j=0}^{m}\Gamma(\theta_j+r_j)}{\Gamma\left(\sum_{j=0}^{m}(\theta_j+r_j)\right)}$$

$$= \frac{\prod_{j=0}^{m}\theta_j^{[r_j]}}{\left\{\sum_{j=0}^{m}\theta_j\right\}^{\left[\sum_0^m r_j\right]}}.$$

In particular the covariance between X_i and X_j is

$$(33.1) \quad \frac{\theta_i\theta_j}{\Theta(\Theta+1)} - \frac{\theta_i\theta_j}{\Theta^2} = -\frac{\theta_i\theta_j}{\Theta^2(\Theta+1)}$$

where $\Theta = \sum_{j=0}^{m}\theta_j$. Since

$$(33.2) \quad E[Y_i] = \theta_i/\Theta \quad \text{and} \quad \operatorname{var}(Y_i) = \frac{\theta_i(\Theta-\theta_i)}{\Theta^2(\Theta+1)},$$

then

$$\text{(33.3)} \qquad \operatorname{corr}(Y_i,Y_j) = -\sqrt{\frac{\theta_i\theta_j}{(\Theta - \theta_i)(\Theta - \theta_j)}}.$$

It can be seen, either by integrating out $y_{s+1},\ldots,y_m$ from (31) or by considering the derivation of the distribution given at the beginning of this section, that the variables $Y_1, Y_2,\ldots,Y_s$ $(s < m)$ have a standard joint Dirichlet distribution with parameters $\theta_1,\theta_2,\ldots,\theta_s;\Theta - \sum_{j=1}^{s}\theta_j$.

It immediately follows, that the conditional joint distribution of

$$Y_j' = Y_j\left[1 - \sum_{i=1}^{s} Y_i\right]^{-1} \qquad (j = s + 1,\ldots,m),$$

given $Y_1,\ldots,Y_s$, is a standard Dirichlet distribution with parameters $\theta_{s+1},\ldots,\theta_m,\theta_0$. (In particular, the distribution of Y_j', given $Y_1,\ldots,Y_s$, is standard beta with parameters $\theta_j, \sum_{i=s+1}^{m}\theta_i + \theta_0 - \theta_j$.)

This is in fact a characterization of the Dirichlet distribution (provided that the Y's must be positive random variables with continuous density functions, and $\sum_{j=1}^{m} Y_j \leq 1$), given by Darroch and Ratcliff [9].

An orthonormal expansion (see Chapter 34, Section 4) of a two-dimensional Dirichlet distribution, with Jacobi polynomials as the orthonormal functions, has been described by Lee [43].

The use of a Dirichlet distribution as an approximation to a multinomial distribution (Johnson [31]) has been discussed in Chapter 11, Section 2.4.

From the structure of the Dirichlet distribution, as described in this Section, it follows (see Chapter 24, Section 2) that the random variables

$$Z_j = Y_j\left[\sum_{i=j}^{m} Y_i\right]^{-1} \qquad (j = 1,2,\ldots,m)$$

are mutually independent standard beta variables, with parameters θ_j, $\sum_{i=j+1}^{m}\theta_i$ respectively. There are clearly relations among these parameters.

If we now let these parameters have *general* values, so that Z_j is distributed as a standard beta variable with parameters a_j,b_j, the corresponding Y's have a *generalized Dirichlet distribution* described by Connor and Mosimann [7].

The joint density function is (replacing Y's by X's)

$$\text{(34)} \quad p_{\mathbf{X}}(\mathbf{x}) = \left(\prod_{j=1}^{m} B(a_j,b_j)\right)^{-1}\left(1 - \sum_{j=1}^{m} x_j\right)^{b_m-1} \times \prod_{j=1}^{m}\left[x_j^{a_j-1}\left(1 - \sum_{i=1}^{j-1} x_i\right)^{b_{j-1}+(a_j+b\ )}\right] \qquad \left(0 \leq x_j;\sum_{j=1}^{m} x_j \leq 1\right).$$

The lower moments of this distribution are

$$(35.1)\qquad E[X_j] = \frac{a_j}{a_j+b_j}\prod_{i=1}^{j-1}\frac{b_i+1}{a_i+b_i};$$

$$(35.2)\qquad \text{var}(X_j) = E[X_j]\left\{\frac{a_j+1}{a_j+b_j+1}\prod_{i=1}^{j-1}\frac{b_i+1}{a_i+b_i+1} - E[X_j]\right\};$$

$$(35.3)\qquad \text{cov}(X_j,X_k) = E[X_k]\left\{\frac{a_j}{a_j+b_j+1}\prod_{i=1}^{j-1}\frac{b_i+1}{a_i+b_i+1} - E[X_j]\right\}\qquad (j > k).$$

If $b_{j-1} = a_j + b_j$ $(j = 1,2,\ldots,m)$, we obtain the Dirichlet distribution. Note that in general the marginal distributions corresponding to (34) (except that of X_1) are *not* beta distributions.

A different kind of generalization can be obtained (Craiu and Craiu [8]) by supposing $X_0,X_1,\ldots,X_m$, at the beginning of Section 5, to have *generalized* gamma distribution (as in Section 8.4 of Chapter 17).

Other types of generalization are discussed in the next section.

6. Generalized Multivariate Beta Distribution

There are several classes of distributions called by this name. The Dirichlet distribution may be generalized in the following way (Olkin and Rubin [58]).

Suppose that $S_{(0)},S_{(1)},\ldots,S_{(g)}$ are independent $m \times m$ matrices, with $S_{(j)}$ having the Wishart distribution $W_m(\nu_j\mathbf{S};I)$ $(j = 0,1,\ldots,g)$. Then the joint distribution of the $\frac{1}{2}gm(m+1)$ statistics, which are elements of the g symmetrical matrices

$$\mathbf{Y}_j = \left(\sum_{i=0}^{g}\mathbf{S}_{(i)}\right)^{-1/2}\mathbf{S}_{(j)}\left(\sum_{i=0}^{g}\mathbf{S}_{(i)}\right)^{-1/2}\qquad (j = 1,2,\ldots,g)$$

$\left(\left(\sum_{i=0}^{g}\mathbf{S}_{(i)}\right)^{1/2}\right.$ is a lower triangular matrix$\Big)$, has density function

$$(36)\qquad p_{\mathbf{Y}_1,\ldots,\mathbf{Y}_g}(\mathbf{y}_1,\ldots,\mathbf{y}_g) = \frac{\prod_{j=0}^{g}K(\nu_j;\mathbf{I})}{K(\nu;\mathbf{I})}\left(\prod_{j=1}^{g}|\mathbf{y}_j|^{\frac{1}{2}(\nu_j-m-1)}\right)\left|\mathbf{I}-\sum_{j=1}^{g}\mathbf{y}_j\right|^{\frac{1}{2}(\nu_0-m-1)}$$

for $\mathbf{y}_1,\ldots,\mathbf{y}_g$, $\mathbf{I}-\sum_{j=1}^{g}\mathbf{y}_j$ each positive definite, with $\nu = \sum_{j=0}^{g}\nu_j$ and $K(\nu_j;\mathbf{I})$

defined by (11) of Chapter 38, so that

$$\prod_{j=0}^{g} K(\nu_j;\mathbf{I})/K(\nu,\mathbf{I}) = \Gamma_m(\tfrac{1}{2}\nu)\left[\prod_{j=0}^{g}\Gamma_m(\tfrac{1}{2}\nu_j)\right]^{-1} \qquad (\nu_j \geq m).$$

(Putting $g = 1$ we obtain a multivariate beta distribution. See Eq. 12 of Chapter 39.)

We further note that

$$\mathbf{Y}_j = \left(\mathbf{I} + \sum_{j=1}^{g}\mathbf{Z}_j\right)^{-1/2}\mathbf{Z}_j\left(\mathbf{I} + \sum_{j=1}^{g}\mathbf{Z}_j\right)^{-1/2} \qquad (j = 1,\ldots,g),$$

with

$$\mathbf{Z}_j = \mathbf{S}_{(0)}^{-1/2}\mathbf{S}_j\mathbf{S}_{(0)}^{-1/2} \qquad (j = 1,\ldots,g),$$

also have the joint density function (36).

We note, too, that (36) holds whether symmetrical or triangular square roots are taken. (It is assumed that the square root has positive diagonal elements.)

There are cases when the definition of square root makes some difference to the distribution. Formula (36) itself applies to Wishart matrices with *any* common variance-covariance matrix if the symmetrical square root is used, but not if a triangular square root is used. If $\mathbf{S}_0$ has variance covariance matrix $\mathbf{V}_0$ and $\mathbf{S}_1 \cdots \mathbf{S}_g$ each have the same variance-covariance matrix $\mathbf{V}$, we have a form of "noncentral" multivariate beta distribution. The density function has been given by de Waal [72].

In the same paper, Waal showed that the "multivariate beta I" density (of the $\frac{1}{2}m(m+1)$ different elements of a $m \times m$ symmetrical matrix $\mathbf{Y}$)

$$(37.1) \quad \frac{\Gamma_m(a+b)}{\Gamma_m(a)\Gamma_m(b)}|\mathbf{Y}|^{a-(1/2)(m+1)}|\mathbf{I}-\mathbf{Y}|^{b-(1/2)(m+1)}$$

$$(a,b > \tfrac{1}{2}(m-1); 0 < \mathbf{Y} < \mathbf{I})$$

can be expressed as a product of univariate beta and Dirichlet densities, and that the "multivariate beta II" (inverted "multivariate beta") density

$$(37.2) \quad \frac{\Gamma_m(a+b)}{\Gamma_m(a)\Gamma_m(b)}|\mathbf{Y}|^{a-(1/2)(m+1)}|\mathbf{I}+\mathbf{Y}|^{-(a+b)} \qquad (a,b > \tfrac{1}{2}(m-1); \mathbf{Y} > 0)$$

can be expressed as a product of univariate inverted beta and inverted Dirichlet densities.

Mitra [50] has shown that for any fixed $m \times 1$ vector $\mathbf{b}$ ($\neq \mathbf{0}$), the ratios $\mathbf{b}'\mathbf{Y}_k\mathbf{b}/\mathbf{b}'\mathbf{b}$ and $\mathbf{b}'\mathbf{b}/\mathbf{b}'\mathbf{Y}_k^{-1}\mathbf{b}$ have standard beta distributions with parameters $\frac{1}{2}\nu_k, \frac{1}{2}\left(\sum_{j=0}^{g}\nu_j - \nu_k\right)$ and $\frac{1}{2}(\nu_k - m + 1), \frac{1}{2}\left(\sum_{j=0}^{g}\nu_j - \nu_k\right)$ respectively. Furthermore, if $\mathbf{S}_{(g+1)}$ has an independent Wishart distribution with degrees of freedom $\sum_{j=0}^{g} \nu_j$, then $\mathbf{S}_{(g+1)}^{1/2}\mathbf{Y}_k(\mathbf{S}_{(g+1)}^{1/2})'$ and $\mathbf{S}_{(g+1)}^{1/2}(\mathbf{I}-\mathbf{Y}_k)(\mathbf{S}_{(g+1)}^{1/2})'$ also have Wishart distributions with the same variance-covariance matrix as $\mathbf{S}_{(g+1)}$ and degrees of freedom ν_k, and are mutually independent.

Also, if $\mathbf{Y}_k^*, \mathbf{Y}_k^{**}$ are independently distributed as $\mathbf{Y}_k$ with (in an obvious notation) $\nu_k^* = \sum_{j=0}^{g} \nu_j^{**}$, then $\mathbf{Y}_k^{*1/2}\mathbf{Y}_k^{**}(\mathbf{Y}_k^{*1/2})'$ has a distribution of the same form with ν_k replaced by ν_k^{**} *and* $\sum_{j=0}^{g} \nu_j$ by $\sum_{j=0}^{g} \nu_j^* - \nu_k^{**}$. (Mitra takes the square roots to be lower triangular matrices.) Khatri [33] gives a different approach to and some extensions of these results.

A corresponding generalization of the multivariate inverted beta distribution (see Section 7), also due to Olkin and Rubin [58], is obtained as the joint distribution of the $\frac{1}{2}gm(m+1)$ statistics which are elements of

$$\mathbf{Y}_{(j)} = \mathbf{S}_{(0)}^{-1/2}\mathbf{S}_{(j)}\mathbf{S}_{(0)}^{-1/2} \qquad (j = 1,2,\ldots,g), \tag{38}$$

where symmetrical square roots are used.

This has the density function

$$p_{\mathbf{Y}_{(1)},\ldots,\mathbf{Y}_{(g)}}(\mathbf{y}_1,\ldots,\mathbf{y}_g) = \frac{\prod_{j=0}^{g}\Gamma_m(\frac{1}{2}\nu_j)}{\Gamma_m(\frac{1}{2}\nu)}\left|\mathbf{I}+\sum_{j=1}^{g}\mathbf{y}_j\right|^{-\frac{1}{2}(\nu-m-1)}\prod_{j=1}^{g}|\mathbf{y}_j|^{\frac{1}{2}(\nu_j-m-1)}, \tag{39}$$

where $\nu = \sum_{j=1}^{g} \nu_j$.

If $\mathbf{S}_{(0)}^{1/2}$ is replaced by the lower triangular matrix (with positive diagonal elements) $\mathbf{T}_0$ such that $\mathbf{S}_{(0)} = \mathbf{T}_0\mathbf{T}_0'$ (see Chapter 38, Section 2), it is found that the joint distribution of the elements of

$$\mathbf{Y}_{(j)} = \mathbf{T}_0^{-1}\mathbf{S}_{(j)}\mathbf{T}_0'^{-1} \qquad (j = 1,2,\ldots,g) \tag{40}$$

has the density function

$$p_{\mathbf{Y}_{(1)},\ldots,\mathbf{Y}_{(g)}}(\mathbf{y}_1,\ldots,\mathbf{y}_g) = \frac{\prod_{j=0}^{g}\Gamma_m(\frac{1}{2}\nu_j)}{\Gamma_m(\frac{1}{2}\nu)}\left|\mathbf{I}+\sum_{j=1}^{g}\mathbf{y}_j\right|^{-\frac{1}{2}(\nu-m-1)}\left[\prod_{j=1}^{m}\left|\left(\mathbf{I}+\sum_{j=1}^{g}\mathbf{y}_j\right)^{[i]}\right|\right], \tag{41}$$

where, in this formula, $\mathbf{A}^{[i]}$ denotes the leading minor composed of the first i rows and i columns of $\mathbf{A}$. Tan [67] calls (36) and (41) generalized multivariate beta densities I and II respectively.

Related distributions have been described in Section 2 of Chapter 39.

Complex analogs of these distributions are discussed systematically in Tan [66].

Mitra [51] has considered the distribution of $\mathbf{T} = \mathbf{S}/(\text{tr } \mathbf{V}^{-1}\mathbf{S})$ and shows that the joint distribution of the $\{\frac{1}{2}m(m+1)-1\}$ distinct elements of $\mathbf{T}$, excluding t_{mm}, is (for $\nu \geq m$)

$$(42) \qquad p_{\mathbf{T}}(\mathbf{t}) = \frac{\Gamma(\frac{1}{2}\nu m)}{\sigma^{mm}\Gamma_m(\frac{1}{2}\nu)} \cdot \frac{|\mathbf{t}|^{\frac{1}{2}(\nu-j-1)}}{|\mathbf{V}|^{(1/2)\nu}} \qquad (\mathbf{t} > 0; \text{tr } \mathbf{V}^{-1}\mathbf{t} = 1),$$

where σ^{mm} is the lower right-hand diagonal element of $\mathbf{V}^{-1}$.

Note that if $\mathbf{LVL}' = \mathbf{I}$ ($\mathbf{L}$ being a $m \times m$ matrix), then the first $(m-1)$ diagonal elements of $\mathbf{LTL}'$ have a joint standard Dirichlet distribution with parameters $\frac{1}{2}\nu,\frac{1}{2}\nu,\ldots,\frac{1}{2}\nu;\frac{1}{2}\nu$.

7. Multivariate Inverted Beta (Inverted Dirichlet) Distribution

If $X_0,X_1,\ldots,X_k$ are independent random variables, with X_j distributed as χ^2 with ν_j degrees of freedom $(j = 0,1,\ldots,k)$ then the joint distribution of

$$Y_j = X_j/X_0 \qquad (j = 1,\ldots,k)$$

has the density function

$$(43) \quad p_{Y_1,\ldots,Y_k}(y_1,\ldots,y_k) = \frac{\Gamma(\frac{1}{2}\nu)}{\prod_{j=0}^{k}\Gamma(\frac{1}{2}\nu_j)} \cdot \frac{\prod_{j=1}^{k} y_j^{(1/2)\nu_j-1}}{\left(1+\sum_{j=1}^{k} y_j\right)^{(1/2)\nu}}$$

$$(0 < y_j; j = 1,2,\ldots,m)$$

with $\nu = \sum_{j=0}^{k} \nu_j$.

Since (43) is a probability density function

$$\int_0^\infty \cdots \int_0^\infty \left(1+\sum_{j=1}^{k} y_j\right)^{-(1/2)\nu} \prod_{j=1}^{k} y_j^{(1/2)\nu_j-1}\, dy_1 \cdots dy_k = \frac{\prod_{j=0}^{k}\Gamma(\frac{1}{2}\nu_j)}{\Gamma(\frac{1}{2}\nu)}.$$

Hence, provided that, $\sum_{j=1}^{k} r_j < \frac{1}{2}\nu$,

$$(44) \qquad \mu'_{r_1,r_2,\ldots,r_k} = E\left[\prod_{j=1}^{k} Y_j^{r_j}\right] = \frac{\Gamma(\frac{1}{2}\nu - r)}{\Gamma(\frac{1}{2}\nu)} \prod_{j=1}^{k} \frac{\Gamma(\frac{1}{2}\nu_j + r_j)}{\Gamma(\frac{1}{2}\nu_j)}$$

$$= \prod_{j=1}^{k} (\tfrac{1}{2}\nu_j)^{[r_j]}/(\tfrac{1}{2}\nu - 1)^{(r)},$$

if $r_1,r_2,\ldots,r_k$ are positive integers, where $r = \sum_{j=1}^{k} r_j$, $M^{[N]} = M(M+1)\cdots(M+N-1)$, and $M^{(N)} = M(M-1)\cdots(M-N+1)$. Formula (44) can also be obtained by noting that

$$E\left[\prod_{j=1}^{k} Y_j^{r_j}\right] = E\left[X_0^{-r} \prod_{j=1}^{k} X_j^{r_j}\right] = E[X_0^{-r}] \prod_{j=1}^{k} E[X_j^{r_j}].$$

If $\frac{1}{2}\nu_j$, in (43), is replaced by θ_j $(j = 0,\ldots,k)$, we obtain the *standard inverted Dirichlet distribution* (Tiao and Guttman [69])

$$(45) \qquad p(y_1,\ldots,y_k) = \frac{\Gamma\left(\sum_0^k \theta_j\right)}{\prod_{j=0}^{k} \Gamma(\theta_j)} \frac{\prod_{j=1}^{k} y_j^{\theta_j - 1}}{\left(1 + \sum_{j=1}^{k} y_j\right)^{(1/2)\sum_0^k \theta_j}} \qquad (0 < y_j).$$

Here $\theta_j > 0$ for all j, but the θ_j's need not be integers or integers plus $\frac{1}{2}$ (as perhaps implied by the derivation from χ^2). The distribution (45) can be obtained by supposing X_j to have a standard gamma distribution with parameter θ_j.

Note that $Y_j/Y_{j'} = X_j/X_{j'}$ so the distribution of this ratio is that of the ratio of two independent gamma variables (see Chapter 26). Also, since the conditional distribution of X_0, given that $X_j/X_0 = y_j$, is that of $(1 + y_j)^{-1} \times$ (standard gamma variable with parameter $(\theta_0 + \theta_j)$), the conditional distribution of $Y_{j'}$, given that $Y_j = y_j$, is that of $(1 + y_j) \times$ (ratio of two independent standard gamma variables with parameters $\theta_{j'}, \theta_0 + \theta_j$). Hence

$$(46.1) \quad E[Y_{j'} \mid Y_j = y_j] = (1 + y_j)\theta_{j'}(\theta_0 + \theta_j - 1)^{-1}, \qquad (\theta_0 + \theta_j > 1)$$

$$(46.2) \quad \operatorname{var}(Y_{j'} \mid Y_j = y_j) = (1 - y_j)^2\theta_{j'}(\theta_0 + \theta_j + \theta_{j'} - 1)(\theta_0 + \theta_j - 1)^{-2}(\theta_0 + \theta_j - 2)^{-1}$$

Also,

$$(46.3) \quad \left\{\begin{aligned} \operatorname{cov}(Y_j, Y_{j'}) &= \theta_j\theta_{j'}(\theta_0 - 1)^{-2}(\theta_0 - 2)^{-1} \\ \operatorname{corr}(Y_j, Y_{j'}) &= [\theta_j\theta_{j'}(\theta_0 + \theta_j - 1)^{-1}(\theta_0 + \theta_{j'} - 1)^{-1}]^{1/2} \end{aligned}\right\} \qquad (\theta_0 > 2).$$

From the structure of the inverted Dirichlet distribution we see that the conditional distribution of $Y_1,\ldots,Y_m$ given $X_0 = x_0$ is simply the product of independent $x_0^{-1}\chi^2_{\nu_j}$ densities, so that

$$(47) \quad p_{Y_1,\ldots,Y_m|X_0}(y_1,\ldots,y_m \mid x_0) = \prod_{j=1}^{m} [(\tfrac{1}{2}x_0)^{(1/2)\nu_j}\{\Gamma(\tfrac{1}{2}\nu_j)\}^{-1} y_j^{(1/2)\nu_j - 1} e^{-(1/2)x_0 y_j}]$$

$$\left(x_0 > 0; y_j > 0; \sum_1^m y_j = 1\right)$$

and

$$p_{X_0,Y_1,\ldots,Y_m}(x_0,y_1,\ldots,y_m) = [\prod \{\Gamma(\tfrac{1}{2}\nu_j)\}^{-1}]x_0^{(1/2)\sum_0^m \nu_j-1}\left[\prod_{j=1}^m y_j^{(1/2)\nu_j-1}\right] \times \exp\left[-\tfrac{1}{2}x_0\left(1+\sum_{j=1}^m y_j\right)\right]$$

$$\left(x_0 > 0; y_j > 0; \sum_1^m y_j < 1\right).$$

This is termed by Roux [60] a *Dirichlet-gamma* distribution. Roux's result, quoted in Chapter 34, Section 6, shows that this is the *only* joint distribution of "multivariate exponential-type" [Chapter 34, equation (30)′] for which $Y_1,\ldots,Y_m$ have joint density function (43) and their conditional distribution given $X_0 = x_0$ is (47).

Roux [60a] has shown that a very wide range of distributions, including various forms of multivariate beta, and also many of the distributions encountered in Chapters 38 and 39 can be expressed in terms of generalized hypergeometric functions (see equations (31) of Chapter 38).

8. Multivariate *F* Distributions

If, in Section 7, we had considered the joint distribution of $F_j = (X_j/\nu_j)(X_0/\nu_0)^{-1}$ $(j = 1,\ldots,m)$ we would have obtained a *multivariate F distribution.* This is the normal null hypothesis joint distribution of the mean square ratios in an analysis of variance table in which there is a residual sum of squares X_0, with ν_0 degrees of freedom, and m independent "effect" sums of squares $X_1,\ldots,X_m$, with $\nu_1,\ldots,\nu_m$ degrees of freedom respectively. The joint density function is

$$(48)\quad p_{F_1,\ldots,F_m}(f_1,\ldots,f_m) = \frac{\Gamma(\tfrac{1}{2}\nu)\prod_{j=0}^m \nu_j^{(1/2)\nu_j}}{\prod_{j=0}^m \Gamma(\tfrac{1}{2}\nu_j)} \frac{\prod_{j=1}^m f_j^{(1/2)\nu_j-1}}{\left(\nu_0+\sum_{j=1}^m \nu_j f_j\right)^{(1/2)\nu}} \qquad (0 < f_j)$$

with $\nu = \sum_{j=0}^m \nu_j$. (See, for example, Finney [12].)

Tables of upper percentage points of $\max(F_1,\ldots,F_m)$ for the special case $\nu_1 = \nu_2 = \cdots = \nu_m = \nu$ were given by Finney [15]. More extensive tables have been published subsequently, including tables of upper 10, 5, 2.5, and 1% points, for $\nu_0 = 1(1)19$; $\nu = 5(1)45$; $m = 2(1)12$ by Armitage and Krishnaiah [1]. (For 1% point, $\nu = 5$ is omitted.)

Kimball [35] has shown that

$$\Pr[(F_1 \le f_1) \cap (F_2 \le f_2)] \ge \Pr[F_1 \le f_1]\Pr[F_2 \le f_2].$$

Olkin [57] showed that if $\nu_1 = \nu_2$ and $f_1 = f_2 = f$, then

$$\Pr[(F_1 \le f) \cap (F_2 \le f)] \ge 2\Pr[F_1 \le f] - \Pr[F_1 \le 2f].$$

Hewett and Bulgren [22] have shown that if $\nu_1 = \nu_2 = \cdots = \nu_m = \nu$

$$\Pr\left[\bigcap_{j=1}^{m} (a < F_j < b)\right] \geq \{\Pr[a < F_{\nu,\nu_0} < b]\}^m. \tag{49}$$

(F_{ν,ν_0} as defined in Chapter 26.) Numerical studies show that the right-hand side of (49) is quite a good approximation to the left when $m = 2$. Accuracy increases as ν_0 increases, but decreases as ν increases. (Error is less than 0.01 for $\nu = 2, \nu_0 > 4$ and for $\nu < 20, \nu_0 = 40$, for example.)

A *generalized* multivariate F distribution with $\nu_2\nu_0$ degrees of freedom may be defined (Krishnaiah [36], Krishnaiah and Armitage [37]) as the joint distribution of

$$Z_j = (Y_j/\nu)(Y_0/\nu_0)^{-1} \qquad (j = 1,2,\ldots,m),$$

where $Y = (Y_1, Y_2, \ldots, Y_m)$ has a multivariate χ^2 distribution (as defined by Krishnaiah and Rao [39]), with ν degrees of freedom, and Y_0 is independent of $\mathbf{Y}$, and is distributed as χ^2 with ν_0 degrees of freedom.

Clearly the marginal distributions (of $Z_1, \ldots, Z_m$) are each F_{ν_j,ν_0} distributions. Krishnaiah [36] gives the following formula for the joint density function:

$$p_{\mathbf{Z}}(\mathbf{z}) = \sum_{j=0}^{\infty} \frac{\Gamma(\frac{1}{2}\nu + j)}{j!\Gamma(\frac{1}{2}\nu)} \sum_{a_1}^{j}{}^{*} \cdots \sum_{a_m}^{j}{}^{*} K(a_1,\ldots,a_m;\mathbf{R}) \tag{50}$$

$$\times \sum_{j_1=0}^{a_1} \cdots \sum_{j_m=0}^{a_m} \frac{(-1)^{\sum_i j_i} \prod_{i=1}^{m} \binom{a_i}{j_i}}{\prod_{i=1}^{m} (a_i + \frac{1}{2}\nu - j_i - 1)!}$$

$$\times \frac{(\nu/\nu_0)^{(1/2)m\nu + \sum_i (a_i - j_i)} \Gamma\left(\sum_i (a_i - j_i) + \frac{1}{2}(\nu_0 + m\nu)\right)}{\Gamma(\frac{1}{2}\nu_0)}$$

$$\times \frac{\prod_{k=1}^{m} z_k^{(1/2)\nu_0 - 1 + a_k - j_k}}{\left[1 + (\nu/\nu_0)\sum_{k=1}^{m} z_k\right]^{\sum_i (a_i - j_i) + \frac{1}{2}(\nu_0 + m\nu)}} \qquad (0 < z_k; k = 1,\ldots,m),$$

where $\sum^* \cdots \sum^*$ denotes summation with at least two nonzero a's and $K(a_1,\ldots,a_m;\mathbf{R})$ is defined by

$$\sum_{a_1}^{r}{}^{*} \cdots \sum_{a_m}^{r}{}^{*} K(a_1,\ldots,a_m;\mathbf{R}) y_1^{a_1} \cdots y_m^{a_m}$$

$$\equiv \left[\sum_{i<j}\sum C_{ij} y_i y_j + \sum_{i<j<k}\sum\sum C_{ijk} y_i y_j y_k + \cdots + C_{12\cdots m} y_1 \cdots y_m\right]^r,$$

with

$$C_{12\cdots r} = (-1)^r \begin{vmatrix} 0 & \rho_{12} & \cdots & \rho_{1r} \\ \rho_{12} & 0 & \cdots & \rho_{2r} \\ \cdot & & & \\ \cdot & & & \\ \cdot & & & \\ \rho_{1r} & \rho_{2r} & \cdots & 0 \end{vmatrix}.$$

By considering the joint distribution of

$$(51) \qquad F_j = [Y_j(\nu p_j)^{-1}]/[Y_0/\nu_0] \qquad (j = 1,\ldots,m),$$

where $Y_1,\ldots,Y_m$ have the joint density function (22), and Y_0, independent of $Y_1,\ldots,Y_m$, has a $\chi^2_{\nu_0}$ distribution, Jensen **[26]** has obtained a more generalized multivariate F distribution. An inequality analogous to (25) also holds for this distribution.

For the special case $m = 2$, when Y_1, Y_2 have the joint distribution (12) with $\nu = (n - 1)$, we have from (12)

$$\Pr\left[\bigcap_{j=1}^{2}(Z_j \le z_j)\right] = \sum_{t=0}^{\infty} c_t \Pr\left[\bigcap_{j=1}^{2}(F_j^{(t)} \le (1 + 2t\nu^{-1})^{-1} z_j/(1 - \rho^2))\right]$$

where $F_1^{(t)}, F_2^{(t)}$ have the joint distribution (48) with $m = 2$, $\nu_1 = \nu_2 = \nu + 2t$ (and c_t's are given in (12)). Bulgren **[5]** has shown that if ν is even

$$\Pr\left[\bigcap_{j=1}^{2}(Z_j \le z_j)\right]$$
$$= (1 - \rho^2)^{(1/2)\nu} \sum_{j=0}^{\infty} \frac{\Gamma(\frac{1}{2}\nu + j)}{\Gamma(\frac{1}{2}\nu)} \frac{\rho^{2j}}{j!}\Bigg[I_{d_2/(1+d_2)}(\tfrac{1}{2}\nu + j, \tfrac{1}{2}\nu_0)$$
$$- (1 + d_1)^{-(1/2)\nu_0} \sum_{s=0}^{(1/2)\nu + j - 1} \frac{\frac{1}{2}\nu_0 + s}{\Gamma(\frac{1}{2}\nu)s!}\left(\frac{d_1}{1 + d_1}\right)^{s} I_{d_2/(1+d_1+d_2)}(\tfrac{1}{2}\nu + j, \tfrac{1}{2}\nu_0 + s)\Bigg],$$

where $d_j = (\nu/\nu_0)z_j/(1 - \rho^2) \qquad (j = 1,2)$.

Bulgren **[5]** also suggested the approximation

$$\Pr\left[\bigcap_{j=1}^{2}(Z_j \le z_j)\right] \doteqdot \prod_{j=1}^{2} \Pr[F_{\nu,\nu_0} \le z_j/(1 - \rho^2)],$$

but numerical examples did not exhibit good accuracy. In view of the remark following (16), the approximation

$$\Pr\left[\bigcap_{j=1}^{2}(Z_j \le z_j)\right] \doteqdot \prod_{j=1}^{2} \Pr[F_{\nu',\nu_0} \le z_j/(1 - 2\rho^2\nu^{-1})]$$

with $\nu' = (\nu - 2\rho^2)/(1 - \rho^2)$ might be considered.

Hewett and Bulgren [22] have shown that

$$\Pr\left[\bigcap_{j=1}^{2}(a \le Z_j \le b)\right] \ge \{\Pr[a \le F_{\nu,\nu_0} \le b]\}^2.$$

This inequality does not give quite as close a bound when $\rho \neq 0$ as that indicated in the remarks following (49).

9. Whittle Distribution

Martin [45] has used the multivariate beta distribution as a compounding distribution for the parameters of a discrete multivariate distribution called the *Whittle distribution.* Since we did not include this distribution in Chapter 11, we give a brief summary here. This is the distribution of the number of transitions (F_{ij}) from state i to state j among n consecutive transitions in a Markov chain with N states and transition matrix $\mathbf{P} = (p_{ij})$.

The probability of obtaining a set of values $\mathbf{F}$ $(= (f_{ij})) = \mathbf{f}$ (where $\mathbf{F}$,$\mathbf{f}$ are $N \times N$ matrices) depends on the initial state, say u, of the chain and is equal to

$$(52) \qquad |F^*_{\mathbf{vu}}| \prod_{i=1}^{N}(f_{i.}!) \prod_{i=1}^{N}\prod_{j=1}^{N}(P_{ij}^{f_{ij}}/f_{ij}!),$$

with

$$f_{i.} = \sum_{j=1}^{N} f_{ij}, \qquad f_{.j} = \sum_{i=1}^{N} f_{ij},$$

where (a) $\mathbf{v}$ is the unique solution of the equations

$$f_{i.} - f_{.i} = \delta_{iu} - \delta_{iv} \qquad (i = 1,\dots,N)$$

(δ_{ij} is a Kronecker delta), (b) $F^*_{\mathbf{vu}}$ is the (v,u)th minor in the $N \times N$ matrix with (i,j)th element equal to

$$\begin{cases} \delta_{ij} - f_{ij}/f_{i.} & \text{if } f_{i.} > 0, \\ \delta_{ij} & \text{if } f_{i.} = 0. \end{cases}$$

Equation (52) defines the *Whittle distribution.*

The expected value of F_{ij} is

$$(53) \qquad p_{ij} \times ((u,i)\text{th element of } (\mathbf{I} + \mathbf{P} + \mathbf{P}^2 + \cdots + \mathbf{P}^{n-1}))$$

Martin [45] gives formulas for the variances and covariances of the F's.

The distribution obtained by compounding each set of p_{ij} $(j = 1,\dots,N)$ by an independent Dirichlet distribution is termed by Martin a *beta-Whittle distribution.*

REFERENCES

[1] Armitage, J. V. and Krishnaiah, P. R. (1964). *Tables for Studentized Largest Chi-Square and Their Applications*, Report ARL 64-188, Aerospace Research Laboratories Wright-Patterson Air Force Base, Ohio.

[2] Bens, G. B. and Jensen, D. R. (1967). *Percentage Points of the Bonferroni Chi-Square Statistics*, Technical Report No. 3, Department of Statistics, Virginia Polytechnic Institute, Blacksburg.

[3] Blumenson. L. E. and Miller, K. S. (1963). Properties of generalized Rayleigh distributions, *Annals of Mathematical Statistics*, **34,** 903–910.

[4] Bose, S. S. (1935). On the distribution of the ratio of variances of two samples drawn from a given normal bivariate correlated population, *Sankhyá*, **2,** 65–72.

[5] Bulgren, W. G. (1969). Representations of the multivariate *t* and multivariate *F* distribution, In *Empirical Bayes Estimation and Computing in Statistics* (Ed. T. A. Atchison and H. F. Martz), pp. 199–211. *Math Series No. 6*, Texas Tech University, Lubbock, Texas.

[6] Cheriyan, K. C. (1941). A bivariate correlated gamma-type distribution function, *Journal of the Indian Mathematical Society*, **5,** 133–144.

[7] Connor, R. J. and Mosimann, J. E. (1969). Concepts of independence for proportions with a generalization of the Dirichlet distribution, *Journal of the American Statistical Association*, **64,** 194–206.

[8] Craiu, M. and Craiu, V. (1969). Repartitia Dirichlet generalizatá, *Analele Universitatii Bucuresti, Mathematicá-Mecanicá*, **18,** No. 2, 9–11.

[9] Darroch, J. N. and Ratcliff, D. (1971). Characterization of the Dirichlet distribution, *Journal of the American Statistical Association*, **66,** 641–643.

[10] D'jachenko, Z. N. (1961). On moments of bivariate γ-distribution, *Izvestiya Vysschych Uchebnych Zavedeniĭ Matematika*, **1** (20), 55–65. (In Russian.)

[11] D'jachenko, Z. N. (1962). On a form of bivariate γ-distribution, *Nauchnye Trudy Leningradskoi Lesotekhnicheskoi Akademii*, **94,** 5–17. (In Russian.)

[12] D'jachenko, Z. N. (1962). Distribution surfaces of γ type, *Trudy VI Vsesoyuznogo Soveshchaniya po Teorii Verojatnostei, Matematicheskoi Statistike, Vilnjus*, 389–395. (In Russian.)

[13] Eagleson, G. K. (1964). Polynomial expansions of bivariate distributions, *Annals of Mathematical Statistics*, **35,** 1208–1215.

[14] Finney, D. J. (1938). The distribution of the ratio of estimates of the two variances in a sample from a normal bivariate population, *Biometrika*, **30,** 190–192.

[15] Finney, D. J. (1941). The joint distribution of variance ratios based on a common error mean square, *Annals of Eugenics, London*, **11,** 136–140.

[16] Fomin, Ye. A. (1970). Maximum value distribution for realization of discrete random time processes, *Problemy Peredachi Informatsii*, **6,** 99–103. (In Russian.)

[17] Gaver, D. P. (1970). Multivariate gamma distributions generated by mixture, *Sankhyā, Series A*, **32,** 123–126.

[18] Ghirtis, G. C. (1967). Some problems of statistical inference relating to double-gamma distribution, *Trabajos de Estadística*, **18,** 67–87.

[19] Griffiths, R. C. (1969). The canonical correlation coefficients of bivariate gamma distributions, *Annals of Mathematical Statistics*, **40,** 1401–1408.

[20] Griffiths, R. C. (1969). A class of infinitely divisible bivariate gamma distributions, *Sankhyā, Series A*, **31,** 473–476.

[20a] Griffiths, R. C. (1970). Infinitely divisible multivariate gamma distributions, *Sankhyā, Series A*, **32,** 393–404.

[21] Gupta, R. P. and Kabe, D. G. (1970). The noncentral multivariate beta distribution in planar case, *Trabajos de Estadística*, **21,** 61–67.

[21a] Hamdan, M. A. and Martinson, E. O. (1971). The bivariate gamma correlation surface, *South African Statistical Journal*, **5,** 67–69.

[22] Hewett, J. and Bulgren, W. G. (1971). Inequalities for some multivariate *f*-distributions with applications, *Technometrics*, **13,** 397–402.

[23] Holla, M. S. and Bhattacharya, S. K. (1965). A bivariate gamma distribution in life testing, *Defence Science Journal* (*India*), **15,** 65–74.

[24] Jensen, D. R. (1969). An inequality for a class of bivariate chi-square distributions, *Journal of the American Statistical Association*, **64,** 333–336.

[25] Jensen, D. R. (1969). Limit properties of noncentral multivariate Rayleigh and chi square distributions, *SIAM Journal on Applied Mathematics*, **17,** 802–814.

[26] Jensen, D. R. (1970). The joint distribution of traces of Wishart matrices and some applications, *Annals of Mathematical Statistics*, **41,** 133–145.

[27] Jensen, D. R. (1970). The joint distribution of quadratic forms and related distributions, *Australian Journal of Statistics*, **12,** 13–22.

[28] Jensen, D. R. (1970). A generalization of the multivariate Rayleigh distribution, *Sankhyā, Series A*, **32,** 193–206.

[29] Jensen, D. R. and Howe, R. B. (1968). Probability content of the bivariate chi-square distribution over rectangular regions, *Virginia Journal of Science*, **19,** 233–239.

[30] Jensen, D. R. and Jones, M. Q. (1969). Simultaneous confidence intervals for variances, *Journal of the American Statistical Association*, **64,** 324–332.

[31] Johnson, N. L. (1960). An approximation to the multinomial distribution; some properties and applications, *Biometrika*, **47,** 93–102.

[32] Johnson, N. L. (1962). Some notes on the investigation of heterogeneity in interactions, *Trabajos de Estadística*, **13,** 183–199.

[33] Khatri, C. G. (1970). A note on Mitra's paper "A density free approach to the matrix variate beta distribution," *Sankhyā, Series A*, **32,** 311–318.

[34] Kibble, W. F. (1941). A two-variate gamma type distribution, *Sankhyā*, **5,** 137–150.

[35] Kimball, A. W. (1951). On dependent tests of significance in the analysis of variance, *Annals of Mathematical Statistics*, **22**, 600–602.

[36] Krishnaiah, P. R. (1964). *Multiple Comparison Tests in the Multivariate Case*, Report ARL 64-124, Aerospace Research Laboratories, Wright-Patterson Air Force Base, Ohio.

[37] Krishnaiah, P. R. and Armitage, J. V. (1970). On a multivariate F distribution, *Essays in Probability and Statistics* (*S. N. Roy Memorial Volume*), Chapel Hill: University of North Carolina Press, pp. 439–468.

[38] Krishnaiah, P. R., Hagis, P. and Steinberg, L. (1963). A note on the bivariate chi-distribution, *SIAM Review*, **5**, 140–144.

[39] Krishnaiah, P. R. and Rao, M. M. (1961). Remarks on a multivariate gamma distribution, *American Mathematical Monthly*, **68**, 342–346.

[40] Krishnamoorthy, A. S. and Parthasarathy, M. (1951). A multivariate gamma-type distribution, *Annals of Mathematical Statistics*, **22**, 549–557 (correction: **31**, 229).

[41] Krishnan, M. (1967). The noncentral bivariate chi distribution, *SIAM Review*, **9**, 708–713.

[42] Kshirsagar, A. M. (1961). The non-central multivariate beta distribution, *Annals of Mathematical Statistics*, **32**, 104–111.

[43] Lee, P. A. (1971). A diagonal expansion for the 2-variate Dirichlet probability density function, *SIAM Journal of Applied Mathematics*, **21**, 155–165.

[44] Lukacs, E. and Laha, R. G. (1964). *Applications of Characteristic Functions*, London: Griffin (Griffin's Statistical Monograph No. 14).

[45] Martin, J. J. (1967). *Bayesian Decision Problems and Markov Chains*, New York: John Wiley and Sons, Inc. (Publications in Operations Research No. 13), Chapter 6.

[46] Mauldon, J. G. (1959). A generalization of the Beta distribution, *Annals of Mathematical Statistics*, **30**, 509–520.

[47] Miller, K. S. (1964). *Multidimensional Gaussian Distributions*, New York: John Wiley and Sons, Inc.

[48] Miller, K. S., Bernstein, R. I. and Blumenson, L. E. (1958). Generalized Rayleigh processes, *Quarterly of Applied Mathematics*, **16**, 137–145. (Correction, *ibid.*, **20**, 395.)

[49] Miller, K. S. and Sackrowitz, H. (1967). Relationships between biased and unbiased Rayleigh distributions, *SIAM Journal of Applied Mathematics*, **15**, 1490–1495.

[50] Mitra, S. K. (1970). A density free approach to the matrix variate beta distribution, *Sankhyā*, *Series A*, **32**, 81–88.

[51] Mitra, S. K. (1970). Analogues of multivariate beta (Dirichlet) distribution, *Sankhyā*, *Series A*, **32**, 189–192.

[52] Moran, P. A. P. (1967). Testing for correlation between non-negative variates, *Biometrika*, **54**, 385–394.

[53] Moran, P. A. P. (1969). Statistical inference with bivariate gamma distributions, *Biometrika*, **56,** 627–634.

[54] Moran, P. A. P. (1970). The methodology of rain making experiments, *Review of the International Statistical Institute*, **38,** 105–115. (Discussion, 115–119.)

[55] Moran, P. A. P. and Vere-Jones, D. (1969). The infinite divisibility of multivariate gamma distributions, *Sankhyā, Series A*, **31,** 191–194.

[56] Mosimann, J. E. (1962). On the compound multinomial distribution, the multivariate beta-distribution, and correlations among proportions, *Biometrika*, **49,** 65–82.

[57] Olkin, I. (1971). *Monotonicity properties of Dirichlet integrals with applications to the multinomial distribution and the ANOVA test*, Technical Report No. 137, Depts of Operations Research and Statistics, Stanford University.

[58] Olkin, I. and Rubin, H. (1964). Multivariate beta distributions and independence properties of the Wishart distribution, *Annals of Mathematical Statistics*, **35,** 261–269.

[59] Ramabhadran, V. R. (1951). A multivariate gamma-type distribution, *Sankhyā*, **11,** 45–46.

[60] Roux, J. J. J. (1971). A characterization of a multivariate distribution, *South African Statistical Journal*, **5,** 27–36.

[60a] Roux, J. J. J. (1971). On generalized multivariate distributions, *South African Statistical Journal*, **5,** 91–100.

[61] Sarmanov, I. O. (1968). A generalized symmetric gamma correlation, *Doklady Akademii Nauk SSSR*, **179,** 1279–1285 (*Soviet Mathematics Doklady*, **9,** 2, 547–550).

[62] Sarmanov, I. O. (1970). Gamma correlation process and its properties, *Doklady Akademii Nauk, SSSR*, **191,** 30–32. (In Russian.).

[63] Sarmanov, I. O. (1970). An approximate calculation of correlation coefficients between functions of dependent random variables, *Matematicheskie Zametki*, **7,** 617–625. (In Russian.) English translation in *Mathematical Notes, Academy of Sciences of the USSR* **7,** 373–377.

[64] Sarmanov, O. V. (1966). Generalized normal correlation and two-dimensional classes of Fréchet, *Doklady Akademii Nauk SSSR*, **168,** 32–35.

[65] Srivastava, M. S. (1968). On the distribution of a multiple correlation matrix; Non-central multivariate beta distributions, *Annals of Mathematical Statistics*, **39,** 227–232.

[66] Tan, W. Y. (1968). Some distribution theory associated with complex Gaussian distribution, *Tamkang Journal*, **7,** 263–302.

[67] Tan, W. Y. (1969). Note on the multivariate and the generalized multivariate Beta distributions, *Journal of the American Statistical Association*, **64,** 230–241.

[68] Tiao, G. C. and Afonja, B. (1969). *Some Approximations and Uses of the Dirichlet Distributions. Preliminary Report*, Abstract, *Annals of Mathematical Statistics*, **40,** 1514.

[69] Tiao, G. C. and Guttman, I. (1965). The inverted Dirichlet distribution with applications, *Journal of the American Statistical Association*, **60,** 793–805. (Correction, **60,** 1251–1252.)

[70] Troskie, C. G. (1967). Noncentral multivariate Dirichlet distributions, *South African Statistical Journal*, **1,** 21–32.

[71] Vere-Jones, D. (1967). The infinite divisibility of a bivariate gamma distribution, *Sankhyā, Series A*, **27,** 421–422.

[72] Waal, D. J. de (1970). Distributions connected with a multivariate Beta statistic, *Annals of Mathematical Statistics*, **41,** 1091–1095.

[73] Wagle, B. (1968). Multivariate beta distribution and a test for multivariate normality, *Journal of the Royal Statistical Society, Series B*, **30,** 511–516.

[74] Wicksell, S. D. (1933). On correlation surfaces of Type III, *Biometrika*, **25,** 121–133.

[75] Zaharov, V. K., Sarmanov, O. V., and Sevastjanov, B. A. (1969). Sequential χ^2 tests, *Matematicheskii Sbornik*, **79,** 444–460. (In Russian.)

41

Multivariate Extreme Value and Exponential Distributions

1. Bivariate Extreme-Value Distributions—General

1.1. *Definition*

Let (X_i, Y_i) be independent pairs of random variables, each having the same continuous joint cumulative distribution function $F(x,y)$. We then consider the joint distribution of $X_{\max} = \max(X_1, \ldots, X_n)$, $Y_{\max} = (Y_1, \ldots, Y_n)$. Since $X_1, \ldots, X_n$ are independent, identically distributed continuous random variables, it will usually be possible (as described in Chapter 21) to find linear transformations

$$X_{(n)} = a_n X_{\max} + b_n \qquad (a_n > 0)$$

such that $X_{(n)}$ has a limiting distribution (as $n \to \infty$) which is one of the three types of extreme-value distributions. There will also, of course, be a transformation

$$Y_{(n)} = c_n Y_{\max} + d_n \qquad (c_n > 0)$$

with similar properties.

The limiting joint distribution of $X_{(n)}$ and $Y_{(n)}$ as $n \to \infty$ is a *bivariate extreme-value distribution.*

1.2. *Properties*

The joint cumulative distribution function of $X_{\max}$ and $Y_{\max}$ is $[F(x,y)]^n$. Denoting the bivariate extreme value cumulative distribution function by $F_{(\infty)}(x,y)$, we have

$$F_{(\infty)}(x,y) = \lim_{n\to\infty} [F(a_nx + b_n, c_ny + d_n)]^n. \tag{1}$$

This equation is commonly referred to as the "postulate of stability." It is a natural extension of the univariate Fréchet-Fisher-Tippett equation [(5) of Chapter 21]. Clearly, if X_i and Y_i are mutually independent, so will be $X_{\max}$ and $Y_{\max}$, and $X_{(n)}$ and $Y_{(n)}$, and the limiting distribution will also be that of two independent random variables. The converse, however, is not necessarily true. Geffroy [6] has shown that the condition

$$\lim_{x,y\to\infty} \frac{1 - F_X(x) - F_Y(y) + F_{X,Y}(x,y)}{1 - F_{X,Y}(x,y)} = 0 \tag{2}$$

is sufficient for asymptotic independence of $X_{\max}$ and $Y_{\max}$, even though $F_{X,Y}(x,y) \neq F_X(x)F_Y(y)$. Condition (2) is satisfied, for example, by the following:

(a) The bivariate normal distribution with

$$|\rho| \neq 1$$

(Sibuya [30]).

(b) Bivariate distributions of type

$$F_{X,Y}(x,y) = F_X(x)F_Y(y)(1 + \alpha[1 - F_X(x)][1 - F_Y(y)])$$

(Gumbel [8]) and generalizations due to Farlie [3] (see Chapter 34, Section 7).

(c) Bivariate exponential distributions of type

$$F_{X,Y}(x,y) = 1 - e^{-x} - e^{-y} - \exp(-x - y - \theta xy) \qquad (x,y \geq 0;\ 0 \leq \theta \leq 1)$$

(see Gumbel [9] and Section 3.2 of this chapter).

(d) The bivariate logistic distribution (Gumbel [11])

$$F_{X,Y}(x,y) = (1 + e^{-x} + e^{-y})^{-1}$$

and, indeed, any joint distribution satisfying the relation

$$\frac{1}{F_{X,Y}(x,y)} = \frac{1}{F_X(x)} + \frac{1}{F_Y(y)} - 1. \tag{3}$$

The marginal distribution of a bivariate extreme-value distribution may be any one of the three extreme-value types. There are thus $\binom{3}{2} + 3 = 6$

possible pairs of types. The two marginal types do not completely specify the joint distribution (just as, e.g., marginal normality does not ensure bivariate normality), but they do imply quite severe restrictions on it, since the cumulative distribution function must also satisfy the stability postulate (1).

Geffroy [6], Gumbel [7], Sibuya [30], and Oliveira [22–24] have obtained a number of more or less equivalent results on the forms of bivariate extreme-value distributions. Their results may be summarized as follows.

If $F_{(\infty)}(x,y)$ is the joint cumulative distribution function of a bivariate extreme-value distribution, and $F_{1(\infty)}(x),F_{2(\infty)}(y)$ the corresponding univariate functions, then

$$(4)\quad -\log F_{(\infty)}(x,y) = -\log F_{1(\infty)}(x) - \log F_{2(\infty)}(y) + g\left(\frac{\log F_{2(\infty)}(y)}{\log F_{1(\infty)}(x)}\right)(-\log F_{1(\infty)}(x)),$$

where $g(t)$ is a continuous convex function with $\max(-t,-1) \leq g(t) \leq 0$. Note that it follows from (4) that

$$(5)\qquad F_{(\infty)}(x,y) \geq F_{1(\infty)}(x)F_{2(\infty)}(y)$$

for any bivariate extreme-value distribution.

It is of interest to note that if $F_{(\infty)}(x,y),G_{(\infty)}(x,y)$ are two bivariate extreme-value distributions, so is their weighted geometric mean

$$[F_{(\infty)}(x,y)]^{\beta}[G_{(\infty)}(x,y)]^{1-\beta} \qquad (0 \leq \beta \leq 1)$$

(Gumbel and Goldstein [13]).

Asymptotic distributions of minimum values are equivalent to (minimum) extreme-value distributions, as can be seen by changing the signs of all variables. As such, they do not require separate treatment.

2. Special Bivariate Extreme-Value Distributions

Gumbel [7, 12] has described two general forms for bivariate extreme-value distributions in terms of the marginal (univariate extreme-value) distributions:

1. *Type A*

$$(6)\quad F_{(\infty)}(x,y) = F_{1(\infty)}(x)F_{2(\infty)}(y)\exp\left[-\theta\left\{\frac{1}{\log F_{1(\infty)}(x)} + \frac{1}{\log F_{2(\infty)}(y)}\right\}^{-1}\right].$$

2. *Type B*

$$(7)\qquad F_{(\infty)}(x,y) = \exp[-\{(-\log F_{1(\infty)}(x))^{m} + (-\log F_{2(\infty)}(y))^{m}\}^{1/m}].$$

In (6), θ is a parameter ($0 \leq \theta < 1$), in (7), m is a parameter ($m \geq 1$). If $\theta = 0$ in (6), X and Y are independent; if $m = 1$ in (7), X and Y are independent.

We now suppose that each marginal distribution is of the standard Type I extreme-value form, so that

$$F_{1(\infty)}(x) = \exp(-e^{-x}); \qquad F_{2(\infty)}(y) = \exp(-e^{-y}).$$

Each of these distributions has expected value γ ($= 0.577 \cdots$) and variance $\pi^2/6$. Since Types II and III can be obtained from Type I by simple transformations, much of our analysis will be relevant to bivariate extreme-value distributions with marginal distributions of these other types.

Oliveira [22, 23] showed that a bivariate distribution with standard Type I extreme-value marginal distributions can be defined by a cumulative distribution function of the form

$$F_{X_1,X_2}(x_1,x_2) = \exp[-(e^{-x_1} + e^{-x_2})g(x_2 - x_1)]. \tag{8}$$

If a density function exists, the function $g(\cdot)$ must satisfy the conditions

$$\lim_{t\to\pm\infty} g(t) = 1, \tag{9.1}$$

$$\frac{d}{dt}[(1 + e^{-t})g(t)] \leq 0, \tag{9.2}$$

$$\frac{d}{dt}[(1 + e^{t})g(t)] \geq 0, \tag{9.3}$$

$$(1 + e^{-t})g''(t) + (1 - e^{-t})g'(t) \geq 0. \tag{9.4}$$

Type A is obtained by taking

$$g(t) = 1 - \tfrac{1}{4}\theta \operatorname{sech}^2 \tfrac{1}{2}t. \tag{10.1}$$

Type B is obtained by taking

$$g(t) = (e^{mt} + 1)^{1/m}(e^t + 1)^{-1}. \tag{10.2}$$

A third type (Oliveira [27]), which we shall call Type C, is obtained by taking

$$g(t) = (e^t + 1)^{-1}\{1 - \phi + \max(e^t,\phi)\} \qquad (0 < \phi < 1). \tag{10.3}$$

2.1. *Type A Distributions*

For these distributions,

$$F_{X,Y}(x,y) = \exp[-e^{-x} - e^{-y} + \theta(e^x + e^y)^{-1}] \qquad (0 \leq \theta \leq 1) \tag{11}$$

and the joint density function is

$$(12)\quad p_{X,Y}(x,y) = e^{-(x+y)}[1 - \theta(e^{2x} + e^{2y})(e^x + e^y)^{-2} + 2\theta e^{2(x+y)}(e^x + e^y)^{-3} + \theta^2 e^{2(x+y)}(e^x + e^y)^{-4}]\exp[-e^{-x} - e^{-y} + \theta(e^x + e^y)^{-1}].$$

$F_{X,Y}(x,y)$ is an increasing function of θ. The median of the common distribution of X and Y is

$$(13)\qquad \mu = -\log(\log 2) = 0.36651.$$

We note that, since $\exp(-e^{-\mu}) = \frac{1}{2}$,

$$(14.1)\qquad F_{X,Y}(\mu,\mu) = \exp(-2e^{-\mu} + \tfrac{1}{2}\theta e^{-\mu}) = (\tfrac{1}{4})^{1-\theta/4}$$

(while $F_X(\mu)F_Y(\mu) = \frac{1}{4}$).

Also

$$(14.2)\qquad F_{X,Y}(0,0) = (e^{-2})^{1-\theta/4}.$$

The value $\tilde{\mu}$ such that $F_{X,Y}(\tilde{\mu},\tilde{\mu}) = \frac{1}{4}$ satisfies the equation

$$(2 - \tfrac{1}{2}\theta)e^{-\tilde{\mu}} = 2\log 2$$

and so

$$(15)\qquad \tilde{\mu} = \log(1 - \tfrac{1}{4}\theta) - \log(\log 2) \doteqdot \log(1 - \tfrac{1}{4}\theta) + 0.3665.$$

(Since $0 \le \theta \le 1$; $0.3665 - \log(\frac{4}{3}) = 0.0787 \le \tilde{\mu} \le 0.3665$.) The mode of the common distribution of X and Y is at zero. The mode of the joint distribution is at

$$(16)\qquad x = y = \log\left[\frac{(2-\theta)(4-\theta)}{2\theta}\left\{\sqrt{\frac{1}{2} + \frac{2}{(2-\theta)^2}} - 1\right\}\right].$$

Some numerical values are given in Table 1.

The shape of the density function (12) is not easily assessed from its analytical expression, nor is it easy to obtain expressions for product moments. However, Gumbel and Mustafi [14] have shown that a useful idea of the way in which the density varies with θ can be obtained by studying the behavior of $p_{X,Y}(x,x)$ (i.e., on the diagonal line $y = x$) as θ varies. Figure 1 (taken from [14]) shows values of $p_{X,Y}(x,x)$ for $\theta = 0$ and $\theta = 1$. For intermediate values of θ, $p_{X,Y}(x,x)$ lie between the values shown. As θ increases, the joint distribution tends to concentrate along the diagonal $x = y$.

Although the population product moment correlation is difficult to evaluate, the grade correlation (Konijn [17]) defined by

$$\bar{\rho} = 12\int_{-\infty}^{\infty}\int_{-\infty}^{\infty} F_{X,Y}(x,y)\, dF_X(x)\, dF_Y(y) - 3$$

TABLE 1

Type A distribution			Type B distribution		
Parameter θ	Mode at $x = y =$	Grade correlation	Parameter m	Mode at $x = y =$	Correlation
0	0.0000	0.0000	1.0	0.0000	0.0000
0.1	−0.0125	0.0509	1.5	−0.1150	0.5556
0.2	−0.0255	0.1031	2.0	−0.1346	0.7500
0.3	−0.0385	0.1571	2.5	−0.1282	0.8400
0.4	−0.0514	0.2127	3.0	−0.1155	0.8889
0.5	−0.0649	0.2702	3.5	−0.1026	0.9184
0.6	−0.0790	0.3296	4.0	−0.0912	0.9375
0.7	−0.0926	0.3909	4.5	−0.0815	0.9506
0.8	−0.1071	0.4542	5.0	−0.0733	0.9600
0.9	−0.1219	0.5198	6.0	−0.0606	0.9722
1.0	−0.1362	0.5894	7.0	−0.0514	0.9796
			8.0	−0.0444	0.9844
			9.0	−0.0391	0.9877
			10.0	−0.0348	0.9900
			∞	0.0000	1.0000

is much simpler. In fact

$$(17)\quad \bar{\rho} = 3(2 - \tfrac{1}{4}\theta)^{-1}\left[1 + (2\theta - \tfrac{1}{4}\theta^2)^{-1} \tan^{-1}\left\{(2\theta - \tfrac{1}{4}\theta^2)^{1/2}\left(2 - \frac{\theta}{2}\right)^{-1}\right\}\right] - 3.$$

Table 1 shows some values of $\bar{\rho}$ for a few values of θ.

2.2. *Type B Distributions*

For these distributions

$$(18)\qquad F_{X,Y}(x,y) = \exp[-(e^{-mx} + e^{-my})^{1/m}] \qquad (m \geq 1)$$

and the joint density function is

$$(19)\quad p_{X,Y}(x,y) = e^{-m(x+y)}(e^{-mx} + e^{-my})^{-2+1/m} \times \{m - 1 + (e^{-mx} + e^{-my})^{1/m}\}\exp[-(e^{-mx} + e^{-my})^{1/m}].$$

Since $\lim_{m\to\infty}(e^{-mx} + e^{-my})^{1/m} = \max(e^{-x},e^{-y})$,

$$(20)\qquad \lim_{m\to\infty} F_{X,Y}(x,y) = \min[\exp(-e^{-x}), \exp(-e^{-y})] = \min(F_X(x),F_Y(y)).$$

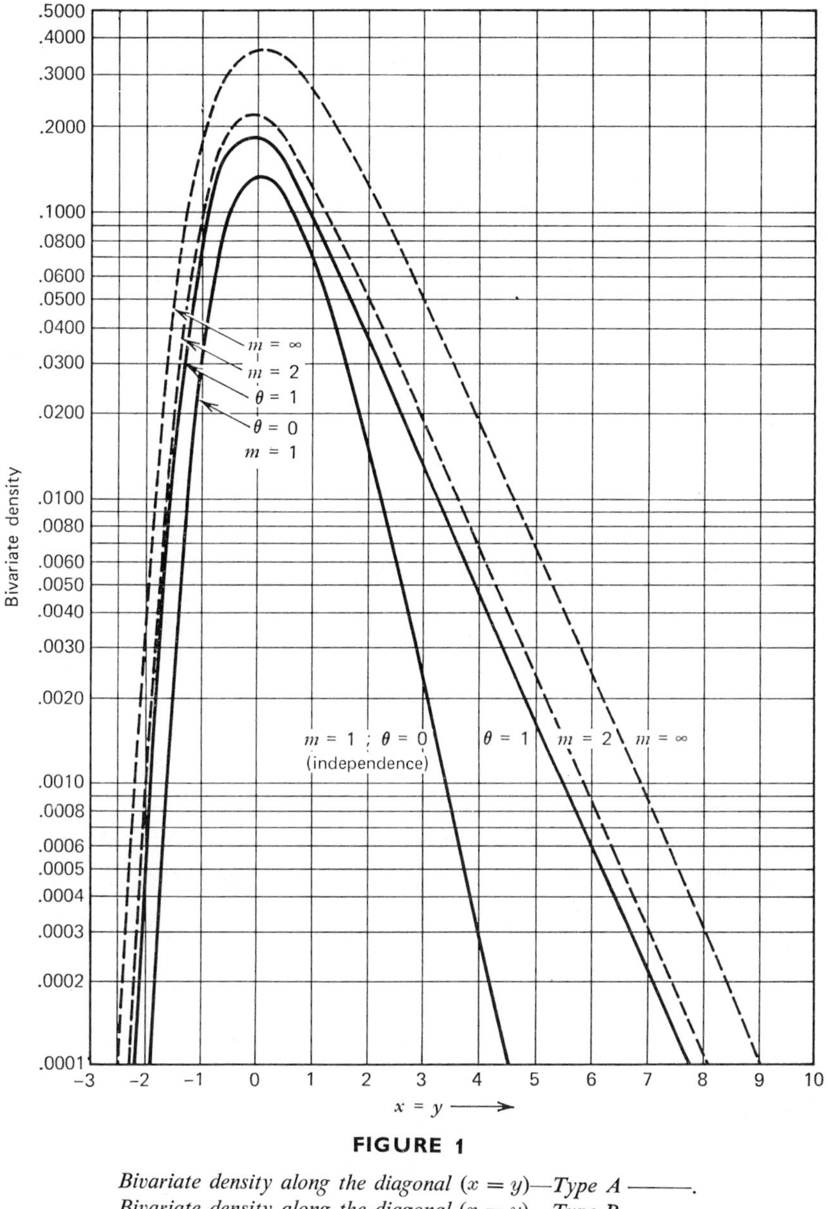

FIGURE 1

Bivariate density along the diagonal ($x = y$)—Type A ———.
Bivariate density along the diagonal ($x = y$)—Type B - - - -.

With the univariate median value μ defined in (10), we find, for Type B distributions,

(21.1) $$F_{X,Y}(\mu,\mu) = (\tfrac{1}{2})^{2^{1/m}}$$

and also

(21.2) $$F_{X,Y}(0,0) = (e^{-1})^{2^{1/m}}$$

[compare (14.1) and (14.2)].

The value $\tilde{\mu}$ such that $F_{X,Y}(\tilde{\mu},\tilde{\mu}) = \frac{1}{4}$ satisfies the equation

$$\exp[-2^{1/m}e^{-\tilde{\mu}}] = \tfrac{1}{4}$$

and so

(22) $$\tilde{\mu} = -\log_e(\log_e 2) - \frac{m-1}{m}\log_e 2.$$

(Since $m \geq 1$; $0.3665 - \log_e 2 = -0.3266 \leq \tilde{\mu} \leq 0.3665$.)

The mode of the joint distribution is at

(23) $$x = y = (1 + m^{-1})\log_e 2 - \log_e[\sqrt{(m-1)^2 + 4} - m + 3].$$

Some numerical values are given in Table 1.

Oliveira [22] has shown that m and the population product moment correlation, ρ, are related by the simple formula

(24) $$m = (1 - \rho)^{-1/2}; \qquad \rho = 1 - m^{-2}.$$

Values of ρ for $m = 1.0(0.5)5.0(1)10,\infty$ are given in Table 1.

Figure 1 (based on Gumbel and Mustafi [14]) shows $p_{X,Y}(x,x)$ (i.e., values on the diagonal $x = y$) for $m = 1,2,\infty$. Note that, for $m = 1$, the graph is the same as that for a Type A distribution with $\theta = 0$ shown in Figure 1. Both correspond to independence, with

$$p_{X,Y}(x,y) = p_X(x)p_Y(y) = e^{-(x+y)}\exp(-e^{-x} - e^{-y}).$$

It is interesting to note that $(X - Y)$ has a logistic distribution, with

(25) $$\Pr[X - Y \leq t] = (1 + e^{-mt})^{-1}.$$

[We have already noted this for the mutual independence case ($m = 1$) in Chapter 21, Section 8.] This property does not hold for Type A distributions.

2.3. *Type C Distributions*

For these distributions

(26) $$F_{X,Y}(x,y) = \exp[-\max\{e^{-x} + (1-\phi)e^{-y}, e^{-y}\}] \qquad (0 < \phi < 1).$$

The distribution (26) can be generated as the joint distribution of X and

$$Y = \max(X + \log \phi, Z + \log(1 - \phi)),$$

where X,Z are mutually independent and each has a standard Type I extreme-value distribution.

A notable feature of this distribution is that it has a singular component on the line $Y = X + \log \phi$, since

$$(27) \quad \Pr[Y = X + \log \phi] = \Pr[X + \log \phi \geq Z + \log(1 - \phi)] = \Pr[Z - X \leq \log\{\phi/(1 - \phi)\}] = \phi$$

(see Eq. 25 with $m = 1$).

The correlation between X and Y is

$$(28) \quad -6\pi^{-2} \int_0^{\phi} (1 - t)^{-1} \log t \, dt$$

and the grade correlation [cf. (17)] is

$$(29) \quad 3\phi/(2 + \phi).$$

The median of each marginal distribution is, of course, $\mu = -\log \log 2$. Note that

$$(30.1) \quad F_{X,Y}(\mu,\mu) = \tfrac{1}{4}(2^{\phi})$$

[compare with (14.1) and (21.1)] and

$$(30.2) \quad F_{X,Y}(0,0) = (e^{-2})^{1-\phi/2}$$

[compare with (14.2) and (21.2)].

The value $\tilde{\mu}$ such that $F_{X,X}(\tilde{\mu},\tilde{\mu}) = \frac{1}{4}$ satisfies the equation

$$\exp[-(2 - \phi)e^{-\tilde{\mu}}] = \tfrac{1}{4}$$

and so

$$(31) \quad \tilde{\mu} = -\log\left[\frac{\log 2}{1 - \frac{1}{2}\phi}\right].$$

2.4. *Estimation*

For distributions of each type (A, B, and C), four further parameters (making five in all) can be introduced as location and scale parameters for the two variables. Their values can be calculated from the separate marginal distributions of the variables, using the methods described in Chapter 21.

In order to estimate the "association parameter" (θ or m, as the case may be) from a random sample of size m we can use the observed frequencies in the 2×2 table formed by dichotomizing each variable at its sample median.

Using formulas (14.1) and (21.1) we obtain estimators θ^*,m^* of θ,m respectively by equating the observed proportions, $\hat{p}$, of the n pairs of values, for which both X and Y exceed their sample medians, to

$$(\tfrac{1}{4})^{1-\theta^*/4} \qquad \text{for Type A;}$$

$$(\tfrac{1}{2})^{2^{1/m^*}} \qquad \text{for Type B;}$$

leading to estimators

$$\theta^* = 4 + \frac{2\log\hat{p}}{\log 2} = 4 + 2.8854\log\hat{p}, \tag{32.1}$$

$$m^* = \left[\log\left(-\frac{\log\hat{p}}{\log 2}\right)\right]^{-1}\log 2 = [0.5288 + 1.4427\log(-\log\hat{p})]^{-1}. \tag{32.2}$$

The variance of θ^* is actually infinite, since $\Pr[\hat{p} = 0] > 0$, but if $(\hat{p} = 0)$ is excluded from the distribution of $\hat{p}$, then

$$\operatorname{var}(\theta^*) \doteqdot \frac{4}{n(\log 2)^2}\,[\tfrac{1}{2}\{F_{(\infty)}(\mu,\mu)\}^{-1} - 1], \tag{33.1}$$

where n is the sample size. This may be estimated as

$$8.3255(\tfrac{1}{2}\hat{p}^{-1} - 1)n^{-1}.$$

The variance of m^{*-1} is also infinite, but excluding $(\hat{p} = 0)$ we have

$$\operatorname{var}(m^{*-1}) \doteqdot \frac{1}{n(\log 2)^2}\,[\tfrac{1}{2}\{F_\infty(\mu,\mu)\}^{-1} - 1]\,\frac{1}{[-\log F_\infty(\mu,\mu)]^2}. \tag{33.2}$$

This may be estimated as

$$2.0814(\tfrac{1}{2}\hat{p}^{-1} - 1)(-\log\hat{p})^{-2}n^{-1}.$$

Some values for (33.1) and (33.2), taken from **[14]**, are given in Table 2.

From (14.1) (noting that $0 \le \theta \le 1$) it can be seen that, for Type A, $F_{X,Y}(\mu,\mu)$ lies between $\frac{1}{4}$ and $(\frac{1}{4})^{0.75} = 0.35355$.

For Type B, $F_{X,Y}(\mu,\mu)$ lies between $\frac{1}{4}$ and $\frac{1}{2}$. If $\hat{p}$ lies outside these limits, formulas (33.1) and (33.2), respectively, cannot be used. Of course, observations of this kind might well be regarded as evidence that a Type A, or a Type B, extreme-value distribution is not appropriate.

An alternative estimator of θ, for Type A distributions, is obtained by solving (17) for θ, with $\bar{\rho}$ replaced by the sample grade correlation. For Type B distributions, m is easily estimated by replacing ρ in (24) by the sample (product moment) correlation coefficient.

Posner et al. **[28]** have proposed a method of estimation of θ or m based on the distribution of $|X_1 - X_2|$. They show that, in the general case (8),

$$P[\alpha < X_1 - X_2 < \beta] = h(\beta) - h(\alpha),$$

TABLE 2

Variances of Estimators of the Parameters

	Approximate value			Approximate value
	(A)	(B)		
$F_{X,Y}(\mu,\mu)$	$n\,\mathrm{var}(\theta^*)$	$n\,\mathrm{var}(m^{*-1})$	$F_{X,Y}(\mu,\mu)$	$n\,\mathrm{var}(m^{*-1})$
0.25	8.32548	1.08304	0.36	0.77548
0.26	7.68506	1.05879	0.37	0.73976
0.27	7.09208	1.03423	0.38	0.70207
0.28	6.54145	1.00919	0.39	0.66213
0.29	6.02880	0.98359	0.40	0.61975
0.30	5.55032	0.95722	0.41	0.57473
0.31	5.10271	0.93004	0.42	0.52682
0.32	4.68308	0.90175	0.43	0.47570
0.33	4.28888	0.87234	0.44	0.42108
0.34	3.91787	0.84158	0.45	0.36270
0.35	3.56806	0.80934	0.46	0.30015
			0.47	0.23305
			0.48	0.16099
			0.49	0.08347
			0.50	0.00000

with

$$h(t) = (1 + e^{-t})^{-1} + g'(t)/g(t).$$

In particular, for example,

$$\Pr[|X_1 - X_2| < \delta] = \frac{e^\delta - 1}{e^\delta + 1} + 2\frac{g'(\delta)}{g(\delta)} = P(\delta). \tag{35}$$

The variance of the estimator so obtained depends markedly on δ. For large sample size (n), and Type A distributions,

$$n\,\mathrm{var}(\hat{\theta}) \doteqdot P(\delta)[1 - P(\delta)]g(\delta). \tag{36}$$

Oliveira [27] has described several methods of estimating ϕ for Type C distributions. An estimator that he considers to be particularly useful is

$$\tilde{\phi} = \min(\exp[\min_j(Y_j - X_j)],1). \tag{37}$$

The cumulative distribution function of $\tilde{\phi}$ is

$$\Pr[\tilde{\phi} \le t] = \begin{cases} 0 & \text{for } t < \phi, \\ 1 - [(1-\phi)^{-1}t + 1]^{-n} & \text{for } \phi \le t < 1, \\ 1 & \text{for } t \ge 1. \end{cases} \tag{38}$$

Note that

$$\Pr[\tilde{\phi} = \phi] = 1 - (1 - \phi)^n$$

and

$$\Pr[\tilde{\phi} = 1] = (1 - \phi)^n(2 - \phi)^{-n}.$$

The estimator $\tilde{\phi}$ necessarily has a positive bias but

$$\lim_{n\to\infty} \Pr[\tilde{\phi} = \phi] = 1.$$

The expected value of $\tilde{\phi}$ is

$$\phi + \frac{1}{n-1}(1 - \phi)^n\{1 - (2 - \phi)^{-(n-1)}\}. \tag{39}$$

3. Bivariate Exponential Distributions

These are distributions for which both marginal distributions are exponential. There are a number of different bivariate exponential distributions. We first describe distributions that are simple special cases of multivariate gamma distributions, already discussed in Chapter 40. Usually, the marginal distributions will be standard exponential. Scale and location parameters can be introduced for each variable by appropriate linear transformations.

Putting $m = \nu = 2$, $\lambda_1 = \sigma_1(1 - \rho)$, $\lambda_2 = \sigma_2(1 - \rho)$, $b_1 = \rho$, $K = \rho^{-1}(1 - \rho)^{-1}$ in equation (21) of Chapter 40 we obtain

$$p_{X_1,X_2}(x_1,x_2) = \frac{1}{\sigma_1\sigma_2(1-\rho)} \exp\left[-\frac{1}{(1-\rho)}\left(\frac{x_1}{\sigma_1} + \frac{x_2}{\sigma_2}\right)\right] \cdot I_0\left(\frac{2\sqrt{\rho}}{1-\rho}\sqrt{\frac{x_1x_2}{\sigma_1\sigma_2}}\right)$$

A detailed study of this distribution has been given by Nagao and Kadoya [21a]. They describe how to estimate the parameters by moments, and give charts to assist in obtaining maximum likelihood estimators.

3.1. *Special Case of Bivariate Chi-Square*

If U_0, U_1, U_2 are independent unit normal variables, then

$$X_j = U_0^2 + U_j^2 \qquad (j = 1,2)$$

are independent χ_2^2 (i.e., exponential) variables. The joint moment generating function of X_1 and X_2 is

$$\begin{aligned} E[\exp\{t_1(U_0^2 + U_1^2) + t_2(U_0^2 + U_2^2)\}] &= E[e^{(t_1+t_2)U_0^2}]E[e^{t_1U_1^2}]E[e^{t_2U_2^2}] \\ &= [\{1 - 2(t_1 + t_2)\} \\ &\quad \times (1 - 2t_1)(1 - 2t_2)]^{-1/2}. \end{aligned} \tag{40}$$

From Section 2 of Chapter 40, we find that (a) the conditional distribution of U_0^2, given $X_j = x_j$, is a beta distribution over the range $(0,x_j)$ with parameters $\frac{1}{2},\frac{1}{2}$; hence (b) the conditional distribution of X_2, given $X_1 = x_1$, is that of $(U^2 + x_1Z)$ where U,Z are independent, U is a unit normal variable, and

$$p_Z(z) = \frac{1}{\pi}[z(1-z)]^{-1/2} \qquad (0 < z < 1).$$

Hence

$$E[X_2 \mid X_1 = x_1] = 1 + \tfrac{1}{2}x_1; \tag{41.1}$$

$$\operatorname{var}(X_2 \mid X_1 = x_1) = 2 + \tfrac{1}{8}x_1^2; \tag{41.2}$$

$$\mu_3(X_2 \mid X_1 = x_1) = 8; \tag{41.3}$$

$$\mu_4(X_2 \mid X_1 = x_1) = 60 + \tfrac{3}{2}x_1^2 + \tfrac{3}{128}x_1^4. \tag{41.4}$$

The correlation between X_1 and X_2 is clearly $\frac{1}{2}$.

The joint density function is

$$\left(\frac{1}{2\pi}\right)^3 e^{-\frac{1}{2}(x_1+x_2)} \int_0^{\min(x_1,x_2)} t^{-1/2}(x_1 - t)^{-1/2}(x_2 - t)^{-1/2} e^{\frac{1}{2}t}\, dt, \tag{42}$$

which is not of simple form.

Note that if U_0^2,U_1^2,U_2^2 are each supposed to have χ_2^2 distributions (i.e., exponential), the joint density function of X_1 and X_2 takes the simple form

$$p(x_1,x_2) = \tfrac{1}{4}[e^{-\frac{1}{2}\max(x_1,x_2)} - e^{-\frac{1}{2}(x_1+x_2)}] \qquad (x_1,x_2 > 0). \tag{43}$$

This is not a bivariate exponential distribution, since the marginal distributions are not exponential, but χ_4^2 distributions.

3.2. *Gumbel's Bivariate Exponential Distributions*

(i) Gumbel [9] has studied the joint cumulative distribution function

$$F_{x,y}(x,y) = 1 - e^{-x} - e^{-y} + e^{-(x+y+\theta xy)} \qquad (x > 0; y > 0; 0 \le \theta \le 1). \tag{44}$$

The marginal distributions of X and Y are each standard exponential. The joint density function is

$$p_{X,Y}(x,y) = e^{-x-y-\theta xy}\{(1 + \theta x)(1 + \theta y) - \theta\} \qquad (x,y > 0). \tag{45}$$

If $\theta = 0$, X and Y are independent. The conditional density function of Y, given X, is

$$p(y \mid x) = e^{-y(1+\theta x)}\{(1 + \theta x)(1 + \theta y) - \theta\} \qquad (y \ge 0). \tag{46}$$

By direct integration, we find

$$(47.1)\quad E[Y \mid X = x] = \int_0^\infty [(1 + \theta x - \theta)y + \theta(1 + \theta x)y^2]e^{-y(1+\theta x)}\,dy$$
$$= (1 + \theta x - \theta)(1 + \theta x)^{-2} + 2\theta(1 + \theta x)^{-2}$$
$$= (1 + \theta + \theta x)(1 + \theta x)^{-2}.$$

Generally (for r a positive integer)

$$(47.2)\qquad \mu_r'(Y \mid X = x) = \frac{r!(1 + \theta x + r\theta)}{(1 + \theta x)^{r+1}},$$

from which

$$(47.3)\qquad \operatorname{var}(Y \mid X = x) = \frac{(1 + \theta + \theta x)^2 - 2\theta^2}{(1 + \theta x)^4}.$$

From (47.1)

$$E[XY] = \int_0^\infty x(1 + \theta + \theta x)(1 + \theta x)^{-2}e^{-x}\,dx$$

$$= \theta^{-1}\left[1 - (1 - \theta)\int_0^\infty (1 + \theta x)^{-1}e^{-x}\,dx - \theta\int_0^\infty (1 + \theta x)^{-2}e^{-x}\,dx\right].$$

Integrating by parts

$$\int_0^\infty (1 + \theta x)^{-2}e^{-x}\,dx = \theta^{-1} - \theta^{-1}\int_0^\infty (1 + \theta x)^{-1}e^{-x}\,dx.$$

Hence

$$E[XY] = \int_0^\infty (1 + \theta x)^{-1}e^{-x}\,dx = \theta^{-1}e^{1/\theta}\int_{\theta^{-1}}^\infty e^{-z}z^{-1}\,dz$$
$$= \theta^{-1}e^{1/\theta}Ei(\theta^{-1}),$$

and so (for $\theta > 0$)

$$(48)\qquad \operatorname{corr}(X,Y) = -\theta^{-1}e^{1/\theta}Ei(\theta^{-1}) - 1.$$

As $\theta \to 0$, the correlation tends to zero (X and Y are independent for $\theta = 0$). As θ increases the correlation decreases, reaching a minimum value of -0.40365 for $\theta = 1$.

(ii) Gumbel [9] studied a second system of bivariate exponential distributions. This is a special application of a general formula:

$$F_{X,Y}(x,y) = F_X(x)F_Y(y)[1 + \alpha\{1 - F_X(x)\}\{1 - F_Y(y)\}] \qquad (-1 \le \alpha \le 1),$$

proposed by Morgenstern [21] (see Chapter 34, Section 7). Putting $F_X(x) = e^{-x}(x > 0)$, $F_Y(y) = e^{-y}(y > 0)$, we obtain

$$(49) \qquad F_{X,Y}(x,y) = (1 - e^{-x})(1 - e^{-y})(1 + \alpha e^{-x-y}) \qquad (x,y \geq 0),$$

with the density function

$$(50) \qquad p_{X,Y}(x,y) = e^{-(x+y)}\{1 + \alpha(2e^{-x} - 1)(2e^{-y} - 1)\}.$$

The X and Y each have standard exponential distributions. The two variables are independent if (and only if) α is zero. The conditional density function of Y, given X, is

$$p(y \mid x) = e^{-y}\{(1 + \alpha(2e^{-x} - 1)(2e^{-y} - 1)\},$$

so that

$$\Pr[Y \leq y \mid X = x] = [1 - \alpha(2e^{-x} - 1)](1 - e^{-y}) + \alpha(2e^{-x} - 1)(1 - e^{-2y}).$$

The conditional distribution is a proper mixture of the two cumulative distribution functions $(1 - e^{-y})$ and $(1 - e^{-2y})$ provided that

$$0 < 1 - \alpha(2e^{-x} - 1) < 1.$$

For $\alpha > 0$, this is equivalent to $x < \log 2$; for $\alpha < 0$, it is equivalent to $\log 2 < x$. The rth moment of Y about zero, given $X = x$, is

$$(51.1) \qquad \mu'_r = r![1 - \alpha(2e^{-x} - 1) + 2^{-r}\alpha(2e^{-x} - 1)]$$
$$= r![1 - \alpha(1 - 2^{-r})(2e^{-x} - 1)].$$

In particular

$$(51.2) \qquad E(Y \mid X = x) = 1 - \tfrac{1}{2}\alpha(2e^{-x} - 1) = 1 + \tfrac{1}{2}\alpha - \alpha e^{-x},$$

$$(51.3) \qquad \operatorname{var}(Y \mid X = x) = 1 + \tfrac{1}{2}\alpha - \tfrac{1}{4}\alpha^2 - (\alpha - \alpha^2)e^{-x} - \alpha^2 e^{-2x}.$$

Also

$$E[XY] = \int_0^\infty x(1 + \tfrac{1}{2}\alpha - \alpha e^{-x})e^{-x}\,dx = 1 + \tfrac{1}{4}\alpha,$$

$$(52) \qquad \operatorname{corr}(X, Y) = \tfrac{1}{4}\alpha.$$

Note that since $|\alpha| \leq 1$, the correlation cannot exceed $\frac{1}{4}$ or be less than $-\frac{1}{4}$.

(iii) Gumbel [9] also briefly considered bivariate exponential distributions with joint cumulative distribution function

$$F(x,y) = 1 - e^{-x} - e^{-y} + \exp[-(x^m + y^m)^{1/m}].$$

When $m = 1$, the two variables are independent.

3.3. *Freund's Bivariate Exponential Distribution*

Freund [5] considered the joint distribution arising from the following situation. Suppose that an instrument has two components A and B with life times X and Y having density functions (when both components are operation) $p_X(x) = \alpha e^{-\alpha x}$; $p_Y(y) = \beta e^{-\beta y}$ $(\alpha,\beta > 0; x,y > 0)$. The X and Y are dependent in that a failure of either component changes the parameter of the life distribution of the other component. Thus when A fails, the parameter for Y becomes β'; when B fails, the parameter for X becomes α'. There is no other dependence. Thus the joint density function of X and Y is

$$(53)\qquad p_{X,Y}(x,y) = \begin{matrix} \alpha\beta' \exp[-\beta' y - (\alpha + \beta - \beta')x] & (0 \le x < y), \\ \alpha'\beta \exp[-\alpha' x - (\alpha + \beta - \alpha')y] & (0 \le y \le x). \end{matrix}$$

The marginal distributions are (provided that $\alpha + \beta \neq \alpha'$)

$$(54.1)\qquad p_X(x) = \frac{(\alpha - \alpha')(\alpha + \beta)e^{-(\alpha+\beta)x}}{x + \beta - \alpha'} + \frac{\alpha'\beta e^{-\alpha' x}}{\alpha + \beta - \alpha'} \qquad (x > 0)$$

and (provided that $\alpha + \beta \neq \beta'$)

$$(54.2)\qquad p_Y(y) = \frac{(\beta - \beta')(\alpha + \beta)e^{-(\alpha+\beta)x}}{\alpha + \beta - \beta'} + \frac{\alpha\beta' e^{-\beta' y}}{\alpha + \beta - \beta} \qquad (y > 0).$$

The marginal distributions are exponential only in the special case $\alpha' = \beta' = \alpha + \beta$, when

$$(54.3)\qquad p_X(x) = \alpha' e^{-\alpha' x} \qquad (x > 0),$$

$$(54.4)\qquad p_Y(y) = \beta' e^{-\beta' y} \qquad (y > 0).$$

The general joint moment generating function is

$$(55)\qquad E[e^{t_1 x + t_2 y}] = \frac{1}{\alpha + \beta - t_1 - t_2}\left[\frac{\beta}{1 - t_1/\alpha'} + \frac{\alpha}{1 - t_2/\beta'}\right],$$

from which we obtain

$$(56.1)\qquad E[X] = \frac{\alpha' + \beta}{\alpha'(\alpha + \beta)}; \qquad E[Y] = \frac{\beta' + \alpha}{\beta'(\alpha + \beta)},$$

$$(56.2)\qquad \operatorname{var}(X) = \frac{\alpha'^2 + 2\alpha\beta + \beta^2}{\alpha'^2(\alpha + \beta)^2}; \qquad \operatorname{var}(Y) = \frac{\beta'^2 + 2\alpha\beta + \alpha^2}{\beta'^2(\alpha + \beta)^2},$$

$$(56.3)\qquad \operatorname{corr}(X,Y) = (\alpha'\beta' - \alpha\beta)\{(\alpha'^2 + 2\alpha\beta + \beta^2)(\beta'^2 + 2\alpha\beta + \alpha^2)\}^{-1/2}.$$

Note that $-\frac{1}{3} < \operatorname{corr}(X,Y) < 1$. In many applications $\alpha' > \alpha, \beta' > \beta$ (i.e., lifetime tends to be shorter when the other component is out of action). In such cases the correlation is positive.

The conditional density function of Y, given X (if $\alpha + \beta \neq \alpha'$), is

$$(57)\qquad p(y \mid x) = \begin{cases} \dfrac{\alpha\beta'(\alpha + \beta - \alpha')e^{-\beta' y - (\alpha+\beta-\beta')x}}{(\alpha - \alpha')(\alpha + \beta)e^{-(\alpha+\beta)x} + \alpha'\beta e^{-\alpha' x}} & (y \ge x), \\[2ex] \dfrac{\alpha'\beta(\alpha + \beta - \alpha')e^{-(\alpha+\beta-\alpha')y - \alpha' x}}{(\alpha - \alpha')(\alpha + \beta)e^{-(\alpha+\beta)x} + \alpha'\beta e^{-\alpha' x}} & (0 \le y < x). \end{cases}$$

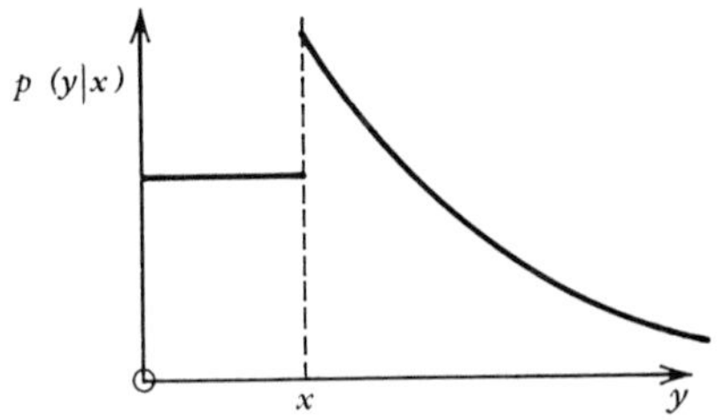

FIGURE 2

Conditional density of Y, given X = x (figure is drawn for α > β).

This is made up of two different exponential functions of y, one for $0 < y \leq x$, the other for $y > x$. It is straightforward to show that

$$(58)\quad E[Y \mid X = x] = \frac{[\alpha\beta'^{-1}(\alpha+\beta-\alpha')(1+\beta' x) - \alpha'\beta(\alpha+\beta-\alpha')^{-1}\{1+[\alpha+\beta-\alpha']x\} \times e^{-(\alpha+\beta)x} + \alpha'\beta(\alpha+\beta-\alpha')^{-1}e^{-\alpha' x}]}{(\alpha-\alpha')(\alpha+\beta)e^{-(\alpha+\beta)x} + \alpha'\beta e^{-\alpha' x}}.$$

The situation is much simpler if $\alpha' = \beta' = \alpha + \beta$. Then

$$(59)\qquad p_{X,Y}(x,y) = \begin{cases} \alpha(\alpha+\beta)e^{-(\alpha+\beta)y} & (0 \leq x < y), \\ \beta(\alpha+\beta)e^{-(\alpha+\beta)x} & (0 \leq y < x), \end{cases}$$

and, using (54.3),

$$(60)\quad p_{Y|X}(y \mid x) = \begin{cases} \alpha(\alpha+\beta)\{\alpha+\beta(\alpha+\beta)x\}^{-1}e^{-(\alpha+\beta)(y-x)} & (y > x), \\ \beta(\alpha+\beta)\{\alpha+\beta(\alpha+\beta)x\}^{-1} & (0 \leq y < x). \end{cases}$$

Over the range 0 to x, the conditional distribution of Y, given $X = x$, is rectangular. For larger values of Y it is a decreasing exponential (see Fig. 2). In this case, the regression of Y on X is

$$(61)\qquad E[Y \mid X = x] = \{\alpha + \beta(\alpha+\beta)x\}^{-1}\{\alpha + \tfrac{1}{2}\beta(\alpha+\beta)x\}.$$

Returning to the general situation it is possible to consider a limiting case as $\alpha' \to \infty$, that is, such that if A has not failed prior to B then it must fail simultaneously with B. In this case we have the linear regression

$$(62)\qquad E[Y \mid X = x] = x + \alpha[(\alpha+\beta)\beta']^{-1}$$

and the correlation coefficient is

$$\beta'(\alpha^2 + 2\alpha\beta + \beta'^2)^{-1/2}.$$

(Similar results are, of course, obtained if the limiting case as $\beta' \to \infty$ is considered.)

3.4. *The Bivariate Exponential Distributions of Marshall and Olkin*

The univariate exponential distribution derives considerable importance from its role as the distribution of waiting time in a Poisson process. It is natural to inquire whether a similar relationship exists between some bivariate exponential distribution and the waiting times in a suitably defined two-dimensional Poisson process. One such possibility, investigated by Marshall and Olkin [19] and later generalized by them [18], will now be described.

We first assume a two-component system, subjected to "shocks" that are always "fatal." These shocks are assumed to be governed by independent Poisson processes with parameters $\lambda_1,\lambda_2,\lambda_{12}$ according as the shock applies to component 1 only, component 2 only, or both components. Then the joint cumulative distribution function of the *negative* lifetimes X_1,X_2 of the two components is

$$(63)\quad F_{X_1,X_2}(x_1,x_2) = \exp[+\lambda_1 x_1 + \lambda_2 x_2 + \lambda_{12}\min(x_1,x_2)] \qquad (x_1,x_2 < 0).$$

(Note that $\Pr[X_1 \leq x_1] = \Pr[\text{lifetime} \geq -x_1]$.) Alternatively, writing $Y_j = -X_j$ $(j = 1,2)$, we have

$$(64)\quad \Pr\left[\bigcap_{j=1}^{2}(Y_j > y_j)\right] = \exp[-\lambda_1 y_1 - \lambda_2 y_2 - \lambda_{12}\max(y_1,y_2)] \qquad (y_1,y_2 > 0).$$

(This means that times between shocks are independently exponentially distributed with expected values $\lambda_1^{-1},\lambda_2^{-1},\lambda_{12}^{-1}$ respectively.) A similar distribution is obtained when the shocks are "fatal" with fixed probability, though the values of the λ's in (63) are changed. It is clear that in this case, also, the marginal distributions of lifetimes $Y_1 = -X_1$ and $Y_2 = -X_2$ are exponential, with expected values $(\lambda_1 + \lambda_{12})^{-1},(\lambda_2 + \lambda_{12})^{-1}$ respectively. The joint moment generating function of X_1 and X_2 is

$$(65)\quad E[\exp(t_1X_1 + t_2X_2)] = \frac{(\lambda + t_1 + t_2)(\lambda_1 + \lambda_{12})(\lambda_2 + \lambda_{12}) + \lambda_{12}t_1t_2}{(\lambda + t_1 + t_2)(\lambda_1 + \lambda_{12} + t_1)(\lambda_2 + \lambda_{12} + t_2)},$$

where $\lambda = \lambda_1 + \lambda_2 + \lambda_{12}$. The correlation between X_1 and X_2 (and between Y_1 and Y_2) is $\lambda_{12}/(\lambda_1 + \lambda_2 + \lambda_{12})$. A characterization of this distribution is that there exist independent exponential variables Z_1,Z_2,Z_3 such that $Y_1 = \min(Z_1,Z_3)$ and $Y_2 = \min(Z_2,Z_3)$. It is important to note that this distribution is a *mixed* distribution, since

$$\Pr[Y_1 = Y_2] = \Pr[\text{first "fatal shock" affects both components}] = \frac{\lambda_{12}}{\lambda_1 + \lambda_2 + \lambda_{12}} > 0.$$

Nevertheless, the marginal distributions are each continuous. If (Y_{1j}, Y_{2j}) $(j = 1,\ldots,n)$ are n independent pairs of variables, each having the distribution (64), then the following consistent estimators of λ_1, λ_2, and λ_{12} have been proposed by Arnold [1]:

$$(66)\qquad \hat{\lambda}_t = n^{-1}\sum_{j=1}^{n} W_{tj}/T \qquad (t = 1,2),$$

$$\hat{\lambda}_{12} = n^{-1}\sum_{j=1}^{n} W_{3j}/T,$$

where

$$W_{1j} = 1 \quad \text{if} \quad Y_{1j} < Y_{2j}, \qquad 0 \text{ otherwise},$$

$$W_{2j} = 1 \quad \text{if} \quad Y_{1j} > Y_{2j}, \qquad 0 \text{ otherwise},$$

$$W_{3j} = 1 \quad \text{if} \quad Y_{1j} = Y_{2j}, \qquad 0 \text{ otherwise},$$

and

$$T = (n-1)\sum_{j=1}^{n} \min(Y_{1j}, Y_{2j}).$$

Saw [29] has generalized (64) by replacing $\max(y_1,y_2)$ by an increasing function of $\max(y_1,y_2)$. This can be interpreted as arising from a situation in which the joint failure rate can vary with time. The marginal distributions are still exponential. A particular function suggested by Saw is

$$\lambda\int_0^{\max(y_1,y_2)} t(\gamma + t)^{-1}\,dt = \lambda[\max(y_1,y_2) - \gamma\log\{\gamma + \max(y_1,y_2)\}]$$

for which

$$(67)\quad \Pr(Y_1 > y_1) \cap (Y_2 > y_2)] = [\gamma + \max(y_1,y_2)]^{\lambda\gamma}\exp\{-(\lambda_1 y_1 + \lambda_2 y_2 + \lambda\max(y_1,y_2))\} \qquad (y_1 > 0, y_2 > 0).$$

3.5. *Moran's Bivariate Exponential Distribution*

Moran [20] has constructed a bivariate distribution with marginal exponential distributions as the joint distribution of

$$(68)\qquad X_1 = \tfrac{1}{2}(U_1^2 + U_2^2) \qquad \text{and} \qquad X_2 = \tfrac{1}{2}(U_3^2 + U_4^2),$$

where U_1,U_2,U_3,U_4 are all unit normal variables; (U_1,U_3) and (U_2,U_4) are mutually independent, but each pair has a bivariate normal distribution with correlation ω. The joint characteristic function of X_1 and X_2 is

(69) $$\{(1 - it_1)(1 - it_2) + \omega^2 t_1 t_2\}^{-1} = \sum_{j=0}^{\infty} [(1 - it_1)(1 - it_2)]^{-(j+1)}(-\omega^2 t_1 t_2)^j.$$

Noting that

$$\frac{(-t_1t_2)^j}{(1 - it_1)^{j+1}(1 - it_2)^{j+1}} = \prod_{k=1}^{2} [(1 - it_k)^{-1}\{(1 - it_k)^{-1} - 1\}^j]$$
$$= \prod_{k=1}^{2} \left\{ \sum_{g=0}^{j} (-1)^g \binom{j}{g} (1 - it_k)^{-(g+1)} \right\},$$

and remembering (Chapter 17, Section 2) the characteristic function of a gamma variable, we see that

(70) $$p_{X_1,X_2}(x_1,x_2) = \sum_{j=0}^{\infty} \omega^{2j} \left[\prod_{k=1}^{2} \left\{ \sum_{g=0}^{j} (-1)^g \binom{j}{g} (g!)^{-1} x_k^g e^{-x_k} \right\} \right].$$

From the structure of (68) it is clear that

(71) $$\begin{cases} E[X_j] = 1, \\ \text{var}(X_j) = 1, \\ \text{corr}(X_1,X_2) = \text{cov}(X_1,X_2) = \frac{1}{2} \text{cov}(U_1^2,U_3^2) = \omega^2. \end{cases}$$

This distribution is a special case of the multivariate gamma distribution of Section 3 in Chapter 40 (corresponding to $m = 2$, $n = 2$).

4. Multivariate Exponential Distributions

Weinman [31] has extended Freund's bivariate exponential distribution to a multivariate exponential distribution in the following way. Suppose that a system has m identical components with times to failure $X_1,X_2,\ldots,X_m$. These each have the exponential distribution

$$p_X(x) = \theta_0^{-1} \exp(-x/\theta_0) \qquad (x > 0; \theta_0 > 0).$$

It is further supposed that if k components have failed (and not been replaced), the conditional joint distribution of the lifetimes of the remaining $(m - k)$ components is that of independent random variables, each having the distribution

$$p_X(x) = \theta_k^{-1} \exp(-x/\theta_k) \qquad (x > 0; \theta_k > 0).$$

Weinman shows that the joint density of $X_1,\ldots,X_m$ is then

(72) $$p(x_1,\ldots,x_m) = \prod_{j=0}^{m-1} [\theta_j^{-1} \exp\{-(m - j)\theta_j^{-1}(x_{j+1} - x_j)\}],$$

where $x_0 = 0$ and $x_1 \le x_2 \le \cdots \le x_m$ are the m x_j's arranged in increasing order of magnitude. The moment generating function is

$$E\left[\exp\left(\sum_{j=1}^{m} t_j X_j\right)\right] = (m!)^{-1} \sum_p{}^* \prod_{j=0}^{m-1} \left[1 - \left(\theta_j \sum_{i=j+1}^{m} t_{p(i)}\right) \Big/ (m-j)\right]^{-1},$$

where $\{t_{p(t)}, \ldots, t_{p(m)}\}$ is one of the $m!$ possible permutations of $t_1, \ldots, t_m$ and Σ^* denotes summation over all such permutations. The distribution is clearly symmetrical in $X_1, \ldots, X_m$. For each j $(= 1,2, \ldots, m)$

$$(73.1) \qquad E[X_j] = m^{-1} \sum_{j=0}^{m-1} \theta_j,$$

$$(73.2) \quad \operatorname{var}(X_j) = m^{-2}\left[\sum_{j=0}^{m-1} (m+j)(m-j)^{-1}\theta_j^2 + 2\sum_{j<j'}\sum j(m-j)\theta_j\theta_{j'}\right].$$

Also,

$$(73.3) \quad \operatorname{cov}(X_j, X_{j'}) = m^{-2}(m-1)^{-1}\left[\sum_{j=0}^{m-1}\left(m - \frac{m+j}{m-j}\right)\theta_j^2 - 2\sum_{j<j'}\sum j(m-j)\theta_j\theta_{j'}\right].$$

The joint moment generating function of the *ordered* variables $X_1' \leq X_2' \leq \cdots \leq X_m'$ has the relatively simple form

$$\prod_{j=0}^{m-1}\left[1 - \left(\theta_j \sum_{i=j+1}^{m} t_i\right)(m-j)^{-1}\right]^{-1}.$$

[The joint density of $X_1', \ldots, X_m'$ is of course $m!$ times the density in (72).] From this we find

$$(74.1) \qquad E[X_j'] = \sum_{i=0}^{j-1} (m-i)^{-1}\theta_i,$$

$$(74.2) \qquad \operatorname{var}(X_j') = \sum_{i=0}^{j-1} (m-i)^{-2}\theta_i^2,$$

and, for $j < j'$,

$$(74.3) \qquad \operatorname{cov}(X_j', X_{j'}') = \operatorname{var}(X_j').$$

We note that since the distribution of $X^{1/c}$ is Weibull if X has an exponential distribution, *multivariate Weibull* distributions can be constructed as the joint distributions of $X_1^{1/c_1}, \ldots, X_m^{1/c_m}$ where $X_1, \ldots, X_m$ have a joint multivariate exponential distribution.

Marshall and Olkin [18] have generalized their bivariate exponential distribution (described in Section 3.4) in the following way. In a system of m components the distribution of times between "fatal shocks" to the combination $\{a_1, \ldots, a_s\}$ of components is supposed to have an exponential distribution with expected value $\lambda_{a_1,\ldots,a_s}^{-1}$. The $2^{m-1} - 1$ different distributions of this kind are supposed to be a mutually independent set. The resulting joint distribution of lifetimes $Y_1, \ldots, Y_m$ of the components is

$$\text{(75)} \quad \Pr\left[\bigcap_{j=1}^{m}(Y_j > y_j)\right]$$
$$= \exp\left[-\sum_{j=1}^{m}\lambda_j y_j - \sum_{j_1<j_2}\sum \lambda_{j_1 j_2}\max(y_{j_1}, y_{j_2})\right.$$
$$\left. - \sum_{j_1<j_2<j_3}\sum\sum \lambda_{j_1 j_2 j_3}\max(y_{j_1}, y_{j_2}, y_{j_3}) - \cdots - \lambda_{12\cdots m}\max(y_1, \ldots, y_m)\right].$$

This, of course, is also a mixed distribution, as in the bivariate case.

Arnold [1] has pointed out that estimation of the λ's by standard maximum likelihood or moment methods is not simple. He has suggested the following method of estimation which exploits the singular nature of the distribution.

We define

$$Z_{a_1,\ldots,a_s} = \begin{cases} 1 & \text{if } \; Y_{a_1} = Y_{a_2} = \cdots = Y_{a_s} < Y_j \\ & \qquad\qquad \text{for all } \; j \neq a_1, a_2, \ldots, a_s, \\ 0 & \text{otherwise.} \end{cases}$$

Given n independent sets $\mathbf{Y}_j = (Y_{1j}, \ldots, Y_{mj})$ each having the joint distribution (75), the estimator of $\lambda_{a_1,\ldots,a_s}$, is, in an obvious notation,

$$\text{(76)} \qquad \left[n^{-1}\sum_{j=1}^{n} Z_{a_1,\ldots,a_s,(j)}\right]\left[(n-1)^{-1}\sum_{j=1}^{n}\min(Y_{1j}, \ldots, Y_{mj})\right]^{-1}.$$

The numerator and denominator of (76) are mutually independent. The estimator is unbiased and has variance

$$[n(n-2)]^{-1}\lambda_{a_1,\ldots,a_s}[(n-1)\lambda + \lambda_{a_1,\ldots,a_s}],$$

where λ = sum of $\lambda_{a_1,\ldots,a_s}$'s over all possible sets $\{a_1, \ldots, a_s\}$.

Note that if n is not large, many of the estimators (76) will have the value zero. In fact for each $\mathbf{Y}_j$, only one Z (at most) will not be zero, so there must be at least $(2^m - 1 - n)$ estimators with zero values.

A further example of a multivariate exponential distribution is obtained by taking $\nu = 2$ in the joint distribution of Krishnamoorthy and Parthasarathy (Chapter 40, Section 3). The joint characteristic function (from (18.1) of Chapter 40) is

$$\text{(77)} \qquad E\left[\exp\left(i\sum_{j=1}^{m} t_j Y_j\right)\right] = |\mathbf{I}_m - 2i\mathbf{R}\mathbf{D}_t|^{-1},$$

where $\mathbf{R}$ is a correlation matrix and $\mathbf{D}_t = \operatorname{diag}(t_1, \ldots, t_m)$. Since $|\mathbf{I}_m - 2i\mathbf{R}\mathbf{D}_t|$ is a polynomial in $(1 - 2it_1), \ldots, (1 - 2it_m)$, the joint distribution can be expressed formally as a mixture of a finite number of χ^2 distributions.

REFERENCES

[1] Arnold, B. C. (1968). Parameter estimation for a multivariate exponential distribution, *Journal of the American Statistical Association*, **63,** 848–852.

[2] Downton, F. (1970). Bivariate exponential distributions in reliability theory, *Journal of the Royal Statistical Society*, *Series B*, **32,** 408–417.

[3] Farlie, D. J. G. (1960). The performance of some correlation coefficients for a general bivariate distribution, *Biometrika*, **47,** 307–323.

[4] Fréchet, M. (1951). Sur les tableau de corrélation dont les marges sont données, *Annales de l'Université de Lyon*, *Ser. III*, **14,** 53–77.

[5] Freund, R. J. (1961). A bivariate extension of the exponential distribution, *Journal of the American Statistical Association*, **56,** 971–977.

[6] Geffroy, J. (1958, 1959). Contribution à la théorie des valeurs extrêmes, *Publications de l'Institut de Statistique de l'Université de Paris*, **7,** 37–121; **8,** 123–184.

[7] Gumbel, E. J. (1958). *Statistics of Extremes*, 2nd ed., New York: Columbia University Press.

[8] Gumbel, E. J. (1958). Distributions à plusieurs variables dont les marges sont données (with remarks by M. Fréchet), *Comptes Rendus de l'Académie des Sciences*, *Paris*, **246,** 2717–2720.

[9] Gumbel, E. J. (1960). Bivariate exponential distributions, *Journal of the American Statistical Association*, **55,** 698–707.

[10] Gumbel, E. J. (1961). Multivariate exponential distributions, *Bulletin of the International Statistical Institute*, **39**(2), 469–475.

[11] Gumbel, E. J. (1961). Bivariate logistic distributions, *Journal of the American Statistical Association*, **56,** 335–349.

[12] Gumbel, E. J. (1965). *Two Systems of Bivariate Extremal Distributions*, 35th Session of the International Statistical Institute, Beograd, No. 69.

[13] Gumbel, E. J. and Goldstein, N. (1964). Analysis of empirical bivariate extremal distributions, *Journal of the American Statistical Association*, **59,** 794–816.

[14] Gumbel, E. J. and Mustafi, C. K. (1967). Some analytical properties of bivariate extremal distributions, *Journal of the American Statistical Association*, **62,** 569–588.

[15] Harris, R. (1966). *Reliability Applications of a Bivariate Exponential Distribution*, University of California Operations Research Center, ORC 66–36.

[16] Konijn, H. S. (1957). On a class of two-dimensional random variables and distribution functions, *Sankhyā*, **18,** 167–172.

[17] Konijn, H. S. (1959). Positive and negative dependence of two random variables, *Sankhyā*, **21,** 269–280.

[18] Marshall, A. W. and Olkin, I. (1967). A multivariate exponential distribution, *Journal of the American Statistical Association*, **62,** 30–44.

[19] Marshall, A. W. and Olkin, I. (1967). A generalized bivariate exponential distribution, *Journal of Applied Probability*, **4,** 291–302.

[20] Moran, P. A. P. (1967). Testing for correlation between non-negative variates, *Biometrika*, **54,** 385–394.

[21] Morgenstern, D. (1956). Einfache Beispiele zweidimensionaler Verteilungen, *Mitteilungsblatt für mathematische Statistik*, **8,** 234–235.

[21a] Nagao, M. and Kadoya, M. (1971). Two-variate exponential distribution and its numerical table for engineering application, *Bulletin of the Disaster Prevention Research Institute*, **20,** No. 3, 183–215.

[22] Oliveira, J. T. de (1961). La représentation des distributions extrêmales bivariées, *Bulletin of the International Statistical Institute*, **33,** 477–480.

[23] Oliveira, J. T. de (1958). Extremal distributions, *Revista da Faculdade de Ciencias, Lisboa, Serie A*, **7,** 215–227.

[24] Oliveira, J. T. de (1963). Structure theory of bivariate extremes; Extensions. *Estodes de Matemática, Estatística e Econometria*, **7,** 165–195.

[25] Oliveira, J. T. de (1964). L'indépendance dans les distributions extrêmales bivariées, *Publications de l'Institut de Statistique de l'Université de Paris*, **13,** 137–141.

[26] Oliveira, J. T. de (1968). Extremal processes: Definitions and properties, *Publications de l'Institut de Statistique de l'Université de Paris*, **18,** (2), 25–36.

[27] Oliveira, J. T. de (1970). Biextremal distributions: Statistical decision, *Trabajos de Estadistica*, **21,** 107–117.

[28] Posner, E. C., Rodemich, E. R., Ashlock, J. C., and Lurie, Sandra (1969). Application of an estimator of high efficiency in bivariate extreme value theory, *Journal of the American Statistical Association*, **64,** 1403–1414.

[29] Saw, J. G. (1969). *A bivariate exponential density and a test that two identical components in parallel behave independently*, Technical Report No. 22, Department of Industrial and Systems Engineering, University of Florida, Gainsville.

[30] Sibuya, M. (1960). Bivariate extreme statistics, I, *Annals of the Institute of Statistical Mathematics, Tokyo*, **19,** 195–210.

[31] Weinman, D. G. (1966). *A multivariate extension of the exponential distribution*, Ph.D. thesis, Arizona State University.

42

Miscellaneous Real Multivariate Distributions

1. Introduction

It is possible to build up multivariate distributions by placing requirements on certain marginal and array distributions. For example, specifications of the (marginal) distribution of X_1 and of the array distribution of X_2, given X_1, suffices to specify the joint distribution of X_1 and X_2. It is often the case, with multivariate distributions built up in these ways, that we have quite a clear idea of the structure of the distributions, even though the explicit analytic form for the joint density function may be very complicated or even unmanageable. While it is not easy to test the validity of models containing such distributions by direct comparison of observed and theoretical frequencies, indirect comparisons (e.g., of observed and theoretical regression functions) are possible and can be of much value. Such is the case, for example, with the multivariate gamma distribution described in Section 2 of Chapter 40.

In this chapter we describe some further distributions of this kind.

2. Beta-Stacy Distribution

This is the name given by Mihram and Hultquist [26] to a bivariate distribution constructed in the following way.

(i) X_1 has a generalized gamma distribution of the kind described by Stacy (see Chapter 17, Section 8.4), with

$$(1)\quad p_{X_1}(x_1) = [\Gamma(\alpha)]^{-1}ca^{-\alpha c}x_1^{\alpha c-1}\exp[-(x_1/a)^c] \qquad (x_1 > 0;\alpha,c,a > 0).$$

(Note that if $\alpha = 1$, this is a Weibull distribution; hence the distribution that we construct is then a multivariate Weibull distribution.)

(ii) The conditional distribution of X_2, given $X_1 = x_1$, is beta with range $(0,x_1)$, so that

$$(2)\quad p_{X_2|X_1}(x_2 \mid x_1) = \frac{1}{B(\theta_1,\theta_2)}\cdot\frac{x_2^{\theta_1-1}(x_1-x_2)^{\theta_2-1}}{x_1^{\theta_1+\theta_2-1}} \qquad (x_1 > 0;\theta_1,\theta_2 > 0).$$

Note that if $\theta_1 = \theta_2 = 1$, then $X_2 \mid X_1$ has a unit rectangular distribution. One might say that "X_2 is a randomly chosen function of X_1."

The joint distribution has the density function

$$(3)\quad p(x_1,x_2) = \frac{1}{\Gamma(\alpha)B(\theta_1,\theta_2)}\frac{c}{a^{\alpha c}}x_1^{\alpha c-\theta_1-\theta_2}x_2^{\theta_1-1}(x_1-x_2)^{\theta_2-1}\exp[-(x_1/a)^c] \qquad (0 < x_2 < x_1).$$

The special form of this distribution with $c = 1$ (so that X_1 has a gamma distribution) was obtained in 1934 by McKay [25] as the joint distribution of Y_1 and $Y_1 + Y_2$, where Y_1, Y_2 are independent gamma variables.

The (r_2)th moment (about zero) of X_2, given X_1, is

$$(4)\qquad E[X_2^{r_2} \mid X_1] = X_1^{r_2}B(\theta_1 + r_2,\ \theta_2)/B(\theta_1,\theta_2).$$

Hence the (r_1,r_2)th product moment of X_1 and X_2 is

$$(5)\qquad E[X_1^{r_1}X_2^{r_2}] = E[X_1^{r_1+r_2}]B(\theta_1 + r_2,\ \theta_2)/B(\theta_1,\theta_2) = \frac{a^{r_1+r_2}\Gamma(\alpha + c^{-1}(r_1+r_2))\Gamma(\theta_1 + r_2)\Gamma(\theta_1+\theta_2)}{\Gamma(\alpha)\Gamma(\theta_1)\Gamma(\theta_1+\theta_2+r_2)}.$$

In particular from (4)

$$(6.1)\qquad E[X_2 \mid X_1] = \frac{\theta_1}{\theta_1+\theta_2}X_1 \qquad \text{(regression is linear)},$$

$$(6.2)\qquad \operatorname{var}(X_2 \mid X_1) = \frac{\theta_1\theta_2}{(\theta_1+\theta_2)^2(\theta_1+\theta_2+1)}X_1^2.$$

Also,

$$(7.1)\qquad E[X_2] = \frac{\theta_1}{\theta_1+\theta_2}E[X_1] = \frac{a\theta_1}{\theta_1+\theta_2}\frac{\Gamma(\alpha+c^{-1})}{\Gamma(\alpha)}$$

and

$$(7.2)\quad \operatorname{var}[X_2] = \frac{a^2\theta_1}{\theta_1+\theta_2}\frac{1}{\Gamma(\alpha)}\left[\frac{\theta_1+1}{\theta_1+\theta_2+1}\Gamma(\alpha+2c^{-1}) - \frac{\theta_1}{\theta_1+\theta_2}\frac{\{\Gamma(\alpha+c^{-1})\}^2}{\Gamma(\alpha)}\right].$$

For c large,

$$(7.1)'\qquad E[X_2] \doteqdot \frac{a\theta_1}{\theta_1+\theta_2}[1+c^{-1}\psi(\alpha)],$$

$$(7.2)'\qquad \operatorname{var}(X_2) \doteqdot \frac{2a^2\theta_1\theta_2\psi(\alpha)}{(\theta_1+\theta_2)^2(\theta_1+\theta_2+1)}.$$

($\psi(\cdot)$ is the digamma function defined in Chapter 1, Section 3.)

In general it is not possible to obtain a simple explicit formula for the marginal density function of X_2. If θ_2 is a positive integer, then

$$(8.1)\quad p_{X_2}(x_2) = \frac{1}{\Gamma(\alpha)B(\theta_1,\theta_2)}\sum_{j=0}^{\theta_2-1}(-1)^j\binom{\theta_2-1}{j}a^{-(\theta_1+j)}x_2^{\theta_1+j-1} \times \int_{(x_2/a)^c}^{\infty} y^{\alpha-c^{-1}(\theta_1+j)-1}e^{-y}\,dy.$$

In particular, for $\theta_2 = 1$,

$$(8.2)\qquad p_{X_2}(x_2) = \frac{\theta_1 x_2^{\theta_1-1}}{a^{\theta_1+1}\Gamma(\alpha)}\int_{(x_2/a)^c}^{\infty} y^{\alpha-c^{-1}\theta_1-1}e^{-y}\,dy.$$

Returning the general case, the covariance between X_1 and X_2 is

$$(9.1)\qquad \operatorname{cov}(X_1,X_2) = \frac{\theta_1}{\theta_1+\theta_2}\operatorname{var}(X_1)$$

and the correlation is

$$(9.2)\quad \operatorname{corr}(X_1,X_2) = \left[\theta_1(\theta_1+\theta_2+1) \times \frac{\Gamma(\alpha)\Gamma(\alpha+2c^{-1}) - \{\Gamma(\alpha+c^{-1})\}^2}{(\theta_1+1)(\theta_1+\theta_2)\Gamma(\alpha)\Gamma(\alpha+2c^{-1}) - \theta_1(\theta_1+\theta_2+1)\{\Gamma(\alpha+c^{-1})\}^2}\right]^{1/2}.$$

As c tends to infinity, the correlation tends to zero. For $c = 1$ (corresponding to a "beta-gamma" bivariate distribution) the correlation is

$$(9.3)\qquad \left[1+\frac{(1+\alpha)\theta_2}{\theta_1(\theta_1+\theta_2+1)}\right]^{-1/2}.$$

Mihram and Hultquist [26] obtain the remarkable general result that if the conditional density function of X_2, given X_1, is as in (2), then the distribution of $X_1 - X_2$ will be the same as that of X_2, with θ_1 and θ_2 reversed, provided *only* that the density function of X_1 is a symmetric function of θ_1 and θ_2.

(This condition is trivially satisfied for the beta-Stacy distribution, since the density function of X_1 does not depend on θ_1 or θ_2 at all.)

Given n independent pairs of random variables (X_{1j},X_{2j}) $(j = 1,\ldots,n)$, each having the beta-Stacy distribution as defined by (3), the Cramér-Rao lower bounds for the variance of unbiased estimators of θ_1, θ_2, α, a, and c are, respectively,

(10.1) $$n^{-1}\{\psi'(\theta_1) - \psi'(\theta_1 + \theta_2)\}^{-1} \qquad (\text{for } \theta_1),$$

(10.2) $$n^{-1}\{\psi'(\theta_2) - \psi'(\theta_1 + \theta_2)\}^{-1} \qquad (\text{for } \theta_2),$$

(10.3) $$n^{-1}\{\psi^{-1}(\alpha)\}^{-1} \qquad (\text{for } \alpha),$$

(10.4) $$n^{-1}a^2\alpha^{-1}c^{-2} \qquad (\text{for } a),$$

(10.5) $$n^{-1}c^2\{1 + \alpha[\psi'(\alpha + 1) + \{\psi(\alpha + 1)\}^2]\}^{-1} \qquad (\text{for } c),$$

where $\psi(\cdot),\psi'(\cdot)$ are the digamma and trigamma functions, respectively, as defined in Section 3 of Chapter 1.

Note that the parameters separate into two groups (θ_1,θ_2) and (α,a,c). This is in accordance with a general result of Rao [32].

The statistics

$$\prod_{j=1}^{n}(X_{2j}/X_{1j}) \qquad \text{and} \qquad \prod_{j=1}^{n}(1 - X_{2j}/X_{1j})$$

are jointly sufficient for θ_1 and θ_2. If c is known, then

$$\prod_{j=1}^{n}X_{1j} \qquad \text{and} \qquad \sum_{j=1}^{n}X_{1j}^c$$

are jointly sufficient for α and a. Of course, if c is known, then calculations are simplified by using the variable $Y = X_1^c$ in place of X_1. The joint distribution of Y and X_2 is a "beta-gamma" distribution.

If c is not known, maximum likelihood equations for estimators $\hat{\theta}_1$, $\hat{\theta}_2$, $\hat{\alpha}$, $\hat{a}$, and $\hat{c}$ are

(11.1) $$\sum_{j=1}^{n}\log\left(\frac{X_{2j}}{X_{1j}}\right) = n[\psi(\hat{\theta}_1) - \psi(\hat{\theta}_1 + \hat{\theta}_2)],$$

(11.2) $$\sum_{j=1}^{n}\log\left(1 - \frac{X_{2j}}{X_{1j}}\right) = n[\psi(\hat{\theta}_2) - \psi(\hat{\theta}_1 + \hat{\theta}_2)],$$

(11.3) $$\sum_{j=1}^{n}\log X_{1j} = n[\log\hat{a} + \hat{c}^{-1}\psi(\hat{\alpha})],$$

(11.4) $$\sum_{j=1}^{n}X_{1j}^{\hat{c}} = n\hat{\alpha}\hat{a}^{\hat{c}},$$

(11.5) $$\hat{\alpha}\sum_{j=1}^{n}\log(X_{1j}/\hat{a}) - \sum_{j=1}^{n}(X_{1j}/\hat{a})^{\hat{c}}\log(X_{1j}/\hat{a}) = -n\hat{c}^{-1}.$$

Note that (11.3) to (11.5), from which $\hat{\alpha}$, $\hat{a}$, and $\hat{c}$ may be found, depend only on X_{1j}'s; and (11.1) and (11.2), from which $\hat{\theta}_1$ and $\hat{\theta}_2$ may be found, depend only on (X_{2j}/X_{1j})'s.

If it is expected that c may be less than 1, then care should be taken, since the maximum likelihood estimators may not be solutions of (11.3) to (11.5).

Although a is a parameter of the marginal distribution of X_1, and not of X_2, it is possible to estimate a with fair accuracy from values of X_2 alone. Mihram and Hultquist [26] point out that if θ_1, θ_2, α, and c are known, then there are two unbiased estimators of a:

$$\tilde{a}_1 = \left[\frac{\Gamma(\theta_1)\Gamma(\alpha)\Gamma(\theta_1+\theta_2+n^{-1})}{\Gamma(\theta_1+n^{-1})\Gamma(\alpha+(nc)^{-1})\Gamma(\theta_1+\theta_2)}\right]^n \prod_{j=1}^{n} X_{2j}^{1/n} \tag{12.1}$$

and

$$\tilde{a}_2 = \frac{(\theta_1+\theta_2)\Gamma(\alpha)}{n\theta_1\Gamma(\alpha+c^{-1})}\sum_{j=1}^{n} X_{2j}. \tag{12.2}$$

(Note that if $\theta_1 = \theta_2 = 1$, then

$$\tilde{a}_1 = [(1+n^{-1})\Gamma(\alpha)/\Gamma(\alpha+(nc)^{-1})]^n \prod_{j=1}^{n} X_{2j}^{1/n};$$

$$\tilde{a}_2 = 2n^{-1}\Gamma(\alpha)\{\Gamma(\alpha+c^{-1})\}^{-1}\sum_{j=1}^{n} X_{2j}.\Big)$$

We have

$$\operatorname{var}(\tilde{a}_1) = a^2\left\{\left[\frac{\Gamma(\alpha)\Gamma(\theta_1)\Gamma(\alpha+2[nc]^{-1})\Gamma(\theta_1+2n^{-1})\{\Gamma(\theta_1+\theta_2+n^{-1})\}^2}{\Gamma(\theta_1+\theta_2)\Gamma(\theta_1+\theta_2+2n^{-1})\{\Gamma(\alpha+[nc]^{-1})\Gamma(\theta_1+n^{-1})\}^2}\right]^n - 1\right\}; \tag{13.1}$$

$$\operatorname{var}(\tilde{a}_2) = a^2 n^{-1}\left\{\frac{(\theta_1+1)(\theta_1+\theta_2)\Gamma(\alpha+2c^{-1})\Gamma(\alpha)}{\theta_1(\theta_1+\theta_2+1)[\Gamma(\alpha+c^{-1})]^2} - 1\right\}; \tag{13.2}$$

$$\operatorname{cov}(\tilde{a}_1,\tilde{a}_2) = a^2\left\{\frac{1+(n\theta_1)^{-1}}{1+[n(\theta_1+\theta_2)]^{-1}}\cdot\frac{\Gamma(\alpha)\Gamma(\alpha+[n+1][nc]^{-1})}{\Gamma(\alpha+c^{-1})\Gamma(\alpha+[nc]^{-1})} - 1\right\}. \tag{13.3}$$

An unbiased estimator of the form

$$\tilde{a}_3 = C\tilde{a}_1 + (1-C)\tilde{a}_2$$

has minimum variance if

$$C = \frac{\operatorname{var}(\tilde{a}_2) - \operatorname{cov}(\tilde{a}_1,\tilde{a}_2)}{\operatorname{var}(\tilde{a}_1) + \operatorname{var}(\tilde{a}_2) - 2\operatorname{cov}(\tilde{a}_1,\tilde{a}_2)}.$$

Table 1 (expanded from Johnson and Kotz [17]) shows some values of the

TABLE 1

Comparison of Estimators of a

c	α	θ_1	θ_2	n	$a^{-2}n\,\mathrm{var}(\hat{a}_1)$	$a^{-2}n\,\mathrm{var}(\hat{a}_2)$	$\mathrm{corr}(\hat{a}_1,\hat{a}_2)$	C	$a^{-2}n\,\mathrm{var}(\hat{a}_3)$
0.5	0.5	0.5	0.5	10	30.3		0.33	0.29	13.9
				20	27.7		0.32	0.32	13.4
				50	25.2	16.5	0.32	0.35	13.1
				100	24.2		0.32	0.36	12.9
				∞	23.0		0.32		
		0.5	1.0	100	25.0	20.0	0.30	0.42	14.4
		1.0	0.5		21.1	13.0	0.35	0.32	10.7
		1.0	1.0		21.5	14.6	0.33	0.36	11.5
		1.0	2.0		21.8	16.5	0.32	0.40	12.3
		2.0	1.0		20.6	12.1	0.35	0.30	10.1
		2.0	2.0		20.7	13.0	0.34	0.33	10.6
		1.0	5.0		22.0	19.0	0.31	0.45	13.3
		5.0	1.0		20.3	11.0	0.36	0.27	9.5
		5.0	5.0	10	22.6		0.37	0.26	10.3
				20	22.0		0.36	0.27	10.1
				50	20.9	11.7	0.35	0.29	10.0
				100	20.4		0.35	0.29	9.9
				∞	19.9				

0.5	2.0	0.5	0.5	10	5.7		0.58	0.29	3.7
		↓	↓	20	5.8		0.57	0.29	3.6
				50	5.9	4.0	0.56	0.29	3.6
				100	5.9		0.55	0.29	3.6
				∞					
		0.5	1.0	100	6.6	5.0	0.53	0.36	4.3
		1.0	0.5	↓	3.3	3.0	0.64	0.44	2.6
		1.0	1.0		3.6	3.4	0.62	0.47	2.8
		1.0	2.0		3.8	4.0	0.60	0.52	3.1
		2.0	1.0		2.8	2.75	0.66	0.48	2.3
		2.0	2.0		2.9	3.0	0.65	0.51	2.5
		1.0	5.0		4.1	4.7	0.58	0.59	3.4
		5.0	1.0		2.6	2.4	0.68	0.44	2.1
		5.0	5.0	10	2.7		0.69	0.47	2.3
		↓	↓	20	2.7		0.68	0.48	2.2
				50	2.7	2.6	0.67	0.48	2.2
				100	2.7		0.67	0.48	2.2
				∞					

TABLE 1 (*Continued*)

c	α	θ_1	θ_2	n	$a^{-2}n\ \mathrm{var}(\hat{a}_1)$	$a^{-2}n\ \mathrm{var}(\hat{a}_2)$	$\mathrm{corr}(\hat{a}_1,\hat{a}_2)$	C	$a^{-2}n\ \mathrm{var}(\hat{a}_3)$
1.0	0.5	0.5	0.5	10	8.07		0.58	0.08	3.47
				20	8.23		0.57	0.08	3.46
				50	8.26	3.50	0.56	0.08	3.46
				100	8.25		0.56	0.09	3.46
		↓	↓	∞					
		0.5	1.0	100	9.00	4.40	0.53	0.16	4.24
		1.0	0.5		5.62	2.60	0.61	0.07	2.58
		1.0	1.0		5.92	3.00	0.59	0.13	2.94
		1.0	2.0		6.18	3.50	0.58	0.19	3.34
		2.0	1.0		5.15	2.375	0.62	0.06	2.36
		2.0	2.0		5.26	2.60	0.61	0.10	2.56
		1.0	5.0		6.41	4.14	0.55	0.27	3.80
		5.0	1.0	↓	4.93	2.09	0.63	0.18	2.08
		5.0	5.0	10	4.61		0.65	0.06	2.26
				20	4.83		0.64	0.06	2.26
				50	4.97	2.27	0.63	0.06	2.26
				100	5.01		0.62	0.06	2.26
		↓	↓	∞					

1.0	2.0	0.5	0.5	10	3.29		0.72	−0.13	1.22
				20	3.60		0.70	−0.12	1.22
				50	3.80	1.25	0.68	−0.12	1.22
				100	3.86		0.68	−0.12	1.22
		↓	↓	∞					
		0.5	1.0	100	4.59	1.70	0.66	−0.05	1.69
		1.0	0.5	↓	1.34	0.80	0.80	−0.07	0.80
		1.0	1.0		1.63	1.00	0.78	0.00	1.00
		1.0	2.0		1.89	1.25	0.76	0.10	1.24
		2.0	1.0		0.89	0.69	0.85	0.08	0.69
		2.0	2.0		1.00	0.80	0.84	0.16	0.79
		1.0	5.0		2.10	1.57	0.73	0.23	1.52
		5.0	1.0		0.68	0.54	0.87	0.06	0.54
		5.0	5.0	10	0.75		0.88	0.19	0.63
				20	0.75		0.87	0.18	0.63
				50	0.76	0.64	0.87	0.18	0.63
				100	0.76		0.86	0.18	0.63
		↓	↓	∞					

TABLE 1 (Continued)

c	α	θ_1	θ_2	n	$a^{-2}n$ var$(\hat{a}_1)$	$a^{-2}n$ var$(\hat{a}_2)$	corr$(\hat{a}_2,\hat{a}_2)$	C	$a^{-2}n$ var$(\hat{a}_3)$
2.0	0.5	0.5	0.5	10	3.90		0.72	−0.15	1.31
		↓	↓	20	4.21		0.70	−0.14	1.31
		↓	↓	50	4.40	1.36	0.69	−0.14	1.31
		↓	↓	100	4.46		0.69	−0.14	1.31
		↓	↓	∞					
		0.5	1.0	100	5.19	1.83	0.66	−0.07	1.81
		1.0	0.5	↓	1.93	0.88	0.79	−0.18	0.86
		1.0	1.0	↓	2.22	1.09	0.77	−0.11	1.08
		1.0	2.0	↓	2.47	1.36	0.74	−0.004	1.36
		2.0	1.0	↓	1.47	0.77	0.81	−0.18	0.75
		2.0	2.0	↓	1.58	0.88	0.80	−0.10	0.88
		1.0	5.0	↓	2.69	1.69	0.72	+0.12	1.67
		5.0	1.0	↓	1.26	0.62	0.82	−0.26	0.59
		5.0	5.0	10	1.24		0.83	−0.18	0.70
		↓	↓	20	1.29		0.82	−0.17	0.70
		↓	↓	50	1.33	0.71	0.81	−0.17	0.70
		↓	↓	100	1.34		0.81	−0.17	0.70
		↓	↓	∞					

2.0	2.0	0.5	0.5	10	2.71		0.77	−0.28	0.59
		↓	↓	20	3.05		0.75	−0.26	0.59
				50	3.28	0.70	0.74	−0.25	0.59
				100	3.37		0.74	−0.24	0.59
				∞					
		0.5	1.0	100	4.09	1.04	0.71	−0.20	0.95
		1.0	0.5	↓	0.86	0.36	0.85	−0.41	0.31
		1.0	1.0		1.15	0.51	0.84	−0.34	0.47
		1.0	2.0		1.40	0.70	0.82	−0.22	0.67
		2.0	1.0		0.41	0.27	0.92	−0.48	0.26
		2.0	2.0		0.52	0.36	0.90	−0.32	0.35
		1.0	5.0		1.61	0.94	0.79	−0.54	0.94
		5.0	1.0		2.01	1.64	0.96	−0.52	1.59
		5.0	5.0	10	2.72		0.95	−0.18	2.34
		↓	↓	20	2.75		0.94	−0.18	2.34
				50	2.76	2.35	0.94	−0.18	2.34
				100	2.77		0.94	−0.17	2.34
				∞					

TABLE 2

Minimum Variance of Unbiased Estimator of a $[V = a^{-2} n \operatorname{var}(\hat{a})]$

$c =$	0.5				1.0				2.0			
n	α	V	α	V	α	V	α	V	α	V	α	V
10		8.67		2.05		2.00		0.50		0.51		0.126
20		8.36		2.02		2.00		0.50		0.50		0.125
50	0.5	8.15	2.0	2.01	0.5	2.00	2.0	0.50	0.5	0.50	2.0	0.125
100		8.08		2.00		2.00		0.50		0.50		0.125
∞		8.00		2.00		2.00		0.50		0.50		0.125

variance and resulting values of C for various values of the parameters c, α, θ_1, and θ_2. The final column also shows the minimized variance of the unbiased estimator $\tilde{a}_3$. Note that although $n \operatorname{var}(\tilde{a}_1)$ increases as n decreases, over the range shown, it must ultimately decrease to the (constant) value of $n \operatorname{var}(\tilde{a}_2)$, when $n = 1$. The limiting $(n = \infty)$ values are calculated from the formulas

$$(14.1) \qquad a^{-2} \lim_{n\to\infty} n \operatorname{var}(\tilde{a}_1) = c^{-2}\psi'(\alpha) + \psi'(\theta_1) - \psi'(\theta_1 + \theta_2);$$

$$(14.2) \qquad a^{-2} \lim_{n\to\infty} n \operatorname{cov}(\tilde{a}_1, \tilde{a}_2) = \theta_1^{-1} - (\theta_1 + \theta_2)^{-1} + c^{-1}[\psi(\alpha + c^{-1}) - \psi(\alpha)].$$

The reduction in variance achieved by using $\tilde{a}_3$ is certainly worthwhile for $c = 0.5$, but for $c = 1.0$ and 2.0 it does not seem to be of much importance. Generally, $\tilde{a}_1$ has a smaller variance than $\tilde{a}_2$, but this is not always so.

The minimum variance unbiased estimator of a is

$$(15) \qquad \hat{a} = \frac{\Gamma(n\alpha)}{\Gamma(n\alpha + c^{-1})} \left(\sum_{j=1}^{n} X_{1j}^{c} \right)^{1/c}.$$

Its variance is

$$(16.1) \qquad \operatorname{var}(\hat{a}) = a^2 \left[\frac{\Gamma(n\alpha)\Gamma(n\alpha + 2c^{-1})}{\{\Gamma(n\alpha + c^{-1})\}^2} - 1 \right]$$

and

$$(16.2) \qquad a^{-2} \lim_{n\to\infty} n \operatorname{var}(\hat{a}) = c^{-2}\alpha^{-1}.$$

Some values of $\operatorname{var}(\hat{a})$ are given in Table 2 (see also Johnson and Kotz [17]). Comparison of Tables 1 and 2 shows that the variables $\{X_{2j}\}$ often provide unbiased estimators of a with variances no more than twice as great as that of $\hat{a}$, which uses observed values of $\{X_{1j}\}$.

Good estimators based on $\{X_{2j}\}$ are to be expected when the correlation between X_1 and X_2 is high. If θ_1 and θ_2 are large (and particularly if θ_2/θ_1 is also large) we do in fact find that the estimators $\hat{a}_1,\hat{a}_2$ are especially good.

3. Multivariate Pareto Distributions

The joint distribution with density function

$$(17)\quad p_{X_1,X_2}(x_1,x_2) = a(a+1)(\theta_1\theta_2)^{a+1}(\theta_2x_1+\theta_1x_2-\theta_1\theta_2)^{-(a+2)}$$
$$(a>0;x_1>\theta_1>0;x_2>\theta_2>0)$$

has marginal distributions with density functions

$$p_{X_j}(x_j) = a\theta_j^a x_j^{-(a+1)} \qquad (x_j>\theta_j>0, j=1,2).$$

The X_j have Pareto distributions (with parameters a,θ_j), so that the joint distribution may be called a *bivariate Pareto* distribution. Note that the marginal distributions share a common value of the parameter a. From (6) of Chapter 19 we have (for $j = 1,2$)

$$(18.1)\qquad E[X_j] = a\theta_j(a-1)^{-1} \qquad (a>1),$$

$$(18.2)\qquad \text{var}(X_j) = a\theta_j^2(a-1)^{-2}(a-2)^{-1} \qquad (a>2).$$

The conditional distribution of X_2 given X_1 has density function

$$(19)\quad p_{X_2|X_1}(x_2 \mid x_1) = \theta_1(a+1)(\theta_2x_1)^{a+1}(\theta_1x_2+\theta_2x_1-\theta_1\theta_2)^{-(a+2)}$$
$$(x_2>\theta_2).$$

This is a nonstandard Pareto distribution. $[(\theta_1X_2+\theta_2(x_1-\theta_1))$ has a conditional distribution, given $X_1 = x_1$ which is standard Pareto with parameters $a+1,\theta_2x_1$.]

From (19)

$$(20.1)\qquad E[X_2 \mid X_1] = \theta_2[1+X_1(\theta_1a)^{-1}],$$

$$(20.2)\qquad \text{var}(X_2 \mid X_1) = (\theta_2/\theta_1)^2X_1^2(a+1)a^{-2}(a-1)^{-1}.$$

From (20.1) we find, for $a > 2$,

$$(20.3)\quad \text{cov}(X_1,X_2) = \theta_2E[X_1]+\theta_2(\theta_1a)^{-1}E[X_1^2]-a^2\theta_1\theta_2(a-1)^{-2}$$
$$= \theta_1\theta_2(a-1)^{-2}(a-2)$$

and

$$(20.4)\quad \text{corr}(X_1,X_2) = a^{-1}.$$

Mardia [23a] has studied order statistics of the multivariate Pareto distribution.

Given observed values of n independent pairs of random variables (X_{1j},X_{2j}), each having the joint distribution (17), maximum likelihood estimators of θ_1,θ_2, and a are given by

$$\hat{\theta}_1 = \min(X_{11},\ldots,X_{1n}), \tag{21.1}$$

$$\hat{\theta}_2 = \min(X_{21},\ldots,X_{2n}), \tag{21.2}$$

$$\hat{a} = (S^{-1} - \tfrac{1}{2}) + (S^{-2} + \tfrac{1}{4})^{1/2}, \tag{21.3}$$

where

$$S = n^{-1}\sum_{j=1}^{n} \log(\hat{\theta}_1^{-1}x_1 + \hat{\theta}_2^{-1}x_2 - 1).$$

Note that $\hat{\theta}_j$ has the Pareto distribution

$$\Pr[\hat{\theta}_j \le K] = 1 - (\theta_j/K)^{an} \qquad (j = 1,2) \qquad (K > \theta_j)$$

and

$$E[\hat{\theta}_j] = \theta_j\{1 - (an)^{-1}\}^{-1}; \qquad (an > 1),$$

$$\operatorname{var}(\hat{\theta}_j) = \theta_j^2 an(an-1)^{-1}(an-2)^{-1} \qquad (an > 2).$$

The joint distribution of $\hat{\theta}_1$ and $\hat{\theta}_2$ is defined by

$$\Pr[(\hat{\theta}_1 > K_1) \cap (\hat{\theta}_2 > K_2)] = (\theta_1\theta_2)^{na}(\theta_2K_1 + \theta_1K_2 - K_1K_2)^{-na} \tag{22}$$

which is of the same form as the joint distribution (17) of X_{1j} and X_{2j}, with a replaced by na. The correlation between $\hat{\theta}_1$ and $\hat{\theta}_2$ is therefore [from (20.4)] equal to $(na)^{-1}$.

Equation (17) can be generalized to give the *multivariate Pareto* density function

$$p_{X_1,\ldots,X_m}(x_1,\ldots,x_m) = a(a+1)\cdots(a+m-1)\left(\prod_{j=1}^{m}\theta_j\right)^{-1}\left(\sum_{j=1}^{m}\theta_j^{-1}x_j - m + 1\right)^{-(a+m)} \qquad (x_j > \theta_j > 0). \tag{23}$$

Any subset of the X's has a joint density of the same form as (23). The conditional density of $X_{s+1},\ldots,X_m$, given $X_1 = x_1, X_2 = x_2,\ldots,X_s = x_s$, is also of the same form, with a replaced by $(a+s)$, θ_j by $\theta_j\left(\sum_{i=1} \theta_i^{-1}x_i - s + 1\right)$, and, of course, m by $(m-s)$.

Mardia [23] has also defined *multivariate Pareto distributions of the second kind* (*type 2*) in the following way. We first note that if

$$p_X(x) = a\theta^a x^{-(a+1)} \qquad (x > \theta > 0; a > 0),$$

then $\log(X/\theta)$ has a standard exponential distribution (Chapter 18). If $X_1, X_2, \ldots, X_m$ each have Pareto distributions

$$p_{X_j}(x_j) = a_j \theta_j^{a_j} x_j^{-(a_j+1)} \qquad (x_j > \theta_j > 0; a_j > 0),$$

then the variables

$$Y_j = a_j \log(X_j/\theta_j) \qquad (j = 1, 2, \ldots, m)$$

will have some form of standard multivariate exponential distribution (see Chapter 41). To each such form of joint distribution will correspond a multivariate Pareto distribution for the X_j's.

Mardia [23] has considered in detail the bivariate case ($m = 2$) when the joint distribution of Y_1 and Y_2 has the density function

$$(24.1) \quad p_{Y_1,Y_2}(y_1,y_2) = (1-\rho^2)^{-1} I_0\left(\frac{2\rho\sqrt{(y_1 y_2)}}{1-\rho^2}\right) \exp\left(-\frac{y_1+y_2}{1-\rho^2}\right),$$

$$(y_1, y_2 > 0),$$

where $I_0(\cdot)$ is a modified Bessel function of the first kind and zero order. It follows from (24.1) that the joint density function of X_1 and X_2 is

$$(24.2) \quad p_{X_1,X_2}(x_1,x_2) = \frac{a_1 a_2}{x_1 x_2 (1-\rho^2)} [(\theta_1/x_1)^{a_1} (\theta_2/x_2)^{a_2}]^{1/(1-\rho^2)}$$

$$\times I_0\left[\frac{2\rho\sqrt{a_1 a_2 (\log(x_1/\theta_1))(\log(x_2/\theta_2))}}{1-\rho^2}\right] \qquad (x_1 > \theta_1; x_2 > \theta_2).$$

We have

$$(25.1) \qquad E[X_2 \mid X_1] = \frac{a_2 \theta_2}{a_2 - 1 + \rho^2}\left(\frac{X_1}{a_1}\right)^{a_1\rho^2/(a_1-1+\rho^2)},$$

$$(25.2) \quad \operatorname{var}(X_2 \mid X_1) = a_2 \theta_2^2 \left[\frac{(X_1/\theta_1)^{2a_1\rho^2/(a_1-2+2\rho^2)}}{a_1 - 2 + 2\rho^2} - \frac{(X_1/\theta_1)^{2a_1\rho^2/(a_1-1+\rho^2)}}{a_1 - 1 + \rho^2}\right],$$

and

$$(25.3) \qquad \operatorname{corr}(X_1, X_2) = \frac{\rho^2\sqrt{a_1 a_2 (a_1 - 2)(a_2 - 2)}}{(a_1 - 1)(a_2 - 1) - \rho^2} \qquad (a_1, a_2 > 2).$$

The maximum likelihood estimators of θ_1, θ_2, a_1, and a_2 are the same as for univariate Pareto distributions (see Chapter 19). Mardia [23] has shown that the maximum likelihood estimator of ρ^2 satisfies the equation

$$(26) \qquad \hat{\rho} = n^{-1} \sum_{j=1}^{n} g_j [I_1(2\hat{\rho} g_j/(1-\hat{\rho}^2))/I_0(2\hat{\rho} g_j/(1-\hat{\rho}^2))],$$

where

$$g_j = [\{\log(X_{1j}/\hat{\theta}_1)\}\{\log(X_{2j}/\hat{\theta}_2)\}]^{1/2}[\{\log(\hat{G}_1/\hat{\theta}_1)\}\{\log(\hat{G}_2/\hat{\theta}_2)\}]^{-1/2},$$

with

$$\hat{G}_j = \prod_{i=1}^{n} X_{ji}^{1/n}.$$

A consistent estimator of ρ^2 which is much easier to compute than (26) is the sample product moment correlation between $\log X_{1j}$ and $\log X_{2j}$. This has approximate variance

$$n^{-1}(1 - \rho^4)(2\rho^4 + 6\rho^2 + 1).$$

For the general multivariate case ($m \geq 2$) Mardia [23] supposes that $Y_1, Y_2, \ldots, Y_m$ have the multivariate exponential distribution of Krishnamoorthy and Parthasarathy [see equation (66) of Chapter 41].

Note that, for the second kind of multivariate Pareto distributions, a_1 and a_2 need not be equal (as they must be for the first kind of distribution). It is of interest to inquire what kind of multivariate exponential distribution the variables $Y_j = a \log(X_j/\theta_j)$ have when the X's have a multivariate Pareto distribution of the first kind. From (17) we find that

$$(27) \quad p_{Y_1,\ldots,Y_m}(y_1,\ldots,y_m) = \frac{a^{(m)}}{a^m}\left[\sum_{j=1}^{m} e^{y_j/a} - m + 1\right]^{-(a+m)} \exp\left(\sum_{j=1}^{m} y_j/a\right)$$

$$(y_j > 0; j = 1,2,\ldots,m).$$

Other multivariate Pareto distributions can be constructed from the different multivariate exponential distributions described in Chapter 41, by applying the transformation $X_j = \theta_j \exp(Y_j/a_j)$. Conversely, multivariate exponentials can be obtained from multivariate Pareto distributions. For example, from (23) we obtain (taking $a_j = a$) the joint density function

$$(28.1) \quad p_{Y_1,\ldots,Y_m}(y_1,\ldots,y_m) = a^{-m+1}(a+1)\cdots(a+m-1)$$

$$\times \left(\sum_{j=1}^{m} e^{y_j/a} - m + 1\right)^{-(a+m)} \exp\left(a^{-1}\sum_{j=1}^{m} y_j\right) \qquad (y_j > 0).$$

We note that

$$(28.2) \qquad \Pr\left[\bigcap_{j=1}^{m} (Y_j \geq y_j)\right] = \left(\sum_{j=1}^{m} e^{y_j/a} - m + 1\right)^{-a}.$$

The marginal distributions are each exponential.

4. Multivariate Burr Distribution

Burr's [4] distribution (Chapter 12, Section 4.5) with cumulative distribution function

$$(29) \qquad \Pr[X \leq x] = 1 - (1 + x^c)^{-k} \qquad (c,k > 0; x > 0)$$

can be obtained as a mixture of Weibull distributions

$$\Pr[X \le x] = 1 - \exp(-\theta x^c) \qquad (\theta > 0; x > 0)$$

compounded with respect to θ, which has a gamma distribution

$$p_\theta(t) = [\Gamma(k)]^{-1} t^{k-1} e^{-t} \qquad (t > 0).$$

If it is supposed that for θ fixed, the variables $X_1, X_2, \ldots, X_m$ are conditionally independent with

$$\Pr[X_j \le x_j] = 1 - \exp(-\alpha_j \theta x_j^{c_j}) \qquad (\theta, \alpha_j, c_j > 0; x_j > 0)$$

for $j = 1, 2, \ldots, m$, then the joint (unconditional) density function of $X_1, X_2, \ldots, X_m$ is

$$(30)\quad p(x_1, \ldots, x_m) = \frac{\Gamma(k+m)}{\Gamma(k)} \left(1 + \sum_{j=1}^m \alpha_j x_j^{c_j}\right)^{-(k+m)} \prod_{j=1}^m (\alpha_j c_j x_j^{c_j - 1})$$

$$(x_j > 0; j = 1, \ldots, m).$$

From the genesis of this distribution it is clear that each X_j has a Burr distribution. In fact $\alpha_j^{1/c_j} X_j$ has a standard Burr distribution of form (29) with c replaced by c_j. It is reasonable, therefore, to call the distribution defined by (30) a *multivariate Burr* distribution. (Takahasi [35].)

It is also clear that the joint density function of any subset of the X's is of the form (30), with appropriate changes in the parameters. Using the formula for the joint density of $X_2, \ldots, X_m$ we obtain the conditional density function of X_1, given $X_2, \ldots, X_m$:

$$(31)\quad p(x_1 \mid x_2, \ldots, x_m) = \frac{(k+m-1)\alpha_1 c_1}{1 + \sum_{j=2}^m \alpha_j x_j^{c_j}} \frac{x_1^{c-1}}{\left[1 + \alpha_1 x_1^{c_1 - 1} \left(1 + \sum_{j=2}^m \alpha_j x_j^{c_j}\right)^{-1}\right]^{k+m}}$$

$$(x_1 > 0).$$

Hence

$$(32)\quad \Pr\left[(X_1 \le x_1) \,\middle|\, \bigcap_{j=2}^m (X_j = x_j)\right]$$

$$= 1 - \left[1 + \alpha_1 x_1^{c_1 - 1} \left(1 + \sum_{j=2}^m \alpha_j x_j^{c_j}\right)^{-1}\right]^{-(k+m-1)},$$

and so the conditional distribution of

$$\left[\alpha_1 \Big/ \left(1 + \sum_{j=2}^m \alpha_j x_j^{c_j}\right)\right]^{1/c_1} X_1$$

is of the standard form (29) with c replaced by c_1 *and* k by $(k + m - 1)$. It follows that

$$(33)\quad E[X_1^r \mid X_2,X_3,\ldots,X_m]$$
$$= \left[\alpha_1^{-1}\left(1 + \sum_{j=2}^{m}\alpha_j X_j^{c_j}\right)\right]^{r/c_1}(k + m - 1)B(1 + rc_1^{-1},k + m - 1 - rc_1^{-1}),$$

provided that $r < (k + m - 1)c_1$. (For larger values of r the expected value is infinite.) In particular, the regression function of X_1 on $X_2,X_3,\ldots,X_m$ is

$$(34)\quad E[X_1 \mid X_2,\ldots,X_m]$$
$$= \left[\alpha_1^{-1}\left(1 + \sum_{j=2}^{m}\alpha_j X_j^{c_j}\right)\right]^{1/c_1}(k + m - 1)B(1 + c_1^{-1},k + m - 1 - c_1^{-1}).$$

Note that this is an increasing function of each X_j. Putting $m = 2$ in (34) we obtain

$$E[X_1 \mid X_2] = [\alpha_1^{-1}(1 + \alpha_2 X_2^{c_2})]^{1/c_1}(k + 1)B(1 + c_1^{-1},k + 1 - c_1^{-1}).$$

Remembering that $\alpha_2^{1/c_2}X_2$ has a standard Burr distribution, we find

$$E[X_1X_2] = \alpha_1^{-1/c_1}B(1 + c_1^{-1},k + 1 - c_1^{-1})(k + 1)$$
$$\times \int_0^\infty kc_2\alpha_2x_2^{c_2}(1 + \alpha_2x_2^{c_2})^{-(k+1-c_1^{-1})}\,dx_2$$
$$= \alpha_1^{-1/c_1}\alpha_2^{-1/c_2}\Gamma(1 + c_1^{-1})\Gamma(1 + c_2^{-1})\Gamma(k - c_1^{-1} - c_2^{-1})/\Gamma(k),$$

hence

$$(35)\quad \operatorname{cov}(X_1,X_2) = \alpha_1^{-1/c_1}\alpha_2^{-1/c_2}\Gamma(1 + c_1^{-1})\Gamma(1 + c_2^{-1})$$
$$\times \left[\frac{\Gamma(k - c_1^{-1} - c_2^{-1})}{\Gamma(k)} - \frac{\Gamma(k - c_1^{-1})}{\Gamma(k)}\frac{\Gamma(k - c_2^{-1})}{\Gamma(k)}\right].$$

For c_1,c_2 large, so that

$$\Gamma(A - c_j^{-1}) \risingdotseq \Gamma(A) - c_j^{-1}\Gamma'(A) + \tfrac{1}{2}c_j^{-2}\Gamma''(A)$$
$$= [1 - c_j^{-1}\psi(A) + \tfrac{1}{2}c_j^{-2}\psi'(A)]\Gamma(A) + \tfrac{1}{2}\{c_j^{-1}\psi(A)\}^2,$$

$$(35)'\quad \operatorname{cov}(X_1,X_2) \doteqdot \alpha_1^{-1/c_1}\alpha_2^{-1/c_2}\Gamma(1 + c_1^{-1})\Gamma(1 + c_2^{-1})(c_1c_2)^{-1}\psi'(k).$$

Since

$$\operatorname{var}(X_j) = \alpha_j^{-2/c_j}\left[\frac{\Gamma(1 + 2c_j^{-1})\Gamma(k - 2c_j^{-1})}{\Gamma(k)} - \left\{\frac{\Gamma(1 + c_j^{-1})\Gamma(k - c_j^{-1})}{\Gamma(k)}\right\}^2\right],$$

it can be seen that the correlation between X_1 and X_2 does not depend on α_1 or α_2. For c_1,c_2 large we have

$$\operatorname{var}(X_j) \doteqdot \alpha_j^{-2/c_j}c_j^{-2}(\psi'(k) + \psi'(1)),$$

hence

$$\text{corr}(X_1,X_2) \doteq \frac{\psi'(k)}{\psi'(k)+\psi'(1)} = \frac{\psi'(k)}{\psi'(k)+\pi^2/6}. \tag{36}$$

For $m = 2$, the cumulative distribution function corresponding to (30) is

$$F_{X_1,X_2}(x_1,x_2) = 1-(1+\alpha_1 x_1^{c_1})^{-1}+(1+\alpha_2 x_2^{c_2})^{-1} + (1+\alpha_1 x_1^{c_1}+\alpha_2 x_2^{c_2})^{-1}. \tag{37}$$

Durling [9] (see also [10]) has generalized this formula by adding $r\alpha_1\alpha_2 x_1^{c_1}x_2^{c_2}$ to the last expression in parentheses. This does not affect the marginal distributions but introduces greater flexibility in the shape of the joint distribution.

5. Multivariate Logistic Distributions

A multivariate logistic distribution has been described by Gumbel [14]. In standard form, it has the density function

$$p_{Y_1,\ldots,Y_m}(y_1,\ldots,y_m) = m!\left\{1+\sum_{j=1}^m e^{-y_j}\right\}^{-(m+1)} \exp\left(-\sum_{j=1}^m y_j\right) \quad (y_j>0) \tag{39}$$

corresponding to a joint cumulative distribution function

$$F_{Y_1,\ldots,Y_m}(y_1,\ldots,y_m) = \left(1+\sum_{j=1}^m e^{-y_j}\right)^{-1}. \tag{40}$$

From (40) it is clear that each Y has the standard logistic distribution

$$F_{Y_j}(y_j) = \{1+e^{-y_j}\}^{-1} \tag{41}$$

and that any subset of Y's has a joint distribution of form (40). The conditional distribution of $Y_{s+1},\ldots,Y_m$ given $Y_1,\ldots,Y_s$ is defined by

$$\begin{aligned} p(y_{s+1},\ldots,y_m \mid y_1,\ldots,y_s) &= \frac{p(y_1,\ldots,y_m)}{p(y_1,\ldots,y_s)} \\ &= \frac{m!\left\{1+\sum_1^s e^{-y_j}\right\}^{s+1}}{s!\left\{1+\sum_1^s e^{-y_j}\right\}^{m+1}} \exp\left(-\sum_{j=s+1}^m y_j\right) \\ &= m^{(m-s)}\left\{1+\sum_{j=1}^s e^{-y_j}\right\}^{-(m-s)} \left\{1+\frac{\sum_{j=s+1}^m e^{-y_j}}{1+\sum_{j=1}^s e^{-y_j}}\right\}^{-(m+1)} \exp\left(-\sum_{j=s+1}^m y_j\right). \end{aligned} \tag{42}$$

The variables

$$Z_i = Y_i + \log\left(1 + \sum_{j=1}^{s} e^{-Y_j}\right) \qquad (i = s + 1,\ldots,m)$$

have the joint conditional density

(43) $$p(z_{s+1},\ldots,z_m \mid y_1,\ldots,y_s) = m^{(m-s)}\left\{1 + \sum_{i=s+1}^{m} e^{-z_i}\right\}^{-(m+1)} \exp\left(-\sum_{s+1}^{m} z_i\right)$$

corresponding to

(44) $$F(z_{s+1},\ldots,z_m \mid y_1,\ldots,y_s) = \left\{1 + \sum_{i=s+1}^{m} e^{-z_i}\right\}^{-(s+1)}.$$

Note that this means that the conditional joint distribution of $Y_{s+1},\ldots,Y_m$, given $Y_1,\ldots,Y_s$ is always of the same shape *and* scale, and varies only in regard to location parameters (i.e., the array variation is homoscedastic). In particular the conditional distribution of Z_1, given $Y_2,\ldots,Y_m$, is the same as that of the maximum of m independent random variables, each having the standard logistic distribution (41). The conditional density function of Z_1 is

(45) $$p_{Z_1}(z \mid y_2,\ldots,y_m) = me^{-z}(1 + e^{-z})^{-(m+1)}.$$

This is sometimes called a "generalized logistic" distribution, though it differs from both of the generalized logistic distributions described in Section 11 of Chapter 22.

Since $E[Z_1 \mid Y_2,\ldots,Y_m] = \psi(1) - \psi(m)$,

(46.1) $$E[Y_1 \mid Y_2,\ldots,Y_m] = \psi(1) - \psi(m) - \log\left(1 + \sum_{j=2}^{m} e^{-Y_j}\right) = \sum_{1}^{m-1} j^{-1} - \log\left(1 + \sum_{j=2}^{m} e^{-Y_j}\right).$$

In particular, putting $m = 2$

(46.2) $$E[Y_1 \mid Y_2] = 1 - \log(1 + e^{-Y_2})$$

and also

(46.3) $$\operatorname{var}(Y_1 \mid Y_2) = \psi'(1) + \psi'(2) = \tfrac{1}{3}\pi^2 - 1.$$

The joint moment generating function of $Y_1,\ldots,Y_m$ corresponding to (39) is

$$E\left[\exp\left(\sum_{1}^{m} t_j Y_j\right)\right] = m!\int_0^\infty\cdots\int_0^\infty \left(1 + \sum_{1}^{m} v_j\right)^{-(m+1)} \prod_{j=1}^{m} v_j^{-t_j}\, dv_1 \cdots dv_m$$

(using the transformation $v_j = e^{-y_j}$). The multiple integral may be evaluated using results in Chapter 40, Section 7, giving

(47) $$E\left[\exp\left(\sum_{1}^{m} t_j Y_j\right)\right] = \left[\prod_{j=1}^{m} \Gamma(1 - t_j)\right]\Gamma\left(1 + \sum_{j=1}^{m} t_j\right),$$

from which

$$\text{(48)} \qquad \operatorname{cov}(Y_i, Y_j) = \psi'(1) = \pi^2/6 \qquad (\text{for all } i \neq j).$$

Since

$$\operatorname{var}(Y_i) = 2\psi'(1) = \pi^2/3 \qquad (\text{for all } i),$$

the correlation between each pair of variables Y_i, Y_j is $\frac{1}{2}$.

The general form of multivariate logistic distribution corresponding to the standard form (39) is obtained by applying the transformations $Y_j = (X_j - \theta_j)/\sigma_j$ for $j = 1, \ldots, m$, giving

$$\text{(49)} \quad p_{X_1,\ldots,X_m}(x_1, \ldots, x_m)$$

$$= m!\left(\prod_{j=1}^{m} \sigma_j\right)^{-1}\left[1 + \sum_{j=1}^{m} \exp\{-(x_j - \theta_j)\sigma_j^{-1}\}\right]^{-1} \exp\left\{\sum_{j=1}^{m} (x_j - \theta_j)\sigma_j^{-1}\right\}.$$

The cumulative distribution function of X_j is

$$F_{X_j}(x_j) = [1 + \exp\{-(x_j - \theta_j)\sigma_j^{-1}\}]^{-1}$$

and the parameters θ_j, σ_j may be estimated from each marginal distribution, using the methods described in Chapter 22. (Note that there are no other parameters, affecting the shape of the joint distributions.)

However, Moore [28] has shown how estimators of improved accuracy may be obtained by using grouped (contingency table) multivariate data. He takes a bivariate logistic distribution, with $\sigma_1 = \sigma_2 = 1$, and considers estimation of θ_1 and θ_2 by application of a general method of estimation using data from two-way contingency tables with boundaries defined by assuming σ known (and taking it equal to one). We suppose the data divided into a 4×4 table with boundaries at the $(1 + e)^{-1}$, $\frac{1}{2}$, and $(1 + e^{-1})^{-1}$ sample quantiles as shown in Fig. 1. The estimator of θ_1 is then (in terms of $\hat{p}_{ij}$, the observed proportion in the cell ij, and the quantiles $\hat{X}_{i\alpha}$) as shown in the figure:

$$\begin{aligned}
&0.36\hat{X}_{11} + 0.36\hat{X}_{12} + 0.28\hat{X}_{13} \\
&-0.06\hat{X}_{21} + 0.02\hat{X}_{22} + 0.04\hat{X}_{23} \\
&+3.06\hat{p}_{11} + 2.76\hat{p}_{21} + 1.54\hat{p}_{31} \\
&+1.72\hat{p}_{12} + 1.69\hat{p}_{22} + 1.02\hat{p}_{32} \\
&+0.83\hat{p}_{13} + 0.82\hat{p}_{23} + 0.52\hat{p}_{33} \\
&-1.07.
\end{aligned}$$

There is a similar formula for an estimator of θ_2. These formulas are more efficient than the corresponding (univariate) sample means or medians. Their efficiency is 84.6%, as compared with 81% for means and 61.2% for medians.

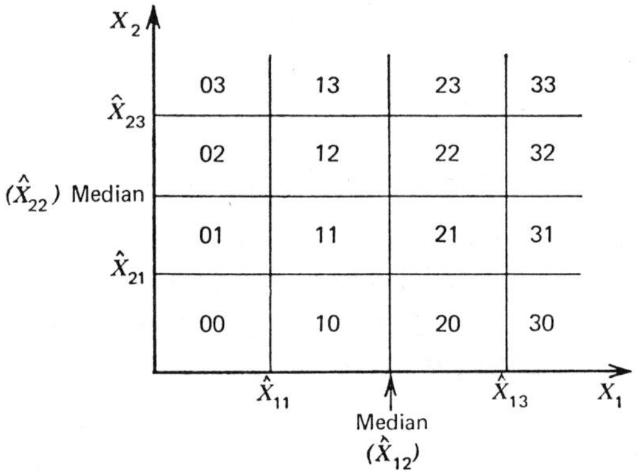

FIGURE 1

Gumbel [14] also developed a *second bivariate logistic* distribution by applying the general formula [see Chapter 34, equation (39)]:

$$F(x_1,x_2) = F(x_1)F(x_2)[1 + \alpha\{1 - F(x_1)\}\{1 - F(x_2)\}]$$

to give

$$F_{X_1,X_2}(x_1,x_2) = (1 + e^{-x_1})^{-1}(1 + e^{-x_2})^{-1} \times [1 + \alpha e^{-x_1-x_2}(1 + e^{-x_1})^{-1}(1 + e^{-x_2})^{-1}] \quad (-1 < \alpha < 1). \tag{50}$$

[Durling [9] has developed a "bivariate logit" method of analysis of bivariate quantal response data based on an assumed joint distribution of form (50).] The regression function of X_2 on X_1 is

$$E[X_2 \mid X_1] = \alpha[2(1 + e^{-X_1})^{-1} - 1], \tag{51}$$

which is an increasing function of X_1. Note that as X_1 increases from $-\infty$ to $+\infty$, $E[X_2 \mid X_1]$ increases from $-\alpha$ to α. The correlation between X_1 and X_2 is

$$\operatorname{corr}(X_1,X_2) = 3\pi^{-2}\alpha. \tag{52}$$

6. Distributions Classified by Functional Form

In Section 3 of Chapter 37 we noted that the special form of multivariate t distribution when the common denominator has 1 degree of freedom is a *multivariate Cauchy distribution.* It has joint probability density function (in standard form)

$$p_{Y_1,\ldots,Y_m}(y_1,\ldots,y_m) = \pi^{-\frac{1}{2}(m+1)}\Gamma(\tfrac{1}{2}(m+1))\left(1 + \sum_{j=1}^{m} y_j^2\right)^{-\frac{1}{2}(m+1)}. \tag{53}$$

Ferguson [11] has shown that this multivariate Cauchy distribution is characterized by the fact that *any* linear function of $Y_1, \ldots, Y_m$ has a (univariate) Cauchy distribution.

Multivariate Cauchy of type (53) and multivariate normal distributions with variance-covariance matrix $\mathbf{I}\sigma^2$ belong to the class of *radial* or *spherical distributions* studied by Lord [22] and Box and Hunter [3].

For these distributions

$$p_{X_1,\ldots,X_m}(x_1,\ldots,x_m) \propto f\left(\sum_{j=1}^{m} x_j^2\right). \tag{54}$$

Box and Hunter [3] have shown that for *any* such distribution

$$E\left[\prod_{j=1}^{m} X_j^{\alpha_j}\right] = \begin{cases} 0 & \text{if one (or more) } \alpha_j \text{ is odd,} \\ K_\alpha \prod_{j=1}^{m} \left[\dfrac{\alpha_j!}{(\frac{1}{2}\alpha_j)!}\right] & \text{if all } \alpha\text{'s are even,} \end{cases} \tag{55}$$

where $\alpha = \sum_{j=1}^{m} \alpha_j$ and K_α depends on α only.

The only spherical distribution for which the X's are independent are spherical multinormal distributions.

Kelker [21a] has shown that $\left[\sum_{j=1}^{\nu_1} X_j^2\right]\left[\sum_{j=1}^{\nu_1+\nu_2} X_j^2\right]^{-1}$ has a beta distribution with parameters $\frac{1}{2}\nu_1, \frac{1}{2}\nu_2$. (This has been noted, for spherical multinormal distributions, in Section 2 of Chapter 24.) Kelker also considers the distributions of linear transforms of spherically distributed variables. (See also Thomas [37]).

Baldessari [1] shows that for z real or complex

$$\underset{\sum_{j=1}^{n} x_j^2 \le r^2}{\int \cdots \int} f\left(z \sum_{j=1}^{n} t_j x_j\right) dx_1 \cdots dx_n \tag{56}$$
$$= \frac{\pi^{\frac{1}{2}(n-1)}}{\Gamma[(n+1)/2]} \int_{-r}^{r} (r^2 - y^2)^{\frac{1}{2}(n-1)} f\left(zy\sqrt{\sum_{j=1}^{n} t_j^2}\right) dy.$$

He then applies this to find the characteristic function of *two classes* of multivariate distributions:

1. Class *A*

$$p(x_1,\ldots,x_n) = Kf\left(\sum_{j=1}^{n} x_j\right) \qquad \left(\sum_{j=1}^{n} (x_j - a)^2 \le r^2\right), \tag{57}$$

with

$$K^{-1} = \pi^{\frac{1}{2}(n-1)}\left[\Gamma\left(\frac{n+1}{2}\right)\right]^{-1} \int_{-r}^{r} (r^2 - y^2)^{\frac{1}{2}(n-1)} f(na + y\sqrt{n})\, dy.$$

The characteristic function is

(58) $\phi_{X_1,\ldots,X_n}(t_1,\ldots,t_n)$

$$= K\frac{\pi^{\frac{1}{2}(n-1)}}{\Gamma(\frac{1}{2}n)}\exp\left(ia\sum_{j=1}^{n}t_j\right)\iint_{y_1^2+y_2^2\le r^2} f(na+y_1\sqrt{n})(r^2-y_1^2-y_2)^{\frac{1}{2}(n-2)}$$

$$\times \exp[(S_1y_1+S_2y_2)]\,dy_1\,dy_2,$$

where

$$S_1=\left[n^{-1}\sum_{j=1}^{n}t_j^2\right]^{1/2};\qquad S_2=\left[\sum_{j=1}^{r-1}\frac{\left\{\sum_{k=1}^{j}t_k-jt_{j+1}\right\}^2}{j(j+1)}\right]^{1/2}.$$

2. Class B

(59) $$p(x_1,\ldots,x_n)=Kf\left(\sum_{j=1}^{n}(x_j-a_j)^2\right)\qquad\left(\sum(x_j-a_j)^2\le r^2\right),$$

with

$$K^{-1}=\pi^{(1/2)n}[\Gamma(\tfrac{1}{2}n)]^{-1}\int_0^{r^2}y^{(1/2)n-1}f(y)\,dy.$$

The characteristic function is

(60) $\phi_{X_1,\ldots,X_n}(t_1,\ldots,t_n)$

$$=K^{-1}\pi^{\frac{1}{2}(n-1)}[\Gamma(\tfrac{1}{2}(n-1))]^{-1}\exp\left(i\sum_{j=1}^{n}a_jt_j\right)$$

$$\times\int_{-r}^{r}\int_{0}^{r^2-x^2}y_1^{\frac{1}{2}(n-3)}f(y_1+y_2^2)\exp\left\{iy_2\sqrt{\sum_{j=1}^{n}t_j^2}\right\}dy_1\,dy_2.$$

(*Note.* In B one can get rid of a_j's by using $x_j'=x_j-a_j$. The essential feature is the form of the characteristic functions.)

Elliptically symmetric distributions have density functions depending only on quadratic functions of the variables. (They include *spherically symmetric* distributions as special cases.) McGraw and Wagner [24] give a number of examples of bivariate distributions, some of which are set out in Table 3.

It is pointed out in [24] that some elliptically symmetric functions can be constructed by writing

$$p_{\mathbf{X}}(\mathbf{x})=cg(Q(\mathbf{x})),$$

where c is a constant, $g(\cdot)$ is a univariate density function, and $Q(\mathbf{x})$ is a quadratic function of $\mathbf{x}$. (This does not give useful results for *all* $g(\cdot)$, but does so for many important cases.)

TABLE 3

Bivariate Elliptically Symmetric Distributions

Family	Marginal distributions $p_X(x)$	Joint distributions $p_{X_1,X_2}(x_1,x_2)$*
Gaussian	$[2\pi\sigma^2]^{-1/2}\exp\{-\frac{1}{2}x^2/\sigma^2\}$	$[2\pi\sigma^2(1-\rho^2)^{1/2}]^{-1}\exp\{-q^2/\sigma^2\}$
Laplace	$[2\sigma^2]^{-1/2}\exp\{-\sqrt{2}\,\lvert x\rvert/\sigma\}$	$[\pi\sigma^2(1-\rho^2)^{1/2}]^{-1} K_0(\sqrt{2}q/\sigma)$†
Pearson Type II ($\nu > 0$)	$\frac{A^{-2\nu}}{\sqrt{\pi}}\frac{\Gamma(\nu+1)}{\Gamma(\nu+\frac{1}{2})}(A^2-x^2)^{\nu-1/2}; \quad \lvert x\rvert < A$	$\frac{\nu[1-\rho^2]^{-1/2}}{\pi A^{2\nu}}(A^2-q^2)^{\nu-1}; \quad \lvert q\rvert < A$
Bessel (generalized Laplace) ($\nu > \frac{1}{4}$)	$\frac{[\pi a^2]^{-1/2}}{2^{\nu-1/2}\Gamma(\nu)}\left(\frac{\lvert x\rvert}{a}\right) K_{\nu-1/2}\left(\frac{\lvert x\rvert}{a}\right)$	$\frac{[1-\rho^2]^{-1/2}}{\pi a^2 2^\nu \Gamma(\nu)}\left(\frac{q}{a}\right)^{\nu-1}$
Pearson Type VII ($a,\nu > 0$)	$\frac{a^{2\nu}\Gamma(\nu+\frac{1}{2})}{\sqrt{\pi}\Gamma(\nu)}[a^2+x^2]^{-\nu-1/2}$	$\frac{\nu[1-\rho^2]^{-1/2}}{\pi a^{-2\nu}}[a^2+q^2]^{-\nu-1}$

* $q = (1-\rho^2)^{-1/2}(x_1^2 - 2\rho x_1 x_2 + x_2^2)^{1/2}$

† $K_\nu(\cdot)$ is a modified Bessel function of the second kind (Chapter 12, Section 4.4).

7. Miscellaneous

We give here a few examples of special multivariate distributions. None is used widely, but all have some interest.

Simoni [34] has considered natural generalizations of the univariate distribution derived by Subbotin (see Chapter 23, Section 5). These have density functions proportional to

$$\exp[-r^{-1}\{(\mathbf{x}-\boldsymbol{\xi})'\mathbf{A}(\mathbf{x}-\boldsymbol{\xi})\}^{r/2}] \qquad (\mathbf{A} \text{ positive definite}), \tag{61}$$

where $r > 1$. For $r = 2$ one obtains a multinormal distribution.

Further generalizations can be constructed by considering the joint distribution of $Y_1, \ldots, Y_k$ $(k \leq m)$, with

$$\mathbf{Y} = \mathbf{C}\mathbf{X} + \boldsymbol{\eta}$$

($\mathbf{C}$ is a nonsingular $k \times m$ matrix), where $X_1, \ldots, X_m$ have independent (univariate) Subbotin distributions with a common value of θ, so that

$$p_{\mathbf{X}}(\mathbf{x}) \propto \exp\left[-\sum_{j=1}^{m} |x_j - \xi_j|^\theta\right].$$

When θ is an integer it is possible to write the joint density of $\mathbf{Y}$ in the form

$$p_{\mathbf{Y}}(\mathbf{y}) \propto \exp[-(\text{homogeneous form of order } \theta \text{ in } \mathbf{y})].$$

Goodman and Kotz [12] have generalized this to allow the homogeneous form to be unrestricted (except for being positive definite) and have shown that the joint density can be written

$$(61)' \quad p_{\mathbf{Y}}(\mathbf{y}) = \frac{1}{|\mathbf{C}|\,[2\Gamma(1+\theta^{-1})]^k} \times \exp\left[-\sum \cdots \sum b_{i_1} \cdots b_{i_\theta}(y_{i_1} - \eta_{i_1}) \cdots (y_{i_\theta} - \eta_{i_\theta})\right]$$

$$(i_j = 1, \ldots, k \text{ for all } j),$$

where $\mathbf{C}$ is a $k \times k$ matrix such that

$$\sum \cdots \sum b_{i_1} \cdots b_{i_\theta} c_{i_1 r_1} \cdots c_{i_\theta r_\theta} = 1 \qquad \text{if} \quad r_1 = r_2 = \cdots = r_\theta,$$

otherwise being equal to zero; and $\sum \cdots \sum$ denotes summation over $1 \leq i_j \leq k$ for all $j = 1, \ldots, \theta$.

Goodman and Kotz show that the marginal distributions of (61)′ are not of the same form. They can be represented as infinite mixtures of reflected generalized gamma distributions (Chapter 17, equation (70)).

Washburn [38] has considered the path of a particle moving at uniform speed (V) in 2 dimensions, in a succession of independent randomly oriented steps, the lengths of time spent on each step having the same exponential distribution. If the particle starts from the origin, at time zero, and the probability that the time spent in any given step exceeds t is $\exp(-\alpha t)$, then the joint density function of the coordinates X_1,X_2 after time t is

$$(62)\quad p_{X_1,X_2}(x_1,x_2 \mid t) = [2\pi(Vt)^2]^{-1}[\alpha t/\sqrt{1-(x_1^2+x_2^2)(Vt)^{-2}}] \times \exp[-\alpha t\{1-\sqrt{1-(x_1^2+x_2^2)(Vt)^{-2}}\}], \quad (x_1^2+x_2^2 < (Vt)^2).$$

Washburn [38] also shows that the conditional joint density of X_1 and X_2, given that $n(\geq 1)$ steps have been completed in time t, is

$$(63)\quad p_{X_1,X_2}(x_1,x_2 \mid t,n) = [2\pi(Vt)^2]^{-1} f_n\left(\frac{x_1^2+x_2^2}{V^2t^2}\right),$$

where

$$f_n(z) = \begin{cases} n(1-z)^{(1/2)n-1} & \text{for } 0 \leq z \leq 1, \\ 0 & \text{for } z > 1. \end{cases}$$

There are many examples of joint distributions of normal variables that are not multinormal. (In particular, Pierce and Dykstra [31] show that if

$$p_{\mathbf{X}}(\mathbf{x}) = \left[1 + \prod_{j=1}^{m} (x_j e^{-(1/2)x_j^2})\right] \prod_{j=1}^{m} [(\sqrt{2\pi})^{-1} e^{-(1/2)x_j^2}],$$

then, although each subset of $X_1,\ldots,X_m$ has a joint multinormal distribution with variance covariance matrix $\boldsymbol{I}$, the complete set is not multinormally distributed.) The one we choose now to describe also provides an example in which zero correlation does not imply independence, even for normally distributed variables. (See also Chapter 35, Section 9.)

If Y and X are mutually independent, Y having a standard beta distribution [Chapter 24, equation (2)] with parameters $\frac{1}{2}(\nu-1),\frac{1}{2}(\nu-1)$ and X a χ_ν distribution (Chapter 17) then $(2Y-1)X$ has a unit normal distribution.

Patil [30] has considered the joint distribution of

$$Z_1 = (2Y_1 - 1)X; \qquad Z_2 = (2Y_2 - 1)X,$$

where Y_1, Y_2, and X are mutually independent and Y_1, Y_2 each have the same distribution as Y. Although the marginal distributions are normal, and the correlation between Z_1 and Z_2 is zero, the variables are not independent. In fact, we have (for even product moments)

$$(64)\quad E[Z_1^{2r_1}Z_2^{2r_2}] = \Gamma(\tfrac{1}{2}\nu + r_1 + r_2) \prod_{j=1}^{2} \left[\frac{(2r_j)!}{r_j!\,\Gamma(\tfrac{1}{2}\nu + r_j)}\right],$$

from which

$$\text{corr}(Z_1^2,Z_2^2) = \nu^{-1}. \tag{65}$$

(All product moments $E[Z_1^{s_1}Z_2^{s_2}]$, with either s_1 or s_2 odd, are zero.)

The regression of Z_2^2 on Z_1^2 is linear:

$$E[Z_2^2 \mid Z_1^2] = 1 - \nu^{-1} + \nu^{-1}Z_1^2. \tag{66}$$

The joint density function is rather complicated:

$$p_{Z_1,Z_2}(z_1,z_2) = \frac{\exp[-\frac{1}{2}\max(z_1^2,z_2^2)]}{2^{(1/2)\nu}\Gamma(\frac{1}{2}\nu)\{B[(\nu-1)/2,\frac{1}{2}]\}^2} \times \int_0^\infty t^{\frac{1}{2}(\nu-3)}(t+|z_1^2-z_2^2|)^{\frac{1}{2}(\nu-3)} \times (t+\max(z_1^2,z_2^2))^{-\frac{1}{2}(\nu-3)}e^{-(1/2)t}\,dt. \tag{67}$$

Patil [30] has given explicit formulas for the cases $\nu = 3$ and $\nu = 5$.

We also note that Kale [20] has pointed out that if $\mathbf{X}$ has the joint density function

$$p_{\mathbf{X}}(\mathbf{x}) = \begin{cases} \prod_{j=1}^m [(\sqrt{2\pi})^{-1}e^{-(1/2)x_j^2}] + (\alpha/\sqrt{2\pi e})^m \prod_{j=1}^m x_j & (\text{all } |x_j| < 1), \\ \prod_{j=1}^m [(\sqrt{2\pi})^{-1}e^{-(1/2)x_j^2}] & \text{otherwise,} \end{cases}$$

with α sufficiently small, so that $p_{\mathbf{X}}(\mathbf{x}) \geq 0$, then

(i) any subset of $r(<m)$ of the variates $X_1,\ldots,X_m$ has a joint multinormal distribution but

(ii) $X_1,\ldots,X_m$ do not have a joint multinormal distribution.

Miller [27] has shown that if $X_1,\ldots,X_m,Y$ have a joint multinormal distribution with expected value vector $\mathbf{0}$ and variance-covariance matrix

$$\mathbf{V} = \begin{pmatrix} \mathbf{V}_1 & \mathbf{h} \\ \mathbf{h}' & \sigma^2 \end{pmatrix},$$

where $\mathbf{V}_1$ is the variance-covariance matrix of $(X_1,\ldots,X_m)$ and σ^2 is the variance of Y, then the joint density of $\mathbf{Z}' = (Z_1,\ldots,Z_m)$, where $Z_j = X_jY$ is

$$p_{\mathbf{Z}}(\mathbf{z}) = 2\,|\mathbf{V}|^{1/2}\,(2\pi)^{-\frac{1}{2}(m+1)}(\sigma^{-2}\mathbf{z}'\mathbf{V}_1\mathbf{z})^{-\frac{1}{4}(m-1)} \times \exp(-\mathbf{V}'\mathbf{z})K_{\frac{1}{2}(m-1)}(\sigma\sqrt{\mathbf{z}'\mathbf{V}_1\mathbf{z}}), \tag{68}$$

where $K_\nu(\cdot)$ is the modified Bessel function of the second kind of order ν (see Chapter 12, Section 4.4).

If $X_1,\ldots,X_m$ have the same distribution as above, but Y is independent of the X's and has a χ_ν distribution, then

(69) $$p_{\mathbf{Z}}(\mathbf{z}) = |\mathbf{V}_1|^{1/2}\,[\pi^{(1/2)m}2^{\frac{1}{2}(m+\nu-2)}\Gamma(\tfrac{1}{2}\nu)]^{-1}(\mathbf{z}'\mathbf{V}_1\mathbf{z})^{\frac{1}{4}(\nu-m)}K_{\frac{1}{2}(\nu-m)}(\sqrt{(\mathbf{z}'\mathbf{V}_1\mathbf{z})}).$$

In Chapter 33, distributions of Kolmogorov-Smirnov type were discussed. Multivariate forms of these statistics, derived from comparison of sample cumulative distribution functions with each other, or with theoretical values, are not widely used. Papers by Bickel [2], Kiefer [21], and Tanaka [36] contain suggestions on possible multivariate test statistics of this type but do not give any new distributions.

An m-dimensional form of Smirnov's ω^2-criterion (Chapter 33, Section 2) can be defined in the following way:

(70) $$\omega_{n,m}^2 = n\int_0^1\cdots\int_0^1[\hat{F}(\mathbf{x}) - F_{\mathbf{X}}(\mathbf{x})]^2\,dF_{\mathbf{X}}(\mathbf{x}),$$

where $\hat{F}(\mathbf{x})$ = proportion of sets $(X_{1j},\ldots,X_{mj})$ $(j = 1,\ldots,n)$ for which the event $\bigcap_{g=1}^{m}(X_{gj} \le x_g)$ occurs. For the special case when $X_1,\ldots,X_m$ are continuous independent and identically distributed, so that

$$F_{\mathbf{X}}(\mathbf{x}) = \prod_{g=1}^{m} F_{X_g}(x_g) = \prod_{g=1}^{m} F(x_g),$$

where $F(\cdot)$ is a fixed mathematical function, Dugué [6, 7] has shown that the limiting characteristic function of $\omega_{n,m}^2$, as $n \to \infty$, is

(71) $$\left[i2^{m-1}\frac{d}{dt}C_m(t)\right]^{-1/2},$$

where

(72.1) $$C_1(t) = \cos\sqrt{2it}$$

and

(72.2) $$C_m(t) = \prod_{j=1}^{\infty} C_{m-1}(\pi^{-2}(j-\tfrac{1}{2})^{-2}t). \qquad (m \ge 2)$$

The function $[C_m(t)]^{-1/2}$ is itself the characteristic function of a Brownian motion (distance) distribution in m dimensions derived by Dugué [6] (and, for $m = 1$, by Cameron and Martin [5]).

Gupta and Wasan [15] have defined a "*bivariate (time) density function of Brownian motion*" as

(73) $$p_{X_1,X_2}(x_1,x_2) = \left[2\pi(1-\rho^2)^{1/2}\left(\tfrac{1}{4} + \frac{1}{2\pi}\sin^{-1}\rho\right)\right]^{-1} \times \exp[-\tfrac{1}{2}(1-\rho^2)^{-1}(x_1^{-1} - 2\rho(x_1x_2)^{-1/2} + x_2^{-1})] \qquad (0 < x_j).$$

This is, in fact, the joint distribution of Y_1^{-2}, Y_2^{-2} where Y_1, Y_2 have a standardized bivariate normal distribution, truncated to the positive quadrant $(Y_1 > 0, Y_2 > 0)$. Properties of this function follow directly from this relation.

In [15], also, there is defined a *bivariate (time) distribution of Brownian motion with positive drift*, which is the joint distribution of X_1 and X_2 when X_1 and $(X_2 - X_1)$ are independently distributed with the special inverse Gaussian density of the form

$$p_X(x) = \theta(2\pi x^3)^{-1/2} \exp\{-\tfrac{1}{2}x^{-1}(x - \theta)^2\} \qquad (x > 0) \tag{74}$$

obtained by putting $\mu = \theta$, $\lambda = \theta^2$ in (4.1) of Chapter 15.

For the particular case when the distributions of X_1 and $X_2 - X_1$ are identical (i.e., $\theta_1 = \theta_2 = \theta$) the maximum likelihood estimator of θ, given n independent pairs of values (X_{1j}, X_{2j}), is

$$\hat{\theta} = T^{-1}(1 + \sqrt{1 + T}), \tag{75}$$

where

$$T = n^{-1} \sum_{j=1}^{n} [(X_{2j} - X_{1j})^{-1} + X_{1j}^{-1}].$$

A wide class of multivariate distributions can be generated from the following model. Suppose that $T_1, T_2, \ldots, T_n$ are independently distributed with a common probability density function $f(\cdot)$, such that $\Pr[T_j \leq 0] = 0$. Then the joint probability density function of

$$X_j = \sum_{i=1}^{j} T_i \qquad (j = 1, \ldots, n)$$

is

$$p_{\mathbf{X}}(\mathbf{x}) = \prod_{j=1}^{n} f(x_j - x_{j-1}) \qquad (0 \leq x_1 \leq x_2 \leq \cdots \leq x_n), \tag{76}$$

with $x_0 = 0$.

Models of this kind are used to represent the joint distribution of times of occurrence of events in "random sequences." Further families can be obtained by forming the conditional distribution of $X_1, X_2, \ldots, X_{n-1}$ given X_n. This represents the joint distribution of the fractions into which the interval 0 to X_n is divided by the times of occurrence of the first $(n - 1)$ events.

As an example, suppose that

$$f(t) = \{\Gamma(\alpha)\}^{-1} t^{\alpha-1} e^{-t} \qquad (t > 0),$$

so that

$$p_{X_1, \ldots, X_n}(x_1, \ldots, x_n) = \{\Gamma(\alpha)\}^{-n} \left[\prod_{j=1}^{n} (x_j - x_{j-1})^{\alpha-1}\right] e^{-x_n}$$
$$(0 \leq x_1 \leq \cdots \leq x_n).$$

In this case $X_n = \sum_{j=1}^{n} T_j$ has the density function

$$p_{X_n}(x_n) = \{\Gamma(n\alpha)\}^{-1} x_n^{n\alpha-1} e^{-x_n} \qquad (x_n > 0),$$

and so

$$(77) \quad p_{X_1,\ldots,X_{n-1}|X_n}(x_1,\ldots,x_{n-1} \mid x_n)$$
$$= \Gamma(n\alpha)\{\Gamma(\alpha)\}^{-n}\left[\prod_{j=1}^{n}\left(\frac{x_j - x_{j-1}}{x_n}\right)^{\alpha-1}\right] x_n^{-(n-1)}$$
$$(0 \leq x_1 \cdots \leq x_{n-1} \leq x_n).$$

The conditional distribution of $T_1,\ldots,T_{n-1}$, given X_n is, in fact, a Dirichlet distribution of the kind described in Chapter 40.

Another method of construction is to use mixtures (see Chapter 34, Section 1) with $X_1,\ldots,X_m$ mutually independent in each component of the mixture. The joint cumulative distribution function is then

$$F_{\mathbf{X}}(\mathbf{x}) = \sum_{j=1}^{k} \omega_j \prod_{i=1}^{m} F_{ij}(x_i)$$

where $F_{ij}(x_i)$ is the cumulative distribution function of X_i in the jth component. Generally $X_1,\ldots,X_m$ are not independent in the overall distribution, though if $F_{ij}(x_j)$ does not depend on i, then X_j is independent of all the other variables. An example of a distribution of this kind with the F_{ij}'s all gamma distributions (Chapter 17) with common scale factor, but different shape parameters, can be found in Schotz and Zelen [33].

In Chapter 34 (Section 5) we have discussed joint distributions formed by transformation of variables in multinormal distributions. If we start from other multivariate distributions, other kinds of transformation may be appropriate.

We consider here transformations of Dirichlet distributions (see Chapter 40, Section 5). A simple transformation, which gives useful results, is the power transformation $X = Y^{\lambda}$. Suppose that $Y_1, Y_2,\ldots,Y_m$ have the joint density function (31) of Chapter 40 (i.e., Dirichlet with parameters $\theta_1,\theta_2,\ldots,\theta_m;\theta_0$). For new variables

$$X_j = Y_j^{\lambda_j} \qquad (j = 1,\ldots,m),$$

with $\lambda_j > 0$ we have a joint distribution with the following properties.

(i) $0 < X_j; \sum_{j=1}^{m} X_j^{1/\lambda_j} < 1$.

(ii) The conditional distribution of X_j $(j \leq s)$, given $X_{s+1},\ldots,X_m$, is that of $Z_j^{\lambda_j}$, where Z_j is distributed as

$$\left(1-\sum_{i=s+1}^{m} X_i^{1/\lambda_i}\right)\left(\text{beta variable with parameters } \theta_j, \sum_{i=1}^{s}\theta_i+\theta_0-\theta_j\right). \tag{78}$$

(iii) From (ii), the multiple regression of X_j on $X_{s+1},\ldots,X_m$ is

$$E[X_j \mid X_{s+1},\ldots,X_m] = C\left(1-\sum_{i=s+1}^{m} X_i^{1/\lambda_i}\right)^{\lambda_j}, \tag{79}$$

where

$$C = B\left(\theta_j+\lambda_j, \sum_{i=1}^{s}\theta_i+\theta_0-\theta_j\right) \Big/ B\left(\theta_j, \sum_{i=1}^{s}\theta_i+\theta_0-\theta_j\right).$$

If $\lambda_j < 0$, these properties remain unchanged, except that X_j now takes values not less than 1.

The same transformations may be applied to variables $Y_1, Y_2,\ldots,Y_m$ having any kind of multivariate gamma distribution (see Chapter 40). The marginal distributions are now those of powers of gamma variables. Figure 2 gives a representation of values of α_3, α_4 $(\sqrt{\beta_1}, \beta_2)$ for such variables.

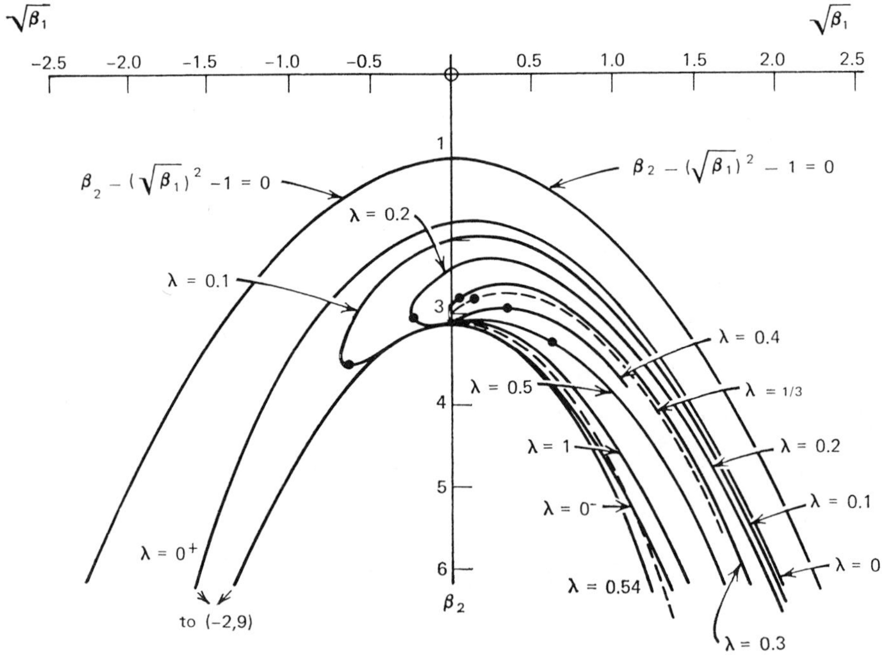

FIGURE 2

For univariate distributions, the *Tukey lambda* transformation [16]

$$X = aY^\lambda - (1 - Y)^\lambda$$

of standard uniform (see Chapter 25) variates Y gives a variety of useful distribution, by suitable choice of a and λ. The special case of *symmetrical Tukey lambda* transformations obtained by putting $a = 1$ has been studied by Joiner and Rosenblatt [19]. Note that in each of the cases $\lambda = 1$ and $\lambda = 2$, the symmetrical transformation is $X = 2Y - 1$, giving a new distribution of the same shape as the original.

If it is desired to apply transformations of this kind to Dirichlet distributions we are led to consider cases when Y has a general standard beta, rather than a uniform, distribution. This is because, if $Y_1, Y_2, \ldots, Y_m$ have a joint Dirichlet distribution, then at most one of $Y_1, \ldots, Y_m$ can have a uniform distribution. (Johnson and Kotz [18].)

If Y has a standard beta distribution with parameters θ, ϕ, then the distribution of $X = Y^\lambda - (1 - Y)^\lambda$ has rth moment

$$\mu_r'(X) = [B(\theta,\phi)]^{-1} \sum_{j=0}^{r} \binom{r}{j} (-1)^j B(\theta + (r - j)\lambda, \phi + j\lambda)$$

for $\lambda > 0$ or $\lambda < 0$. (The transition case $\lambda = 0$ corresponds to $X = \log\{Y/(1 - Y)\}$.)

Modal values of the density function of Y occur at values corresponding to $X = x$ where $u = x/(1 - x)$ satisfies the equation

$$u^{\lambda-1} = \frac{(\phi - \lambda)u - (\theta - 1)}{\theta - \lambda - (\phi - 1)u}. \tag{80}$$

(If $\lambda = \theta + \phi - 1$, this gives

$$u = \left(\frac{\theta - 1}{\phi - 1}\right)^{(\lambda-1)^{-2}}.)$$

If transformations $X_j = Y^{\lambda_j} - (1 - Y_j)^{\lambda_j}$ are applied to variables $Y_1, \ldots, Y_m$ having a joint standard Dirichlet distribution, the conditional distribution of Y_j ($j \le s$) given $Y_{s+1}, \ldots, Y_m$ does not have as simple a form as for the power transformation discussed above. (Johnson and Kotz [18].)

REFERENCES

[1] Baldessari, B. (1965). Osservazioni sulle funzioni caratteristiche di alcune classi di v.c. n-dimensionali, *Pubblicazioni della Seconda Serie dell'Istituto di Calcolo delle Probabilità dell'Università di Roma*, **49,** 1–11.

[2] Bickel, P. (1969). A distribution free version of the Smirnov two sample test in the p-variate case, *Annals of Mathematical Statistics*, **40,** 1–23.

[3] Box, G. E. P. and Hunter, J. S. (1957). Multi-factor experimental designs for exploring response surfaces, *Annals of Mathematical Statistics*, **28,** 195–241.

[4] Burr, I. W. (1942). Cumulative frequency functions, *Annals of Mathematical Statistics*, **13,** 215–232.

[5] Cameron, R. H. and Martin, W. T. (1944). The Wiener's measure of Hilbert neighborhoods in the space of real continuous function, *Journal of Mathematics and Physics* (*MIT*), **23,** 195–209.

[6] Dugué, D. (1967). Fonctions caractéristiques d'intégrales Browniennes, *Revue Roumaine de Mathématiques Pures et Appliquées*, **12,** 1207–1215.

[7] Dugué, D. (1968). Fonction caractéristique de ω_n^2 multidimensionnel de von Mises. Fonctions caractéristiques bidimensionelles liées au mouvement Brownien, *Comptes Rendus*, *Académie des Sciences*, *Paris*, **226,** 834–836.

[8] Dugué, D. (1969). Characteristic functions of random variables connected with Brownian motion and of the von Mises multidimensional ω_n^2, in *Multivariate Analysis*, Vol. 2, P. R. Krishnaiah, Ed., New York: Academic Press, pp. 289–301.

[9] Durling, F. C. (1969). *Bivariate Probit, Logit and Burrit Analysis*, THEMIS Report No. 41, Department of Statistics, Southern Methodist University, Dallas, Texas.

[10] Durling, F. C., Owen, D. B., and Drane, J. W. (1970). A new bivariate Burr distribution (Abstract) *Annals of Mathematical Statistics*, **41,** 1135.

[11] Ferguson, T. S. (1962). A representation of the symmetric bivariate Cauchy distribution, *Annals of Mathematical Statistics*, **33,** 1256–1266.

[12] Goodman, I. and Kotz, S. (1971). Structural properties of multivariate θ-generalized distributions, (Abstract) *Annals of Mathematical Statistics*, **42,** 1475.

[13] Gullota, B. (1953). Sulla estensione della legge di probabilità di Cauchy, *Giornale dell'Istituto Italiano degli Attuari*, **16,** 38–50.

[14] Gumbel, E. J. (1961). Bivariate logistic distributions, *Journal of the American Statistical Association*, **56,** 335–349.

[15] Gupta, R. P. and Wasan, M. T. (1969). Bivariate time distribution of Brownian motion, *Trabajos de Estadística*, **20,** 117–128.

[16] Hastings, C., Mosteller, F., Tukey, J. W., and Winsor, C. P. (1947). Low moments for small samples: a comparative study of order statistics, *Annals of Mathematical Statistics*, **18,** 413–426.

[17] Johnson, N. L. and Kotz, S. (1972). Comparisons among estimators of a scale parameter of the Beta-Stacy distribution, *Journal of the American Statistical Association*, **67**, 203–205.

[18] Johnson, N. L. and Kotz, S. (1970). *Generalized and Multivariate Tukey Lambda Distributions*, Presented at Detroit meeting, Biometric Society.

[19] Joiner, B. L. and Rosenblatt, Joan R. (1971). Some properties of range in samples from Tukey's symmetric lambda distributions. *Journal of the American Statistical Association*, **66**, 394–399.

[20] Kale, B. K. (1970). Normality of linear combinations of nonnormal random variables, *American Mathematical Monthly*, **77**, 992–995.

[21] Kiefer, J. (1959). K-sample analogues of the Kolmogorov-Smirnov and Cramér-von Mises tests, *Annals of Mathematical Statistics*, **30**, 420–449.

[21a] Kelker, D. (1970). Distribution theory of spherical distributions and a location-scale parameter generalization, *Sankhyā*, *Series A*, **32**, 419–430.

[22] Lord, R. D. (1954). The use of Hankel transforms in statistics. I. General theory and examples, *Biometrika*, **41**, 44–55.

[23] Mardia, K. V. (1962). Multivariate Pareto distributions, *Annals of Mathematical Statistics*, **33**, 1008–1015.

[23a] Mardia, K. V. (1964). Some results on the order statistics of the multivariate normal and Pareto type 1 populations, *Annals of Mathematical Statistics*, **35**, 1815–1818.

[24] McGraw, D. K. and Wagner, J. F. (1968). Elliptically symmetric distributions, *IEEE Transactions on Information Theory*, **14**, 110–120.

[25] McKay, A. T. (1934). Sampling from batches, *Journal of the Royal Statistical Society*, *Series B*, **1**, 207–216.

[26] Mihram, G. A. and Hultquist, R. A. (1967). A bivariate warning-time/failure-time distribution, *Journal of the American Statistical Association*, **62**, 589–599.

[27] Miller, K. S. (1965). Some multivariate density functions of products of Gaussian variates, *Biometrika*, **52**, 645–646.

[28] Moore, D. S. (1969). Asymptotically nearly efficient estimators of multivariate location parameters, *Annals of Mathematical Statistics*, **40**, 1809–1823.

[29] Morgenstern, D. (1956). Einfache Beispiele zweidimensionaler Verteilungen, *Mitteilungsblatt für Mathematische Statistik*, **8**, 234–235.

[30] Patil, S. A. (1969). A bivariate distribution of product of beta variables and square root of chi square variable, *Sankhyā*, *Series B*, **31**, 25–28.

[31] Pierce, D. A. and Dykstra, R. L. (1969). Independence and the normal distribution, *American Statistician*, **23**, No. 4, 39.

[32] Rao, C. R. (1945). Information and the accuracy attainable in the estimation of statistical parameters, *Bulletin of the Calcutta Mathematical Society*, **37**, 81–91.

[33] Schotz, W. E. and Zelen, M. (1971). Effect of length sampling bias on labeled mitotic index scores, *Journal of Theoretical Biology*, **32**, 383–404.

[34] Simoni, S. de (1968). Su una estensione dello schema delle curve normali di ordina *r* alle variabili doppie, *Statistica* (*Bologna*), **28**, 151–170.

[35] Takahasi, K. (1965). Note on the multivariate Burr's distribution, *Annals of the Institute of Statistical Mathematics, Tokyo*, **17**, 257–260.

[36] Tanaka, M. (1970). Estimation and testing hypotheses for one, two or several samples from general multivariate distributions, *Annals of Mathematical Statistics*, **41**, 1999–2020.

[37] Thomas, D. H. (1970). Ph.D. Thesis, Wayne State University.

[38] Washburn, A. (1969). Probability density of a moving particle, *Operations Research*, **17**, 861–871.

Augmented Cumulative Index

Numbers preceding parentheses indicate volume numbers (1–Discrete Distribution, 2–Continuous Univariate 1, 3–Continuous Univariate 2, 4–Continuous Multivariate); numbers in parentheses are page numbers.

The symbol ↔ denotes "associations" between different distributions.

Entries appearing in Table of Contents are generally not included in this index.

Index of References by Topics

In this Index, chapter numbers are given in bold type, followed by reference numbers in parentheses. The system of classification is necessarily somewhat imprecise, but it is hoped all major references in each category are included. The following classification categories are given:

Applications, in other sciences:

INDEX OF REFERENCES BY TOPICS

INDEX OF REFERENCES BY TOPICS

Corrections

Discrete Distributions (Chapters *1–11*)

Page	Position	Present Text	Corrected Text
5	l. 14	$n![(n-r)!r]^{-1}$	$n![(n-r)!r!]^{-1}$
10	eq. (60)	$\|B_2\|_r$	$\|B_{2r}\|$
11	l. 4	$B_5(x) = x^5 - \frac{5}{2}x^2 + \cdots$	$B_5(x) = x^5 - \frac{5}{2}x^4 + \cdots$
12	l. 14	$H_4(x) = x^4 - 6x + 3$	$H_4(x) = x^4 - 6x^2 + 3$
19	eq. (104)	$\mu_{(r)}$	$\mu_{(j)}$
20	l. 8	$\exp[t(\cdots)]$	$E[\exp[t(\cdots)]]$
21	l. 5f	uth	$(u-1)$th
24	l. 5f	θ	θ_j
31	eq. (1)	$(e^{r+s}-1)^{-2}$	$(e^{r+s}-1)^{-1}$
52	eq. (10)	$N\binom{N-1}{[Np]}\cdots$	$2N\binom{N-1}{[Np]}\cdots$
95	l. 9f	Section 9	Section 10
105	eq. (43.2)	$\text{var}(\mathbf{x}) = (1-e^{-\theta})^{-1}\cdots$	$\text{var}(\mathbf{x}) = \theta(1-e^{-\theta})^{-1}$
126	eq. (14)	$\mu'_{(j)} =$	$\mu_{(j)} = \cdots$
127	21f	$\Pr[x \geq X]$	$\Pr[x \leq X]$
131	eq. (27)	$\bar{\mathbf{x}}^2/(\mathbf{s}^2 - \bar{\mathbf{x}}^2)$	$\bar{\mathbf{x}}^2/(\mathbf{s}^2 - \bar{\mathbf{x}})$

l. = line; f = from foot; eq. = equation.

Page	Position	Present Text	Corrected Text
139	[6]	*Biometrics*, 8, 340–342	*Technometrics*, **8,** 345–350
326	l. 14		
185	eq. (3)	$+(e^{-a}a^{k+1} - \cdots)$	$+(b-a)^{-1}(e^{-a}a^{k+1} - \cdots)$
186	l. 11f	$\cdots\binom{N}{j} = \cdots$	$\cdots\binom{N}{j}p^jq^{N-j} = \cdots$
188	eq. (19)	$\cdots e^{-j\phi}(j\phi)^k\binom{X}{j}\cdots$	$\cdots e^{-j\phi}j^k\binom{X}{j}\cdots$
191	l. 8f	Schumway	Shumway
196	eq. (40)	$1+\beta^{-1}\log(Q-Pt)$	$1+\beta\log(Q-Pt)$
197	ll. 7f, 5f, 3f	Change p to q and q to p; also change λ to θ	
198	eq. (50)	(but not θ to λ)	
198	l. 6f	$\theta q^{-1}(p/q)^{r-1}$	$r!\theta q^{-1}(p/q)^{r-1}$
199	l. 8f	$\log(P_1/P_0)$	(P_1/P_0)
199	eq. (55)	$\log(\mathbf{f}_1/\mathbf{f}_0)$	$(\mathbf{f}_1/\mathbf{f}_0)$
206	eq. (74.2)	$(c+1)\mathbf{f}_c\hat{\boldsymbol{\lambda}}^{-1}$	$(c+1)\mathbf{f}_{c+1}\hat{\boldsymbol{\lambda}}^{-1}$
207	l. 4f	$[-k\log(1-\theta)]^{-k}$	$[-k\log(1-\theta)]^{-1}$
214	[**37**]	(1947)	(1957)
217	l. 14	$-\frac{1}{2}(1-e^{-\phi})$	$-\lambda(1-e^{-\phi})$
224	l. 8	is	of
224	l. 9	of usually	usually
226	ll. 17, 18	he, He	she, She
228	eq. (22)	$P_{k-1} = \cdots$	$P_{k+1} = \cdots$
230	l. 1f	Add $= n^{(r)}\prod_{j=0}^{r-1}\left[\frac{P+j\alpha}{1+j\alpha}\right]$	
234	l. 4	(42)	(43)

Continuous Univariate Distributions—1 (Chapters *12–21*)

Page	Position	Present Text	Corrected Text
3	l. 5	X_n'	X_1'
3	eq. (6) (twice)	$a_j - a_{j-1}$	$a_j - a_{j-1} - 1$
3	l. 11	x_1, x_2, x_s	$x_{a_1}, x_{a_2}, x_{a_s}$
4	eq. (12)	Y_{a_0}'	Y_{a_j}'
5	eq. (15.1)	$E[X_r') = X_r' + \cdots$	$E[X_r'] = \xi_r' + \cdots$
49	l. 1f	$-n[(n-1)n]^{-\frac{1}{2}}\cdots$	$-(n-1)[(n-1)n]^{-\frac{1}{2}}\cdots$
52	l. 10	$E[X \mid X_j - \bar{X}]$	$E[\bar{X} \mid X_j - \bar{X}]$
56	eq. (28)″	$+14x^2$	$-14x^2$

Page	Position	Present Text	Corrected Text
56	l.9	(28)′	(28)″
56	11. after (i)	$\ldots .]^{-k}$	$\ldots .]^{k}$
98	[**61**]	David, H. A.	David, H. T.
105	[**209**]	*Changes*	*Chances*
133	[**34**] [**35**]	particles	particulate substances
133	[**34**]	**207,** 369–388	**215,** 27–37
177	Table 1 Top last column	U_ν^2	U_ε^2
179	l. 1f	$e^{-\frac{1}{2}x}$	$\dfrac{e^{-\frac{1}{2}x}}{x-\nu+2}$
	l. 1f	$(x-\nu+2)^2+4\nu$	$(x-\nu+2)^2+4x$
193	l. 11	$e^{-X'_{n-r_2}t/\beta}$	$e^{-X'_{n-r_2}t/\hat{\beta}}$
237	l. 12f	$\cdots 2n$ degrees $\cdots$	$2(n-1)$ degrees $\cdots$
237	l. 9f	$\cdots \chi^2_{2n} \cdots$	$\cdots \chi^2_{2(n-1)} \cdots$ (twice)
273	l. 6f	[**19**]	[**20**]
287	eq. (38)	$\cdots (1-ky)^{k-1}]$	$\cdots (1-ky)^{k^{-1}}]$

Continuous Univariate Distributions—2 (Chapters *22–33*)

Page	Position	Present Text	Corrected Text
3	l. 7	$\theta=\alpha+\beta\log(\eta\beta)$	$\theta=\beta$ and $\xi=\alpha+\beta\log(\eta\beta)$
3	l. 6 and 11		delete 1 −
53	l. 2	$p \pm q$	$p+q$
60	eq. (6)	$\left(\dfrac{2}{h}\right)^{n-1}\ldots$	$\frac{1}{2}h^{-n}\ldots$
60	eq. (7)	$2\left(\dfrac{2}{h}\right)^{n-1}\ldots$	$h^{-n}\ldots$
60	eq. (8)	$\left(\dfrac{2}{h}\right)^{n-1} n(\frac{1}{2}-\lvert a'-a-\frac{1}{2}\rvert)^{n-2}$	$\frac{1}{2}h^{-n}n(h-\lvert a'-a\rvert)^{n-1}$
96	eq. (4.4)	$\frac{1}{2}+\{1+\cdots$	$\frac{1}{2}+\frac{1}{2}\{1+\cdots$
108	eq. (21)	$8x+3$	$8\nu+3$
112	l. 10f	$t^2>n\geq 1$	$t^2>\nu\geq 1$
	l. 6f	$z=[\nu^{\frac{1}{2}}c_\nu\alpha]^{2/\nu}$	$z=[\nu^{\frac{1}{2}}c_\nu^{-1}(1-\alpha)]^{2/\nu}$
191	l. 8	$B(\frac{1}{2}\nu_1+j,\frac{1}{2}\nu_1)$	$B(\frac{1}{2}\nu_1+j,\frac{1}{2}\nu_2)$
209	l. 15	$b=\Gamma(\frac{1}{2}\nu)\sqrt{\cdots}$	$b=[2(\nu-2)^{-1}\{\Gamma(\frac{1}{2}\nu)/\Gamma(\frac{1}{2}(\nu-1))\}^2-1]^{\frac{1}{2}}$
209	eq. (17.1)	$\sinh^{-1}\dfrac{bE(t_\nu')}{a}$	$\dfrac{1}{b}\sinh^{-1}\dfrac{bE(t_\nu')}{a}$
248	[**30**]	**32**	*Series B*, **32,** 381–394

Acknowledgments

FIGURE 1, Page 18	Adapted from N. L. Johnson (1949). Bivariate distributions based on simple translation systems, *Biometrika*, **36,** 297–304.
FIGURE 1, Pages 88–89	Adapted from F. Y. Borden (1971). *Three-D.* Unpublished, Pennsylvania State University.
FIGURE 5, Page 100	Adapted from D. P. Tihansky (1970). *Properties of the Bivariate Normal Cumulative Distribution.* Rand Corporation Report P4400, Santa Monica, California.
FIGURE 1, Page 255	Adapted from E. J. Gumbel and C. K. Mustafi (1967). Some analytical properties of bivariate extremal distributions, *Journal of the American Statistical Association*, **62,** 569–588.
FIGURE 2, Page 304	Adapted from N. L. Johnson and S. Kotz (1972). Power transformations of gamma variables, *Biometrika*, **59,** 226–229.

TABLE 1, Page 8	Adapted from W. P. Elderton and N. L. Johnson (1969). *Systems of Frequency Curves.* London: Cambridge University Press. p. 138.
TABLE 2, Page 17	Adapted from N. L. Johnson (1949). Bivariate distributions based on simple translation systems, *Biometrika*, **36,** 297–304.
TABLE 3, Page 28	Adapted from C. E. V. Leser (1942). Inequalities for multivariate frequency distributions, *Biometrika*, **32,** 284–293.
TABLE 1, Page 50	Adapted from R. H. Bacon (1963). Approximations to multivariate normal orthant probabilities, *Annals of Mathematical Statistics*, **34,** 191–198.
Pages 57–58	Adapted from F. N. David and C. L. Mallows (1961). The variance of Spearman's rho in normal samples, *Biometrika*, **48,** 19–28.

TABLE 2, Page 64	Adapted from I. Olkin and J. W. Pratt (1958). Unbiased estimation of certain correlation coefficients, *Annals of Mathematical Statistics*, **29,** 201–211.
TABLE 4, Page 69	Adapted from I. Guttman (1970). Construction of β-content tolerance regions at confidence level γ for large samples from the k-variate normal distribution, *Annals of Mathematical Statistics*, **41,** 376–400.
TABLE 4, Page 117	Adapted from G. M. Tallis (1963). Elliptical and radial truncation in normal populations, *Annals of Mathematical Statistics*, **34,** 940–944.
TABLE 1, Pages 166–167	Adapted from J. Wishart (1928). The generalized product moment distribution in samples from a normal multivariate population, *Biometrika*, **20A,** 32–52.
TABLE 2, Page 171	Adapted from A. G. Constantine (1963). Some non-central distribution problems in multivariate analysis, *Annals of Mathematical Statistics*, **34,** 1270–1284. A. T. James (1954). Normal multivariate analysis and the orthogonal group, *Annals of Mathematical Statistics*, **25,** 40–75.
TABLE 1, Page 190	Adapted from T. Sugiyama (1968). Mimeo Series No. 590, Institute of Statistics, University of North Carolina, Chapel Hill.
TABLE 2, Page 191	Adapted from K. C. S. Pillai and T. C. Chang (1969). An approximation to the c.d.f. of the largest root of a covariance matrix, *Annals of the Institute of Statistical Mathematics, Tokyo*, **6** (Supplement), 115–124.
TABLE 2, Page 259	Adapted from E. J. Gumbel and C. K. Mustafi (1967). Some analytical properties of bivariate extremal distributions, *Journal of the American Statistical Association*, **62,** 569–588.
TABLE 3, Page 297	Adapted from D. K. McGraw and J. F. Wagner (1968). Elliptically symmetric distributions, *IEEE Transactions on Information Theory*, **14,** 110–120.